READINGS IN THE PHYSICAL SCIENCES

READINGS IN THE PHYSICAL SCIENCES

Edited by

HARLOW SHAPLEY

HELEN WRIGHT

SAMUEL RAPPORT

New York

APPLETON-CENTURY-CROFTS, INC.

6125-6

PRINTED IN THE UNITED STATES OF AMERICA
E 79872

Preface

It is the task of general education to provide the kinds of learning and experience that will enable the student . . . to apply habits of scientific thought to both personal and civic problems, and to appreciate the implications of scientific discoveries for human welfare . . . ; [to] bring to the general student understanding of the fundamental nature of the physical world in which he lives and of the skills by which this nature is discerned. That the student grasp the processes involved in scientific thought and understand the principles of scientific method is even more important than that he should know the data of the sciences.

The aim of the editors in preparing *Readings in the Physical Sciences* is stated succinctly in the above quotation from *Higher Education for American Democracy* (A Report of the President's Commission on Higher Education, Washington, December, 1947). To obtain the selections, many books and articles were examined. The emphasis has been on contemporary work. Such emphasis is necessary because of the rapid advance of the physical sciences in recent years. But also an attempt has been made to give the student historical perspective on each individual science. The selections have been drawn largely from writings in the English language, for translations frequently lack the flair that is apt to excite the imagination of the student; moreover, almost all the topics which rightfully belong in a *Readings* of this sort have been discussed in English in more than adequate fashion.

We have attempted to select articles that will be read for their intrinsic interest, even though a number of technical selections are included. It is hoped that in this way the student will be induced to continue reading on his own volition; to help him an extensive bibliography is appended. Short biographical sketches and an index have also been included.

The thanks of the editors are extended to the various publishers and authors who have granted permission to reprint. For their helpful suggestions in both over-all planning and in the selection of individual articles, the editors also thank: S. G. Bergquist, Michigan State College; J. W. Buchta, University of Minnesota; William E. Cadbury, Jr., Haverford College; R. H. Carleton, Michigan State College; Sidney J. French, Colgate University; J. Osborn Fuller, Ohio State University; C. E. Hesthal, Ohio State University; C. L. Henshaw, Colgate University; C. J. Lapp, National Research Council; J. W. McGrath, Kent State University; S. R. Powers, Teachers College, Columbia University.

H. S.
H. W.
S. R.

To the Student

This book is designed to give the reader some understanding of the physical world as revealed by science, some idea of the habits of thought which have built the edifice of modern science, and some conception of how these habits can be used to solve many of the complex problems, scientific or otherwise, of contemporary living. To achieve this aim, the editors have selected articles that approach the problems of science in a variety of ways.

The first of these approaches is *historical.* As George Sarton, the great historian of science, has said: "The only way of humanizing scientific labor is to inject into it a little of the historical spirit, the spirit of reverence for the past—the spirit of reverence for every witness of good will throughout the ages." Through reading original material, such as Galileo's fascinating account of his first telescopic observation of the revolution of the satellites around Jupiter, or selections from Lavoisier's classic "On the Nature of Water and on the Experiments Adduced in Proof of the Possibility of Its Change into Earth" (contained in "The Method of the Inductive Sciences" by Ida Freund), we see the first of the great experimenters at work. Galileo built on the work of Copernicus and others before him; his work was in turn used by those who followed to develop whole new sciences and to foster the true scientific spirit.

In over-all historical surveys, like the admirable account given by Bumstead of the development of physics, and in discussions of the solutions of individual problems, like Conant's "Combustion," we see the slow emergence of science from the mists of ignorance and superstition, its gradual development after numberless false starts, its widening influence on human civilization, and finally its place in the modern world. In examples from the fields of astronomy, physics, and chemistry, we see how facts have been collected, how concepts and definitions arose, how assumptions and hypotheses were introduced and theories and physical laws evolved. Every theory has led to further theory which, when proved or eliminated by observation, has made for further knowledge.

Our second approach to the problems of science is through an examination of the *scientific method and its implications.* Not only in the section labeled "Science and Scientific Method," but throughout the book the student will see how a particular mental attitude, an eagerness to know, and a willingness to accept the results of observation and experiments have achieved results which unscientific medieval man would have considered literally miraculous. There is hardly an article among those that follow which does not illuminate some phase of scientific method. It is worth noting that not only in science, but also in art, politics, and the social sciences, indeed in every phase of daily life, the scientific approach can help in distinguishing the real from the apparent, the true from the false, and fact from opinion. The tested methods of the physical sciences should be more widely used for the solution of many of the crucial problems of living.

The third approach is through articles on *research*. In each section of the book some of the greatest modern scientists tell of their work and what they have learned from it. Not all of the great are here, of course, for many have not written in terms which can be understood by those with little scientific background. Yet some of the greatest, like Eddington in astronomy and Whitehead in mathematics, have also been among the most gifted writers. New vistas are opened by their accounts of great advances.

Some of the discussions of modern concepts, such as that on "How the Stars Use Atomic Energy" by George Gamow, require a background of knowledge. Gamow's article will be found much more comprehensible after an examination of Jeans on "Exploring the Atom" in the Physics section. In the same way "From Cyzicus to Neptune" in the Mathematics section illuminates and is illuminated by a number of articles under Astronomy. These two examples illustrate the increasing interrelations among the sciences. Astronomy relies first on mathematics, then on physics, even to an extent on chemistry. The study of geology would now be impossible without an understanding of the part that physics and chemistry play in the interpretation of our observations of rocks and minerals. So it has become with all the sciences, until in many cases the boundary lines are no longer distinguishable.

A fourth approach used in this volume is the examination of *tools and apparatus*. The inventor of the tools by which great scientific discoveries have been made has often been relegated to a minor position in the annals of fame. Yet his contribution is vital. In the section on Astronomy, Aitken shows how the spectroscope, in conjunction with the photographic plate, has literally revolutionized modern astronomy. No doubt some of our greatest discoveries in this field will be made through the use of the great 200-inch telescope on Mt. Palomar. In an entirely different field, George W. Gray shows how engineers have utilized a new apparatus, the wind tunnel, to make otherwise impossible advances in modern aviation. The refinement of tools and apparatus in modern times has made possible discoveries far beyond the imagination of scientists of previous ages.

Special note should be made of the *Bibliography*, which constitutes the fifth approach. It has been prepared with care, but its value depends entirely on the coöperation of the reader. In it are listed volumes that offer varied information on the numerous facets of science. In Sir James Frazer's *Golden Bough* are described the earliest origins of science in the wondering of primitive man. In George Sarton's *Introduction to Science* is the story of beginnings in Babylon, Arabia, and Greece. The story is continued through biographies of the great scientists, through studies of scientific philosophy and method, and through explanations of practical applications of pure research.

In all of the ways described above an attempt has been made to open the door to an understanding of the physical sciences. Some of this book's readers will doubtless follow in the footsteps of those who have made our scientific world possible. The synoptic pictures here given for the individual sciences may point their interest toward a particular field. It is conceivable that a few may even make notable contributions in the physical sciences. For these few, the selections should give some idea of the immensity of the field, and the necessarily coöperative nature of their labor.

For the vast majority who will not specialize in scientific work, it is worth repeating that the world of the physical sciences offers a perspective and a point of view which are valuable in every field. "It is because we have failed to assimilate science into our culture," writes President Conant, "that so many feel spiritually lost in this modern world. For when an idea is assimilated it becomes part of an integrated complex of ideas and proves itself an element of strength."

Contents

Part Four: MATHEMATICS

Part Five: PHYSICS

Part Six: CHEMISTRY

II

SCIENCE AND SCIENTIFIC METHOD

JUST what is scientific method? Hundreds of definitions have been attempted. The results of the method are obvious enough, influencing our tiniest waking actions and our most monumental speculations. The ways the results have been obtained are more difficult to appreciate—partly because they have been so diverse. The discoveries have resulted from infinite capacity to take pains, as in the isolation of radium by the Curies; or from almost divine flashes of illumination, as in the case of much of Newton's work. Lord Keynes, in a paper read at the Newton Tercentenary celebration in England, wrote, "I fancy his pre-eminence is due to his muscles of intuition being the strongest and most enduring with which a man has ever been gifted. I believe that Newton could hold a problem in his mind for hours and days and weeks until it surrendered to him its secret . . . 'so happy in his conjectures,' says de Morgan, 'as to seem to know more than he could possibly have any means of proving.' "

On rare occasions the line of discovery has been direct and easy. Usually it has seemed obvious after the fact, yet almost always it has occurred after many false starts and erroneous hypotheses, as you will appreciate when you have read President Conant's article on "Combustion." Yet these false starts have contributed their work in building the articulated structure which is science. No experiment, if it has been accurately performed, can be said to be truly wasted; and it is a willingness to accept the results obtained, to subordinate authority to these results even though they have sometimes seemed to defy the evidence of the senses, that is one touchstone of the scientific spirit.

In the opening selection in this section, some of the world's greatest scientific minds, from Aristotle to Einstein, give you brief glimpses of their philosophies, their methods, their understanding of the relation of sciences to daily life. What the scientific method is, how the scientist works and thinks, what tremendous spiritual rewards await his success are all illuminated. Here are mentioned the kinds of investigation and the types of investigators, the necessity for inquisitive spirit and questioning attitude, the need to subordinate beautiful speculation to ugly fact, the disappointments of the search, the ecstasy of accomplishment.

Fittingly, our first long selection is by a scientist who was one of the very greatest scientific writers. T. H. Huxley it was who, more than any other single person, defeated the wave of reaction that followed the publication of Darwin's theory of evolution. He was a master of lucid and persuasive exposition as well as a born fighter, and these qualities are exhibited in "The Method of Scientific Investigation." Each one of us, every day, says Huxley, uses the basic techniques of science, applies its basic principles. Whether we are ferreting out the burglar who steals the spoons or defining the motions of the heavenly bodies, the processes are intrinsically the same. To a degree, the least of us can paraphrase M. Jourdain in Molière's play, "I have been a scientist all my life."

A twentieth-century scientist, the famous geologist W. M. Davis, carries Huxley's thesis a step farther in "The Reasonableness of Science." His fable of the tides, with four characters representing four aspects of scientific research, is drawn from his own specialized experience. As we shall see, his illustration applies equally well to any other science from astronomy to biology. In fact, one purpose of this book is to show how the same general rules apply in each of the sciences, how a theory of the internal constitution of the stars may influence an experiment in nuclear physics, how beautifully articulated is the whole body of scientific knowledge.

Joseph Priestley, discoverer of oxygen, wrote in his *History of Electricity* some hundred and seventy-five years ago, "From Natural Philosophy have flowed all those great inventions by means of which mankind in general is able to subsist with more ease, and in greater numbers upon the face of the earth. Hence arise the capital advantages of men above brutes, and of civilization above barbarity." Here Priestley is pointing out that it is "pure" science from which application and practical benefits flow. Faraday's theoretical studies in electromagnetism resulted in Edison's electric bulb. A mathematical equation by Einstein held the clue to the power of the atomic bomb. Never before has the relation between pure and applied science been so important; yet many individuals tend to be confused by it. William F. Durand, a noted pioneer in aerodynamics, a subject in which theory and practice are intimately connected, discusses the relation between the two in "Science and Engineering." He points out that while both are essential, one can follow only where the other leads. It is a thesis which not only students but legislators and opinion makers should take to heart.

It is not alone for its practical value that science deserves the serious attention of the student. There are unique ways in which science offers stimulation to the mind as well as opportunity for service. Bertrand Russell, noted equally as philosopher, teacher, and mathematician, explains how this is so in "The Place of Science in a Liberal Education." It is a selection from his book *Mysticism and Logic*, which is recommended to the beginner and indeed to the specialist in science.

Our next two selections, dealing with the scientist as creator and as human being, are by writers who have no immediate connection with the physical sciences. In "Imagination Creatrix," John Livingston Lowes, a great authority on English literature, elaborating on the idea of Lord Keynes quoted above, shows how the thought processes of Coleridge in creating "The Ancient Mariner" were similar to those of Newton in his garden at Woolsthorpe, how in fact all great creative impulses, be they in the arts or sciences, have much in common. It is a beautiful and inspiring piece.

La Farge, the novelist and ethnologist, does more than discuss the scientist's problem as a human being. He shows how each step in research, often discouragingly minute and sometimes seemingly entirely wasted, is a stepping stone which may end in great results.

Today as science is advancing at a stupendous rate and social, economic, and political development lags far behind, there is constantly greater need of understanding the implications of scientific advance. The philosopher Irwin Edman of Columbia considers this thesis as he looks toward the future in "Science and the Dream of Happiness." If we are to live in the world where the atomic bomb exists, we must learn to get along with one another or perish.

A layman with an intimate knowledge of scientific research through his long association with the Rockefeller Foundation, Raymond B. Fosdick, paints a realistic picture of the frightening prospects which have resulted from scientific advance. Unlike many wishful thinkers, he admits that he is ignorant of the road that leads to a solution. All he can do is pose the problem. It is for the student of today to find the answer tomorrow to the question asked in "A Layman Looks at Science."

THOUGHTS ON SCIENCE:

ARISTOTLE TO EINSTEIN

The search for truth is in one way hard and in another way easy, for it is evident that no one can master it fully nor miss it wholly. But each adds a little to our knowledge of Nature, and from all the facts assembled there arises a certain grandeur.

ARISTOTLE

All sciences are connected; they lend each other material aid as parts of one great whole, each doing its own work, not for itself alone, but for the other parts; as the eye guides the body and the foot sustains it and leads it from place to place.

ROGER BACON

The invention all admired; and each how he
To be the inventor wish'd; so easy it seemed
Once found, which yet unfound most would have thought
Impossible!

JOHN MILTON

The World little knows how many thoughts and theories which have passed through the mind of a scientific investigator have been crushed in silence and secrecy by his own severe criticism and adverse examinations; that in the most successful instances not a tenth of the suggestions, the hopes, the wishes, the preliminary conclusions have been realized.

MICHAEL FARADAY

I have steadily endeavored to keep my mind free so as to give up any hypothesis, however much beloved (and I cannot resist forming one on every subject) as soon as the facts are shown to be opposed to it.

CHARLES DARWIN

The ever-recurring tragedy in the realm of science is a beautiful theory killed by an ugly fact.

While awaiting the birth of his first child, on December 31, 1856, Huxley entered in his journal his ambitions for the future:

To smite all humbugs, however big; to give a nobler tone to science; to set an example of abstinence from petty personal controversies, and of toleration for everything but lying: to be indifferent as to whether the work is recognised as mine or not, so long as it is done.

T. H. HUXLEY

The child just awakening into consciousness of the world, knows no problem. The bright flower, the ringing bell, are all new to it; yet it is surprised at nothing. The out and out Philistine, whose only thoughts lie in the beaten path of his every-day pursuits, likewise has no problems. Everything goes its wonted course, and if perchance a thing go wrong at times, it is at most a mere object of curiosity and not worth serious consideration. In fact, the question "Why?" loses all warrant in relations where we are familiar with every aspect of events. But the capable and talented young man has his head full of problems; he has acquired, to a greater or less degree, certain habitudes of thought, and at the same time he is constantly observing what is new and unwonted, and in his case there is no end to the questions, "Why?"

Thus, the factor which most promotes scientific thought is the gradual widening of the field of experience. We scarcely notice events we are accustomed to; the latter do not really develop their intellectual significance until placed in contrast with something to which we are unaccustomed. Things that at home are passed by unnoticed, delight us when abroad, though they may appear in only slightly different forms. The sun shines with heightened radiance, the flowers bloom in brighter colors, our fellowmen accost us with lighter and happier looks. And, returning home, we find even the old familiar scenes more inspiring and suggestive than before.

Every motive that prompts and stimulates us to modify and transform our thoughts, proceeds from what is new, uncommon, and not understood. Novelty excites wonder in persons whose fixed habits of thought are shaken and disarranged by what they see. But the element of wonder never lies in the phenomenon or event observed; its place is in the person observing. People of more vigorous mental type aim at once at an *adaptation of thought* that will conform to what they have observed. Thus does science eventually become the natural foe of the wonderful. The sources of the marvellous are unveiled, and surprise gives way to calm interpretation.

ERNST MACH

The first experiment a child makes is a physical experiment: the suction-pump is but an imitation of the first act of every new-born infant. Nor do I think it calculated to lessen that infant's reverence, or to make him a worse citizen, when his riper experience shows him that the atmosphere was his helper in extracting the first draught from his mother's breast. The child grows, but is still an experimenter: he grasps at the moon, and his failure teaches him to respect distance. At length his little fingers acquire sufficient mechanical tact to lay hold of a spoon. He thrusts the instrument into his mouth, hurts his gums, and thus learns the impenetrability of matter. He lets the spoon fall, and jumps with delight to hear it rattle against the table. The experiment made by accident is repeated with intention, and thus the young student receives his first lessons upon sound and gravitation. There are pains and penalties, however, in the path of the enquirer: he is sure to go wrong, and Nature is just as sure to inform him of the fact. He falls down stairs, burns his fingers, cuts his hand, scalds his tongue, and in this way learns the conditions of his physical well being. This is Nature's way of proceeding, and it is wonderful what progress her pupil makes. His enjoyments for a time are physical, and the confectioner's shop occupies the foreground of human happiness; but the blossoms of a finer life are already beginning to unfold themselves, and the relation of cause and effect dawns upon the boy. He begins to see that the present condition of things is not final, but depends upon one that has gone before, and will be succeeded by another. He becomes a puzzle to himself; and to satisfy his newly awakened curiosity, asks all manner of inconvenient questions. The needs and tendencies of human nature express themselves through these early yearnings of the child. As thought ripens, he desires to know the character and causes of the phenomena presented to his observation; and unless this desire has been granted for the express purpose of having it repressed, unless the attractions of natural phenomena be like the blush of the forbidden fruit, conferred merely for the purpose of exercising our self-denial in letting them alone; we may fairly claim for the study of Physics the recognition that it answers to an impulse implanted by nature in the constitution of man.

JOHN TYNDALL

When you believe you have found an important scientific fact, and are feverishly curious to publish it, constrain yourself for days, weeks, years sometimes, fight yourself, try and ruin your own experiments and only proclaim your discovery after having exhausted all contrary hypotheses. But when, after so many efforts you have at last arrived at a certainty, your joy is one of the greatest which can be felt by a human soul.

Referred to himself as:

A man whose invincible belief is that science and peace will triumph over ignorance and war, that nations will unite, not to destroy but to build, and that the future will belong to those who will have done most for suffering humanity. But whether our efforts are or are not favored by life, let us be able to say, when we come near to the great goal, "I have done what I could."

LOUIS PASTEUR

It was a great step in science when men became convinced that, in order to understand the nature of things, they must begin by asking, not whether a thing is good or bad, noxious or beneficial, but of what kind it is? and how much is there of it? Quality and quantity were then first recognised as the primary features to be discovered in scientific inquiry.

CLERK MAXWELL

This creative use of the imagination is not only the fountain of all inspiration in poetry and art, but is also the source of discovery in science, and indeed supplies the initial impulse to all development and progress. It is the creative power of imagination which has inspired and guided all the great discoveries in science.

SIR WILLIAM HUGGINS

Accurate and minute measurement seems to the non-scientific imagination a less lofty and dignified work than looking for something new. But nearly all the grandest discoveries of science have been but the rewards of accurate measurement—patient long-continued labor in the minute sifting of numerical results.

LORD KELVIN

We especially need imagination in science. It is not all mathematics, nor all logic, but it is somewhat beauty and poetry.

MARIA MITCHELL

We should not compare the advances of science with the transformations of a city whose antiquated buildings are ruthlessly demolished to make way for new ones, but rather to the ceaseless evolution of new zoological types, each developing to the point where—seemingly unique to the ignorant—it yet reveals to trained eyes the living vestiges of the labors of past centuries. Therefore we must never believe that discarded theories have been either sterile or in vain.

HENRI POINCARÉ

Let the mind rise from victory to victory over surrounding nature, let it but conquer for human life and activity not only the surface of the earth but also all that lies between the depth of the sea and the outer limits of the atmosphere; let it command for its service prodigious energy to flow from one part of the universe to the other, let it annihilate space for the transference of its thoughts. Only science, exact science about human nature itself, and the most sincere approach to it by the aid of the omnipotent scientific method, will deliver man from his present gloom and will purge him from his contemporary share in the sphere of interhuman relations.

Study, compare and accumulate facts. As perfect as is the structure of a bird's wing, the bird would never be able to fly if its wings were not supported by air. Facts are the air of the scientist; without them you would never be able to fly. Without them your theories are useless efforts.

Learn the a.b.c.'s of science before ascending its heights. Never reach for the next step before having mastered the preceding one.

IVAN PAVLOV

The only way of humanizing scientific labor is to inject into it a little of the historical spirit, the spirit of reverence for the past,—the spirit of reverence for every witness of good will throughout the ages. However abstract science may become, it is essentially human in its origin and growth. Each scientific result is a fruit of humanity, a proof of its virtue. The almost unconceivable immensity of the universe revealed by his own efforts does not dwarf man except in a purely physical way; it gives a deeper meaning to his life and thought. Each time that we understand the world a little better, we are also able to appreciate more keenly our relationship to it. There are no natural sciences as opposed to humanities; every branch of science or learning is just as natural or as humane as you make it. Show the deep human interest of science and the study of it becomes the best vehicle of humanism one could devise; exclude that interest, teach scientific knowledge only for the sake of information and professional instruction, and the study of it, however valuable from a purely technical point of view, loses all educational value. Without history, scientific knowledge may become culturally dangerous; combined with history, tempered with reverence, it will nourish the highest culture.

GEORGE SARTON*

In ancient days two aviators procured to themselves wings. Daedalus flew safely through the middle air and was duly honored on his landing. Icarus soared upwards to the sun till the wax melted which bound his wings and his flight ended in fiasco. In weighing their achievements, there is something to be said for Icarus. The classical authorities tell us that he was only "doing a stunt," but I prefer to think of him as the man who brought to light a serious constructional defect in the flying machines of his day. So, too, in Science. Cautious Daedalus will apply his theories where he feels confident they will safely go; but by his excesses of caution their hidden weaknesses remain undiscovered. Icarus will strain his theories to the breaking-point till the weak points gape. For the mere adventure? Perhaps partly; that is human nature. But if he is destined not yet to reach the sun and solve finally the riddle of its constitution, we may hope at least to learn from his journey some hint to build a better machine.

A. S. EDDINGTON

The future of our civilization depends upon the widening spread and deepening hold of the scientific habit of mind.

JOHN DEWEY

An engineer is one who, through application of his knowledge of mathematics, the physical and biological sciences and economics, and with aid,

* From *The History of Science and the New Humanism* by George Sarton. New York: Henry Holt and Company, Inc. Reprinted by permission of Brown University. Copyright 1931 by Brown University.

further, from results obtained through observation, experiences, scientific discovery and invention, so utilizes the materials and directs the forces of nature that they are made to operate to the benefit of society. An engineer differs from the technologist in that he must concern himself with the organizational, economic and managerial aspects as well as the technical aspects of his work.

KARL COMPTON

Much of the significance of accumulated knowledge lies in an understanding of the process by which it was accumulated.

JAMES B. CONANT

The process by which the boundaries of knowledge are advanced, and the structure of organized science is built, is a complex process indeed. It corresponds fairly well with the exploitation of a difficult quarry for its building materials and the fitting of these into an edifice; but there are very significant differences. First, the material itself is exceedingly varied, hidden and overlaid with relatively worthless rubble, and the process of uncovering new facts and relationships has some of the attributes of prospecting and exploration rather than of mining or quarrying. Second, the whole effort is highly unorganized. There are no direct orders from architect or quarrymaster. Individuals and small bands proceed about their businesses unimpeded and uncontrolled, digging where they will, working over their material, and tucking it into place in the edifice.

Finally, the edifice itself has a remarkable property, for its form is predestined by the laws of logic and the nature of human reasoning. It is almost as though it had once existed, and its building blocks had then been scattered, hidden, and buried, each with its unique form retained so that it would fit only its own peculiar position, and with the concomitant limitation that the blocks cannot be found or recognized until the building of the structure has progressed to the point where their position and form reveal themselves to the discerning eye of the talented worker in the quarry. Parts of the edifice are being used while construction proceeds, by reason of the applications of science, but other parts are merely admired for their beauty and symmetry, and their possible utility is not in question.

In these circumstances it is not at all strange that the workers sometimes proceed in erratic ways. There are those who are quite content, given a few tools, to dig away unearthing odd blocks, piling them up in the view of fellow workers, and apparently not caring whether they fit anywhere or not. Unfortunately there are also those who watch carefully until some industrious group digs out a particularly ornamental block; whereupon they fit it in place with much gusto, and bow to the crowd. Some groups do not dig at all, but spend all their time arguing as to the exact arrangement of a cornice or an abutment. Some spend all their days trying to pull down a block or two that a rival has put in place. Some, indeed, neither dig nor argue, but go along with the crowd, scratch here and there, and enjoy the scenery. Some sit by and give advice, and some just sit.

On the other hand there are those men of rare vision who can grasp well in advance just the block that is needed for rapid advance on a section of the edifice to be possible, who can tell by some subtle sense where it will be found, and who have an uncanny skill in cleaning away dross and bringing it surely into the light. These are the master workmen. For each of them there can well be many of lesser stature who chip and delve, industriously, but with little grasp of what it is all about, and who nevertheless make the great steps possible.

There are those who can give the structure meaning, who can trace its evolution from early times, and describe the glories that are to be, in ways that inspire those who work and those who enjoy. They bring the inspiration that not all is mere building of monotonous walls, and that there is architecture even though the architect is not seen to guide and order.

There are those who labor to make the utility of the structure real, to cause it to give shelter to the multitude, that they may be better protected, and that they may derive health and well-being because of its presence.

And the edifice is not built by the quarrymen and the masons alone. There are those who bring them food during their labors, and cooling drink when the days are warm, who sing to them, and place flowers on the little walls that have grown with the years.

There are also the old men, whose days of vigorous building are done, whose eyes are too dim to see the details of the arch or the needed form of its keystone, but who have built a wall here and there, and lived long in the edifice; who have learned to love it and who have even grasped a suggestion of its ultimate meaning; and who sit in the shade and encourage the young men. . . .

VANNEVAR BUSH*

Many times a day I realize how much my own outer and inner life is built upon the labors of my fellow-men, both living and dead, and how earnestly I must exert myself in order to give in return as much as I have received. My peace of mind is often troubled by the depressing sense that I have borrowed too heavily from the work of other men.

ALBERT EINSTEIN

* Article entitled "The Builders." Reprinted by permission from *The Technology Review*, January, 1945, edited at the Massachusetts Institute of Technology. Copyright 1945 by the Alumni Association of the Massachusetts Institute of Technology.

>>>-<<<

THE METHOD OF SCIENTIFIC INVESTIGATION *

T. H. HUXLEY

The method of scientific investigation is nothing but the expression of the necessary mode of working of the human mind. It is simply the mode at which all phenomena are reasoned about, rendered precise and exact. There is no more difference, but there is just the same kind of difference, between the mental operations of a man of science and those of an ordinary person, as there is between the operations and methods of a baker or of a butcher weighing out his goods in common scales, and the operations of a chemist in performing a difficult and complex analysis by means of his balance and finely-graduated weights. It is not that the action of the scales in the one case, and the balance in the other, differ in the principles of their construction or manner of working; but the beam of one is set on an infinitely finer axis than the other, and of course turns by the addition of a much smaller weight.

You will understand this better, perhaps, if I give you some familiar example. You have all heard it repeated, I dare say, that men of science work by means of induction and deduction, and that by the help of these operations, they, in a sort of sense, wring from Nature certain other things, which are called natural laws, and causes, and that out of these, by some cunning skill of their own, they build up hypotheses and theories. And it is imagined by many, that the operations of the common mind can be by no means compared with these processes, and that they have to be acquired by a sort of special apprenticeship to the craft. To hear all these large words, you would think that the mind of a man of science must be constituted differently from that of his fellow men; but if you will not be frightened by terms, you will discover that you are quite wrong, and that all these terrible apparatus are being used by yourselves every day and every hour of your lives.

There is a well-known incident in one of Molière's plays, where the author makes the hero express unbounded delight on being told that he had been talking prose during the whole of his life. In the same way, I trust, that you will take comfort, and be delighted with yourselves, on the discovery that you have been acting on the principles of inductive and deductive philosophy during the same period. Probably there is not one who has not in the course of the day had occasion to set in motion a complex train of reasoning, of the very same kind, though differing of course in degree, as that which a scientific man goes through in tracing the causes of natural phenomena.

A very trivial circumstance will serve to exemplify this. Suppose you go

* From *Darwiniana* by T. H. Huxley. Reprinted by permission from Appleton-Century-Crofts, Inc.

into a fruiterer's shop, wanting an apple,—you take up one, and, on biting it, you find it is sour; you look at it, and see that it is hard and green. You take up another one, and that too is hard, green, and sour. The shopman offers you a third; but, before biting it, you examine it, and find that it is hard and green, and you immediately say that you will not have it, as it must be sour, like those that you have already tried.

Nothing can be more simple than that, you think; but if you will take the trouble to analyse and trace out into its logical elements what has been done by the mind, you will be greatly surprised. In the first place, you have performed the operation of induction. You found that, in two experiences, hardness and greenness in apples went together with sourness. It was so in the first case, and it was confirmed by the second. True, it is a very small basis, but still it is enough to make an induction from; you generalise the facts, and you expect to find sourness in apples where you get hardness and greenness. You found upon that a general law, that all hard and green apples are sour; and that, so far as it goes, is a perfect induction. Well, having got your natural law in this way, when you are offered another apple which you find is hard and green, you say, "All hard and green apples are sour; this apple is hard and green, therefore this apple is sour." That train of reasoning is what logicians call a syllogism, and has all its various parts and terms—its major premiss, its minor premiss, and its conclusion. And, by the help of further reasoning, which, if drawn out, would have to be exhibited in two or three other syllogisms, you arrive at your final determination, "I will not have that apple." So that, you see, you have, in the first place, established a law by induction, and upon that you have founded a deduction, and reasoned out the special conclusion of the particular case. Well now, suppose, having got your law, that at some time afterwards, you are discussing the qualities of apples with a friend: you will say to him, "It is a very curious thing,—but I find that all hard and green apples are sour!" Your friend says to you, "But how do you know that?" You at once reply, "Oh, because I have tried them over and over again, and have always found them to be so." Well, if we were talking science instead of common sense, we should call that an experimental verification. And, if still opposed, you go further, and say, "I have heard from the people in Somersetshire and Devonshire, where a large number of apples are grown, that they have observed the same thing. It is also found to be the case in Normandy, and in North America. In short, I find it to be the universal experience of mankind wherever attention has been directed to the subject." Whereupon, your friend, unless he is a very unreasonable man, agrees with you, and is convinced that you are quite right in the conclusion you have drawn. He believes, although perhaps he does not know he believes it, that the more extensive verifications are,—that the more frequently experiments have been made, and results of the same kind arrived at,—that the more varied the conditions under which the same results are attained, the more certain is the ultimate conclusion, and he disputes the question no further. He sees that the experiment has been tried under all sorts of conditions, as to time, place, and people, with the same result; and he says with you, therefore, that the law you have laid down must be a good one, and he must believe it.

In science we do the same thing;—the philosopher exercises precisely the same faculties, though in a much more delicate manner. In scientific inquiry it becomes a matter of duty to expose a supposed law to every possible kind of verification, and to take care, moreover, that this is done intentionally, and not left to a mere accident, as in the case of the apples. And in science, as in common life, our confidence in a law is in exact proportion to the absence of variation in the result of our experimental verifications. For instance, if you let go your grasp of an article you may have in your hand, it will immediately fall to the ground. That is a very common verification of one of the best established laws of nature—that of gravitation. The method by which men of science establish the existence of that law is exactly the same as that by which we have established the trivial proposition about the sourness of hard and green apples. But we believe it in such an extensive, thorough, and unhesitating manner because the universal experience of mankind verifies it, and we can verify it ourselves at any time; and that is the strongest possible foundation on which any natural law can rest.

So much, then, by way of proof that the method of establishing laws in science is exactly the same as that pursued in common life. Let us now turn to another matter (though really it is but another phase of the same question), and that is, the method by which, from the relations of certain phenomena, we prove that some stand in the position of causes towards the others.

I want to put the case clearly before you, and I will therefore show you what I mean by another familiar example. I will suppose that one of you, on coming down in the morning to the parlour of your house, finds that a tea-pot and some spoons which had been left in the room on the previous evening are gone,—the window is open, and you observe the mark of a dirty hand on the window-frame, and perhaps, in addition to that, you notice the impress of a hob-nailed shoe on the gravel outside. All these phenomena have struck your attention instantly, and before two seconds have passed you say, "Oh, somebody has broken open the window, entered the room, and run off with the spoons and the tea-pot!" That speech is out of your mouth in a moment. And you will probably add, "I know there has; I am quite sure of it!" You mean to say exactly what you know; but in reality you are giving expression to what is, in all essential particulars, an hypothesis. You do not *know* it at all; it is nothing but an hypothesis rapidly framed in your own mind. And it is an hypothesis founded on a long train of inductions and deductions.

What are those inductions and deductions, and how have you got at this hypothesis? You have observed, in the first place, that the window is open; but by a train of reasoning involving many inductions and deductions, you have probably arrived long before at the general law—and a very good one it is—that windows do not open of themselves; and you therefore conclude that something has opened the window. A second general law that you have arrived at in the same way is, that tea-pots and spoons do not go out of a window spontaneously, and you are satisfied that, as they are not now where you left them, they have been removed. In the third place, you look at the marks on the window-sill, and the shoemarks outside, and you say that in all previous experience the former kind of mark has never been produced by anything else but the hand of a human being; and the same experience shows that no other animal but man at present wears shoes with hob-nails in them such as would produce the marks in the gravel. I do not know, even if we could discover any of those "missing links" that are talked about, that they would help us to any other conclusion! At any rate the law which states our present experience is strong enough for my present purpose. You next reach the conclusion, that as these kinds of marks have not been left by any other animals than men, or are liable to be formed in any other way than by a man's hand and shoe, the marks in question have been formed by a man in that way. You have, further, a general law, founded on observation and experience, and that, too, is, I am sorry to say, a very universal and unimpeachable one,—that some men are thieves; and you assume at once from all these premisses—and that is what constitutes your hypothesis—that the man who made the marks outside and on the window-sill, opened the window, got into the room, and stole your tea-pot and spoons. You have now arrived at a *vera causa*;—you have assumed a cause which, it is plain, is competent to produce all the phenomena you have observed. You can explain all these phenomena only by the hypothesis of a thief. But that is a hypothetical conclusion, of the justice of which you have no absolute proof at all; it is only rendered highly probable by a series of inductive and deductive reasonings.

I suppose your first action, assuming that you are a man of ordinary common sense, and that you have established this hypothesis to your own satisfaction, will very likely be to go for the police, and set them on the track of the burglar, with the view to the recovery of your property. But just as you are starting with this object, some person comes in, and on learning what you are about, says, "My good friend, you are going on a great deal too fast. How do you know that the man who really made the marks took the spoons? It might have been a monkey that took them, and the man may have merely looked in afterwards." You would probably reply, "Well, that is all very well, but you see it is contrary to all experience of the way tea-pots and spoons are abstracted; so that, at any rate, your hypothesis is less probable than mine." While you are talking the thing

over in this way, another friend arrives. And he might say, "Oh, my dear sir, you are certainly going on a great deal too fast. You are most presumptuous. You admit that all these occurrences took place when you were fast asleep, at a time when you could not possibly have known anything about what was taking place. How do you know that the laws of Nature are not suspended during the night? It may be that there has been some kind of supernatural interference in this case." In point of fact, he declares that your hypothesis is one of which you cannot at all demonstrate the truth and that you are by no means sure that the laws of Nature are the same when you are asleep as when you are awake.

Well, now, you cannot at the moment answer that kind of reasoning. You feel that your worthy friend has you somewhat at a disadvantage. You will feel perfectly convinced in your own mind, however, that you are quite right, and you say to him, "My good friend, I can only be guided by the natural probabilities of the case, and if you will be kind enough to stand aside and permit me to pass, I will go and fetch the police." Well, we will suppose that your journey is successful, and that by good luck you meet with a policeman; that eventually the burglar is found with your property on his person, and the marks correspond to his hand and to his boots. Probably any jury would consider those facts a very good experimental verification of your hypothesis, touching the cause of the abnormal phenomena observed in your parlour, and would act accordingly.

Now, in this suppositious case, I have taken phenomena of a very common kind, in order that you might see what are the different steps in an ordinary process of reasoning, if you will only take the trouble to analyse it carefully. All the operations I have described, you will see, are involved in the mind of any man of sense in leading him to a conclusion as to the course he should take in order to make good a robbery and punish the offender. I say that you are led, in that case, to your conclusion by exactly the same train of reasoning as that which a man of science pursues when he is endeavouring to discover the origin and laws of the most occult phenomena. The process is, and always must be, the same; and precisely the same mode of reasoning was employed by Newton and Laplace in their endeavours to discover and define the causes of the movements of the heavenly bodies, as you, with your own common sense, would employ to detect a burglar. The only difference is, that the nature of the inquiry being more abstruse, every step has to be most carefully watched, so that there may not be a single crack or flaw in your hypothesis. A flaw or crack in many of the hypotheses of daily life may be of little or no moment as affecting the general correctness of the conclusions at which we may arrive; but, in a scientific inquiry, a fallacy, great or small, is always of importance, and is sure to be in the long run constantly productive of mischievous, if not fatal results. . . .

1863

>>><<<

THE REASONABLENESS OF SCIENCE *

W. M. DAVIS

A FABLE OF THE TIDES

Once upon a time—for science also has its fables—there dwelt a hermit on the shore of the ocean, where he observed the tides. He measured the period and the range of their rise and fall and, patiently tabulating his records, discovered that the tides run like clock-work. The interval between two high tides was determined to be about 12 hours and 26 minutes; the range from low water to high water was found to vary systematically, being greater one week and smaller the next, the total variation running its course in 14 days; more singular still, the high tides were found to exhibit an alternating inequality, such that, if they were numbered in order, the even-numbered would be stronger than the odd-numbered for two weeks and then the odd-numbered would be stronger than the even-numbered for two weeks; this cycle of alternating inequality completing itself in 28 days. The hermit then wishing to extend his observations, decided to travel overland to another ocean and learn whether the tides behaved in the same way there also.

Now at the same epoch, but far away in the center of a great continental desert, a recluse lived in a cave, thinking and reflecting. One problem in particular engrossed his thoughts. He knew Newton's law of gravitation, and he asked himself what other consequences ought to follow from it besides the revolution of the planets around the sun and of the moons around their planets. He at last convinced himself that if the earth and the moon attract each other, the moon must produce a system of what he called earth-deforming forces, disposed in such a way as to strain the earth's crust, tending to raise it on the sides of the earth toward the moon and opposite the moon, so that at any one point on the rotating earth, the crust should be raised twice in a lunar day, or every 12 hours and 26 minutes; also, that similar but weaker earth-deforming forces produced by the sun should be combined with those produced by the moon so that the resulting total strains in the earth's crust would be stronger and weaker every 14 days; and furthermore, that as the moon is north of the sky equator for one half of a lunation and south of it for the other half—Alas, that you dwellers in roofed houses are so little acquainted with the sky as not to know of your own seeing that the moon's course does carry it obliquely across the sky equator and back again every month!—but as the moon does move in this manner, the recluse saw that the deforming forces which tend to raise the earth's crust at any point must exhibit a sequence of alternating inequalities

* Oration delivered at the annual meeting of the Harvard Chapter of Phi Beta Kappa, in Cambridge, Mass., June 19, 1922. Reprinted by permission from *The Scientific Monthly*. Copyright, 1922, The Science Press.

every 28 days. And beside these rhythmic variations in a little more than half a day, in 14 days, and in 28 days, he worked out several other variations of even longer periods. But his calculations also showed that the rhythmic forces were too weak to deform the stiff earth's crust perceptibly. "If only," he thought to himself, "some large part of the earth's surface were covered with a deep sheet of water, surely the deforming forces would make the yielding water sheet rise and fall every 12 hours and 26 minutes, with a variation of range every 14 days, and an alternating inequality of rise every 28 days, and so on." He thereupon resolved to travel into other regions and learn, in case a vast sheet of water were anywhere discovered, whether it really did exhibit rhythmic changes of level in systematic periods such as, according to his calculations, it ought to exhibit.

OBSERVATION, INVENTION, AND DEDUCTION

Curiously enough it happened that about this time the hermit reached a caravansery where he met an alert-looking individual who proved to be an inventor—not an inventor of machines but of hypotheses and theories and explanations. The hermit told him about the tides and their periodic variations, and asked: "What do you suppose makes them go?" The inventor thought a moment and then said: "Perhaps the tides rise and fall because Old Mother Earth is slowly breathing; or perhaps, inasmuch as you say the tides vary every 12 hours and 26 minutes, or twice in a lunar day, they may possibly be driven by the moon." "How can they be driven by anything that is so far away in the sky, and why should one moon make two high tides in one lunar day?" asked the hermit. Just then the recluse came in and, approaching the other two, inquired: "Can you tell me whether there is anywhere a vast sheet of water covering a large part of the earth?" "Yes, there is," said the hermit; "it is called the ocean. I have lived on its shores, observing the periodic rise and fall of its waters in the tides and I was just asking the inventor here if he could tell me how they are caused." The inventor repeated his suggestion that the tides might possibly be caused by a sort of earth-breathing, but that they were more probably caused by the moon. "Well, as to that," exclaimed the recluse, "I can tell you how the tides ought to run if the moon has anything to do with them. The moon ought to produce two high tides on opposite sides of the earth, so that as the earth rotates, the tides at any one point ought to rise and fall twice in a lunar day, as you say they do; not only so, they ought to be extra strong every 14 days at new moon and at full moon, because the sun also must have a share in producing them; and besides that, the high tides ought to show an alternating inequality in a period of 28 days; and"—The astonished hermit interrupted—"They do exactly that," he cried, "but how in the world did you know they do so, if you have never seen the ocean?" "I didn't know they did," replied the recluse, "but I was convinced that *if* the earth had an ocean its waters ought to have rhythmic oscillations of the kind I have described, because don't you see——" and he proceeded to explain his calculations.

VERIFICATION

"What are you men talking about?" said a sedate-looking onlooker of judicial aspect. So the hermit, the inventor and the recluse all repeated their stories to him. He pondered a while and then remarked to the inventor—"It looks very much as if your hypothesis about the moon's driving the tides were correct, for it is hardly conceivable that the consequences of lunar attraction, as thought out by the recluse, and the period of the tides, as observed by the hermit, could agree so well unless the moon and the tides stood in a veritable relation of cause and effect; but the hypothesis needs modification because, as the recluse has pointed out, the secondary variations of the tides show that the sun also has something to do with them." "But," interposed the recluse, "there should be, besides those already mentioned, still other periodic variations in the tides if they are really caused by the moon and the sun, and it will demand of the observer at least a year to detect some of the longer ones." "Take your time," said the judicial onlooker, "go back to the ocean and make a long series of records, not only at one point but at many different points on widely separated coasts; and come back here for a second conference 10 or 20 years hence. We may then reach a well established conclusion."

And thus it came to pass that, after long series of tidal observations had been made in many parts of the world, all the rhythmic consequences deduced from the moon-and-sun theory were so fully confirmed by their correspondence with the observed periodic variations of the tides in the ocean, that—in short, it all ended happily: all the world was convinced that the moon and the sun really do drive the tides.

THE FOUR-FACULTY PROCEDURE OF MODERN SCIENCE

But the moral of the fable is yet to be told. The moral is that the observant hermit, the alert inventor, the thoughtful recluse, and the judicial onlooker represent not four different individuals, but only four different mental faculties in a single individual, the trained man of science, who uses his powers of observation to discover the facts of nature, his inventive ingenuity to propose various possible hypotheses for the explanation of the facts, his power of logical reflection to think out, or deduce, from each hypothesis, in accordance with previously acquired, pertinent knowledge, just what ought to happen if the hypothesis were true, and his impartial faculty of verification to decide which hypothesis, if any, is competent to explain the observed facts. In view of the leading part taken by these four faculties in scientific investigation, we may speak of science as involving a four-faculty procedure. But the fable must not be taken to mean that every scientist has all his faculties developed to the full strength needed for the best work; one man may be a patient observer but not active-minded enough to be a good inventor of hypotheses; another may be an ingenious inventor of hypotheses, but too impatient to be a good observer and too flighty to be a good deducer, and so on. Nor must it be understood that the several faculties work independently; as a matter of fact, now this faculty, now that is called into play in irregular sequence, and very frequently they are summoned into conference with one another. If it were not that the phrase is preoccupied in another connection, we might call such conferences "faculty meetings." Furthermore, it must be pointed out that replacement of mental deduction by experiment is essential in problems of certain kinds; that is, the faculty of invention is called upon, after proposing an explanatory hypothesis, to devise special artificial conditions under which natural processes shall themselves be permitted or constrained to determine the consequences of the hypothesis; but mental deduction usually accompanies or follows experimentation, and therefore problems into which experiment enters may still be included under four-faculty science.

THE FALLIBILITY OF SCIENCE

Unfortunately, in all steps of science from observation to verification, mistakes may be made, errors may creep in. It would be profitable to examine some of the more common classes of errors into which scientific investigators are led by the imperfection of their faculties; and it would be still more profitable to set forth the safeguards by which the danger of making errors may be lessened. Brief comment on observation and verification may be made in these respects. Errors commonly associated with observation result from the unconscious extension of visible things into inferred things, and from the attempt to establish generalizations on too narrow a basis. Consciousness of the danger of these errors goes far toward eliminating them. The most common errors associated with verification are a tendency to adopt an imperfectly supported conclusion instead of maintaining a suspended judgment, and an unwillingness, indeed an inability to change an adopted conclusion after it has been invalidated by new evidence.

As to the latter cause of error it may be said that, if proficiency comes from practice, it would be almost worth while occasionally to lead advanced students to a false conclusion and leave them in it for a time, so that they might have actual practice in changing their minds when corrective evidence is later brought forward. Indeed, scientific training can hardly be regarded as completed until it has included the necessity of giving up a cherished opinion. The experience is distinctly an unpleasant one; it causes mental disturbance to the point of sleeplessness; but it is profitable in promoting the maintenance of a mobile state of mind. . . .

THE NATURE OF THEORIZING

There is a popular prejudice against the use of the inventive faculty, ordinarily called theorizing. Theorizing alone, mere theorizing, is certainly of little value; but trained theorizing in proper association with trained observing is absolutely essential to scientific progress. The chief reason for this is that our observing senses are of limited power. We soon reach the conviction that many facts of nature elude direct observation, either because their medium is inherently transparent and intangible, or because their dimensions are submicroscopic, or because their time of occurrence lay in the irrecoverable past. And yet all of these unobservable phenomena are in their own way just as much a part of the natural world as observable phenomena are. If we wish really to understand the natural world, surely those of its phenomena which are not immediately detectable by our limited senses must be detected in some way or other; and the way usually employed is—theorizing. No single observable fact is a complete entity. The world is not so simply constituted. The deeper one inquires into the nature of an observable present-day fact, the more one becomes persuaded that it is in some way or other related to something else that, for the reasons just given, is not observable; and in such an inquiry one soon becomes convinced that the something else is, in spite of our not seeing it, or hearing it or feeling it, in short not sensing it, just as truly a fact of nature as the sensible fact from which our inquiry started out. The sensible facts are discoverable by our senses, the insensible facts by our thoughts. The invention of hypotheses is therefore nothing more than a mental effort to bring insensible facts into causal relation with sensible facts, and such an effort of correlation is praiseworthy even if it is daring.

Now hypotheses when first invented are as a rule not only incomplete, but are also without assurance of being true, especially with regard to insensible facts. Of course they must explain the observed facts that they were invented to explain; they would deserve no consideration at all if they did not do that! But before any one of several competing hypotheses is accepted as true, it must do more; it must explain facts that it was not invented to explain, facts that were perhaps not known when it was invented; and it must do this consistently with all previously acquired knowledge, so that the new explanation shall cohere with the older ones. Not until these exacting demands are satisfied should the correctness of even the best of several competing hypotheses be accepted. It therefore remains, after several hypotheses have been invented, to determine which one of them, if any, is right; that is, to determine whether the imagined insensible facts of any one of the hypotheses are truly counterparts of actual insensible facts. That important task is accomplished, as was shown in the tidal problem, by mentally deducing all the logical consequences of each hypothesis and then matching them with appropriate sensible facts. If the consequences of a hypothesis are numerous, peculiar and complicated, and if, even so, they succeed in matching equally numerous, peculiar and complicated facts, a good share of which were unknown when the hypothesis was invented, then it is highly probable that that hypothesis it true.

Let me add that it is this demand for the verification of a hypothesis after its invention that especially distinguishes modern science from primitive science, as I shall later show more fully; and it is chiefly because of the demand for verification that the modern progress made in the daring search for insensible facts has been so great. . . .

THE CREDULITY OF SCIENCE

It is not to be denied that much credulity is called for in this daring search for the unobservable facts of the natural world. Science, however, is not alone in credulously building up an unseen world to complement the seen world. That has been done by non-science also for ages past. But the credulity involved in the two cases is unlike. In the latter the credulity is whimsical, fantastic, irresponsible, incoherent; in the former it is orderly, controlled, rational, coherent. During the progress of the human race from savagery toward enlightenment, fantastic, incoherent credulity is slowly replaced by rational, coherent credulity. The belief in witchcraft is a good example of irrational credulity. Let me give you an equally good example of rational credulity. The solution of the tidal problem involves a belief in the force of gravitation, by which two bodies like the moon and the earth or the sun and the earth exert a pulling force upon each other. We are familiar with the exertion of a pulling force through material substance, as when one pulls a heavy body with a rope; but the attraction of the sun upon the earth is exerted through what appears to be empty space. Yet in spite of the absence of anything to pull with, the sun's attraction is strong enough to pull the moving earth continually into the curved path of its orbit. How large a rope or cable do you suppose would be required to represent, in material form, the pull exerted through empty space by the sun on the earth? If the cable were made of ordinary telegraph wires, the wires would have to be planted all over the earth's disc about as close together as grass roots in a lawn, and even then the wires would be stretched almost to breaking strength in compelling the earth to turn from a straight tangent into its curved orbit. Scientific credulity accepts that marvel. . . .

THE SCHEME OF THE GEOGRAPHICAL CYCLE

Let us now turn to an altogether different example of scientific inquiry, a geographical inquiry concerning the distribution of plants and animals over the earth's surface. Climate is an important factor in controlling their distribution. Now climate varies not only from equator to pole but also with altitude above sea level. Lowlands are warmer and as a rule drier than highlands. But a lowland may, it is believed, be changed to a highland by the gradual upheaval of its part of the earth's crust; and it is believed further that a highland thus produced must in the course of time be worn down to a lowland again by the still more gradual processes of erosion. A warm lowland with a moderate rainfall may therefore be upheaved into a cool or cold highland with greater rainfall; and after the forces of upheaval have ceased, the cool and rainy highland may be very slowly worn down to a warm and less rainy lowland again. Evidently there must be changes in the flora and fauna of a region while it is undergoing these changes of altitude and of climate. As a lowland is raised into a highland and its climate modified, its former flora and fauna can not survive, because they can not accommodate themselves to the new climatic conditions. They are therefore replaced by immigrants from some neighboring highland or from some lower land nearer the pole. Likewise the occupants of a highland can not survive the changes of climate that take place as it is worn down to a lowland; they are therefore gradually replaced by invaders from some other lowland not too far away. It is instructive to note that these changes of the earth's surface, slow as they may be, are faster as a rule than the evolutionary changes of plants and animals. Hence, in a long view of the earth one would see its plants and animals not only undergoing their extremely slow evolutionary changes, but also making somewhat less slow migrations, prompted by and accompanying the upheavals and downwearings of its surface; and the present distribution of plants and animals is believed to be simply a transitory phase in this long succession of changes.

How different is this problem of the cycle of geographical changes from that of the tides. The rapid changes of the tides are directly observable; they are moreover periodic and their changes can therefore be observed over and over again; and both they and their cause are susceptible of quantitative mathematical treatment. The changes of the geographical cycle are so slow that they can not be followed, they can only be imagined; and there is no reason for believing that such cycles of change are accomplished in a definite period, nor indeed that any given cycle will run its entire course without disturbance; the downwearing of a highland to a lowland may be interrupted during its progress by a new upheaval. Moreover the asserted extinctions and invasions of plants and animals following the changes in the climate of their habitat are only inferences. In a word, this scheme of the geographical cycle is in its very nature highly speculative. Why then should credence be given to it? For the very simple reason that only by believing it can a host of present-day observable facts, inorganic and organic, be brought into reasonable relations. In short, the scheme of the geographical cycle is believed because it works; and therefore, like many other scientific conclusions, it is an excellent example of pragmatic philosophy. . . .

THE NATURE OF SCIENTIFIC DEMONSTRATION

But what does a man mean when he says that he believes the scheme of the geographical cycle, with its imagined yet unseen changes of land forms and its inferred yet unobserved changes in the distribution of plants and animals? He ought not to mean that the truth of the scheme has been absolutely proved, but only that it has been given a very high order of probability; for that is, as a rule, the nature of what is often called scientific demonstration. He ought to recognize also that many generalizations on which the argumentation of the scheme rests are likewise not absolutely proved: for example, the persistence of the present-day order of natural processes through hundreds of millions of years of past time; to say nothing of the unbroken continuity of time itself! Who can prove the truth of those generalizations in any absolute sense? Nevertheless one accepts their truth because he finds, after due inquiry, that they too appear to have a high order of probability.

Now what is the common feature in the problem of the tides and the problem of the geographical cycle, and in all other scientific problems, in virtue of the possession of which they deserve to be called scientific? Evidently not the subjects that they treat, for the subjects of scientific study are remarkably diverse. The common feature inheres not in the content of the problems but in their method; and the common feature of their method is the quality of reasonableness; that is, a spirit of free inquiry, in which no prepossessions are accepted which are not themselves open to scrutiny, in which the conclusions reached are followed wherever they lead, and in which a revision of conclusions is made whenever it is demanded by new facts. Science is therefore not final any more than it is infallible. It is a growth, and its growth is by no means completed. . . .

1922

SCIENCE AND ENGINEERING *

WILLIAM F. DURAND

We shall all agree, I think, that progress in civilization depends upon putting ourselves more and more fully in partnership with nature and thus working with her as an ally or partner in the utilization of her constructive materials, her energies, and her laws.

If we take any one element of our material progress in civilization and

* Presented at the annual meeting of the American Association for the Advancement of Science, Kansas City, Kansas, Dec. 28, 1925, to Jan. 2, 1926. Reprinted from *Mechanical Engineering*, April, 1926, by permission from The American Society of Mechanical Engineers. Copyright 1926 by The American Society of Mechanical Engineers.

trace out its life history, or, to vary the figure, subject it to some form of qualitative analysis, we shall find that it is the terminal product of a vast number of interconnecting lines of human effort and study, all in a sense converging toward this one end and tracing back in orderly progression to perhaps a widely diversified group of what we term "fundamental" or "basic" facts or laws of nature. It is through these laws of nature, as they work out in terms of application to the intricate and vast field of phenomena, that we are able to come into more effective partnership with her and thus enter more fully into the enjoyment of the treasures which she has laid away in store for us.

But what is a fundamental or basic fact or law of nature? Is it more than the momentarily last stage in our attempt to explain the phenomena of nature in terms of a certain limited number of concepts and relations which we term "basic"? But in this process of observation, classification, comparison, and arrangement in sequence, we never reach the last term. Any so-called explanation is only an expression of relation to some other phenomenon or series of phenomena, and so on without limit. The ultimate explanation always lies beyond, and always will.

We may explain the fall of the apple by gravitation, but who shall explain gravitation? We may explain the color of the sea as due to the passage of light into and out of a colloidal solution, but who shall explain light or the nature of its interaction with a colloidal particle? We may explain water as a chemical combination of hydrogen and oxygen, and we may explain the two-to-nine weight ratio by reference to atomic weights and to valencies, and we may attempt to explain atomic weights and valencies and combining proportions through the properties of protons and electrons; but who shall explain to us the proton and the electron? And if perchance the coming years shall bring an explanation of these, it will only be in terms of some other entities or concepts which will then stand for the moment as the ne plus ultra.

If in any particular case we trace out the derivation from the terminal result back to what seems to be the ultimate source, we shall find the structure as a whole resting upon a formation of so-called basic law, the range of application of which is in nowise limited to the particular and narrow purpose in view. As we pass, however, from this foundation forward toward the terminal result, and along numerous and converging lines, the field of application of the studies which we traverse and of the results which they produce becomes progressively narrowed, until finally all converge upon one single terminal purpose as the ultimate expression of this particular combination of nature's building materials.

MATERIAL ELEMENTS OF OUR CIVILIZATION TERMINAL PRODUCTS OF A CONVERGING SERIES OF STUDIES

It thus appears that any particular facility or material element of our civilization of which we today enjoy the use, may be viewed as the terminal product of a series of converging studies, each one of which has proceeded from the general to the particular, and all of which are applicable to wider and wider fields of application, the farther back we go from the particular narrow purpose or terminal end from which we start.

Now, largely as a matter of convenience, there has come about the custom of dividing up this one continuous sequence of investigation and study into phases or stages designated by such terms as "scientific" or "fundamental" research, and "engineering," or "engineering and industrial," research. Actually the sequence is continuous and the point at which one type of research ends and another begins, or the proper designation of any one particular study can often be determined only by an act of arbitrary choice. Any research, no matter by what name we may characterize it, is simply an interrogation of nature, and it is only by the use of secondary and perhaps accidental characteristics that we may find some reason for giving to it one name or another.

In our attempts to understand or to explain the phenomena of nature, we have, as I have already pointed out, reached for the moment certain ultimate terms and concepts. Thus with reference to the inorganic world, we attempt to explain the phenomena with which we come into contact through such concepts as center about the terms "time," "space," "mass," "energy," "force," "the ether molecules," "atoms," "electrons," "protons," "quanta," etc., together with the observed relations between and among these various expressions of the objective world. And when any phenomenon is connected through some observed sequence back to these basic concepts it is said to be explained.

Many researches and a noble army of research workers are concerned with this basic field of activity. Some are concerned with efforts to widen our acquaintance with, and understanding of, these basic counters of which I have just spoken; others are engaged in the search for new and still broader generalizations—still more fundamental counters wherewith to explain our explanations; others still are engaged in the attempt to link up through continuous sequences, apparently remote and empirical observations of fact with these present basic counters. All such activities surely merit the designation of "fundamental research," and the body of knowledge which results therefrom is properly called "fundamental science."

We shall all agree, however, that the results of fundamental research stored away as in a granary and never translated into the service of human needs, have failed of realizing their highest use, and that the ideal is and must be that all knowledge of nature should be turned in some way into expression in terms of service to humanity.

To realize this end there must be, therefore, a vast and diversified field of activity dealing with the applications of these results to specific human problems; and so there have grown up the terms of "applied science" and of "applied" or "engineering" or "industrial" research.

In fundamental research the particular application to human problems is not directly within the field of vision. In applied research it necessarily must be. This fact of the presence or absence of some immediate purpose of a utilitarian character, is very commonly made the basis of determination as to whether the research shall receive one designation or the other.

Again, the economic factor is one which bears a distinctly different relation to these two fields of research. Broadly speaking, in fundamental research we do not count the cost of the terminal product. We are seeking for light on the pathways along which nature moves, and when once this particular bit of pathway is illuminated, our goal is achieved. The cost of producing the terminal product is not a factor in this stage of the study.

If, however, results thus achieved are to be translated into the service of humanity, the process must be within economic reach.

It has in fact become almost a commonplace that research and its application to the demands of civilization must pass through the two stages of, first, a laboratory process or research method, serving to establish the broad features or to demonstrate the general laws involved, and, second, of studies intended to translate the process from the laboratory to the shop, from something possible under laboratory conditions to something economically feasible under industrial conditions.

We remember when aluminum was well enough known in a small sample way and available by what might be termed "laboratory" processes. It only became possible for aluminum to realize its possibilities as a structural element when the processes became so modified as to place the product within the economic range for structural materials.

Again, helium was once known as belonging in a space in the Mendeljeff series, or again as a substance represented by a line in the solar spectrum. Later it became known in a small way through laboratory processes, but at a cost of production which would have rendered impracticable any economic use, had there been any demand of this character. But with the advent of such a demand as a feature of airship construction during the war, and with the discovery of relatively large sources of supply in our Southwestern gas wells, a combination of physics, thermodynamics, and machine design brought the solution, and helium, as a filler for airships, has now become an economic possibility. Doubtless other uses will develop.

The domain of technology and industry teems with like illustrations—the refining of crude oil, the development of the steam turbine and of the internal-combustion engine, the manufacture of dyes, explosives, and fertilizers, of toothpicks and matches, and of thousands of other products of industry from needles to steel nails, from window glass to portland cement and pottery, or from writing paper to rubber tires—all have witnessed the same evolution from the laboratory phase, perhaps crude and imperfect and far outside the economic range, through to the final industrial and economic status.

In this process of development and of economic refinement, moreover, it may happen, and in fact very commonly does, that necessary links in the chain are found to be studies or researches which are, in themselves, distinctly fundamental in character. Thus the economical production of helium required the application of advanced and special studies in thermodynamics. Or again, in many of the chemical industries, such as the production of H_2CO_4 or the fixation of nitrogen, the use of catalyzers has developed as a fundamentally important factor. But some understanding of the operation of catalyzers and some basis for their intelligent and efficient use is only now coming into the light, resulting from studies on the firing line of advanced theory regarding the structure of the atom. Or again, engineering or industrial studies looking toward the development of the most efficient design of devices for securing the interchange of heat between liquids, gases, and vapors separated by metal partitions, are attracting much attention in recent years. Such studies, for their effective prosecution, call upon theories of steam flow, of turbulence and its nature, of the mechanism of heat transfer from one molecule to another, and thence to the most recent theories of the constitution of the molecule and of the atom.

FUNDAMENTAL VERSUS INDUSTRIAL RESEARCH

And so on every hand, studies in which the economical factor is paramount and in which the direct purpose is industrial rather than fundamental, include as essential features, researches and studies which in themselves are distinctly basic in character. And so in the pursuit of any one purpose, stated in industrial terms, there may be found researches and studies in the most diverse fields, and of all types as regards status, from the most thoroughly fundamental to the purely industrial—and all as essential elements in the program of development.

Again, in many cases of research the question asked or the end in view may be of a purely empirical or observational character, perhaps without reference to any useful applications, and likewise without relation to any sequence carrying back to what I have termed our "fundamental counters." It is often of the highest importance that the answers to questions of this character be determined at the earliest practicable moment, leaving to other times or to other agencies the task of connecting them up with more fundamental concepts. In other cases such empirical results are set down simply as so much material, without reference to utilization or terminal purpose, but simply as classified observation, awaiting the time when in adequate amount it may serve as a means for reasoning from such empirical results back to some earlier stage in the sequence leading to the ultimate counters.

But these various interrogations of nature, no matter what the particular relation to their environment, are of the essence of research, and their results constitute the great body of science viewed as a whole. Broadly, we may say that in proportion as the study deals with the phenomena of nature with more remote reference to specific purposes or applications, to such extent is the research the more fundamental in character; and in proportion as it is more narrowly focused on a single or utilitarian purpose, to such extent does it more definitely belong in the engineering or industrial category.

But the important point is not by what name we shall call a given research, but rather to recognize the fact that all types and forms find their place and serve their purpose as essential elements in our continuous approach toward nature and a better understanding of her ways.

If fundamental research is to realize its measure of service to the cause of human progress, it can only do so as it is carried on to useful application through specific studies directed to that end. It is no less true that in our efforts to ally ourselves with nature and to seek from her wherewith to answer the many needs of our modern civilization, we should find ourselves in a blind path without these more fundamental studies to light the way.

Engineering and industrial research are thus indissolubly tied in with fundamental research as a starting point. And these two phases of research are after all only the two indivisible parts of a single procedure which leads us from nature and her infinite complexity of orderly sequence down through to the most humble and simple application to the needs of humanity in its progress along a rising gradient of civilization.

ILLUSTRATIONS SHOWING THE DEPENDENCE OF APPLIED SCIENCE UPON FUNDAMENTAL SCIENCE

At this point, perhaps, some further illustrations may be of use, not in detail but only by way of mere mention, and only in order the better to bring out the intimate dependence of applied science upon fundamental science or otherwise to show the manner in which the results of such fundamental research works through to its goal in terms of useful application to human needs.

In selecting such illustrations, the principal trouble is with the wealth of material. There is, indeed, an embarrassment of riches, and in selecting here and there I shall choose only at random from some of the arbitrary subdivisions into which we partition the field of scientific work.

If we take first that most exact of the sciences, mathematics, we have the foundation of all quantitative measurement and comparison as used throughout the whole domain of engineering and industry. What, again, of logarithms and their expression in the slide rule—that tried and trusty friend of the engineer?

Or again, what of the theory of dimensions, dimensional analysis, and the principles of similitude? The entire art of shipbuilding as a field of engineering and industry is dependent, so far as the determination of matters relating to resistance and propulsion are concerned, upon the application of experimental methods which rest upon these mathematical cornerstones. The same is true of aircraft resistance and propulsion, as well as of many other parts of the domain of engineering and industry where these principles, developed and contributed by the mathematician, furnish a most valuable and indeed a necessary element in the treatment of the problem involved.

Or still again, what of the theory of elasticity and its development at the hands of a long line of illustrious mathematicians? The entire theory of structures and the practice in structural engineering trace for their foundation back to principles which have their roots deep in the physical properties of matter as developed, interpreted, and applied through the aid of mathematics and the labor of mathematicians.

If we turn to another type of illustration, what of Carnot and his immortal principle, or of Fourier and his equally immortal series?

The whole domain of power from heat rests for its economic realization on the principle laid down by Carnot and developed as the product of his own penetrating insight into the laws which nature has laid upon herself in regard to the transformation of heat energy into mechanical work.

It is perhaps doubtful if in the domain of science and engineering there is to be found a more striking example of far-reaching application to the progress of civilization than this product of pure reasoning in the brain of Carnot. The very name of his paper suggests its source in his own mind —"Reflections"—reflections on the motive power of heat.

Again, it seems like a long step between the foretelling of the rise and fall of the tide with such a degree of reliability and precision as to tell just when the commerce of the world may enter our harbors and when it may not, and the investigation of the phenomena of the flow of heat along a metal bar. But all of this and much more has come out of Fourier's classic researches on the latter problem.

Again, in this same domain of heat there are perhaps no problems of greater practical importance than those which relate fundamentally to the transmission of heat from a molecule of one kind to another molecule of a different kind. On this basic problem depend all manner of industrial operations involving the use of heat—steam boilers, condensers, coolers, heaters, heat exchangers of all sorts and for realizing an exchange of heat between solids, liquids, gases, and vapors, in all combinations and in infinite variety of applications in the arts and industries. But the intelligent study of these problems in their terminal applications, all traces back to fundamental problems in physics, and in particular to the mechanism of the exchange of heat energy between molecules of different kinds and at different temperature levels. Any effective study of the terminal problems and their application in the arts and industries is dependent on these fundamental studies; and on the other hand, such studies into the structure of matter and the properties of molecules, leading as they must into the modern electron theory of the constitution of the atom, find some of their most useful applications in industries in pointing the way to a better understanding of the conditions which surround this problem of the transfer of heat energy from one molecule to another.

If we take an illustration from the field of metallurgy, we cannot perhaps find a better one than that furnished by the recent developments in the study of metal crystals and crystal aggregates, as bearing on the physical properties of metals, especially strength, yield point, and hardness.

These fundamental researches have thrown in recent times a flood of light on hitherto most obscure phenomena relative to the properties of metals, and promise ultimately to furnish some measurably satisfactory explanation of the intricate conditions affecting the tempering and hardening of such aggregates as steel and duralumin.

In a high sense, furthermore, these investigations are fundamental since they are not merely the empirical expression of observation, but seek rather to develop an explanation through a study of the relation between the observed terminal phenomena and certain other more basic conditions expressed in terms of crystal structure, and so on in sequence back to fundamental concepts.

The field of chemistry is especially rich in material illustrative of the close dependence of industrial research, as expressed in terms of terminal products, upon fundamental chemical research. To mention only a few, what of fertilizers and explosives, synthetic fuels, synthetic drugs, synthetic silk and now wool and perhaps rubber, the dye industry, paints and varnishes, and like materials? The industrial production of substances such as these traces back to fundamental chemical research as its absolutely essential point of departure. . . .

AERONAUTIC ENGINEERING A FIELD WELL ILLUSTRATING THE ESSENTIAL UNITY THAT MUST CHARACTERIZE ALL RESEARCH WORK

By way of another illustration, let me turn your attention to the field of aeronautics and aeronautic engineering. This happens to be a field in which my own interests have been engaged in recent years, and perhaps for that reason it seems to me to furnish a peculiarly good illustration of that essential unity which must characterize all research work, no matter by what particular name it may be called.

The development of the airplane has resulted through the convergence of three measurably distinct lines of research and study. There is first the field of aerodynamics which deals with the airplane in relation to its sustentation, movement, and behavior in the air; and then there is the field of structural engineering, including the theory of structures in its most refined and complete form; and then again the field of thermodynamics and heat engineering which deals with the ways and means of converting heat energy liberated from liquid fuels into the mechanical work required for propulsion—and all under the limitations of weight and size imposed by the conditions of airplane flight.

We have here at the foundation, mathematics, physics, fluid mechanics, rigid structures and their mechanics, thermodynamics, and chemistry in its relation to many problems of glues, dopes, varnishes, anti-knock fuels, etc. And over and throughout this entire field there have been studies which are truly fundamental in character, serving as stepping stones again for others more immediately related to the airplane as a terminal result, and so continuously focusing more and more directly upon the ultimate goal—the realization of a structure which, supplied with a source of energy, shall, under human control and direction, be able to rise from the earth, move as may be desired in the air, and return again to the earth.

Running throughout this complex of research and study is the continuous demonstration of the extent to which progress toward any one specific goal may require the widest variety of seemingly remote and fundamental studies. As one illustration, the problem of the liquid-fuel-injection engine as adapted to aircraft requirements has for some time been the subject of study. One of the earliest phases of this study has related to ways and means of obtaining a photographic history of the formation and progressive development of a jet of liquid when forced under high pressure through a small aperture. This required an extended and independent study of rapid-motion photography with time exposures infinitesimal in extent. Other problems have related to the mechanics of the formation and flow of periodic jets of liquid through orifices of different form and in the brief time available as a small fraction of the cycle of a high-speed engine of the aircraft type; still others have related to the character of the combustion of such jets and the conditions affecting the progress of flame through them. Again, other needful studies have related to matters bearing on the types of mechanism best suited to meet the particular combination of requirements presented, and still other to matters of design, structural materials, etc.

Certain of these studies are essentially fundamental in character while others are directly focused on specific objectives, but all are essential, and the terminal result is simply the joint product of this complex series of studies, each one of which has contributed some element to the realization of the ultimate goal.

One further illustration in a different field will again show the same interdependence. The law of kinematic similitude, if perfectly realized, permits the determination of the resistance and other conditions of movement in the case of a full-sized body moving relative to a fluid through the use of a small model, geometrically similar and moving with a velocity as determined by the law of similitude. But in the case of airplane structures and air as the fluid, the conditions of similitude can rarely be met. For a small model the velocities become too high for practical realization. It thus results that with small models in normal air there is need of a correction known as the "scale factor" and intended to make up for this lack of fulfillment of the requirements for complete similitude. But the evaluation of such a factor is attended with much difficulty, and to the degree to which the conditions of complete similitude can be approached, to such extent will uncertainty be removed.

Now one method by which these conditions may be more nearly realized is by the use of air under an increased pressure and density instead of air under normal atmospheric conditions. In such case the spacing of the molecules of air in relation to the dimensions of the model may be made similar to that of the molecules of free air in relation to the dimensions of the full-sized body, and thus at workable velocities the conditions of similitude may be realized.

In order to make use of these principles, an air tunnel inclosed in a steel shell and intended for the use of a current of air under high pressure and density has been designed and installed in the laboratory of the National Advisory Committee for Aeronautics at Langley Field, Va., and with this equipment a wide range of research has been carried on, in part broadly fundamental and intended to develop a better understanding of the basic phenomena attending the movement of a solid within a fluid, and in part more immediately directed toward the solution of specific problems in aeronautic engineering.

The design and construction of this piece of laboratory equipment in itself, again, called for the widest variety of investigation into special problems in physics, in the theory of elasticity as applied to structures, and in design and construction.

But if to reach any specific goal, research of varied types must cooperate and interlock, and if, as in many of the preceding illustrations, applied research is continually falling back on phases of fundamental research, it is none the less true that the latter, for its tools and implements, its ways and means, is as continually falling back on applied research and its results. A single illustration will suffice.

A recent visit to the Bureau of Standards in Washington gave opportunity to examine the piece of equipment which is to serve for a really monumental research on the properties of water vapor up to pressures of perhaps 80 atmospheres.

Thus far and for two years and more the work has been concerned with the construction of the apparatus—with searches for suitable materials of construction, with the design of valves and joints, with the study of methods for preventing or minimizing leakage—material, thermal, and electrical. Thus far the research has been wholly in the applied field. With the apparatus completed, the final and fundamental stage will be ushered in.

Illustrations beyond number of this essential interlocking of all types of research may be drawn from any or from all of the fields of activity of the scientist and of the engineer.

CONCLUSION

I have thus attempted to visualize the material elements of our civilization, as complex products of manifold studies, fundamental and applied, interlocking, and tracing back ultimately to the broad and fundamental concepts, through which for the moment, we attempt to interpret the phenomena of nature. Those studies deal with nature in all her aspects and from all avenues of approach. Some deal with what I have called our "basic counters" or with the linking up of observed phenomena with such counters. Others deal more directly with terminal results, and in an immediate or observational way. If we may look upon these various studies and their results as building blocks, then out of this building material we have builded, in almost infinite variety of combination, the terminal products which go to make up the material content of our civilization.

If we seek to compare these two types of building material as they have entered into any one terminal product, or to ask which of the two is the more important, there is no answer to the query. Both are essential, as we have seen.

But if we are thinking in terms of progress, if now and hitherto unknown results are to be realized, then *new* building material must be available, and in the way of such new material we shall agree, I believe, that the products of basic or fundamental research are of greater significance than those resulting from more narrowly focused studies. It is more valuable for us to have some knowledge of the crystalline aggregates which go to make up steel as a basis for explaining its properties, than to record the fact that plunging red-hot steel into water will harden it. It is more important for us to have some working theory of the conduction of electricity in metals than to merely know that copper is a better conductor than iron. It is more important to have some working theory of the molecular constitution of metals and of the results thereon of repeated stress, than to merely record the number of million times any particular sample may withstand a particular repetition of stress before rupture.

A new basic relation in nature, a new linking up of observed phenomena with our basic counters, may open up an entirely new series of practical and useful results. It constitutes a new source, available for use in combination with all other known sources, and with vast and unknown potentialities for useful application.

If, then, we are to carry on along an ascending gradient of human progress, we must look to the provision of new building material or, to vary the figure, of new sources of basic knowledge. Without such, the streams of progress will become dried at the source. Without such continued activity as a nation, we shall be left behind in the world condition.

It perhaps runs with the so-called practical character of our genius, that as a nation our contribution to world progress has lain thus far more largely along lines of applied science than along those more fundamental in character. In the former lines of research and achievement we have made a record in reasonable relation to our endowments and our opportunities. It is not clear that we have made or are making a like record along the latter lines.

As a nation we are spending, year by year, in one form or another, sums which bulk to enormous magnitudes for research along lines of engineering and industrial research. We are not supporting in like proportionate degree research along more fundamental lines. We are cultivating the lower reaches of flowing stream and quiet pool, and, at least in relative degree, we are neglecting the living sources nearer the mountain tops. A more just balance is needed in the support which we are giving to these two lines of effort. . . .

1926

THE PLACE OF SCIENCE IN A LIBERAL EDUCATION *

BERTRAND RUSSELL

I

Science, to the ordinary reader of newspapers, is represented by a varying selection of sensational triumphs, such as wireless telegraphy and aeroplanes, radio-activity and the marvels of modern alchemy. It is not of this aspect of science that I wish to speak. Science, in this aspect, consists of detached up-to-date fragments, interesting only until they are replaced by something newer and more up-to-date, displaying nothing of the systems of patiently constructed knowledge out of which, almost as a casual incident, have come the practically useful results which interest the man in the street. The increased command over the forces of nature which is de-

* Reprinted from *Mysticism and Logic*, by Bertrand Russell, by permission of W. W. Norton & Company, Inc., New York. Copyright 1929 by the publishers.

rived from science is undoubtedly an amply sufficient reason for encouraging scientific research, but this reason has been so often urged and is so easily appreciated that other reasons, to my mind quite as important, are apt to be overlooked. It is with these other reasons, especially with the intrinsic value of a scientific habit of mind in forming our outlook on the world, that I shall be concerned in what follows.

The instance of wireless telegraphy will serve to illustrate the difference between the two points of view. Almost all the serious intellectual labour required for the possibility of this invention is due to three men—Faraday, Maxwell, and Hertz. In alternating layers of experiment and theory these three men built up the modern theory of electromagnetism, and demonstrated the identity of light with electromagnetic waves. The system which they discovered is one of profound intellectual interest, bringing together and unifying an endless variety of apparently detached phenomena, and displaying a cumulative mental power which cannot but afford delight to every generous spirit. The mechanical details which remained to be adjusted in order to utilise their discoveries for a practical system of telegraphy demanded, no doubt, very considerable ingenuity, but had not that broad sweep and that universality which could give them intrinsic interest as an object of disinterested contemplation.

From the point of view of training the mind, of giving that well-informed, impersonal outlook which constitutes culture in the good sense of this much-misused word, it seems to be generally held indisputable that a literary education is superior to one based on science. Even the warmest advocates of science are apt to rest their claims on the contention that culture ought to be sacrificed to utility. Those men of science who respect culture, when they associate with men learned in the classics, are apt to admit, not merely politely, but sincerely, a certain inferiority on their side, compensated doubtless by the services which science renders to humanity, but none the less real. And so long as this attitude exists among men of science, it tends to verify itself: the intrinsically valuable aspects of science tend to be sacrificed to the merely useful, and little attempt is made to preserve that leisurely, systematic survey by which the finer quality of mind is formed and nourished.

But even if there be, in present fact, any such inferiority as is supposed in the educational value of science, this is, I believe, not the fault of science itself, but the fault of the spirit in which science is taught. If its full possibilities were realised by those who teach it, I believe that its capacity of producing those habits of mind which constitute the highest mental excellence would be at least as great as that of literature, and more particularly of Greek and Latin literature. In saying this I have no wish whatever to disparage a classical education. I have not myself enjoyed its benefits, and my knowledge of Greek and Latin authors is derived almost wholly from translations. But I am firmly persuaded that the Greeks fully deserve all the admiration that is bestowed upon them, and that it is a very great and serious loss to be unacquainted with their writings. It is not by attacking them, but by drawing attention to neglected excellences in science, that I wish to conduct my argument.

One defect, however, does seem inherent in a purely classical education —namely, a too exclusive emphasis on the past. By the study of what is absolutely ended and can never be renewed, a habit of criticism towards the present and the future is engendered. The qualities in which the present excels are qualities to which the study of the past does not direct attention, and to which, therefore, the student of Greek civilisation may easily become blind. In what is new and growing there is apt to be something crude, insolvent, even a little vulgar, which is shocking to the man of sensitive taste; quivering from the rough contact, he retires to the trim gardens of a polished past, forgetting that they were reclaimed from the wilderness by men as rough and earth-soiled as those from whom he shrinks in his own day. The habit of being unable to recognise merit until it is dead is too apt to be the result of a purely bookish life, and a culture based wholly on the past will seldom be able to pierce through everyday surroundings to the essential splendour of contemporary things, or to the hope of still greater splendour in the future.

> "My eyes saw not the men of old;
> And now their age away has rolled.
> I weep—to think I shall not see
> The heroes of posterity."

So says the Chinese poet; but such impartiality is rare in the more pugnacious atmosphere of the West, where the champions of past and future fight a never-ending battle, instead of combining to seek out the merits of both.

This consideration, which militates not only against the exclusive study of the classics, but against every form of culture which has become static, traditional, and academic, leads inevitably to the fundamental question: What is the true end of education? But before attempting to answer this question it will be well to define the sense in which we are to use the word "education." For this purpose I shall distinguish the sense in which I mean to use it from two others, both perfectly legitimate, the one broader and the other narrower than the sense in which I mean to use the word.

In the broader sense, education will include not only what we learn through instruction, but all that we learn through personal experience—the formation of character through the education of life. Of this aspect of education, vitally important as it is, I will say nothing, since its consideration would introduce topics quite foreign to the question with which we are concerned.

In the narrower sense, education may be confined to instruction, the imparting of definite information on various subjects, because such information, in and for itself, is useful in daily life. Elementary education—reading, writing, and arithmetic—is almost wholly of this kind. But instruction, necessary as it is, does not *per se* constitute education in the sense in which I wish to consider it.

Education, in the sense in which I mean it, may be defined as *the formation, by means of instruction, of certain mental habits and a certain outlook on life and the world.* It remains to ask ourselves, what mental habits, and what sort of outlook, can be hoped for as the result of instruction? When we have answered this question we can attempt to decide what science has to contribute to the formation of the habits and outlook which we desire.

Our whole life is built about a certain number—not a very small number—of primary instincts and impulses. Only what is in some way connected with these instincts and impulses appears to us desirable or important; there is no faculty, whether "reason" or "virtue" or whatever it may be called, that can take our active life and our hopes and fears outside the region controlled by these first movers of all desire. Each of them is like a queen-bee, aided by a hive of workers gathering honey; but when the queen is gone the workers languish and die, and the cells remain empty of their expected sweetness. So with each primary impulse in civilised man: it is surrounded and protected by a busy swarm of attendant derivative desires, which store up in its service whatever honey the surrounding world affords. But if the queen-impulse dies, the death-dealing influence, though retarded a little by habit, spreads slowly through all the subsidiary impulses, and a whole tract of life becomes inexplicably colourless. What was formerly full of zest, and so obviously worth doing that it raised no questions, has now grown dreary and purposeless: with a sense of disillusion we inquire the meaning of life, and decide, perhaps, that all is vanity. The search for an outside meaning that can *compel* an inner response must always be disappointed: all "meaning" must be at bottom related to our primary desires, and when they are extinct no miracle can restore to the world the value which they reflected upon it.

The purpose of education, therefore, cannot be to create any primary impulse which is lacking in the uneducated; the purpose can only be to enlarge the scope of those that human nature provides, by increasing the number and variety of attendant thoughts, and by showing where the most permanent satisfaction is to be found. Under the impulse of a Calvinistic horror of the "natural man," this obvious truth has been too often misconceived in the training of the young; "nature" has been falsely regarded as excluding all that is best in what is natural, and the endeavour to teach virtue has led to the production of stunted and contorted hypocrites instead of full-grown human beings. From such mistakes in education a better psychology or a kinder heart is beginning to preserve the present generation;

we need, therefore, waste no more words on the theory that the purpose of education is to thwart or eradicate nature.

But although nature must supply the initial force of desire, nature is not, in the civilised man, the spasmodic, fragmentary, and yet violent set of impulses that it is in the savage. Each impulse has its constitutional ministry of thought and knowledge and reflection, through which possible conflicts of impulses are foreseen, and temporary impulses are controlled by the unifying impulse which may be called wisdom. In this way education destroys the crudity of instinct, and increases through knowledge the wealth and variety of the individual's contacts with the outside world, making him no longer an isolated fighting unit, but a citizen of the universe, embracing distant countries, remote regions of space, and vast stretches of past and future within the circle of his interests. It is this simultaneous softening in the insistence of desire and enlargement of its scope that is the chief moral end of education.

Closely connected with this moral end is the more purely intellectual aim of education, the endeavour to make us see and imagine the world in an objective manner, as far as possible as it is in itself, and not merely through the distorting medium of personal desire. The complete attainment of such an objective view is no doubt an ideal, indefinitely approachable, but not actually and fully realisable. Education, considered as a process of forming our mental habits and our outlook on the world, is to be judged successful in proportion as its outcome approximates to this ideal; in proportion, that is to say, as it gives us a true view of our place in society, of the relation of the whole human society to its nonhuman environment, and of the nature of the nonhuman world as it is in itself apart from our desires and interests. If this standard is admitted, we can return to the consideration of science, inquiring how far science contributes to such an aim, and whether it is in any respect superior to its rivals in educational practice.

II

Two opposite and at first sight conflicting merits belong to science as against literature and art. The one, which is not inherently necessary, but is certainly true at the present day, is hopefulness as to the future of human achievement, and in particular as to the useful work that may be accomplished by any intelligent student. This merit and the cheerful outlook which it engenders prevent what might otherwise be the depressing effect of another aspect of science, to my mind also a merit, and perhaps its greatest merit—I mean the irrelevance of human passions and of the whole subjective apparatus where scientific truth is concerned. Each of these reasons for preferring the study of science requires some amplification. Let us begin with the first.

In the study of literature or art our attention is perpetually riveted upon the past: the men of Greece or of the Renaissance did better than any men do now; the triumphs of former ages, so far from facilitating fresh triumphs in our own age, actually increase the difficulty of fresh triumphs by rendering originality harder of attainment; not only is artistic achievement not cumulative, but it seems even to depend upon a certain freshness and *naïveté* of impulse and vision which civilisation tends to destroy. Hence comes, to those who have been nourished on the literary and artistic productions of former ages, a certain peevishness and undue fastidiousness towards the present, from which there seems no escape except into the deliberate vandalism which ignores tradition and in the search after originality achieves only the eccentric. But in such vandalism there is none of the simplicity and spontaneity out of which great art springs: theory is still the canker in its core, and insincerity destroys the advantages of a merely pretended ignorance.

The despair thus arising from an education which suggests no preeminent mental activity except that of artistic creation is wholly absent from an education which gives the knowledge of scientific method. The discovery of scientific method, except in pure mathematics, is a thing of yesterday; speaking broadly, we may say that it dates from Galileo. Yet already it has transformed the world, and its success proceeds with ever-accelerating velocity. In science men have discovered an activity of the very highest value in which they are no longer, as in art, dependent for progress upon the appearance of continually greater genius, for in science the successors stand upon the shoulders of their predecessors; where one man of supreme genius has invented a method, a thousand lesser men can apply it. No transcendent ability is required in order to make useful discoveries in science; the edifice of science needs its masons, bricklayers, and common labourers as well as its foremen, master-builders, and architects. In art nothing worth doing can be done without genius; in science even a very moderate capacity can contribute to a supreme achievement.

In science the man of real genius is the man who invents a new method. The notable discoveries are often made by his successors, who can apply the method with fresh vigour, unimpaired by the previous labour of perfecting it; but the mental calibre of the thought required for their work, however brilliant, is not so great as that required by the first inventor of the method. There are in science immense numbers of different methods, appropriate to different classes of problems; but over and above them all, there is something not easily definable, which may be called *the* method of science. It was formerly customary to identify this with the inductive method, and to associate it with the name of Bacon. But the true inductive method was not discovered by Bacon, and the true method of science is something which includes deduction as much as induction, logic and mathematics as much as botany and geology. I shall not attempt the difficult task of stating what the scientific method is, but I will try to indicate the temper of mind out of which the scientific method grows, which is the second of the two merits that were mentioned above as belonging to a scientific education.

The kernel of the scientific outlook is a thing so simple, so obvious, so seemingly trivial, that the mention of it may almost excite derision. The kernel of the scientific outlook is the refusal to regard our own desires, tastes, and interests as affording a key to the understanding of the world. Stated thus baldly, this may seem no more than a trite truism. But to remember it consistently in matters arousing our passionate partisanship is by no means easy, especially where the available evidence is uncertain and inconclusive. A few illustrations will make this clear.

Aristotle, I understand, considered that the stars must move in circles because the circle is the most perfect curve. In the absence of evidence to the contrary, he allowed himself to decide a question of fact by an appeal to æsthetico-moral considerations. In such a case it is at once obvious to us that this appeal was unjustifiable. We know now how to ascertain as a fact the way in which the heavenly bodies move, and we know that they do not move in circles, or even in accurate ellipses, or in any other kind of simply describable curve. This may be painful to a certain hankering after simplicity of pattern in the universe, but we know that in astronomy such feelings are irrelevant. Easy as this knowledge seems now, we owe it to the courage and insight of the first inventors of scientific method, and more especially of Galileo.

We may take as another illustration Malthus's doctrine of population. This illustration is all the better for the fact that his actual doctrine is now known to be largely erroneous. It is not his conclusions that are valuable, but the temper and method of his inquiry. As everyone knows, it was to him that Darwin owed an essential part of his theory of natural selection, and this was only possible because Malthus's outlook was truly scientific. His great merit lies in considering man not as the object of praise or blame, but as a part of nature, a thing with a certain characteristic behaviour from which certain consequences must follow. If the behaviour is not quite what Malthus supposed, if the consequences are not quite what he inferred, that may falsify his conclusions, but does not impair the value of his method. The objections which were made when his doctrine was new—that it was horrible and depressing, that people ought not to act as he said they did, and so on—were all such as implied an unscientific attitude of mind; as against all of them, his calm determination to treat man as a natural phenomenon marks an important advance over the reformers of the eighteenth century and the Revolution.

Under the influence of Darwinism the scientific attitude towards man has now become fairly common, and is to some people quite natural, though to most it is still a difficult and artificial intellectual contortion. There is, however, one study which is as yet almost wholly untouched by the scientific spirit—I mean the study of philosophy. Philosophers and the public imagine that the scientific spirit must pervade pages that bristle with allusions to ions, germ-plasms, and the eyes of shell-fish. But as the devil can quote Scripture, so the philosopher can quote science. The scientific spirit is not an affair of quotation, of externally acquired information, any more than manners are an affair of the etiquette-book. The scientific attitude of mind involves a sweeping away of all other desires in the interests of the desire to know—it involves suppression of hopes and fears, loves and hates, and the whole subjective emotional life, until we become subdued to the material, able to see it frankly, without preconceptions, without bias, without any wish except to see it as it is, and without any belief that what it is must be determined by some relation, positive or negative, to what we should like it to be, or to what we can easily imagine it to be.

Now in philosophy this attitude of mind has not as yet been achieved. A certain self-absorption, not personal, but human, has marked almost all attempts to conceive the universe as a whole. Mind, or some aspect of it—thought or will or sentience—has been regarded as the pattern after which the universe is to be conceived, for no better reason, at bottom, than that such a universe would not seem strange, and would give us the cosy feeling that every place is like home. To conceive the universe as essentially progressive or essentially deteriorating, for example, is to give to our hopes and fears a cosmic importance which *may*, of course, be justified, but which we have as yet no reason to suppose justified. Until we have learnt to think of it in ethically neutral terms, we have not arrived at a scientific attitude in philosophy; and until we have arrived at such an attitude, it is hardly to be hoped that philosophy will achieve any solid results.

I have spoken so far largely of the negative aspect of the scientific spirit, but it is from the positive aspect that its value is derived. The instinct of constructiveness, which is one of the chief incentives to artistic creation, can find in scientific systems a satisfaction more massive than any epic poem. Disinterested curiosity, which is the source of almost all intellectual effort, finds with astonished delight that science can unveil secrets which might well have seemed for ever undiscoverable. The desire for a larger life and wider interests, for an escape from private circumstances, and even from the whole recurring human cycle of birth and death, is fulfilled by the impersonal cosmic outlook of science as by nothing else. To all these must be added, as contributing to the happiness of the man of science, the admiration of splendid achievement, and the consciousness of inestimable utility to the human race. A life devoted to science is therefore a happy life, and its happiness is derived from the very best sources that are open to dwellers on this troubled and passionate planet.

1929 edition

>>>‹‹‹

IMAGINATION CREATRIX *

JOHN LIVINGSTON LOWES

I

Every great imaginative conception is a vortex into which everything under the sun may be swept. "All other men's worlds," wrote Coleridge once, "are the poet's chaos." In that regard "The Ancient Mariner" is one with the noble army of imaginative masterpieces of all time. Oral traditions —homely, fantastic, barbaric, disconnected—which had ebbed and flowed across the planet in its unlettered days, were gathered up into that marvel of constructive genius, the plot of the *Odyssey*, and out of "a tissue of old *märchen*" was fashioned a unity palpable as flesh and blood and universal as the sea itself. Well-nigh all the encyclopedic erudition of the Middle Ages was forged and welded, in the white heat of an indomitable will, into the steel-knot structure of the *Divine Comedy*. There are not in the world, I suppose, more appalling masses of raw fact than would stare us in the face could we once, through some supersubtle chemistry, resolve that superb, organic unity into its primal elements. It so happens that for the last twenty-odd years I have been more or less occupied with Chaucer. I have tracked him, as I have trailed Coleridge, into almost every section of eight floors of a great library. It is a perpetual adventure among uncharted Ophirs and Golcondas to read after him—or Coleridge. And every conceivable sort of thing which Chaucer knew went into his alembic. It went in *x*—a waif of travel-lore from the mysterious Orient, a curious bit of primitive psychiatry, a racy morsel from Jerome against Jovinian, alchemy, astrology, medicine, geomancy, physiognomy, Heaven only knows what not, all vivid with the relish of the reading—it went in stark fact, "nude and crude," and it came out pure Chaucer. The results are as different from "The Ancient Mariner" as an English post-road from spectre-haunted seas. But the basic operations which produced them (and on this point I may venture to speak from first-hand knowledge) are essentially the same.

As for the years of "industrious and select reading, steady observation, insight into all seemly and generous arts and affairs" which were distilled into the magnificent romance of the thunder-scarred yet dauntless Rebel, voyaging through Chaos and old Night to shatter Cosmos, pendent from the battlements of living sapphire like a star—as for those serried hosts of facts caught up into the cosmic sweep of Milton's grandly poised design, it were bootless to attempt to sum in a sentence here the opulence which countless tomes of learned comment have been unable to exhaust. And what (in apostolic phrase) shall I more say? For the time would fail me to tell

* Reprinted by permission from Houghton Mifflin Company from *The Road to Xanadu* by John Livingston Lowes. Copyright 1927 by John Livingston Lowes.

of the *Æneid*, and the *Orlando Furioso*, and the *Faërie Queene*, and *Don Juan*, and even *Endymion*, let alone the cloud of other witnesses. The notion that the creative imagination, especially in its highest exercise, has little or nothing to do with facts is one of the *pseudodoxia epidemica* which die hard.

For the imagination never operates in a vacuum. Its stuff is always fact of some order, somehow experienced; its product is that fact transmuted. I am not forgetting that facts may swamp imagination, and remain unassimilated and untransformed. And I know, too, that this sometimes happens even with the masters. For some of the greatest poets, partly by virtue of their very greatness, have had, like Faust, two natures struggling within them. They have possessed at once the instincts of the scholar and the instincts of the artist, and it is precisely with regard to facts that these instincts perilously clash. Even Dante and Milton and Goethe sometimes clog their powerful streams with the accumulations of the scholar who shared bed and board with the poet in their mortal frames. "The Professor still lurks in your anatomy"—*Dir steckt der Doktor noch im Leib*—says Mephistopheles to Faust. But when, as in "The Ancient Mariner," the stuff that Professors and Doctors are made of has been distilled into quintessential poetry, then the passing miracle of creation has been performed.

II

But "creation," like "creative," is one of those hypnotic words which are prone to cast a spell upon the understanding and dissolve our thinking into haze. And out of this nebulous state of the intellect springs a strange but widely prevalent idea. The shaping spirit of imagination sits aloof, like God as he is commonly conceived, creating in some thaumaturgic fashion out of nothing its visionary world. That and that only is deemed to be "originality"—that, and not the imperial moulding of old matter into imperishably new forms. The ways of creation are wrapt in mystery; we may only marvel, and bow the head.

Now it is true beyond possible gainsaying that the operations which we call creative leave us in the end confronting mystery. But that is the fated terminus of all our quests. And it is chiefly through a deep-rooted reluctance to retrace, so far as they are legible, the footsteps of the creative faculty that the power is often thought of as abnormal, or at best a splendid aberration. I know full well that this reluctance springs, with most of us, from the staunch conviction that to follow the evolution of a thing of beauty is to shatter its integrity and irretrievably to mar its charm. But there are those of us who cherish the invincible belief that the glory of poetry will gain, not lose, through a recognition of the fact that the imagination works its wonders through the exercise, in the main, of normal and intelligible powers. To establish that, without blinking the ultimate mystery of genius, is to bring the workings of the shaping spirit in the sphere of art within the circle of the great moulding forces through which, in science and affairs and poetry alike, there emerges from chaotic multiplicity a unified and ordered world. . . .

Creative genius, in plainer terms, works through processes which are common to our kind, but these processes are superlatively enhanced. The subliminal agencies are endowed with an extraordinary potency; the faculty which conceives and executes operates with sovereign power; and the two blend in untrammelled interplay. There is always in genius, I imagine, the element which Goethe, who knew whereof he spoke, was wont to designate as "the Dæmonic." But in genius of the highest order that sudden, incalculable, and puissant energy which pours up from the hidden depths is controlled by a will which serves a vision—the vision which sees in chaos the potentiality of Form.

III

. . . "The imagination," said Coleridge once, recalling a noble phrase from Jeremy Taylor's *Via Pacis*, ". . . *sees all things in one.*" It sees the Free Life—the endless flux of the unfathomed sea of facts and images—but it sees also the controlling Form. And when it acts on what it sees, through the long patience of the will the flux itself is transformed and fixed in the clarity of a realized design. For there enter into imaginative creation three factors which reciprocally interplay: the Well, and the Vision, and the Will. Without the Vision, the chaos of elements remains a chaos, and the Form sleeps forever in the vast chambers of unborn designs. Yet in *that* chaos only could creative Vision ever see *this* Form. Nor without the cooperant Will, obedient to the Vision, may the pattern perceived in the huddle attain objective reality. Yet manifold though the ways of the creative faculty may be, the upshot is one: from the empire of chaos a new tract of cosmos has been retrieved; a nebula has been compacted—it may be!—into a star.

Yet no more than the lesser are these larger factors of the creative process—the storing of the Well, the Vision, and the concurrent operation of the Will—the monopoly of poetry. Through their conjunction the imagination in the field of science, for example, is slowly drawing the immense confusion of phenomena within the unfolding conception of an ordered universe. And its operations are essentially the same. For years, through intense and unremitting observation, Darwin had been accumulating masses of facts which pointed to a momentous conclusion. But they pointed through a maze of baffling inconsistencies. Then all at once the flash of vision came. "I can remember," he tells us in that precious fragment of an autobiography—"I can remember the very spot in the road, whilst in my carriage, when to my joy the solution occurred to me." And then, and only then, with the infinite toil of exposition, was slowly framed from the obdurate facts the great statement of the theory of evolution. The leap of the imagination, in a garden at Woolsthorpe on a day in 1665, from the fall of an apple to an architectonic conception cosmic in its scope and grandeur is one of the dramatic moments in the history of human thought. But in that pregnant moment there flashed together the profound and daring observations and conjectures of a long period of years; and upon the instant of illumination followed other years of rigorous and protracted labour, before the *Principia* appeared. Once more there was the long, slow storing of the Well; once more the flash of amazing vision through a fortuitous suggestion; once more the exacting task of translating the vision into actuality. And those are essentially the stages which Poincaré observed and graphically recorded in his "Mathematical Discovery." And that chapter reads like an exposition of the creative processes through which "The Ancient Mariner" came to be. With the inevitable and obvious differences we are not here concerned. But it is of the utmost moment to more than poetry that instead of regarding the imagination as a bright but ineffectual faculty with which in some esoteric fashion poets and their kind are specially endowed, we recognize the essential oneness of its function and its ways with all the creative endeavours through which human brains, with dogged persistence, strive to discover and realize order in a chaotic world.

For the Road to Xanadu is the road of the human spirit, and the imagination voyaging through chaos and reducing it to clarity and order is the symbol of all the quests which lend glory to our dust. And the goal of the shaping spirit which hovers in the *poet's* brain is the clarity and order of pure beauty. Nothing is alien to its transforming touch. "Far or forgot to (it) is near; Shadow and sunlight are the same." Things fantastic as the dicing of spectres on skeleton-barks, and ugly as the slimy spawn of rotting seas, and strange as a star astray within the moon's bright tip, blend in its vision into patterns of new-created beauty, *herrlich, wie am ersten Tag.* Yet the pieces that compose the pattern are not new. In the world of the shaping spirit, save for its patterns, there is nothing new that was not old. For the work of the creators is the mastery and transmutation and reordering into shapes of beauty of the given universe within us and without us. The shapes thus wrought are not that universe; they are "carved with figures strange and sweet, All made out of the carver's brain." Yet in that brain the elements and shattered fragments of the figures already lie, and what the carver-creator sees, implicit in the fragments, is the unique and lovely Form.

1927

>>><<<

SCIENTISTS ARE LONELY MEN *

OLIVER LA FARGE

I

It is not so long ago that, even in my dilettante study of the science of ethnology, I corresponded with men in Ireland, Sweden, Germany, France, and Yucatán, and had some discussion with a Chinese. One by one these interchanges were cut off; in some countries the concept of science is dead, and even in the free strongholds of Britain and the Americas pure science is being—must be—set aside in favor of what is immediately useful and urgently needed. It must hibernate now; for a while all it means is likely to be forgotten.

It has never been well understood. Scientists have never been good at explaining themselves and, frustrated by this, they tend to withdraw into the esoteric, refer to the public as "laymen," and develop incomprehensible vocabularies from which they draw a naïve, secret-society feeling of superiority.

What is the special nature of a scientist as distinguished from a soda-jerker? Not just the externals such as his trick vocabulary, but the human formation within the man? Most of what is written about him is rot; but there is stuff there which a writer can get his teeth into, and it has its vivid, direct relation to all that we are fighting for.

The inner nature of science within the scientist is both emotional and intellectual. The emotional element must not be overlooked, for without it there is no sound research on however odd and dull-seeming a subject. As is true of all of us, an emotion shapes and forms the scientist's life; at the same time an intellectual discipline molds his thinking, stamping him with a character as marked as a seaman's although much less widely understood.

To an outsider who does not know of this emotion, the scientist suggests an ant, putting forth great efforts to lug one insignificant and apparently unimportant grain of sand to be added to a pile, and much of the time his struggle seems as pointless as an ant's. I can try to explain why he does it and what the long-term purpose is behind it through an example from my own work. Remember that in this I am not thinking of the rare, fortunate geniuses like the Curies, Darwin, or Newton, who by their own talents and the apex of accumulated thought at which they stood were knowingly in pursuit of great, major discoveries. This is the average scientist, one among thousands, obscure, unimportant, toilsome.

* Reprinted by permission from Houghton Mifflin Company from *Raw Materials* by Oliver La Farge.

I have put in a good many months of hard work, which ought by usual standards to have been dull but was not, on an investigation as yet unfinished to prove that Kanhobal, spoken by certain Indians in Guatemala, is not a dialect of Jacalteca, but that, on the contrary, Jacalteca is a dialect of Kanhobal. Ridiculous, isn't it? Yet to me the matter is not only serious but exciting. Why?

There is an item of glory. There are half a dozen or so men now living (some now, unfortunately, our enemies) who will pay me attention and respect if I prove my thesis. A slightly larger number, less interested in the details of my work, will give credit to La Farge for having added to the linguistic map of Central America the name of a hitherto unnoted dialect. But not until I have told a good deal more can I explain—as I shall presently—why the notice of so few individuals can constitute a valid glory.

There's the nature of the initial work. I have spent hours, deadly, difficult hours, extracting lists of words, paradigms of verbs, constructions, idioms, and the rest from native informants, often at night in over-ventilated huts while my hands turned blue with cold. (Those mountains are far from tropical.) An illiterate Indian tires quickly when giving linguistic information. He is not accustomed to thinking of words in terms of other words; his command of Spanish is so poor that again and again you labor over misunderstandings; he does not think in our categories of words. Take any schoolchild and ask him how you say, "I go." Then ask him in turn, "Thou goest, he goes, we go." Even the most elementary schooling has taught him, if only from the force of staring resentfully at the printed page, to think in terms of the present tense of a single verb—that is, to conjugate. He will give you, in Spanish, for instance, "*Me voy, te vas, se va, nos vamos,*" all in order. Try this on an illiterate Indian. He gives you his equivalent of "I go," follows it perhaps with "thou goest," but the next question reminds him of his son's departure that morning for Ixtatán, so he answers "he sets out," and from that by another mental leap produces "we are traveling." This presents the investigator with a magnificently irregular verb. He starts checking back, and the Indian's mind being set in the new channel, he now gets "I travel" instead of "I go."

There follows an exhausting process of inserting an alien concept into the mind of a man with whom you are communicating tenuously in a language which you speak only pretty well and he quite badly.

Then of course you come to a verb which really is irregular and you mistrust it. Both of you become tired, frustrated, upset. At the end of an hour or so the Indian is worn out, his friendship for you has materially decreased, and you yourself are glad to quit.

Hours and days of this, and it's not enough. I have put my finger upon the village of Santa Eulalia and said, "Here is the true, the classic Kanhobal from which the other dialects diverge." Then I must sample the others; there are at least eight villages which must yield me up fairly complete word-lists and two from which my material should be as complete as from Santa Eulalia. More hours and more days, long horseback trips across the mountains to enter strange, suspicious settlements, sleep on the dirt floor of the schoolhouse, and persuade the astonished yokelry that it is a good idea, a delightful idea, that you should put "The Tongue" into writing. Bad food, a bout of malaria, and the early-morning horror of seeing your beloved horse's neck running blood from vampire bats ("Oh, but, yes, señor, everyone knows that here are very troublesome the vampire bats"), to get the raw material for proving that Jacalteca is a dialect of Kanhobal instead of . . .

You bring your hard-won data back to the States and you follow up with a sort of detective-quest for obscure publications and old manuscripts which may show a couple of words of the language as it was spoken a few centuries ago, so that you can get a line on its evolution. With great labor you unearth and read the very little that has been written bearing upon this particular problem.

By now the sheer force of effort expended gives your enterprise value in your own eyes. And you still have a year's work to put all your data in shape, test your conclusions, and demonstrate your proof.

Yet the real emotional drive goes beyond all this. Suppose I complete my work and prove, in fact, that Kanhobal as spoken in Santa Eulalia is a language in its own right and the classic tongue from which Jacalteca has diverged under alien influences, and that, further, I show just where the gradations of speech in the intervening villages fit in. Dear God, what a small, dull grain of sand!

But follow the matter a little farther. Jacalteca being relatively well-known (I can, offhand, name four men who have given it some study), from it it has been deduced that this whole group of dialects is most closely related to the languages spoken south and east of these mountains. If my theory is correct, the reverse is true—the group belongs to the Northern Division of the Mayan Family. This fact, taken along with others regarding physical appearance, ancient remains, and present culture, leads to a new conclusion about the direction from which these tribes came into the mountains: a fragment of the ancient history of what was once a great, civilized people comes into view. So now my tiny contribution begins to be of help to men working in other branches of anthropology than my own, particularly to the archaeologists; it begins to help toward an eventual understanding of the whole picture in this area: the important question of, not what these people are to-day, but how they got that way and what we can learn from that about all human behavior including our own.

Even carrying the line of research as far as this assumes that my results have been exploited by men of greater attainments than I. Sticking to the linguistic line, an error has been cleared away, an advance has been made in our understanding of the layout and interrelationship of the many languages making up the Mayan Family. With this we come a step nearer to working out the processes by which these languages became different from one another and hence to determining the archaic, ancestral roots of the whole group.

So far as we know at present, there are not less than eight completely unrelated language families in America north of Panama. This is unreasonable: there are hardly that many families among all the peoples of the Old World. Twenty years ago we recognized not eight, but forty. Some day perhaps we shall cut the total to four. The understanding of the Mayan process is a step toward that day; it is unlikely that Mayan will remain an isolated way of speech unconnected with any other. We know now that certain tribes in Wyoming speak languages akin to those of others in Panama; we have charted the big masses and islands of that group of tongues and from the chart begin to see the outlines of great movements and crashing historical events in the dim past. If we should similarly develop a relationship between Mayan and, let's say, the languages of the Mississippi Valley, again we should offer something provocative to the archaeologist, the historian, the student of mankind. Some day we shall show an unquestionable kinship between some of these families and certain languages of the Old World and with it cast a new light on the dim subject of the peopling of the Americas, something to guide our minds back past the Arctic to dark tribes moving blindly from the high plateaus of Asia.

My petty detail has its place in a long project carried out by many men which will serve not only the history of language but the broad scope of history itself. It goes farther than that. The humble *Pah-Utes* of Nevada speak a tongue related to that which the subtle Montezuma used, the one narrow in scope, evolved only to meet the needs of a primitive people, the other sophisticated, a capable instrument for poetry, for an advanced governmental system, and for philosophical speculation. Men's thoughts make language and their languages make thought. When the matter of the speech of mankind is fully known and laid side by side with all the other knowledges, the philosophers, the men who stand at the gathering-together point of science, will have the means to make man understand himself at last.

Of course no scientist can be continuously aware of such remote possible consequences of his labors; in fact the long goal is so remote that if he kept his eyes on it he would become hopelessly discouraged over the half inch of progress his own life's work will represent. But it was the vision of this which first made him choose his curious career, and it is an emotional sense of the great structure of scientific knowledge to which his little grain will be added which drives him along.

II

I spoke of the item of glory, the half dozen colleagues who will appreciate one's work. To understand that one must first understand the *isola-*

tion of research, a factor which has profound effects upon the scientist's psyche.

The most obvious statement of this is in the public attitude and folk-literature about "professors." The titles and subjects of Ph.D. theses have long been sources of exasperated humor among us; we are all familiar with the writer's device which ascribes to a professional character an intense interest in some such matter as the development of the morals in pre-Aurignacian man or the religious sanctions of the Levirate in northeastern Australia, the writer's intention being that the reader shall say "Oh God!", smile slightly, and pigeonhole the character. But what do you suppose is the effect of the quite natural public attitude behind these devices upon the man who is excitedly interested in pre-Aurignacian molars and who knows that this is a study of key value in tracing the evolution of *Homo sapiens?*

Occasionally some line of research is taken up and made clear, even fascinating, to the general public, as in Zinsser's *Rats, Lice and History*, or de Kruif's rather Sunday-supplement writings. Usually, as in these cases, they deal with medicine or some other line of work directly resulting in findings of vital interest to the public. Then the ordinary man will consent to understand, if not the steps of the research itself, at least its importance, will grant the excitement, and honor the researcher. When we read Eve Curie's great biography of her parents our approach to it is colored by our knowledge, forty years later, of the importance of their discovery to every one of us. It would have been quite possible at the time for a malicious or merely ignorant writer to have presented that couple as archetypes of the "professor," performing incomprehensible acts of self-immolation in pursuit of an astronomically unimportant what's-it.

Diving to my own experience like a Stuka with a broken wing, I continue to take my examples from my rather shallow linguistic studies because, in its very nature, the kind of thing a linguist studies is so beautifully calculated to arouse the "Oh God!" emotion.

It happened that at the suggestion of my letters I embarked upon an ambitious, general comparative study of the whole Mayan Family. The farther in I got the farther there was to go and the more absorbed I became. Puzzle piled upon puzzle to be worked out and the solution used for getting after the next one, the beginning of order in chaos, the glimpse of understanding at the far end. Memory, reasoning faculties, realism, and imagination were all on the stretch; I was discovering the full reach of whatever mental powers I had. When I say that I became absorbed I mean absorbed; the only way to do such research is to roll in it, become soaked in it, live it, breathe it, have your system so thoroughly permeated with it that at the half glimpse of a fugitive possibility everything you have learned so far and everything you have been holding in suspension is in order and ready to prove or disprove that point. You do not only think about your subject while the documents are spread before you; everyone knows that some of our best reasoning is done when the surface of the mind is occupied with something else and the deep machinery of the brain is free to work unhampered.

One day I was getting aboard a trolley car in New Orleans on my way to Tulane University. As I stepped up I saw that if it were possible to prove that a prefixed *s-* could change into a prefixed *y-* a whole series of troublesome phenomena would fall into order. The transition must come through *u-* and, thought I with a sudden lift of excitement, there may be a breathing associated with *u-* and that may make the whole thing possible. As I paid the conductor I thought that the evidence I needed might exist in Totonac and Tarascan, non-Mayan languages with which I was not familiar. The possibilities were so tremendous that my heart pounded. . . . Speculation was useless until I could reach the University and dig out the books, so after a while I calmed myself and settled to my morning ration of Popeye, who was then a new discovery too. As a matter of fact, the idea was no good, but the incident is a perfect example of the "professor mind."

Of course, if as I stepped on to the car it had dawned upon me that the reason my girl's behavior last evening had seemed odd was that she had fallen for the Englishman we had met, the incident would not have seemed so funny, although the nature of the absorption, subconscious thinking, and realization would have been the same in both cases.

I lived for a month with the letter *k*. If we have three words in Quiché, one of the major Mayan languages, beginning with *k,* in Kanhobal we are likely to find that one of these begins with *ch.* Moving farther west and north, in Tzeltal one is likely to begin with *k,* one with *ch,* and the one which began with *ch* in Kanhobal to begin with *ts.* In Hausteca, at the extreme northwest, they begin with *k, ts,* and plain *s* respectively. Why don't they all change alike? Which is the original form? Which way do these changes run, or from which point do they run both ways? Until those questions can be answered we cannot even guess at the form of the mother tongue from which these languages diverged, and at that point all investigation halts. Are these *k's* in Quiché pronounced even faintly unlike? I noticed no difference between the two in Kanhobal, but then I wasn't listening for it. I wished someone properly equipped would go and listen to the Quiché Indians, and wondered if I could talk the University into giving me money enough to do so.

This is enough to give some idea of the nature of my work, and its uselessness for general conversation. My colleagues at Tulane were archaeologists. Shortly after I got up steam they warned me frankly that I had to stop trying to tell them about the variability of *k*, the history of Puctun t^y, or any similar matter. If I produced any results that they could apply, I could tell them about it; but apart from that I could keep my damned sound-shifts and intransitive infixes to myself; I was driving them nuts. My other friends on the faculty were a philosopher and two English professors; I was pursuing two girls at the time but had not been drawn to either because of intellectual interests in common; my closest friends were two painters and a sculptor. The only person I could talk to was myself.

The cumulative effect of this non-communication was terrific. A strange, mute work, a thing crying aloud for discussion, emotional expression, the check and reassurance of another's point of view, turned in upon myself to boil and fume, throwing upon me the responsibility of being my own sole check, my own impersonal, external critic. When finally I came to New York on vacation I went to see my Uncle John. He doesn't know Indian languages but he is a student of linguistics, and I shall never forget the relief, the reveling pleasure, of pouring my work out to him.

Thus at the vital point of his life-work the scientist is cut off from communication with his fellow-men. Instead, he has the society of two, six, or twenty men and women who are working in his specialty, with whom he corresponds, whose letters he receives like a lover, with whom when he meets them he wallows in an orgy of talk, in the keen pleasure of conclusions and findings compared, matched, checked against one another—the pure joy of being really understood.

The praise and understanding of those two or six become for him the equivalent of public recognition. Around these few close colleagues is the larger group of workers in the same general field. They do not share with one in the steps of one's research, but they can read the results, tell in a general way if they have been soundly reached, and profit by them. To them McGarnigle "has shown" that there are traces of an ancient, dolichocephalic strain among the skeletal remains from Pusilhá, which is something they can use. Largely on the strength of his close colleagues' judgment of him, the word gets round that McGarnigle is a sound man. You can trust his work. He's the fellow you want to have analyze the material if you turn up an interesting bunch of skulls. All told, including men in allied fields who use his findings, some fifty scientists praise him; before them he has achieved international reputation. He will receive honors. It is even remotely possible that he might get a raise in salary.

McGarnigle disinters himself from a sort of fortress made of boxes full of skeletons in the cellar of Podunk University's Hall of Science, and emerges into the light of day to attend a Congress. At the Congress he delivers a paper entitled *Additional Evidence of Dolichocephaly among the Eighth Cycle Maya* before the Section on Physical Anthropology. In the audience are six archaeologists specializing in the Maya field, to whom these findings have a special importance, and twelve physical anthropologists including Gruenwald of Eastern California, who is the only other man working on Maya remains.

After McGarnigle's paper comes Gruenwald's turn. Three other physical anthropologists, engaged in the study of the Greenland Eskimo, the Coastal Chinese, and the Pleistocene Man of Lake Mojave respectively, come in.

They slipped out for a quick one while McGarnigle was speaking because his Maya work is not particularly useful to them and they can read the paper later; what is coming next, with its important bearing on method and theory, they would hate to miss.

Gruenwald is presenting a perfectly horrible algebraic formula and a diagram beyond Rube Goldberg's wildest dream, showing *A Formula for Approximating the Original Indices of Artifically Deformed Crania.* (These titles are not mere parodies; they are entirely possible.) The archaeologists depart hastily to hear a paper in their own section on *Indications of an Early Quinary System at Uaxactún.* The formula is intensely exciting to McGarnigle because it was the custom of the ancient Mayas to remodel the heads of their children into shapes which they (erroneously) deemed handsomer than nature's. He and Gruenwald have been corresponding about this; at one point Gruenwald will speak of his colleague's experience in testing the formula; he has been looking forward to this moment for months.

After the day's sessions are over will come something else he has been looking forward to. He and Gruenwald, who have not seen each other in two years, go out and get drunk together. It is not that they never get drunk at home, but that now when in their cups they can be uninhibited, they can talk their own, private, treble-esoteric shop. It is an orgy of release.

III

In the course of their drinking it is likely—if an archaeologist or two from the area joins them it is certain—that the talk will veer from femoral pilasters and alveolar prognathism to personal experiences in remote sections of the Petén jungle. For in my science and a number of others there is yet another frustration.

We go into the field and there we have interesting experiences. The word "adventure" is taboo and "explore" is used very gingerly. But the public mind has been so poisoned by the outpourings of bogus explorers that it is laden with claptrap about big expeditions, dangers, hardships, hostile tribes, the lighting of red flares around the camp to keep the savages at bay, and God knows what rot. (I can speak freely about this because my own expeditions have been so unambitious and in such easy country that I don't come into the subject.) As a matter of fact it is generally true that *for a scientist on an expedition to have an adventure is evidence of a fault in his technique.* He is sent out to gather information, and he has no business getting into "a brush with the natives."

The red-flare, into-the-unknown, hardship-and-danger boys, who manage to find a tribe of pink-and-green Indians, a lost city, or the original, handpainted descendants of the royal Incas every time they go out, usually succeed in so riling the natives and local whites upon whom scientists must depend if they are to live in the country as to make work in the zones they contaminate difficult for years afterward. The business of their adventures and discoveries is sickening. . . .

These men by training express themselves in factual, "extensional" terms, which don't make for good adventure stories. They understandably lean over backward to avoid sounding even remotely like the frauds, the "explorers." And then what they have seen and done lacks validity to them if it cannot be told in relation to the purpose and dominant emotion which sent them there. McGarnigle went among the independent Indians of Icaiché because he had heard of a skull kept in one of their temples which, from a crude description, seemed to have certain important characteristics. All his risks and his maneuverings with those tough, explosive Indians centered around the problem of gaining access to that skull. When he tries to tell an attractive girl about his experiences he not only understates, but can't keep from stressing the significance of a skull with a healed, cloverleaf trepan. The girl gladly leaves him for the nearest broker. . . .

It is too bad both for the scientists and the public that they are so cut off from each other. The world needs now not the mere knowledges of science, but the way of thought and the discipline. It is the essence of what Hitler has set out to destroy; against it he has waged total war within his own domain. It is more than skepticism, the weighing of evidence more even than the love of truth. It is the devotion of oneself to an end which is far more important than the individual, the certainty that the end is absolutely good, not only for oneself but for all mankind, and the character to set personal advantage, comfort, and glory aside in the devoted effort to make even a little progress toward it.

1942

SCIENCE AND THE DREAM OF HAPPINESS *

IRWIN EDMAN

. . . There have been many reasons why the relationship of science to happiness has been obscured. The two words themselves conjure up two different vistas. The first evokes techniques on the one hand and mathematical formulae on the other. Even the immense contributions made to man's comfort and to his efficiency have confused the scientific method and human good, for while chemistry and physics and all the physical sciences have seemed to contribute to man's power, they have not always seemed to promote his serenity and his joy. Happiness, even in the modern period,

* This article was the annual Phi Beta Kappa address delivered before the American Association for the Advancement of Science, St. Louis, Missouri, March 29, 1946. Reprinted by permission from *The American Scholar*, Autumn, 1946. Copyright 1946 by the United Chapters of Phi Beta Kappa.

has seldom been defined in terms borrowed from the scientist. It has been described or expressed in the images and the adorations of the poets. The immense resourcefulness of science seemed to produce not the New Atlantis of which Bacon had dreamed, but the bleak industrial cities, the mass production, the many cheap things produced cheaply, of the Industrial Revolution. Lives as well as goods seemed to have been cheapened by science and, in the accidents of industry or the risks of mechanized war, held cheaply. . . .

It is, therefore, not to be wondered at that since science has emerged in regimental industry and atomic war, happiness has been relegated to the sphere of fantasies bred at once of human desire and of personal and social frustrations. Happiness is compounded of what poets have focused upon, the color and quality, the intensities and the aspirations, the energies and the creativeness of men. And since these were apparently not realized in the world of fact or the world of the physical and geometrizing intellect, they were placed in some golden dream of the past, or some golden vision of timeless essences eternally beheld. Men have fled from the world of fact to a world of significance, significance not in terms of the facts found in the laboratory but of values felt in love, in art, in religion. In the Garden of Eden, the City of God, the Platonized Paradise of pure forms have been found the elements of happiness. Some have taken these fantasies literally and have lived in hope of eventual Heaven. Some have tried to escape from the dreary world of fact to a dream world of frankly imagined values, a reverie instigated by both frustration and desire.

It must be pointed out, however, that during the last three centuries, for reflective and sober-minded persons science itself seemed to provide a realizable dream of happiness. I need hardly remind my hearers that in liberal minds of three centuries past science became closely identified with a confident promise of eventual human felicity. The promise held forth by the increased control of man over Nature seemed to be incalculable. The golden age for three centuries has been placed not in the past but in the future.

> The world's great age begins anew,
> The golden years return.

Nothing seemed impossible for human beings to the audacious imagination of the seventeenth century in England, to the enthusiasts for reason among the eighteenth century philosophers in France. There was, until recently, widely current in liberal spirits a faith in the infinite perfectability of human institutions. All that was needed was first to clear away inherited stupidities and traditional follies, as Voltaire suggested, and to bring the clear light of intelligence to play upon the problems of mankind, from illness and crime to government and business and law. This faith in the fruits of scientific method was carried well into the nineteenth century and even into the twentieth. That hope of progress through science may be said to have come to its first full stop with the beginning of the First World War. It came to another full stop with the news of the atomic bomb.

It seems quite clear by now that human intelligence may span oceans in hours and speak to distant continents in an instant. But the happiness dreamed of, the good society, the heaven on earth seems no whit nearer than it was in Greece, which had no science at all in the modern sense. Everyone who has watched the changing climate of feeling has seen scientific Utopianism fade. It has vanished for reasons given before, but there were others. The major issues of civilization do not seem to be those which are solved either by the engineering uses or theoretical advances in science, or did not, until recently, seem to be so solved. Mass production does not automatically distribute goods equitably; there is in capitalistic and in other societies starvation amid plenty. Instantaneous communication has not produced an era of perpetual good feeling and mutual understanding among nations. The triumph of understanding that emerged in the control of nuclear energy has simply brought a fearful threat of destruction into the world. . . .

The temptation and the provocation have been to abandon science altogether and to say that it is a complex snare and an expensive delusion. Add up its technical triumphs, and they seem to have complicated man's life but not rejoiced it. It has not, on the one hand, provided enough things for all, and it has, on the other, provided elaborate and spirit-destroying luxuries for a few. It has robbed the believer of beliefs he may have had about another world, without providing any ultimate significance or meaning to this one. And today its most celebrated marvel is simply a device for ending the civilization that comes to a climax in a means for destroying itself. I think it not surprising that there should be all kinds of escapes offered to sensitive spirits and credulously accepted by them—escapes into mysticism, other-worldliness, and strange revelations often proffered late in life by scientists who would not think for a moment of offering with so little evidence any hypotheses in their own fields.

Perhaps it would be well for the imagination of men today if the discoveries of astronomers were as popular as those of physicists. In astronomy at least people would be habituated to longer views both in time and space, and since astronomical researches cannot so easily be turned into applied engineering marvels, a confusion between scientific inquiry and the engineering applications of science might be more readily distinguished. There would be, perhaps, less wringing of hands over the necessary fatality of scientific discovery if the public were reminded, for example, that nuclear energies are operative throughout the solar system, and that the atom bomb does not exhaust the possibilities of atomic fission. It is important to point out to those who counsel the abandonment of faith in scientific method because in its application it has not always conduced to human happiness, to consider frankly the ways in which science may and may not be expected to contribute to human welfare. It is equally important to remind the hasty abdicators of intelligence what lurks in the substitution of some other method than that of the patient and responsible inquiry of scientific analysis into human and physical problems. . . .

Insofar as science in itself is an enjoyment and kind of intellectual creation, it is an art. In the sense in which it is a shared enterprise, it is a subtle friendship of the mind. But what is generally meant by the question as to whether science contributes to happiness, is whether it provides the conditions for such realizations as enter into that shared well-being which is a good life in a just society. Scientific inquiry may provide a happy way of life for a few, whose life comes to fulfillment in the processes of analysis itself. But that, also, is not what is generally meant by the contribution that science makes to happiness. The scientific habit of mind may, itself, as I propose to show before the end of this paper, contribute to happiness, through the enlargement and the refinement of intellectual landscape it provides. But the question we are asking is a larger one: How does science contribute both as mental habit and in its practical applications toward the shared well-being of all men—plain men and humanists and scientists in modern civilization?

In the first place, I think it important to realize that if the habit of the scientific approach to the understanding of the world and of ourselves were as widespread as education may gradually make it, men and women generally would be helped to discover what their happiness consists in, and to eliminate the sorrows that come from a misconception of where their possible felicity lies. One of the reasons the "dream of happiness" is so familiar a phrase is that generally speaking there is a resigned suspicion on the part of most people that happiness, in truth and of necessity, is a dream. For most persons, even though they live by the mechanical marvels of the present time and even perhaps imagining that they accept a scientific view of the world, continue to live imaginatively in terms inherited from mythology and religions and illusions. They have long believed that happiness, being as they suspect somehow illicit at best, must have its locus beyond ourselves, beyond this world. Their image of happiness is assembled almost by definition out of impossible goods—ends that mortality cannot hope for, like immortal life, or continuous ecstasy.

The first sense in which the scientific point of view may be a help to felicity is by defining for us the scope and orbit of our possible good. The plain man and the man of letters, and even the man of science, have to this day failed to take with full seriousness and adequate imaginative realization the scientific point of view. They have been impressed with the penny marvels or the expensive miracles of science. But all of them, humanist, scientist, plain man alike, have failed to draw the patent morals of scientific method or that general habit of mind by which it is sustained. They have not learned in any synoptic view of their own lives or of the life of mankind to construct their programs and their hopes and their values on the basis of analysis of the facts themselves. They have not reconsidered "man's hope" in terms of man's actual discoverable situation. The omnipresence of scientific enterprise has not made pervasive the habit of basing possibility in terms of what the actual turns out, upon inquiry, to be.

When the candor and objectivity necessary to scientific inquiry has become a habit of mind among mature men about their personal affairs, and about the affairs of society, illusory goods will no longer be yearned for, and possible goods will beckon as challenges to renewed and liberated life. In the circle of what *can* be done, one can find plenty of materials towards creativeness in the doing, and clarity and delight in the realization. . . .

I should like to deal first with the more obvious and more patent contribution of science to happiness, and with its apparent failure to produce such contributions. On the practical level, there has been disillusion with what science can do for us. All the resources of mass production have not abolished poverty; the mastery of physical control over nature has, at best, provided luxury, often corrupting luxury, for a few. All this has been charged against science itself, as if investigation into the order of nature was, by itself, responsible for disorders in modern society. I think it is necessary, therefore, to distinguish science from its particular social settings, and the special uses or misuses to which it is put in a given society or a given civilization. It is absurd to discuss *in vacuo* what science can or cannot do for human happiness, while tacitly making the assumptions of present political and social organization or the present state of general education. . . .

The question raised by those who ask what contribution science can make to man's happiness is usually, in some form, this question: What do the immense practical resourcefulness and applicability of scientific method portend for the life of man?

It would be banal to recount the contributions science has made to the comfort and the convenience, the health and the longevity of human beings. But almost as early as the first Industrial Revolution itself, it was observed that the mere technical control of vast physical resources did not carry a promise of inevitable joy for mankind, or even of comfort and convenience for all. Mass production of basic necessities has not even assured basic necessities for all. As for the luxuries of transportation and comfort, they that are the direct result of modern techniques, these, too, remain expensively limited to the few. And it was observed also, not very much later than the early days of the Industrial Revolution, that the mere availability of things could kill the spirit rather than nourish it, and make us the victims rather than the masters of our techniques. All that mass production seemed to promise was either widespread mediocrity and regimentation of life, or luxury on the one hand with want on the other. . . .

There has been a good deal of nonsense talked about science and its contribution to personal happiness. As a delight, inquiry itself, for a very few, provides a good. But broadly speaking, scientific investigation is concerned with the solution of problems, and happiness is a name for those aspects of life which are fulfillment and not urgencies demanding solution. To ask whether the scientific itself yields happiness is to ask whether all our well-being comes from the solving of problems. The more realistic question is: Does science provide a way of life for Western man which contributes the conditions of a general well-being among mankind?

Occasionally a voice is raised that says not until we give up the application of science, and even its point of view, will well-being come to modern man. It is easy to point out that in certain simplicities of art, love, friendship, vision are our self-justified moments of life, and that the world of metropolitan standardization, of haste, has corrupted us from our own instinctive and possible goods. There are counsels of return to medievalism in industrial life and in imagination and thought. There are advices to escape to a world of eternal essences, or to our inner soliloquizing selves.

Well, for better or for worse, mass production is now necessary even to keep us alive, and it is impossible to reverse or to forget the instrumentalities science has put at our disposal. It is not impossible, however, to extend the habit of inquiry and the faith in human intelligence to fields still dominated by prejudice, special interest and encrusted tradition.

If such an extension is made, it is impossible to foresee the limits which can be reached by a reliance, not only on the methods of science but on the general and basic elements of scientific faith to contribute to human good and the human sense of well-being. There used to be a fashion among anti-clericals in Europe in the nineteenth century to berate all religion by citing the history of folly, stupidity, hypocrisy and corruption that could be discovered in the background of almost any historic religious institution. In the same way, of late, there have been charges against science itself that are really accusations against certain misuses of science that have been made, especially since the beginning of the nineteenth century. Scientific method has been exploited in the interest of large-scale production primarily for profit rather than for functionalism, just as during the last war there was a concentration of research upon those aspects of theory and engineering practice which would facilitate destruction of our enemies. In other fields as well, the resources of scientific method have been put at the disposal of large-scale commercial interests. The marvels of radio communication have been yoked to serve the interests of advertisers, so that what could be a miraculous agency of enlightenment and taste has become a national broadcasting of banalities. The miracles of the possible cinematic art become the regimental mediocrity of Hollywood industry.

It is important, I think, to remind ourselves that even in the fields where the application of scientific method may contribute to the liberation of the spirit of men everywhere in devices for health, comfort and leisure, it has been prevented from doing so by the accidental incrustations of vested interests, traditional sovereignties, conventional equities. It was not, I think, until the dismaying consequences of the control of atomic energy became apparent that scientists themselves became almost guiltily aware of these facts. If physical research can have as a consequence human destruction, it becomes a paramount obligation of scientists themselves to regard research from the point of view of world citizens and responsible members of the human race. Control of atomic energy is not a question for soldiers, but for members of the general civilization whose very existence is concerned.

But this is true not only of those aspects of science that concerns war; it equally concerns those phases of it that concern peace. It is all very well to talk of science for Science's sake, as poets and aesthetes in the 1900's were speaking of art for Art's sake. The free play of mind and inquiry is as important for society itself—and not simply for the joy of it—as the free play of artistic creation. But the insistence on the free play of intelligence in research is not inconsistent with the responsibility of scientists for a free use in the widest public interest of the fruits of scientific inquiry. As long as the research of the scientist is primarily harnessed to the interests of special economic groups or as an instrument of power politics, the charges against science will remain plausible. The net effect of the achievements of human intelligence at its most spectacularly successful will be human catastrophe at its most revolting. The same will hold true so long as the precision, the objectivity, the freedom of scientific inquiry are limited merely to matters of physical control. Until there is an intellectual climate in which the habits of mind now considered proper to the study and the laboratory are extended to human relations, those crucial fields which determine whether or not science will redound to human welfare will be dominated by superstition, illusion and propaganda.

But supposing scientific method is extended to human affairs—and supposing, we are asked, the application of scientific method is for the common good, not for private greed or nationalistic aggrandizement. Supposing our general health is secured, our longevity lengthened, and the general physical conditions of well-being provided. Supposing our slums do become garden cities, and our leisure made so general that the terrible regimentation of factory work and factory towns will be reduced. Assume, even, that it will be possible for something of the creative crafts and arts to revive during wide general leisure. For it is not impossible to hope that with the extension of scientific inquiry to human ills and the use of physical researches for the commonweal, that these things will be possible.

Will there not, it may quite properly be asked, still be something missing in a world dominated by the scientific point of view? When such a question is asked, what is usually implied is that what is missing is something that traditional religion has provided, and that the dominance of the habit of belief merely in the experimental methods of inquiry will not itself provide. What is implied is that scientific method can give us comfort, convenience, leisure, all the necessities toward felicity—but not felicity, not that which alone keeps life from despair, faith. Wars may be abolished, but there will be death even in great cities, and increased leisure may simply give us pause, more time to brood upon the emptiness of lives without a single comprehensive meaning to give point to them, or an immortality in after-life in which to redeem the failures of this one. Our own personal future is in every case fated to extinction, and there is promised, too, in the long run, extinction of the whole human scene. What dignity or meaning can life have when there is no faith possible in the permanent or ultimate significance of anything that genius ever has accomplished or expressed or felt?

Well, some of the promises of traditional religions, some of the kinds of meaning their mythologies give to life, I cannot pretend are derivable from anything that the method of the sciences or the habit of the scientific mind can yield. But in an important sense, science itself is a faith—an adequate one, and, I suspect, the only reliable one.

Because of the disastrous consequences, the social misuses of science, because of the blind alleys into which industrial civilization and power politics have led us, there is a natural temptation to fly away from that verifiable knowledge and from responsible intelligence, which seem to have served us with nothing but disaster. There is a strong temptation to flee to irresponsible dreams of impossible Heavens, of womb-like and tomb-like inner peace. But like all daydreams, these are narcoses, not solutions. They are precarious and illusory escapes.

Whether or not scientific method can yield the human race all the conditions of felicity, it is clear that in such organized intelligence lies its only hope. And the hope is a fair one. For what scientific method suggests to us and implies for those who stake the human future upon it, is not a Paradise on earth. It is faith that human intelligence joined to good will may make for man a society in which those ills are reduced that are the consequence of ignorance or illusion, those goods are available to all which come within the compass of an adult awareness of what life and human nature can sustain and make possible.

Faith in science is faith in the hope, the fruitfulness and value of the human adventure. It is a faith that action will be, within limits, effective, and that the effects of action will be humanly rewarding. There will be little time or inclination to speculate on the meaninglessness of life, or to allege meaninglessness. Inquiry itself will render so much possible in the way of new discriminations and hitherto unsuspected varieties of goods and value in the world that the world itself will become charged not with one preordained meaning, but with ever-new awarenesses and interests. The habit of inquiry will liberate the spontaneities of imagination. The human adventure, in science itself, in art, in human relations will be sufficient nourishment for a faith in humanity and its future. . . .

Science is now perhaps the only reliable method of knowledge, of responsible inquiry. It is the *sine qua non* of any happiness possible for the race, and the only alternative is, now more than ever, catastrophe. Our knowledge is still power; sometimes, as in the case of the atomic bomb, deadly and terrifying power. But what knowledge is power *for*—that is the issue for scientists and humanists alike.

It may be power for power's sake, in the hands of unscrupulous men. It may be power for humanity's sake, if used by a world opinion itself educated to the point of view of responsible intelligence. Science as the instrument of understanding and of control may provide us eventually with some of the very joys which it has been assumed are open only to traditional worship. The cooperative adventure of human beings may itself yield some of the joy of mystical communion. The sense of partnership in the common human enterprise can give something of the sense of being children born of the same nature and bound by the same fate. And a sense of the perfectibilities possible to man through his cooperative intelligence may well emerge as reverence addressed to possible good.

Happiness, in the sense of a childish ecstasy, may or may not be possible through science. But in the sense of a well-being—a well-being made possible and sustained by the scientific faith itself—science may well contribute to the changing of happiness from a dream into a beckoning possible and an adult idea!

1946

A LAYMAN LOOKS AT SCIENCE *

RAYMOND B. FOSDICK

August 6, 1945—the day the atomic bomb was dropped on Hiroshima—brought home to all of us in dramatic fashion the significance of science in human life. The impact of that bomb has left us stunned and confused. Certainly we laymen are frightened by science as we never were before. And certainly, too, we are bewildered by the power which science has suddenly placed in our laps—bewildered and humbled by our realization of how unequipped we are, in terms of ethics, law, and government, to know how to use it.

That, I think, is the first reaction of a layman to the stupendous reper-

* From *The Scientists Speak,* edited by Warren Weaver. Reprinted by permission from Boni & Gaer, Inc. Copyright 1947 by Boni & Gaer, Inc.

cussion of that bomb on Hiroshima. And the first question that comes to his mind is this: What use are radios and automobiles and penicillin and all the other gifts of science if at the same time this same science hands us the means by which we can blow ourselves and our civilization into drifting dust? We have always been inclined to think of research and technology as being consciously related to human welfare. Now, frankly, we are not so sure, and we are troubled, deeply troubled, by the realization that man's brain can create things which his will may not be able to control.

To the layman it seems as if science were facing a vast dilemma. Science is the search for truth, and it is based on the glorious faith that truth is worth discovering. It springs from the noblest attribute of the human spirit. But it is this same search for truth that has brought our civilization to the brink of destruction; and we are confronted by the tragic irony that when we have been most successful in pushing out the boundaries of knowledge we have most endangered the possibility of human life on this planet. The pursuit of truth has at last led us to the tools by which we can ourselves become the destroyers of our own institutions and all the bright hopes of the race. In this situation what do we do—curb our science or cling to the pursuit of truth and run the risk of having our society torn to pieces?

It is on the basis of this dilemma that serious questions are forming in the public mind. Unless research is linked to a humane and constructive purpose should it not be subject to some kind of restraint? Can our scientists afford to be concerned solely with fact and not at all with value and purpose? Can they legitimately claim that their only aim is the advancement of knowledge regardless of its consequences? Is the layman justified in saying to the scientist: "We look to you to distinguish between that truth which furthers the well-being of mankind and that truth which threatens it"?

One of the scientists who played a leading role in the development of the atomic bomb said to the newspapermen: "A scientist cannot hold back progress because of fears of what the world will do with his discoveries." What he apparently implied was that science has no responsibility in the matter and that it will plunge ahead in the pursuit of truth even if the process leaves the world in dust and ashes.

Is that the final answer? Is there no other answer? Frankly, as a layman I do not know. Offhand, this disavowal of concern for the social consequences of science seems callous and irresponsible. But we may be facing a situation where no other answer is realistic or possible. To ask the scientist to foresee the use—the good or evil of the use—to which his results may be put is doubtless beyond the realm of the attainable. Almost any discovery can be used for either social or antisocial purposes. The German dye industry was not created to deal with either medicine or weapons of war; and yet out of that industry came our sulfa-drugs and mustard gas. When

Einstein wrote his famous transformation equation in 1905 he was not thinking of the atomic bomb, but out of that equation came one of the principles upon which the bomb was based.

Willard Gibbs was a gentle spirit whose life was spent in his laboratory at Yale University and who never dreamed that his work in mathematical physics might have even a remote relationship to war; and yet it is safe to say that his ideas gave added power to the armaments of all nations in both World War I and World War II.

I suspect that the way out of the dilemma is not as simple as the questions now being asked seem to imply. The good and the evil that flow from scientific research are more often than not indistinguishable at the point of origin. Generally they are by-products, or they represent distortions of original purpose, none of which could have been foreseen when the initial discovery was made. We are driven back to a question of human motives and desires. Science has recently given us radar, jet propulsion and power sources of unprecedented magnitude. What does society want to do with them? It can use them constructively to increase the happiness of mankind, or it can employ them to tear the world to pieces. There is scarcely a scientific formula or a process or a commodity which cannot be used for war purposes, if that is what we elect to do with it. In brief, the gifts of science can be used by evil men to do evil even more obviously and dramatically than they can be used by men of good will to do good.

I fear there is no easy way out of our dilemma. I would not absolve the scientists from some measure of responsibility, for they are men of superior training and insight and we are entitled to look to them for help and leadership—more help and leadership, I venture to add, than have thus far been given. However, I note that a considerable number of the scientists who were connected with the atomic bomb project have publicly expressed their apprehension of the consequences of their own creation. "All of us who worked on the atomic bomb," said Dr. Allison of the University of Chicago, "had a momentary feeling of elation when our experiment met with success; but that feeling rapidly changed to a feeling of horror, and a fervent desire that no more bombs would be dropped."

Nevertheless in the long run I do not believe that we shall be successful in making science the arbiter of its own discoveries. Somehow or other society itself must assume that responsibility. The towering enemy of mankind is not science but war. Science merely reflects the social forces by which it is surrounded. When there is peace, science is constructive; when there is war, science is perverted to destructive ends. The weapons which science gives us do not necessarily create war; they make war increasingly more terrible until now it has brought us to the doorstep of doom.

Our main problem, therefore, is not to curb science but to stop war—to substitute law for force and international government for anarchy in the relations of one nation with another. That is a job in which everybody must participate, including the scientists. But the bomb on Hiroshima suddenly woke us up to the fact that we have very little time. The hour is late and our work has scarcely begun. Now we are face to face with this urgent question: "Can education and tolerance and understanding and creative intelligence run fast enough to keep us abreast with our own mounting capacity to destroy?"

That is the question which we shall have to answer one way or the other in this generation. Science must help us in the answer, but the main decision lies within ourselves.

1947

SCIENCE AND SCIENTIFIC METHOD

History and Biography

ALLOTT, KENNETH, *Jules Verne* (New York, The Macmillan Company, 1941).

BATES, RALPH S., *Scientific Societies in the United States* (New York, John Wiley and Sons, Inc., 1945).

BAXTER, JAMES P., *Scientists Against Time* (Boston, Little, Brown and Co., 1946).

BRIDGES, J. H., *The Life and Work of Roger Bacon* (London, Williams and Norgate, Ltd., 1941).

CROWTHER, J. G., *Famous American Men of Science* (New York, W. W. Norton & Company, Inc., 1937).

DAMPIER, SIR WILLIAM, *A History of Science* (New York, The Macmillan Company, 1932).

DAMPIER-WHETHAM, SIR W. C. and WHETHAM, M. D., *Cambridge Readings in the Literature of Science* (New York, The Macmillan Company, 1924).

FRAZER, JAMES G., *The Golden Bough* (Abridged edition, New York, The Macmillan Company, 1940).

GINZBURG, BENJAMIN, *The Adventure of Science* (New York, Simon & Schuster, Inc., 1930).

HUXLEY, LEONARD, editor, *Life and Letters of T. H. Huxley* (New York, D. Appleton and Co., 1900).

JORDAN, DAVID S., editor, *Leading American Men of Science* (New York, Henry Holt and Company, 1910).

KNICKERBOCKER, W. S., *Classics of Modern Science* (New York, Alfred A. Knopf, Inc., 1927).

LIBBY, WALTER, *An Introduction to the History of Science* (Boston, Houghton Mifflin Company, 1917).

LODGE, SIR OLIVER, *Pioneers of Science* (New York, The Macmillan Company, 1922).

MACCURDY, EDWARD, editor, *The Notebooks of Leonardo da Vinci* (New York, Reynal & Hitchcock, 1938).

MEREJKOWSKI, DMITRI, *The Romance of Leonardo da Vinci* (New York, Random House, Inc., 1931).

MERZ, JOHN T., *History of European Thought in the 19th Century*, Vol. 1 (London, William Blackwood & Sons, Ltd., 1903).

MOULTON, F. R. and SCHIFFERES, J. J., *The Autobiography of Science* (New York, Doubleday & Co., Inc., 1945).

SARTON, GEORGE, *The History of Science and the New Humanism* (Cambridge, Harvard University Press, 1937).

———, *Introduction to the History of Science* (Baltimore, The Williams & Wilkins Company, 1927).

THORNDIKE, LYNN, *A History of Magic and Experimental Science* (New York, Columbia University Press, 1923–1941).

TYNDALL, JOHN, *Fragments of Science* (New York, D. Appleton and Co., 1899).

———, *New Fragments* (New York, D. Appleton and Co., 1900).

VEBLEN, THORSTEIN, *The Place of Science in Modern Civilization* (New York, B. W. Huebsch, 1919).

WHITE, A. D., *A History of the Warfare of Science with Theology* (New York, D. Appleton and Co., 1925).

Philosophy, Method

ADAMS, MARY, editor, *Science in the Changing World* (London, Allen & Unwin, Ltd., 1933).

BAKER, JOHN R., *The Scientific Life* (London, Allen & Unwin, Ltd., 1942).

BERNAL, J. D., *The Social Function of Science* (New York, The Macmillan Company, 1939).

BRAGG, SIR WILLIAM, *Creative Knowledge* (New York, Harper & Brothers, 1927).

BUSH, VANNEVAR, *Science—the Endless Frontier* (Washington, U.S. Government Printing Office, 1945).

CLIFFORD, W. K., *The Common Sense of the Exact Sciences* (New York, Alfred A. Knopf, Inc., 1947).

COHEN, MORRIS, and NAGEL, ERNST, *An Introduction to Logic and Scientific Method* (New York, Harcourt, Brace and Company, Inc., 1934).

DEWEY, JOHN, *Problems of Men* (New York, Philosophical Library, 1946).

DINGLE, HERBERT, *Science and Human Experience* (London, Williams and Norgate, Ltd., 1931).

DRACHMAN, J. M., *Studies in the Literature of Natural Science* (New York, The Macmillan Company, 1930).

HUXLEY, JULIAN, *Scientific Research and Social Needs* (London, C. A. Watts & Co., Ltd., 1934).

LEWIS, G. N., *The Anatomy of Science* (London, Oxford University Press, 1926).

MACH, ERNST, *Popular Scientific Lectures* (Chicago, The Open Court, 1895).

PEARSON, KARL, *The Grammar of Science* (London, J. M. Dent & Sons, Ltd., 1937).

POINCARÉ, HENRI, *The Foundations of Science* (New York, Science Press, 1913).

ROBINSON, JAMES H., *The Mind in the Making* (New York, Harper & Brothers, 1921).

RUSSELL, BERTRAND, *Mysticism and Logic* (New York, W. W. Norton & Co., Inc., 1929).

———, *The Scientific Outlook* (London, Allen & Unwin, Ltd., 1931).

SAIDLA, L. E., and GIBBS, W. E., editors, *Science and the Scientific Mind* (New York, McGraw-Hill Book Company, Inc., 1930).

Spencer, Herbert, *Essays—Scientific, Political and Speculative* (New York, D. Appleton and Co., 1910).
Thomson, J. A., *Introduction to Science* (New York, Henry Holt and Company, Inc., 1911).
Thornton, Jesse E., editor, *Science and Social Change* (Washington, The Brookings Institute, 1939).
West, Rebecca, *The Strange Necessity* (New York, Doubleday & Co., Inc., 1928).
Whitehead, Alfred N., *Science and the Modern World,* (New York, The Macmillan Company, 1935).

Development and Applications

Allen, John S., and others, *Atoms, Rocks and Galaxies* (New York, Harper & Brothers, 1942).
Bragg, Sir William, *Concerning the Nature of Things* (New York, Harper & Brothers, 1925).
Davis, Watson, *The Advance of Science* (New York, Doubleday & Co., Inc., 1934).
———, *Science Picture Parade* (New York, Duell, Sloane & Pearce, Inc., 1940).
Dietz, David, *The Story of Science* (New York, Dodd, Mead & Company, 1942).
Eddington, Sir Arthur, *New Pathways in Science* (New York, The Macmillan Company, 1935).
Furnas, C. C., *The Storehouse of Civilization* (New York, Columbia University Press, 1939).
Gray, George W., *The Advancing Front of Science* (New York, Whittlesey House, 1937).
Haldane, J. B. S., *Science and Human Life* (New York, Harper & Brothers, 1933).
Huxley, Julian, and Andrade, E. N. daC., *Simple Science* (New York, Harper & Brothers, 1935).
Huxley, T. H., *Collected Essays* (New York, D. Appleton and Co., 1893-1894).
Kaempffert, Waldemar, *Science—Today and Tomorrow* (New York, The Viking Press, 1942).
Krauskopf, Konrad B., *Fundamentals of Physical Science* (New York, McGraw-Hill Book Company, Inc., 1941).
Mills, John, *The Engineer in Society* (New York, D. Van Nostrand Company, Inc., 1946).
Montgomery, Frank, and Becklund, L. N., *Essays in Science and Engineering* (New York, Farrar & Rinehart, Inc., 1938).
Moulton, F. R., editor, *The World and Man as Science Sees Them* (New York, Doubleday & Co., Inc., 1937).
Rosen, S. M. and Rosen, Laura, *Technology and Society* (New York, The Macmillan Company, 1941).
Sullivan, J. W. N., *Aspects of Science* (New York, Alfred A. Knopf, Inc., 1926).
University of California Faculty Members, *Science in the University* (Berkeley, University of California Press, 1947).

WATKEYS, C. W., and others, *An Orientation in Science* (New York, McGraw-Hill Book Company, Inc., 1938).

WEAVER, WARREN, editor, *The Scientists Speak* (New York, Boni and Gaer, Inc., 1947).

WOODRUFF, LORANDE L., *Development of the Sciences* (1st Series: New Haven, Yale University Press, 1923; 2nd Series: London, Oxford University Press, 1941).

II

ASTRONOMY

ASTRONOMY is the oldest science. When man first began consciously to examine his world, he looked at the stars above. He saw the rising and setting of the sun and moon, the changes in the stars' positions from season to season. The regularity of the movements first led him to a conception of an orderly universe. Unable to understand causes, he first attributed the progressions to the will of the gods. Gradually, out of myth and superstition, he developed a more scientific viewpoint which finally crystallized in the Ptolemaic system.

For Ptolemaic astronomy, erroneous though it was, nevertheless was founded on scientific premises. It did attempt to explain observed phenomena in a logical manner. And like the phlogiston theory, it did succeed in offering causes which were able to satisfy logical and intelligent minds. It is easy now to laugh at those who refused to subscribe to the Copernican theory which overthrew the Ptolemaic hypothesis. It is much less easy to imagine the dislocation of human thought caused by the idea that man was not the center of the universe, that he was an infinitesimal spot on an extremely minor heavenly body; and it is almost as hard to appreciate fully the true genius of a Galileo who could announce the revolution of Jupiter's satellites and further insist that this revolution is "Proof That the Earth Moves."

Many people still consider astronomy an abstract science, far removed from daily life. The addle-pated astronomer was a stock figure of English comedy, but F. R. Moulton explains how completely mistaken is this view in "Influence of Astronomy on Science." One of the men responsible for the Planetesimal Hypothesis of the origin of the solar system, Moulton is an astronomer of note and a writer of charm. His article shows how astronomy has been the bell-wether of scientific advance, how in addition it has had a transcendent influence on almost every aspect of human thought.

The earliest astronomical research had to do with the positions, motions, and distances of the stars. For many centuries it was felt that even to hope to know anything of their physical and chemical natures was ridiculous. Nevertheless, the seemingly miraculous has been accomplished, and in "Driving Back the Dark," R. G. Aitken, formerly Director of the Lick Observatory, tells how the gulf between positional astronomy and modern astrophysics has been bridged. He explains what instruments have been used, what methods employed, what men made outstanding contributions. He perhaps pays insufficient tribute to Joseph Fraunhofer, the orphan boy who lived to discover the dark lines in the solar spectrum and thus paved the way for modern work on the composition of the stars. With spectrum analysis, Sir Norman Lockyer identified helium in the sun even before Sir William Ramsey discovered it on earth! Sir William Huggins used it to measure "Motion in the Line of Sight," a hitherto impossible feat.

Today there remain many unsolved problems in astronomy. Some which deal primarily with our own solar system are discussed in the selections by Whipple and Jeans. In "The Solar System and Its Origin," the Harvard astronomer considers what we do and do not know about the nature and composition of the planets. He examines also one of the outstanding puzzles in astronomy. From Laplace, to Chamberlin and Moulton (author of one article in this section), to Jeans (author of another), there have been numerous theories of the origin of the system. None has yet succeeded in explaining all the known facts.

Sir James Jeans, the well-known scientist and popularizer of science, examines another ancient puzzle in "Is There Life on Other Worlds?" His answer is based not only on facts of temperature and atmosphere but also on mathematical calculation. Only recently has the announcement been made of the discovery of carbon dioxide on Mars. If substantiated, it may be an indication of some low form of life there.

As we proceed outward from our solar system to the stars, the Milky Way and the galaxies, other problems present themselves immediately. How have the sun and the other stars managed to supply energy at the enormous observed rates and for the periods which we believe to be minimum? The latest theory is the result of a meeting between the egregiously large and the extremely small. To quote Eddington, "The road to a knowledge of the stars leads through the atom; and important knowledge of the atom has been reached through the stars." Hans Bethe's explanation of the energy transformation in the sun is here explained by George Gamow, who has himself done extensive work on the structure of atomic nuclei. For his work, Bethe has just been awarded a Nobel Prize.

Out from our own galactic system, one of the greatest modern astronomers, Sir Arthur Eddington, carries us to unimaginable distances in "The Milky Way and Beyond." Eddington is responsible for important work on the internal constitution of the stars. He proved the validity of Einstein's theory by his observation of the gravitational effect of the sun on a star's rays. In the present article he tells the story of another great unsolved problem—that of the expanding universe.

How is such a problem to be solved? Time and again scientists have seemed to come to a dead end in their research—only to find new instruments pointing the way to new interpretations. Thus it was with Fraunhofer's spectroscope. Thus it may be with the 200-inch telescope. As early as 1923, George Ellery Hale had written of the feasibility of an instrument even larger than the Mount Wilson telescope. He and his associates worked for years to help carry the idea to fruition. The results of the Palomar project will be apparent in years to come. A host of individuals have helped create this new instrument, probably the most expensive single scientific instrument in existence. They include some of the country's greatest engineers, a physicist who discovered a new method of increasing reflecting power and durability by spraying aluminum on glass, and a truck driver who, previously untrained, learned the technique of polishing glass so that he might have a part in the project. Sir Harold Spencer Jones, Astronomer Royal of England, describes some of the technical problems which were overcome, in "The 200-Inch Telescope." His article is particularly interesting as showing how applied science and engineering have contributed to the furtherance of pure research. Ira Sprague Bowen, Director of the Mount Wilson-Palomar Observatories, gives us a glimpse of what may be learned, in "Work for the 200-Inch Camera."

Many readers will be puzzled by the concepts of the new cosmogony discussed by Aitken, Eddington, and Bowen. The British astronomer Herbert Dingle helps them understand the problems involved in his "Astronomy and Scientific Ideas." A point Dingle has made elsewhere is worth noting no matter what science is involved. Each problem solved by science merely raises others. In the very nature of things, therefore, it is useless and absurd that we should ask of science that it gives us ultimate solutions.

A THEORY THAT THE EARTH MOVES AROUND THE SUN *

NICHOLAS COPERNICUS

THAT THE UNIVERSE IS SPHERICAL

First of all we assert that the universe is spherical; partly because this form, being a complete whole, needing no joints, is the most perfect of all;

* From *Concerning the Revolutions of the Heavenly Bodies*. Translated by Martha B. Shapley, 1928. Reprinted with her permission.

partly because it constitutes the most spacious form, which is thus suited to contain and retain all things; or also because all discrete parts of the world, I mean the sun, the moon and the planets, appear as spheres; or because all things tend to assume the spherical shape, a fact which appears in a drop of water and in other fluid bodies when they seek of their own accord to limit themselves. Therefore no one will doubt that this form is natural for the heavenly bodies.

THAT THE EARTH IS LIKEWISE SPHERICAL

That the earth is likewise spherical is beyond doubt, because it presses from all sides to its center. Although a perfect sphere is not immediately recognized because of the great height of the mountains and the depression of the valleys, yet this in no wise invalidates the general spherical form of the earth. This becomes clear in the following manner: To people who travel from any place to the North, the north pole of the daily revolution rises gradually, while the south pole sinks a like amount. Most of the stars in the neighborhood of the Great Bear appear not to set, and in the South some stars appear no longer to rise. Thus Italy does not see Canopus, which is visible to the Egyptians. And Italy sees the outermost star of the River, which is unknown to us of a colder zone. On the other hand, to people who travel toward the South, these stars rise higher in the heavens, while those stars which are higher to us become lower. Therefore, it is plain that the earth is included between the poles and is spherical. Let us add that the inhabitants of the East do not see the solar and lunar eclipses that occur in the evening, and people who live in the West do not see eclipses that occur in the morning, while those living in between see the former later, and the latter earlier.

That even the water has the same shape is observed on ships, in that the land which can not be seen from the ship can be spied from the tip of the mast. And, conversely, when a light is put on the tip of the mast, it appears to observers on land gradually to drop as the ship recedes until the light disappears, seeming to sink in the water. It is clear that the water, too, in accordance with its fluid nature, is drawn downwards, just as is the earth, and its level at the shore is no higher than its convexity allows. The land therefore projects everywhere only as far above the ocean as the land accidentally happens to be higher. . . .

WHETHER THE EARTH HAS A CIRCULAR MOTION, AND CONCERNING THE LOCATION OF THE EARTH

Since it has already been proved that the earth has the shape of a sphere, I insist that we must investigate whether from its form can be deduced a motion, and what place the earth occupies in the universe. Without this knowledge no certain computation can be made for the phenomena occurring in the heavens. To be sure, the great majority of writers agree that the earth is at rest in the center of the universe, so that they consider it unbelievable and even ridiculous to suppose the contrary. Yet, when one weighs the matter carefully, he will see that this question is not yet disposed of, and for that reason is by no means to be considered unimportant. Every change of position which is observed is due either to the motion of the observed object or of the observer, or to motions, naturally in different directions, of both; for when the observed object and the observer move in the same manner and in the same direction, then no motion is observed. Now the earth is the place from which we observe the revolution of the heavens and where it is displayed to our eyes. Therefore, if the earth should possess any motion, the latter would be noticeable in everything that is situated outside of it, but in the opposite direction, just as if everything were traveling past the earth. And of this nature is, above all, the daily revolution. For this motion seems to embrace the whole world, in fact, everything that is outside of the earth, with the single exception of the earth itself. But if one should admit that the heavens possess none of this motion, but that the earth rotates from west to east; and if one should consider this seriously with respect to the seeming rising and setting of the sun, of the moon and the stars; then one would find that it is actually true. Since the heavens which contain and retain all things are the common home of all things, it is not at once comprehensible why a motion is not rather ascribed to the thing contained than to the containing, to the located rather than to the locating. This opinion was actually held by the Pythagoreans Heraklid and Ekphantus and the Syracusean Nicetas (as told by Cicero), in that they assumed the earth to be rotating in the center of the universe. They were indeed of the opinion that the stars set due to the intervening of the earth, and rose due to its receding. . . .

REFUTATION OF THE ARGUMENTS, AND THEIR INSUFFICIENCY

It is claimed that the earth is at rest in the center of the universe and that this is undoubtedly true. But one who believes that the earth rotates will also certainly be of the opinion that this motion is natural and not violent. Whatever is in accordance with nature produces effects which are the opposite of what happens through violence. Things upon which violence or an external force is exerted must become annihilated and cannot long exist. But whatever happens in the course of nature remains in good condition and in its best arrangement. Without cause, therefore, Ptolemy feared that the earth and all earthly things if set in rotation would be dissolved by the action of nature, for the functioning of nature is something entirely different from artifice, or from that which could be contrived by the human mind. But why did he not fear the same, and indeed in much higher degree, for the universe, whose motion would have to be as much more rapid as the heavens are larger than the earth? Or have the heavens become infinite just because they have been removed from the center by the inexpressible force of the motion; while otherwise, if they were at rest, they would collapse? Certainly if this argument were true the extent of the heavens would become infinite. For the more they were driven aloft by the outward impulse of the motion, the more rapid would the motion become because of the ever increasing circle which it would have to describe in the space of 24 hours; and, conversely, if the motion increased, the immensity of the heavens would also increase. Thus velocity would augment size into infinity, and size, velocity. But according to the physical law that the infinite can neither be traversed, nor can it for any reason have motion, the heavens would, however, of necessity be at rest.

But it is said that outside of the heavens there is no body, nor place, nor empty space, in fact, that nothing at all exists, and that, therefore, there is no space in which the heavens could expand; then it is really strange that something could be enclosed by nothing. If, however, the heavens were infinite and were bounded only by their inner concavity, then we have, perhaps, even better confirmation that there is nothing outside of the heavens, because everything, whatever its size, is within them; but then the heavens would remain motionless. The most important argument, on which depends the proof of the finiteness of the universe, is motion. Now, whether the world is finite or infinite, we will leave to the quarrels of the natural philosophers; for us remains the certainty that the earth, contained between poles, is bounded by a spherical surface. Why should we hesitate to grant it a motion, natural and corresponding to its form; rather than assume that the whole world, whose boundary is not known and cannot be known, moves? And why are we not willing to acknowledge that the *appearance* of a daily revolution belongs to the heavens, its *actuality* to the earth? The relation is similar to that of which Virgil's *Æneas* says: "We sail out of the harbor, and the countries and cities recede." For when a ship is sailing along quietly, everything which is outside of it will appear to those on board to have a motion corresponding to the movement of the ship, and the voyagers are of the erroneous opinion that they with all that they have with them are at rest. This can without doubt also apply to the motion of the earth, and it may appear as if the whole universe were revolving. . . .

CONCERNING THE CENTER OF THE UNIVERSE

. . . Since nothing stands in the way of the movability of the earth, I believe we must now investigate whether it also has several motions, so that it can be considered one of the planets. That it is not the center of all the revolutions is proved by the irregular motions of the planets, and their varying distances from the earth, which cannot be explained as concentric circles with the earth at the center. Therefore, since there are several central points, no one will without cause be uncertain whether the center of the universe is the center of gravity of the earth or some other central point. I, at least, am of the opinion that gravity is nothing else than a natural force planted by the divine providence of the Master of the World into its parts, by means of which they, assuming a spherical shape, form a unity and a whole. And it is to be assumed that the impulse is also inherent in the sun and the moon and the other planets, and that by the operation of this force they remain in the spherical shape in which they appear; while they, nevertheless, complete their revolutions in diverse ways. If then the earth, too, possesses other motions besides that around its center, then they must be of such a character as to become apparent in many ways and in appropriate manners; and among such possible effects we recognize the yearly revolution.

1543

PROOF THAT THE EARTH MOVES *

GALILEO GALILEI

About ten months ago a report reached my ears that a Dutchman had constructed a telescope, by the aid of which visible objects, although at a great distance from the eye of the observer, were seen distinctly as if near; and some proofs of its most wonderful performances were reported, which some gave credence to, but others contradicted. A few days after, I recieved confirmation of the report in a letter written from Paris by a noble Frenchman, Jaques Badovere, which finally determined me to give myself up first to inquire into the principle of the telescope, and then to consider the means by which I might compass the invention of a similar instrument, which after a little while I succeeded in doing, through deep study of the theory of Refraction; and I prepared a tube, at first of lead, in the ends of which I fitted two glass lenses, both plane on one side, but on the other side one spherically convex, and the other concave. Then bringing my eye to the concave lens I saw objects satisfactorily large and near, for they appeared one-third of the distance off and nine times larger than when they are seen with the natural eye alone. I shortly afterwards constructed another telescope with more nicety, which magnified objects more than sixty times. At length, by sparing neither labour nor expense, I succeeded in constructing for myself an instrument so superior that objects seen through it appear magnified nearly a thousand times, and more than thirty times nearer than if viewed by the natural powers of sight alone.

* From *The Sidereal Messenger*. Translated by E. S. Carlos, 1880.

FIRST TELESCOPIC OBSERVATIONS

It would be altogether a waste of time to enumerate the number and importance of the benefits which this instrument may be expected to confer, when used by land or sea. But without paying attention to its use for terrestrial objects, I betook myself to observations of the heavenly bodies; and first of all, I viewed the Moon as near as if it was scarcely two semidiameters of the Earth distant. After the Moon, I frequently observed other heavenly bodies, both fixed stars and planets, with incredible delight. . . .

DISCOVERY OF JUPITER'S SATELLITES

There remains the matter, which seems to me to deserve to be considered the most important in this work, namely, that I should disclose and publish to the world the occasion of discovering and observing four planets, never seen from the very beginning of the world up to our own times, their positions, and the observations made during the last two months about their movements and their changes of magnitude. . . .

On the 7th day of January in the present year, 1610, in the first hour of the following night, when I was viewing the constellations of the heavens through a telescope, the planet Jupiter presented itself to my view, and as I had prepared for myself a very excellent instrument, I noticed a circumstance which I had never been able to notice before, owing to want of power in my other telescope, namely, that three little stars, small but very bright, were near the planet; and although I believed them to belong to the number of the fixed stars, yet they made me somewhat wonder, because they seemed to be arranged exactly in a straight line, parallel to the ecliptic, and to be brighter than the rest of the stars, equal to them in magnitude. The position of them with reference to one another and to Jupiter was as follows:

Ori. * * O * Occ.

On the east side there were two stars, and a single one towards the west. The star which was furthest towards the east, and the western star, appeared rather larger than the third.

I scarcely troubled at all about the distance between them and Jupiter, for, as I have already said, at first I believed them to be fixed stars; but when on January 8th, led by some fatality, I turned again to look at the same part of the heavens, I found a very different state of things, for there were three little stars all west of Jupiter, and nearer together than on the previous night, and they were separated from one another by equal intervals, as the accompanying figure shows.

Ori. O * * * Occ.

At this point, although I had not turned my thoughts at all upon the approximation of the stars to one another, yet my surprise began to be excited, how Jupiter could one day be found to the east of all the aforesaid fixed stars when the day before it had been west of two of them; and forthwith I became afraid lest the planet might have moved differently from the calculation of astronomers, and so had passed those stars by its own proper motion. I, therefore, waited for the next night with the most intense longing, but I was disappointed of my hope, for the sky was covered with clouds in every direction.

But on January 10th the stars appeared in the following position with regard to Jupiter, the third, as I thought, being

Ori. * * O Occ.

hidden by the planet. They were situated just as before, exactly in the same straight line with Jupiter, and along the Zodiac.

When I had seen these phenomena, as I knew that corresponding changes of position could not by any means belong to Jupiter, and as, moreover, I perceived that the stars which I saw had always been the same, for there were no others either in front or behind, within a great distance, along the Zodiac—at length, changing from doubt into surprise, I discovered that the interchange of position which I saw belonged not to Jupiter, but to the stars to which my attention had been drawn, and I thought therefore that they ought to be observed henceforward with more attention and precision.

Accordingly, on January 11th I saw an arrangement of the following kind:

Ori. * * O Occ.

namely, only two stars to the east of Jupiter, the nearer of which was distant from Jupiter three times as far as from the star further to the east; and the star furthest to the east was nearly twice as large as the other one; whereas on the previous night they had appeared nearly of equal magnitude. I, therefore, concluded, and decided unhesitatingly, that there are three stars in the heavens moving about Jupiter, as Venus and Mercury round the Sun; which at length was established as clear as daylight by numerous other subsequent observations. These observations also established that there are not only three, but four, erratic sidereal bodies performing their revolutions round Jupiter. . . .

These are my observations upon the four Medicean planets, recently discovered for the first time by me; and although it is not yet permitted me to deduce by calculation from these observations the orbits of these bodies, yet I may be allowed to make statements, based upon them, well worthy of attention.

ORBITS AND PERIODS OF JUPITER'S SATELLITES

And, in the first place, since they are sometimes behind, sometimes before Jupiter, at like distances, and withdraw from this planet towards the east and towards the west only within very narrow limits of divergence, and since they accompany this planet alike when its motion is retrograde and direct, it can be a matter of doubt to no one that they perform their revolutions about this planet while at the same time they all accomplish together orbits of twelve years' length about the centre of the world. Moreover, they revolve in unequal circles, which is evidently the conclusion to be drawn from the fact that I have never been permitted to see two satellites in conjunction when their distance from Jupiter was great, whereas near Jupiter two, three, and sometimes all four, have been found closely packed together. Moreover, it may be detected that the revolutions of the satellites which describe the smallest circles round Jupiter are the most rapid, for the satellites nearest to Jupiter are often to be seen in the east, when the day before they have appeared in the west, and contrariwise. Also, the satellite moving in the greatest orbit seems to me, after carefully weighing the occasions of its returning to positions previously noticed, to have a periodic time of half a month. Besides, we have a notable and splendid argument to remove the scruples of those who can tolerate the revolution of the planets round the Sun in the Copernican system, yet are so disturbed by the motion of one Moon about the Earth, while both accomplish an orbit of a year's length about the Sun, that they consider that this theory of the universe must be upset as impossible; for now we have not one planet only revolving about another, while both traverse a vast orbit about the Sun, but our sense of sight presents to us four satellites circling about Jupiter, like the Moon about the Earth, while the whole system travels over a mighty orbit about the Sun in the space of twelve years.

1610

MOTION IN THE LINE OF SIGHT *

SIR WILLIAM HUGGINS

From the beginning of our work upon the spectra of the stars, I saw in vision the application of the new knowledge to the creation of a great method of astronomical observation which could not fail in future to have a powerful influence on the progress of astronomy; indeed, in some respects greater than the more direct one of the investigation of the chemical nature and the relative physical conditions of the stars.

It was the opprobrium of the older astronomy—though indeed one which involved no disgrace, for *à l'impossible nul n'est tenu*—that only that part of the motions of the stars which is across the line of sight could be seen and directly measured. The direct observation of the other component

* From *The Nineteenth Century Review.*

in the line of sight, since it caused no change of place and, from the great distance of the stars, no appreciable change of size or of brightness within an observer's lifetime, seemed to lie hopelessly quite outside the limits of man's powers. Still, it was only too clear that, so long as we were unable to ascertain directly those components of the stars' motions which lie in the line of sight, the speed and direction of the solar motion in space, and many of the great problems of the constitution of the heavens, must remain more or less imperfectly known.

Now as the color of a given kind of light, and the exact position it would take up in a spectrum, depends directly upon the length of the waves, or, to put it differently, upon the number of waves which would pass into the eye in a second of time, it seemed more than probable that motion between the source of the light and the observer must change the apparent length of the waves to him, and the number reaching his eye in a second. To a swimmer striking out from the shore each wave is shorter, and the number he goes through in a given time is greater than would be the case if he had stood still in the water. Such a change of wave length would transform any given kind of light, so that it would take a new place in the spectrum, and from the amount of this change to a higher or to a lower place, we could determine the velocity per second of the relative motion between the star and the earth. . . .

The discovery of the actual velocity of light was made by Roemer in 1675, from observations of the satellites of Jupiter. Now though the effect of motion in the line of sight upon the apparent velocity of light underlies Roemer's determinations, the idea of a change of colour in light from motion between the source of light and the observer was announced for the first time by Doppler in 1841. Later, various experiments were made in connection with this view by Ballot, Sestini, Klinkerfues, Clerk Maxwell, and Fizeau. But no attempts had been made, nor were indeed possible, to discover by this principle the motions of the heavenly bodies in the line of sight. For, to learn whether any change in the light had taken place from motion in the line of sight, it was clearly necessary to know the original wave length of the light before it left the star.

As soon as our observations had shown that certain earthly substances were present in the stars, the original wave lengths of their lines became known, and any small want of coincidence of the stellar lines with the same lines produced upon the earth might safely be interpreted as revealing the velocity of approach or of recession between the star and the earth.

These considerations were present to my mind from the first, and helped me to bear up under my toilsome disappointments: *Studio fallente laborem.* It was not until 1866 that I found time to construct a spectroscope of greater power for this research. It would be scarcely possible, even with greater space, to convey to the reader any true conception of the difficulties which presented themselves in this work, from various instrumental causes, and of the extreme care and caution which were needful to distinguish spurious instrumental shifts of a line from a true shift due to the star's motion.

At last, in 1868, I felt able to announce in a paper printed in the *Transactions of the Royal Society* for that year, the foundation of this new method of research, which, transcending the wildest dreams of an earlier time, enables the astronomer to measure off directly in terrestrial units the invisible motions in the line of sight of the heavenly bodies. . . .

It has become fruitful in another direction, for it puts into our hands the power of separating double stars which are beyond the resolving power of any telescope that can be constructed. Pickering and Vogel have independently discovered by this method an entirely new class of double stars.

Double stars too close to be separately visible unite in giving a compound spectrum. Now, if the stars are in motion about a common centre of gravity, the lines of one star will shift periodically relatively to similar lines of the other star, in the spectrum common to both; and such lines will consequently, at those times, appear double. Even if one of the stars is too dark to give a spectrum which can be seen upon that of the other star, as is actually the case with Algol and Spica,[1] the whirling of the stars about each other may be discovered from the periodical shifting of the lines of the brighter star relatively to terrestrial lines of the same substance. It is clear that as the stars revolve about their common center of gravity, the bright star would be sometimes advancing, and at others receding, relatively to an observer on the earth, except it should so happen that the stars' orbit were perpendicular to the line of sight.

It would be scarcely possible, without the appearance of great exaggeration, to attempt to sketch out even in broad outline the many glorious achievements which doubtless lie before this method of research in the immediate future.

1897

INFLUENCE OF ASTRONOMY ON SCIENCE *

F. R. MOULTON

Many arts and sciences have contributed to the exploration of the celestial regions. Reciprocally the heavens have illuminated and are illuminating many of the sciences that pertain to the earth, for our planet has been found

[1] Spica is now known to be composed of two stars nearly equal in brightness.—Eds.

* Address at the dedication of the Franklin Memorial, May 20, 1938. Published by permission from *The Scientific Monthly*. Copyright 1938 by The Science Press.

to be only a particle in a universe of matter, its life only an incident in the history of the cosmos, and terrestrial phenomena and laws only particular examples of universal events and principles.

What is the foundation on which all science rests? It is what we think of as the orderliness of the universe, the regularities in the sequences of its phenomena. Without orderliness there could be no science, for unless there were a firm conviction that nature is orderly there would be no attempt to discover its order. In this age of science it is difficult to realize that in ancient times men almost universally believed that the physical universe is subject to the whims of capricious gods and goddesses. Then chaos prevailed on the earth and in the heavens above; superstitions cast their terrifying shadows over mankind. But before the dawn of recorded history regularities in such phenomena as the recurring seasons and the phases of the moon had been noted. Even before the time of Aristotle, in the fourth century B.C., the lengths of the month and the year had been measured to within a minute or two, the inclination of the plane of the earth's equator to the plane of its orbit had been determined with considerable accuracy, the causes of eclipses of the sun and of the moon had been discovered, and much progress had been made in developing theories of cycles and epicycles for explaining the apparent motions of the sun, the moon and the planets among the stars. All these great results, depending upon centuries of observations, had been established before any considerable steps had been taken in the development of the sciences that pertain only to things on the earth. It is to the glory of astronomy that in it men thus first perceived that the universe is orderly and entered on the pathway to science.

It may be surprising that order should have been first clearly perceived in phenomena presented by distant things. But distance smooths to imperceptibility the countless little ripples of phenomena which would confuse us with their complexities were we among them, and leaves to our perceptions only the regularly recurring great waves which roll along like the swells of the ocean. Though the moon has more than a thousand measurable cycles in its motion, a few determine all the important characteristics in the succession of its phases. In ever-changing shape, it courses through the night sky when all the distractions of the day are covered by darkness. Inaccessible and somewhat mysterious and with cycles of change short enough to be held easily in the memory, it attracts the attention and makes clear the orderly succession of its phenomena.

One of the principal methods in the development of science is generalization. If the motions of the moon are orderly, then why not the motions of those mysterious wanderers among the stars, the planets? Thus the ancients must have asked themselves the question. Since the planets revolve around the sun instead of around the earth, their apparent motions as observed from this rotating and revolving planet are enormously more complex than those of the moon. Yet long series of observations and endless calculations had led to the discovery of the order in them by the beginning of our era. All who have read the Almagest of Claudius Ptolemy, which was published about 1,800 years ago, have been amazed at his knowledge of the apparent motions of the planets and at the perfection of his theories for explaining them. In only a few other sciences have similar very close correspondences between theories and observed phenomena been reached even at the present day.

The words "order" and "orderliness" have been used as though they have perfectly definite meanings which are generally understood. But we find on examination that it is difficult if not impossible to define them and that it is equally difficult to determine whether natural phenomena are orderly according to any definition that we may adopt. It does not relieve us to say that phenomena are orderly when they obey laws that we can state, for essentially "laws of nature" are only descriptions of phenomena, often in time sequences. There is nothing of compulsion or causality in laws of nature, for they are man-made—and often man-destroyed—formulations of how certain classes of things exist or occur. Consequently, if there is any definite content in such a phrase as a "law of nature" it belongs to a description, whether in words or symbols, that scientists themselves have invented.

Now what properties of a description entitle us to say that the phenomena it describes are orderly? A ready answer would be that the description is simple. But what is simple depends to a large extent upon the information and experience of the person considering it. It depends also upon the terminology or notation in which it is expressed. For example, the unperturbed motion of the earth around the sun is simple to one familiar with the properties of conic sections, but enormously complicated to one who does not have such knowledge. Or, as to notation, explicit formulas describing the complicated motions of the moon fill many pages, but the differential equations which contain implicitly everything pertaining to its motion may be written on a calling card. Simplicity of a description, therefore, does not appear to be a satisfactory criterion for determining whether the phenomena it describes are orderly, for simplicity depends in considerable part upon considerations that are entirely independent of the things described.

Another possible criterion of orderliness of phenomena is whether or not they are cyclical in character. Most of the phenomena with which we are generally familiar are approximately cyclical. Not only do day and night and the seasons endlessly recur, but there are fundamental rhythms in our own lives—the beatings of our hearts, the inhalations and exhalations of our lungs, our periods of activity and repose, the electric potentials that rise and fall in our brains. But phenomena do not exactly repeat themselves. No day ever exactly duplicated another day, no two seasons were ever exactly alike. Although strict periodicity in nature is never found, the approximately cyclical character of phenomena appears to have been fundamental in the origin and development of science and to be fundamental for its progress. Indeed, without repetitions our memories would appear to play only with dreams and our reason would grope in vain for materials for its use. That is, the experiences which are basic in the evolution and exercise of our mental processes are cyclical in character. In general, we feel that we understand phenomena only when we analyze them into series of nearly repeating elementary events. When we have succeeded in such an analysis, we regard the phenomena as orderly, and we are satisfied.

Science was born in astronomy because many celestial phenomena are compounded of relatively few cycles. It flourished long in this science before there were comparable developments in other fields both because of the simplicity of its repetitions and because of the amazing successes of its predictions. For many centuries it alone filled the reason, as well as the imagination, with awe.

Throughout the history of science there have been attempts to discover the *causes* of phenomena instead of simply *how* phenomena occur. To account for the motions of the planets the Greeks invented crystalline spheres, apparently not realizing that if they felt impelled to ascribe causes they should explain also both the crystalline spheres and the reason for their rotation. A parallel case was the invention of the luminiferous ether to carry the transverse waves of radiant energy. These fictitious causes or instruments are in the nature of anthropomorphisms, having their origin in our feeling that by acts of our wills we cause phenomena to occur. In very ancient times men were a little more naive, inventing gods and goddesses as the causes of phenomena. Fundamentally the gods and goddesses of antiquity and the crystalline spheres and ethers of more recent times are alike. All have been introduced arbitrarily in order to make the phenomena of the physical world parallel what we regard as the consequences of our own volitions.

Now and then newly discovered facts or phenomena have compelled the abandonment of irrelevant scaffoldings in our science. Perhaps the earliest clear example was Kepler's derivation from observations of the three laws of planetary motion which he announced more than three hundred years ago. The demonstrated elliptical motions of the planets around the sun at variable angular rates made it impossible to retain as realities the fantastic crystalline spheres of the Greeks. And, similarly, the fact that radiant energy has the properties of both waves and particles eliminates the assumption of a luminiferous ether.

It is remarkable that the history of the theories of the motions of the planets has not had a greater influence on later ideas respecting the essential meaning of "laws of nature." Over and over again, even in astronomy, analogues of the crystalline spheres of the Greeks have been introduced in order to have causes of phenomena, although all we know is the relationships among the phenomena themselves.

One of the greatest and most important changes in point of view in science occurred with the acceptance of the heliocentric theory of the solar system. Although Aristarchus of Samos, three hundred years before the Christian era, clearly formulated the theory that the earth rotates and revolves around the sun, and explained by it the seasons and all the apparent motions of the heavenly bodies, the earth was almost universally believed to be the center of the universe until the time of Copernicus near the middle of the sixteenth century. In spite of his painstaking and convincing comparisons of theory with observations, the heliocentric theory was not generally accepted even by scientists until after the time of Galileo, a century later. Then the solid earth beneath, contrary to accepted common sense, philosophy and theology, suddenly became a spinning particle flying unsupported in the immensity of space. Man found himself removed from his proud position at the center of the universe to the surface of one of its lesser constituents. As vague fears entered his heart that he might not be the principal object of creation, he naturally resented the new and subversive doctrine.

Another reason that the revolution of the earth about the sun was at first difficult to accept was that there was nothing assigned to support it or to cause it to move. This psychological defect in the theory was partly remedied by the discovery of the laws of motion and the law of gravitation, which were regarded as the cause of the motions of the planets and their satellites. Although this cause was a rather intangible set of formulae, it gradually acquired reality in the minds of scientists, as abstract ideas always do with increasing familiarity.

With the formulation of the laws of motion and the discovery of the law of gravitation by Newton, physical science closed a long period, extending from the prehistoric days when men first began to perceive that there is order in the motions of the heavenly bodies down through the centuries of painstaking observations to the time when Kepler laboriously worked out his three laws of planetary motion. With the publication of Newton's "Principia" in 1687, physical science entered on a new and glorious period. The transition from the old to the new was sudden, and the completeness of the revolution in point of view has perhaps never been equalled in science or in any other field of human endeavor.

Previous to the work of Newton descriptions of phenomena had been made by means of tables of values or geometrical constructions or kinematical models. All at once something entirely new was introduced, derivatives of the first and the second orders. With all the background of knowledge and experience we have now, it is difficult for us to realize the revolutionary nature of the new concepts and methods. Let us cast out from our minds Newton's work and think of the problem of describing the path of a projectile in a vacuum. From experience we know that at each instant it has a definite distance and altitude; consequently we can make a table for its coordinates. If we desire its components of velocity we can make a similar table. We can make a diagram of its path and mark off on it intervals of time. The table or the diagram is fairly descriptive of the phenomena—in few fields of science do we have more. But the equations of Newton are universal, containing implicitly complete descriptions of all properties of the motion not only at the surface of the earth but at any other place.

Dynamics originated largely in connection with the problem of explaining the motions of the moon and of the planets, though Galileo had previously gone far in his investigations of the motions of falling bodies. Fortunately the masses of the planets are so small relative to the mass of the sun that each of them moves, at least for several revolutions, almost as though the others do not exist. If it were not for this circumstance, there would not have been any simple laws of planetary motion for Kepler to discover. Without Kepler's laws, Newton could not have verified his theories of the laws of motion and of the law of gravitation. Without the work of Newton or similar work, dynamics would not have been founded and the progress of all science would have been much slower.

Of equal importance in the founding and verifying of the principles of dynamics was the fact that the sun affects the motions of the moon, and the planets interact upon one another; for these perturbations, as they are called, are the consequences of foreign influences which would be most likely to produce unexpected results if any of the laws from which they are derived were erroneous. Newton himself made more verifications of the principles he laid down than have been made even to-day for almost any other law in the whole domain of science. His successors, particularly Lagrange, Laplace and Euler, extended the agreements between theory and observations to thousands. Some of these verifications of theory were of the most involved nature, consisting of a series of consequences, each of which in turn became the cause of other perturbations. For example, the attraction of the sun slightly increases the period of revolution of the moon, the amount depending upon the dimensions and shape of the orbit of the earth. The planets are slowly altering the shape of the orbit of the earth, with the result that the effects of the sun on the orbit of the moon also gradually are changed. Although the cycle of these slight effects are thousands of centuries in length, Laplace worked out all the complicated interactions of forces and obtained theoretical results which were precisely verified by observations.

It was not of much practical importance in everyday matters that Laplace showed that the gravitational interactions of the bodies of the solar system are in harmony, even to many decimals, with the implications of theory. But these amazing demonstrations of the exactness of the law of gravitation were made in the infancy of, or before the birth of, most of the sciences and scientific theories of the present day—a generation before Dalton's founding of the atomic theory of matter, two generations before

Wöhler's first synthesis of an organic compound and Faraday's experiments on the relation between electricity and magnetism, three generations before Joule's and Mayer's formulation of the law of the conservation of energy and Darwin's work on the origin of species, more than a century before chemists and physicists first penetrated into the subatomic world or astronomers had made substantial progress in exploring our galaxy of stars. Even to this day there are no more striking illustrations than the motions of the planets and their satellites that the universe is orderly.

The indirect effects of the triumphs of celestial mechanics during the eighteenth century were the important ones. Whenever in later times chemists were tempted to despair of explaining chemical processes or geologists were assuming creation and cataclysms or biologists were appealing to mysterious vital forces, there arose always before them the shining example of perfect order and comprehensibility in the motions of the heavenly bodies. Whenever scientists or philosophers were inclined to take a narrow view of the cosmos in space or in time, the limitations they were about to impose were contradicted by the immensities of the celestial spaces and the long cycles in the motions of the planets.

It is universally agreed that evolution is one of the most important concepts in science. In a sense it completes science. As has been stated, the basis on which science rests is the orderliness of the universe, and orderliness is essentially the approximately cyclical character of phenomena. But phenomena are not exactly repeated. For example, the cycles of the moon's motion do not exactly recur, nor do the waves on the sea or the characteristics of living organisms. Evolution provides for these continual variations; indeed, it depends on them. The departures from cyclical repetitions of phenomena are not discontinuous or relatively large. They are rather in the nature of slight modifications in the cycles that we regard as essential to order. But when variations occur on the whole in one direction over long periods of time, as they may, the changes eventually become very great. So the fundamental basis of science as enlarged and enriched by the principle of evolution provides us with a universe that is orderly in a limited sense and not essentially unchanging.

Although evolution was adumbrated in the writings of the Greek philosophers, it could not take definite scientific form until recent times. It found its first clear expression in astronomy about a century before Darwin published his "Origin of Species." Curiously it appeared independently in three countries; in England in 1750, in a book by Thomas Wright; in Germany, in 1755, in a brilliant volume by Immanuel Kant; and in France, in 1796, as a chapter in a general survey of astronomy with which Laplace followed the publication of his monumental "Mécanique Céleste." Each of these writers attempted to trace out the evolution of the solar system on the basis of the principles of mechanics.

Of the three theories of planetary evolution, that of Laplace had by far the greatest influence, partly because of the great name of its author, partly because of its relative simplicity and partly because the scientific world was gradually being prepared for such revolutionary ideas. The nebular hypothesis of Laplace, as it was called, gradually became widely accepted in science. It pointed to a long history for the earth and undoubtedly had an important influence in the struggle among geologists over Catastrophism and Uniformitarianism in the early decades of the nineteenth century. It accustomed scientists to thinking of change in long periods of time and thus prepared the way psychologically for the theory of organic evolution. It affected the philosophy of Spencer and its influence extended even to theology. By the beginning of the twentieth it had tinged the thoughts of all the world.

Since all our knowledge of celestial bodies is obtained from the radiant energy we receive from them, astronomers from the time of Galileo have been interested in the properties of light. About 1608 Jan Lippershey used the property of the refraction of light in designing spectacles. Upon hearing of this work, Galileo at once invented the refracting telescope and with it observed craters on the moon, the largest four satellites of Jupiter and spots on the sun. For different reasons each of these discoveries was of great interest and importance. But with increasing telescopic power, difficulties arose because different colors under given conditions are refracted by different amounts. To avoid these defects, telescope makers turned to the use of mirrors until John Dollond, about 1750, discovered how to correct the errors in refraction by using two pieces of glass having approximately compensating properties. Thus about a century before the invention of photography the requirements of astronomy led to the design and construction of achromatic lenses without which good photographs can not be obtained in white light.

One of the properties of light which has come to play a fundamental rôle in recent physical theories is its velocity in vacant space. The fact that light traverses interplanetary spaces with a finite, though very great, velocity was discovered by Römer, in 1675, only sixty-six years after the invention of the telescope. In this day it is difficult to appreciate the rapidity of the development of observational astronomy which led to this discovery or the profound effect it had upon scientific thought. It does not seriously detract from its importance that the value obtained by Römer for the velocity of light was about 20 per cent. too large. The stimulating effect of the discovery that radiant energy is transmitted at a finite velocity is illustrated by the fact that Laplace attempted, but without success, to determine the velocity of gravitation.

Our familiarity with the numbers used in expressing the properties of radiant energy dulls us to the amazing realities they represent. The highest velocities for which scientists were familiar before the time of Römer were those of projectiles and of sound in the atmosphere, or of the order of a mile in five seconds. But light flashes through space at a speed equal to seven times the distance around the earth in a second. The lengths of its waves are of the order of a fifty thousandth of an inch. The number of its mysteriously transverse vibrations in a second is, in the case of yellow light, greater than the number of seconds in 18,000,000 years. These are the quantities that a world familiar only with such things as the diameter of a hair and the speed of the flight of birds were suddenly asked to accept as realities.

For more than a century astronomers lamented the fact that there is dispersion of light because it impaired the excellence of their telescopes. Then they gradually came to realize with the development and application of the spectroscope that the composite character of light and its easy separability into its different wave-lengths place within their hands an instrument of the most extraordinary value. . . .

And what of the results obtained by means of the spectroscope? By its use astronomers have determined the chemical constitution of the sun, its temperature, its period of rotation, the velocities of its violent eruptions, its magnetic condition, its distance from the earth, the density of its atmosphere, and have observed its prominences even when it is not eclipsed. For most scientific purposes the spectroscope has brought the sun down to the earth. It has become a physical laboratory in which the principles of spectrum analysis are verified in the flash spectrum at the time of an eclipse, in which temperatures beyond these of terrestrial laboratories are always available, and in which theories of ionization can be verified. . . .

It would be inexcusable to close these remarks without referring to Michelson's attempt to measure the velocity of the earth with respect to the ether and his failure to find the expected result, for it led eventually to the theory of relativity and entirely new conceptions respecting the nature of the universe and of science. Moreover, it may be noted that nearly all the tests of the validity of the equations of relativity are astronomical in nature.

In summary, science originated in observations of the heavenly bodies, and its anthropomorphic character was successively weakened by the requirements of astronomical theories. The exterior universe has taught us much about our earth and its sciences, and much even about the workings of our own minds. . . .

1938

DRIVING BACK THE DARK *

ROBERT GRANT AITKEN

It was my good fortune, twenty years ago, to walk for a time in the steps of Galileo. At Pisa, I climbed the leaning tower from whose summit he gave his famous demonstration of the laws of falling bodies; at Florence, I had the privilege of holding in my hands and of looking through his little "optic tube," the first telescope directed upon the heavenly bodies; at Padua, I wandered through the halls of the 700-year-old university where for eighteen years he carried on his researches and delivered his lectures before audiences that not uncommonly numbered 2,000 students coming not only from Italy but from all parts of Europe; in Rome, I stood within the old church Santa Maria sopra Minerva where he made formal recantation of heretical doctrines; and at Arcetri, I was admitted to the house and garden where he passed his later years.

For me, this experience will remain an ever-memorable one, because Galileo, who insisted that every theory must be put to the test of observation, who said not merely "Come and hear" but also "Come and see," more truly than any of his predecessors or contemporaries was the forerunner of the modern astronomer. Throughout the ages until the night when he first scanned the heavens with his little telescope, man's universe had been limited by the blue canopy covering the motionless Earth. Within that canopy were the Sun, the Moon, the five bright wandering stars, a few thousand "fixed" stars, and through it plunged an occasional comet or falling star, sent as a warning by an angry God; beyond it lay the darkness of unknown outer space. Galileo was the first to open the canopy and drive back the dark.

To set the heavens wide open and drive back the dark, back even to the outmost "marches and strongholds of space"; that is the astronomer's objective, and the successive generations of the followers of Galileo, armed with more and still more powerful equipment, have been constantly pressing on toward it, sometimes swiftly, sometimes at a more plodding pace, but ever onward, though even today they have not reached their goal and the retreating dark still challenges their advance. . . .

Those who entered upon it did not think of themselves as adventurers engaged in driving back the dark. They were completely engrossed in the study of special objects or classes of objects—the Sun, the planets, the stars, and the nebulae. They were collecting data on their positions, motions, numbers, distances, their various physical properties, data of every kind that might be classified and, later, rationalized by some great generaliza-

* This paper was read at the celebration of the eighty-fifth anniversary of the founding of Mills College. It was printed in *Popular Astronomy*, and is reprinted here in a slightly revised form through the courtesy of the editor of that journal.

tion or theory that would at the same time provide a basis for prediction, and guide and stimulate further observation.

Their record, at the time our special story opens, was a brilliant one. Not only had they carefully surveyed the solar system—the dramatic discovery of the planet Neptune in 1846 testifying alike to the accuracy of their observations and to the degree of refinement they had reached in the development of the theory of planetary motions based upon the Newtonian law of gravitation—but, as Galileo's original optic tube and Newton's first one-inch speculum were gradually replaced by more and more powerful telescopes, they had also penetrated deeply into the greater system of the stars, bringing into view tens of millions of stars, of descending grades of brightness, which the unaided eye can never see.

These stars, they found, were not fixed, but were all in motion, very slowly changing their positions on the face of the sky, and the Sun itself was moving among them in a well-defined direction. They were not all single stars—many thousands of them were double stars, pairs of stars indissolubly united by the bonds of their mutual attraction; they did not all shine with constant light—many of them varied in brightness, in short cycles precisely repeated, or more slowly and less regularly. Here and there, dozens or scores or hundreds of stars were found grouped in clusters like the Pleiades, or sometimes more compactly, as in the globular cluster in Hercules. And intermingled with stars and star groups were thousands of objects called nebulae from their pale, cloudlike light, mostly small and fairly regular in form, but not infrequently, along the Milky Way, revealing amazingly irregular and complicated outlines. And all these stars, bright and faint, single or double, shining steadily or with variable light, "instead," in Sir John Herschel's words, "of being scattered indifferently through space, form a stratum the thickness of which is small in comparison with its length and breadth," the longer diameters lying in the plane of the Milky Way.

Even the age-old problem of measuring the distance to a star had at last been solved and approximately accurate values for the distances of a few of the nearer ones had been determined, providing final proof of the truth of the Copernican doctrine that the Earth revolves about the Sun, and making it clear that the stars must be bodies like the Sun, shining by their own light, and that the Sun itself is but a star. Were the Sun to be removed to the distance of even the nearest stars, it would, like them, become a mere point of light, no brighter than a star of the first magnitude. That this was true had, indeed, become more evident with each successive failure to measure the distance to a star, but its practical value for the extension of our knowledge of the nature of the stars was slow to be realized.

It is indeed a record of great achievements, but it must be pointed out that it is a record of work relating not to the stars themselves, but to their positions, motions, and distances; to the mechanics of the stellar system, and not to its physical nature. So far, the astronomers had been working practically alone, using the telescope and the calculus, and ignoring the physicists and chemists, though they, too, were driving back the dark in their respective fields, gradually bringing to light the secrets hidden in the molecule and the atom.

About the middle of the nineteenth century, this condition began to change. Astronomers, physicists, and chemists began to see the advantage of joining forces in their attacks upon the problems of the universe, the astronomers profiting by instruments and theories developed in terrestrial laboratories and, in turn, opening to the physicists and chemists vast celestial laboratories in which to put their theories to the test of observation under conditions of temperature and pressure beyond their power to secure here on the Earth. The astronomers, too, were beginning to realize the need of coöperation with each other, for it was becoming apparent that only by such coöperation could they accumulate the vast masses of data on the positions, numbers, motions, distances, and the various physical attributes of the stars required as the basis for generalizations and theoretical investigations that would bring more fully into light the structure and the physical nature of the universe.

The change from the older to the newer attitude that heralded the opening of the modern era was, as all such changes are, a gradual one. In a general way, one may say that the older conception that astronomy was concerned only with measures of positions, motions, and distances held exclusive sway until the middle of the nineteenth century and that the conception of a new astronomy concerned with the physical nature of the heavenly bodies had achieved definite recognition twenty-five years later, though it was not until long afterward that it attained its present dominant position.

To set a more specific transition date is well-nigh impossible, there are so many important dates to select from. Shall we take 1850, the year in which the elder Bond at Harvard secured a daguerreotype of the Moon with the 15-inch refractor and also photographed the bright star Vega; 1851, the year in which Humboldt published Schwabe's discovery of sunspot periodicity; 1863, when Secchi classified the brighter stars according to their spectra; or 1864, when Huggins demonstrated that certain of the nebulae are not unresolved star clusters but are vast masses of tenuous gas? All these observations and many others in this transition period were epoch-making, but, if a single date is desired as boundary mark, I should advise no one of them but rather the year 1859, for it was in that year that Kirchhoff and Bunsen formulated the principles of spectrum analysis and that Kirchhoff began to apply them to the analysis of sunlight.

This great generalization, as epoch-making in its way as Darwin's *Origin of Species* which was published in the same year, had no Minerva-like birth; rather, it was the product of slow growth and development, like the corn from the seed in the Gospel parable, "first the blade, then the ear, after that the full corn in the ear." Sir Isaac Newton, it may be claimed, sowed the seed when, nearly two hundred years before, he for the first time clearly established the fact that sunlight passed through a glass prism under proper conditions will be decomposed into rays of light of different colors, which, caught upon a screen, produce the band of colored light, from violet to red, known as a spectrum. The growing plant through blade to ear was nourished by Melville, Wollaston, Fraunhofer, and a host of other experimenters who studied the spectra of sunlight and starlight and of incandescent gases in observatories and laboratories. But the development of the full corn in the ear came only with the decisive experiments of Kirchhoff and Bunsen, and their formulation of principles on the basis of these experiments in 1859. Armed with the spectroscope to apply these great principles to the analysis of the light from the Sun, the stars, and the nebulae, concentrated by the telescope upon the spectroscope's tiny slit, our adventurers in driving back the dark now pressed forward with ardent zeal to the exploration of the well-nigh illimitable field of astronomical physics, a field that even great astronomers as well as the positivist philosopher Comte had but a few years earlier declared to be forever closed to the intellect of man.

The spectroscope, in effect, ignores distance. Let but light, sufficient to affect the eye or to make its imprint on a photographic plate, fall upon the slit and pass through its optical train, and it will analyze that light with equal efficiency whether it comes from a laboratory source a few feet away or from the most distant object in our stellar system. If the source is a star, a body like the Sun with a hot core surrounded by a hot luminous atmosphere, the dark-line absorption spectrum proclaims the fact; if it is a gaseous nebula, a vast mass of luminous vapor under low pressure, the bright-line emission spectrum reveals it. If hydrogen or helium or sodium or any other element in gaseous form exists in the atmosphere of the star or in the nebula, the characteristic line pattern of each element, dark in the solar or stellar spectrum, bright in that of the nebula, makes its presence unmistakable.

But that is only part of the story. A luminous substance, it presently appeared, may, when the physical conditions, and in particular the temperature, are varied, give a variety of spectra, each perfectly definite and characteristic of its chemical composition, and the lines in each spectrum may, moreover, be split or shifted by the action of certain physical forces, or by the motion of the body. The wealth of physical data thus put within our reach is beyond all computation. The spectrum of a star, for example, records its temperature, its density or degree of mechanical pressure, the presence or absence of a magnetic field, even the fact that it is a rotating body. The relative intensities of certain lines in the spectrum measure the star's true luminosity, or the total amount of light it emits, and thus permit us, by comparison with its apparent brightness, to say how far away it is. Again, the shift of the lines from their normal positions toward the violet or toward the red end of the spectrum gives a measure of the star's velocity in the line of sight, toward or away from us, in miles or kilometers a second. "It is," to quote Professor Dingle, "as though a star throws the whole secret of its being into its spectrum, and we have only to learn how to read it aright in order to solve the most abstruse problems of the physical universe."

While the spectroscope is by far the most important instrument for the advancement of knowledge in this great field, it is by no means the only one; in fact, it must be combined with the photographic camera if its full possibilities are to be realized. A visual observation of a spectrum is at best a fleeting one; the observer notes its quality and characteristics, or with the aid of a micrometer measures the positions of the lines in it; then the image for that time is gone. But if a sensitive plate or film replaces the eye, then a permanent record is made that can be examined and measured under a microscope, time and time again, far more accurately than is possible with the eye alone, and that can be reproduced at will for study by others than the original observer. The range and the degree of sensitivity of the eye are also limited. The rays of light in the far violet on the one end of the spectrum and in the extreme red on the other make no impression upon the retina, and light even of the intermediate colors may be too faint to impress it or so brilliant as to dazzle it. The photographic plate, on the other hand, by the use of appropriate dyes, can be made sensitive to light of any color. Moreover, a very short exposure on a slow plate will give a sharp spectrum of the brightest light, and the property the plate possesses, of storing up the minute quantities of light that fall upon it and thus deepening the impression made from minute to minute, permits the astronomer to record the spectrum from exceedingly faint stars or nebulae merely by lengthening the exposure time to many hours.

It was fortunate indeed that the principles of photography were being developed about the same time that the principles of spectrum analysis were being worked out. Some experimental photographs of the Moon were made by Henry Draper as early as 1840; Bond, as we have already said, photographed the Moon and the bright star Vega in 1850; and Draper in 1872 secured a photographic spectrum of Vega showing four dark Fraunhofer lines. But it was not until the dry plate came into use that the full possibilities of the spectrograph began to be appreciated. Sir William Huggins, for the first time, used a dry gelatin plate in 1876 to photograph the spectrum of Vega, an operation then requiring a full hour's exposure time though the light from the brilliant star was concentrated on the slit of the spectrograph with an 18-inch reflecting telescope.

Armed with the spectrograph to analyze light, with the photometer to measure its intensity, long-focus and short-focus cameras to record the images of the heavenly bodies in detail or en masse, and, as time went on, with many other special instruments, our eager adventurers now wandered far and wide over this great new field, examining objects near and far, and, as they advanced, cloud after cloud of darkness rolled away before them, revelation followed revelation with startling rapidity.

On the one hand, they began to study the Sun intensively with special forms of telescopes and spectrographs, for they now came fully to recognize the fact that the Sun, of supreme importance to us as human beings because it is so near us, is, from the cosmic point of view, but an ordinary star, differing in no essential feature from thousands of others known to us. Its nearness permits us to examine its features, sunspots, faculae, prominences, corona, in detail; to study variations in pressure, in temperature, in strength of magnetic and electric field, even to measure the relative abundance of the chemical elements present in its atmosphere at different levels, thus affording knowledge to be kept in mind when analyzing the integrated light received from the more distant stars.

On the other hand, as they pressed forward, they demanded ever more powerful telescopes to penetrate more deeply into space, and it was their good fortune that the progress made by their fellow adventurers in the fields of electrical and mechanical engineering and the mechanic arts made it possible to meet their demands. The 15-inch refractors of 1850 were succeeded by improved refractors of 18, 26, 30, 36, and 40 inches' aperture; the unwieldy and relatively inefficient reflectors of speculum metal gave way to the modern equatorially mounted reflectors of glass coated with silver and these grew in size to 20 inches, 36, 60, and even 100 inches, the largest now receiving on its surface and concentrating at its focus more than 150,000 times as much light as falls on the pupil of the unaided eye. And now the silver coating is being replaced by the still more effective coating of aluminum, and a giant 200-inch reflector is in process of construction.

These new and powerful instruments helped not only the followers of the new astronomy, but were of almost equal value to those engaged upon the problems of the older astronomy of stellar positions, motions, and distances. Indeed, the boundary between the fields of physical astronomy and dynamical astronomy is as vague and ill-defined as that separating the older from the newer era. It was, for example, the measures of the orbital motions in visual double-star systems, combined with the measures of the distances of these systems, that brought us our first accurate knowledge of the masses of the stars. Again, the measures of the relative intensities of certain lines in a star's spectrum, in conjunction with researches in terrestrial laboratories, gave us knowledge of the star's true luminosity, the total amount of light it actually emits, and this knowledge, combined with measures of the star's apparent brightness, told us how far away the star is.

So the adventurers in the new field joined forces with those already at work in the old, as well as with their colleagues working in terrestrial laboratories. This spirit of coöperation is, in fact, one of the fundamental characteristics of modern astronomy, and it is in very large measure responsible for the progress that has been made. . . .

It is through the use of such powerful instruments and by such close coöperation of astronomers with their fellow astronomers and with the adventurers in other fields of science that we have reached our present concept of the great stellar system to which our Sun belongs. For the ten million or, at most, one hundred million stars envisaged by astronomers when California became a state, we now count fully thirty billion, scattered singly, in pairs, or in groups through a region of space so vast that, in Sir James Jean's graphic comparison, space is less filled with stars than St. Paul's great cathedral is filled with flies when but half a dozen are liberated at different points within it; we have fairly accurate measures of the distances, motions, luminosities, temperatures, and masses of thousands of the nearer of these stars, and values that are statistically reliable for millions more, and know that, with a few fascinating exceptions, all these stars, large and small, bright and faint, ten times as hot as the Sun or of such low temperature that they glow only with feeble red light, fall into well-defined categories, and that, despite the inconceivably great volume of space through which they are scattered, they constitute a finite system built on the general plan adumbrated in the theories held by astronomers in Sir William Herschel's day.

For the stars, single, double or multiple, or grouped in open clusters like the Pleiades, the great irregular nebulosities like the Orion nebula, and that cloud of incredibly tenuous light-scattering and light-absorbing material which, as we have lately discovered, fills the vast spaces between the stars, all tend to concentrate toward the central plane of the Milky Way. It is a lens-shaped system, the diameters of whose central plane are perhaps six times its thickness and are so great that light may take one hundred thousand or possibly even one hundred and fifty thousand years to pass from bound to bound of the Milky Way.[1]

And notwithstanding its stupendous dimensions and its infinite variety of content, it is an organic unity. The building blocks are the same throughout. The light from the farthest stars within it reveals no new chemical element, gives evidence of the existence of no forces not known to us here; and the whole gigantic system, as we have recently discovered, is rotating about its center, in a period of about two hundred and twenty million years.

Far indeed have the followers of Galileo gone, driving back the dark before them, until this whole vast stellar system has come into the light; but even so they are not satisfied; indeed, there never was a time "since

[1] The recent investigations of the absorption of light in space, especially along and near the plane of the Milky Way, and the revelation to us by the new red-sensitive photographic plates of the existence of multitudes of stars hitherto hidden from us by this cosmic dust, will compel a revision of the dimensions set down here and of the number of stars in our stellar system. Studies along these lines are now in progress.

ever the Earth began" when they were so eager to press forward to new light as they are today. There are dark spots still to be explored even in our solar system, and more, far more, in the great stellar system. They are probing into these with telescopes large and small and with all the auxiliary instruments modern ingenuity can devise, and they will not be content until the last dark spot has yielded up its secrets.

Nor are they content with merely reaching the boundaries of our stellar system; they want to know what lies beyond, hidden in the darkness of outer space, and they are pressing forward to find out. This is the great adventure of the present day, for it is only within the past decade or two that powerful telescopes and more potent methods of using them have made it possible for astronomers to penetrate the outer dark.

The story of this latest adventure, which in the revelations it is making is comparable with the one on which Galileo and his successors embarked more than three centuries ago, has a prologue that dates back to 1750, when Thomas Wright of Durham, an English instrument maker and private tutor, assuming the uniformity of nature, put forward on purely speculative grounds an original theory of the universe, which, five years later, was elaborated by the great philosopher, Immanuel Kant. According to this theory, our great stellar system is but one of many scattered through infinite space, some of the nearest of which are even revealed to us in the nebulae which were beginning to be discovered. The theory found confirmation in the researches of the Herschels, who not only catalogued thousands of nebulae but showed that the great majority were small, elliptical objects, which, it was later found, do not, like the stars, tend to crowd toward the plane of the Milky Way, but rather to avoid it. Many of these, moreover, the powerful reflectors of Sir William Herschel and of the Earl of Rosse resolved into clusters of faint stars. Others, including the few which the Earl of Rosse found to have a definite spiral structure, were thought to be unresolved simply because they were too distant.

This "island universe" theory, so prophetic of recent actual discoveries, was generally accepted as late as 1864 when Sir William Huggins found that some at least of the nebulae possessed the bright-line spectra characteristic of gaseous objects, but in the later decades of the nineteenth century it was practically abandoned, and every object visible in the telescope was regarded by astronomers generally as part of one great stellar system.

It was Keeler who laid the foundations for its revival when, in the paper prepared just before his death in 1900, he estimated, on the basis of his photographs taken with the Crossley reflector of the Lick Observatory, that no less than one hundred and twenty thousand faint nebulae were within the reach of that telescope and that most of them were spiral or elliptical in form, adding that in his opinion these were facts of great significance in theories of cosmogony. To find out how significant, we must first know the distance of these nebulae, and that means that we must have a plummet line long enough to sound the abysmal depths of space in which they lie. The story of its discovery is one of the many fascinating romances of astronomy.

Who, in his sober senses, would ever dream that pulsating stars, varying in their brightness in a particular manner, could give us any information of the distance of the Great Nebula in Andromeda and of other nebulae still farther away? The type star of this class, Delta Cephei, was discovered by John Goodricke, a deaf mute who died in 1786 at the early age of 22 years. Its characteristics are a rapid rise from minimum light to maximum, a slower decline to minimum again, the star at maximum being nearly twice as bright as at minimum, and the accurate repetition of this pulsation, both in the degree of light change and in its period, which is 5 days, 8 hours, 47 minutes, and 35.3056 seconds—and, as Kipling would have said, you must not forget that fraction of a second, for it is accurately computed. A dozen or two stars are known, within the limits of our stellar system, which have precisely the same characteristics of rapid rise in brightness to a maximum of two or even four times the minimum light, the slower fall to minimum again, and the accurate repetition of the variation, in periods so short as to be measured in days, not months. All of them are so far away that it is extremely difficult to measure their distances with precision, and all of them, accordingly, must be stars of great intrinsic brightness.

Now it has been found that there are many such Cepheid variables in the Magellanic Clouds, and, while engaged in measuring the brightness of a number of those in the Smaller Cloud on photographs taken on different nights, Miss Leavitt of Harvard Observatory noticed, in 1908, that the brighter the star at its median point between minimum and maximum light, the longer the time required to complete its cycle of light variation. Four years later she was able to say that this period-luminosity relationship was a definite mathematical one. The relationship must, therefore, be a physical characteristic of stars of this type, because we may say that all the stars in the Cloud are practically at the same distance from us, just as we may say that Trafalgar Square and the Tower of London are at the same distance from us here in Berkeley. It follows, from the uniformity of nature, that the same relationship applies to all Cepheid variable stars wherever they may be found, and that, therefore, if we can ascertain the true luminosity of any one of them, we shall be able to measure the luminosity of all of them by determining the period of light variation accurately. Then by comparing this, their true luminosity, with their apparent brightness, we shall be able to say how far away they are. Such determinations were made for some of the Cepheids in our own stellar system, approximately at first, and then more accurately, and our plummet line was ready for our use.

The Great Nebula in Andromeda and a number of others can be partially resolved into stars and groups of stars by the powerful 100-inch reflecting telescope, and many of these stars prove to be Cepheid variables showing the same period-luminosity relationship as those in the Magellanic Clouds. But they are so faint as to be almost at the limit of the power of that great telescope and must therefore be very distant. In fact, we find that light from the Andromeda Nebula, traveling at the rate of 186,000 miles a second, takes 680,000 years to reach us, and that others of the nearer nebulae are more distant still.

The distances of these nearer nebulae once established, other criteria, besides the Cepheid variables, were soon developed to measure the distances of nebulae more remote, until, relying always upon the uniformity of nature, it has been possible to set a value of 246,000,000 light years upon the distance of the remotest nebula so far measured directly with the spectrograph and to say that, on the average, the faintest and most distant nebula visible with the 100-inch telescope is approximately 500,000,000 light years out in space! [1] Double that value to give a diameter of nearly a billion light years to the volume of space now partially brought into the light!

Surveys made with our powerful modern reflectors indicate that no less than 100,000,000 nebulae, 100,000,000 stellar systems, many of them quite comparable in size and in splendor of content with our own great Milky Way system, are scattered through this prodigious volume of observable space. Like the stars in our stellar system, they occur singly, in pairs, in smaller groups or in larger clusters, but just as the stars in our system are, on the average, separated from each other by distances of the order of 5 or 6 light years, so these great stellar systems, on the average, are separated from each other by distances of the order of 2,000,000 light years.

Observations of the shift of the lines in their spectra indicate, moreover, that they are all in motion, traveling away from us with velocities far greater than those of the stars and velocities that increase with their distance from us. If we may rely upon the criterion for velocity measurement that holds true for the radial velocities of the stars in our own system, namely, that the greater the shift of the lines toward the red the greater the speed of travel away from us, this means that the universe as a whole is expanding, every system in it increasing its distance from every other system. If this is not so, then some hitherto quite unknown property of space is operating to slow up the velocity of light as it speeds toward us through space for millions of years.

All this knowledge of Sun, planets, and stars is of inestimable practical value to man, whether he realizes it or not. In 1675, King Charles II founded the Royal Observatory and commanded the Reverend John Flamsteed, the first Astronomer Royal, "to apply himself with the most exact care and diligence to Rectifying the Tables of the Motions of the Heavens and the Places of the Fixed Stars," in order to improve the art of navigation. At the

[1] It is very difficult to distinguish between these extremely faint nebulae (of about the twenty-second photographic magnitude) and tiny star images, but Dr. Hubble estimates that the most remote nebula that can now be distinguished with the 100-inch telescope is at least 750,000 light years distant.

present day, the navigator of an airplane flying out of sight of everything but Sun and stars makes a higher demand for accurate methods of determining time and position from the stars. And the astronomer's purely disinterested studies of the well-nigh incredible forces at play in the Sun, and of the methods by which its output of radiation has been kept at an almost uniform rate through the ages, are a matter of the first importance to man in his investigations of conditions in our upper atmosphere and of their influence not only on weather conditions but also on radio transmission and aviation in the stratosphere. If further evidence is desired of the practical value of astronomy, it may be found in the fact that our government has called so many astronomers from their peaceful studies of the stars to assist in the work of improving instruments and methods of war and defense.

But all this will always be secondary. The astronomer's chief aim and object, the purpose for which he builds enormous telescopes and studies in minute detail the structure of every object near or far and seeks to learn the laws governing all its phenomena, is to lift man's thought to a truer concept of the nature of this ever expanding and changing, dynamic universe of which our earth is so small a part.

Small wonder that astronomers long for the completion of the great 200-inch reflector which will penetrate twice as far into space as the 100-inch, give us a volume of space to explore that is eightfold larger than the one now open to us, resolve more distant nebulae into stars, and thus permit us, working always in the spirit of Galileo, to put our present results and theories to the test of further observation.

And when shall come the end? When will these adventurers in driving back the dark rest content? Never! As long as Earth endures and Sun and stars continue to shine, so long will the followers of Galileo march on toward new light.

> "No deep-set boundary-mark in Space or Time
> Shall halt or daunt them. Who that once has seen
> How truth leads on to truth shall ever dare
> To set a bound to knowledge?"

1944

THE SOLAR SYSTEM AND ITS ORIGIN *

FRED L. WHIPPLE

The five bright planets have been known to man for many thousands of years, but in antiquity as mysterious celestial deities whose very motions

* Reprinted from *Earth, Moon and Planets* by Fred L. Whipple, The Blakiston Company, Philadelphia, by permission from the publishers. Copyright 1941 by The Blakiston Company.

seemed to reflect the caprices of superhuman beings. The old Greek and Roman legends are well known. Mars was the God of War, Venus the Goddess of Love, while Mercury was a sort of messenger boy. And thus the planets remain today—to the poets, that is, and to others for whom imagery is the essence of life. But to the scientist the planets have assumed a new character; the massive spheres of stone and iron and gas are even more interesting and exciting individually than were their mythical other-selves. Their motions are now a matter of mathematical calculation, not of caprice. The question of what lies within and beneath the cloud-filled atmosphere of Venus is, for the scientist, more conducive to mental activity than the folklore of dead generations.

Each planet acquires more individuality and becomes more interesting as the astronomer, by observation and reasoning, deduces additional facts. Every year some of the problems of the preceding year are solved and new ones, once beyond the expectation of solution, appear within reach. To appreciate the current discoveries and deductions in planetary astronomy, we must be familiar with the fund of knowledge already accumulated. . . .

The planets are really so small compared to the vast distances between them, and their reflected sunlight is so weak in comparison with the great brilliancy of the Sun, that all of them can never show to good advantage from any one location. As a vantage spot for observations, our present position on the Earth is actually quite satisfactory, except for the thick atmosphere above us. Since we must surmount this obstacle, we might as well, in imagination, go out farther from the Sun to about the distance of Jupiter. From there the inner part of the solar system is easily visible. The orbits of the planets show first that the Sun is almost exactly in the center. The reason is very simple; the Sun possesses 99.866 per cent of the entire mass, so that by gravitational attraction it completely dominates the motions of the planets.

We notice next that the orbits lie almost in a plane, very close to the *ecliptic* or the plane of the Earth's orbit about the Sun. This favoritism on the part of the planets in adopting a common plane of motion is probably not due to chance. Although no rigorous proof has been given, it is possible that Jupiter is responsible, because this planet is 317 times as massive as the Earth and possesses seven tenths of the combined mass of all the planets. Jupiter is certainly the master planet and by gravitational attraction may have regulated the orbits of the others. There is the more likely possibility, of course, that the planets were all formed in a plane—but we must investigate this matter later on.

Mercury, the smallest planet, moves in the smallest orbit of all, but one that is tipped from the common plane with an inclination of seven degrees, while the other inner planets keep within about three degrees of the plane.

For measuring distances in the solar system we must use a larger unit than for distances on the Earth. The most convenient is the astronomical unit (A.U.), which equals the mean of the greatest and least distances from the Earth to the Sun, technically called the Earth's mean distance. In miles it is 92,870,000, the zeros shouting that we do not know what numbers to put in for them, and that we are not very certain about even the number seven. This basic astronomical unit is very difficult to measure accurately in miles, and is known barely to one part in ten thousand.

The distance to the Sun is enormous in terms of ordinary distances on the Earth. An airplane, moving with the velocity of sound, 750 miles per hour, would require fourteen years for the trip (necessarily one-way), while a cannon projectile moving a mile per second would arrive in a little less than three years. If such distances seem large, remember that we spend our lives confined to one of the smaller planets of the solar system, and are denied the privilege of a "fuller" existence in the universe at large. The astronomical unit is actually much too small for conveniently listing the distances between the stars; a much larger unit is used for that purpose.

Mercury has a mean distance from the Sun of only 0.39 astronomical units, Venus 0.72, the Earth 1.00, Mars 1.52, and Jupiter 5.20, a rather uniform sequence of increasing distances except for the large gap between Mars and Jupiter. In this gap we find more than a thousand small planets called asteroids that fill the space where a planet might well move. These asteroids range from mountain size, a mile or so in diameter, up to Ceres which is about 480 miles across—comparable to a large island. Pallas comes second with a diameter of 304 miles and Vesta third, 240 miles. There are certainly no large asteroids that have not been discovered but there must be many smaller ones, perhaps 40,000 that could be photographed with the larger telescopes. These fly-weight planets, although contributing a negligible part to the mass of the system (perhaps 1/500 of the Earth's mass), provide astronomers with a great amount of work in observation and calculation. They are fine test specimens for theories of various kinds and may eventually assist materially in finding the key to the origin of the system.

The planets themselves have much of the character of the ancient gods for whom they were named. Mercury is indeed swift and small, characteristic of a messenger. It requires only 88 days for a complete revolution about the Sun, less than one fourth the length of our year. Its diameter is only 0.4 that of the Earth. Even this small diameter, 3,100 miles, is enough greater than the diameter of Ceres to distinguish Mercury definitely as a planet rather than as a large asteroid. The period of rotation remains quite uncertain at present but probably equals the period of revolution about the Sun. The planet is, unfortunately, so small and always remains so close to the Sun as observed from the Earth, that surface markings are difficult to discern.

Venus is certainly the "sister" planet of the Earth. The diameter is almost identical (97.3 per cent), the period of revolution about the Sun somewhat shorter (225 days), and the mass about 0.8. Venus too is cloaked with a large atmosphere; it is this opaque atmosphere that hides the surface features so completely that we cannot be certain of the rate of rotation. From indirect evidence we judge the period probably to be long—more than three weeks. The actual observations of both of these inner planets are made difficult by the circumstance that we can see only part of the sunlit face at any time. When nearest to the Earth, only a thin crescent of Venus can be seen, as is the case for the Moon when new, because the bodies are almost on a line between the Earth and the Sun. . . .

Mars may best be described as a pygmy Earth (one half its diameter) with a thin atmosphere, distinct surface features, but no oceans. It moves more slowly about the Sun, in 687 days. Mars, however, boasts two moons or satellites, while Mercury and Venus have none. These two satellites are little more than medals for Mars, the God of War, since the largest, Phobos, is only fifteen miles across. Deimos, the smaller, is just one half of Phobos in diameter. The existence of these Lilliputian satellites, strangely enough, was narrated by Jonathan Swift in his "Gulliver's Travels," some one hundred and fifty years before their discovery in 1877. According to Gulliver's account, the astronomers of the cloud island, Laputa, possessed small but most excellent telescopes and had "discovered two lesser stars, or satellites, which revolve about Mars; whereof the innermost is distant from the center of the primary planet exactly three of his diameters, and the outermost, five; the former revolves in the space of ten hours, and the latter in twenty-one and a half."

These periods of revolution are remarkably close to the truth, for Phobos revolves about Mars in 7 h. 39 m. while Deimos requires 30 h. 18 m. The mythical distances from the center of Mars, are, however, too great; Phobos is distant only 1.4 of the planet's diameter, and Deimos 3.5 diameters. It would be enlightening to have learned more of the Laputian discoveries, but Gulliver mentions only that they had "observed ninety-three different comets, and settled their periods with great exactness."

The rapid motion of Phobos makes this satellite unique in the solar system. Its period of revolution is less than the Martian day, 24 h. 37 m. As seen from the surface of Mars, Phobos would rise in the west and set in the east!

Before going on to the outermost planets, we note that the four planets Mercury, Venus, Earth, and Mars are really very much alike, of somewhat the same size, and all fairly dense, as though they were made of stone or iron. They are justly classed as the *terrestrial* planets because of their similarity to the Earth. Probably Pluto is much like the Earth or Venus. Jupiter, Saturn, Uranus and Neptune, on the other hand, are of an entirely different species, giants compared to the Earth, and only about as dense as water. . . .

Jupiter is conspicuous as the greatest of the planets. It has eleven times the diameter of the Earth, but rotates faster than any other planet, its day being slightly less than ten hours in length. It rotates so fast, indeed, that the equator is much bulged out by the centrifugal force. Since Jupiter is only a third denser than water we are not surprised to find that it possesses an enormously thick atmosphere, how thick we cannot know. The depth of the atmosphere, if indeed there is a distinct solid surface below, can be calculated only on the basis of estimates of the chemical composition and temperatures within the planet. Ammonia and methane (marsh gas) are known to be present in the gigantic clouds that we can see from outside. These markings are certainly clouds because their forms are ever changing. The general structure is banded parallel to the equator as though clouds were being blown along by "trade winds" that result from the rapid rotation.

The atmospheres of the other giant planets are very similar to that of Jupiter, the differences being attributable in a large measure to the fact that the planets farther from the Sun are colder at their surfaces. Neptune, 30 A.U. from the Sun, is a frigid world by our standards because it receives only $\frac{1}{900}$ as much heat and light from the Sun as we receive. Solid carbon dioxide (dry ice) near its melting point is hot compared to the probable temperature at the surface of Neptune, about —330° F. Nitrogen gas would be frozen, likewise oxygen.

Although the giant planets are cold and uninhabitable, their great masses and wide separation in space allow them to control astonishingly large families of satellites. Jupiter is again first, with eleven moons, Saturn is second with nine, while Uranus has four and Neptune only one. Of these, the four brightest of Jupiter's family, one of Saturn's, and the single satellite of Neptune are about the size of our Moon, while the others range in diameter from that of small asteroids to about half the Moon. The systems of Jupiter and Saturn are really miniature solar systems in every respect except that the primary planets do not send out light by themselves but shine by reflected sunlight only. The great planets are more massive when compared to their largest satellites than is the Sun when compared to Jupiter or Saturn.

The similarity with the whole solar system is even more striking in the system of Saturn because this planet controls not only nine satellites, equal to the number of known planets about the Sun, but also possesses a family of miniature asteroids, which comprise the great rings. These rings are so close to Saturn itself that in the early telescopes they looked like ears or appendages. Galileo, who was the first scientist of the modern world to see Jupiter's four bright satellites, sometimes drew Saturn as consisting of three pieces—a central body with symmetrical side sections. We know now that the rings are made of small fragments of matter revolving about Saturn in nearly a plane, relatively thinner than a sheet of paper. When seen at different angles they present different appearances, from invisibility, if seen edge on, to wide rings at the brightest angle possible.

On beyond Neptune lies the more recently discovered Pluto. Little is known about Pluto as a planet. Our best information suggests that it is slightly smaller and less massive than the Earth, but its rate of rotation is uncertain. Probably there is no atmosphere because the surface seems to reflect sunlight very poorly; the planets with heavy atmospheres reflect much better than those with thin atmospheres. The Moon is an especially poor reflector, and Pluto may be even worse.

To complete this quick introduction to the solar family, some mention must be made of the ever-baffling comets. These strange wanderers have excited more superstitious fear in the human mind than any other class of celestial bodies. Today their continued existence is in itself a major riddle of the solar system and the phenomena that they manifest are far from well explained. Most comets move in exceedingly elongated orbits, approaching the Sun for only a very small fraction of one period of revolution. When distant from the Sun they become too faint for observation but they brighten enormously at perihelion, when closest to the Sun. At this time they become so active that they waste an appreciable part of their substance into space, and produce a great coma of gases and small dust particles about their nuclei. The strong sunlight forces these gases and dust back from the comet in a great tail, sometimes multiple and always complicated in structure. . . .

No longer can the philosopher in his easy chair expect to solve the basic problems of the origin and evolution of the solar system. A great array of observational facts must be explained by a satisfactory theory, and the theory must be consistent with the principles of dynamics and modern physics. All of the hypotheses so far presented have failed, when physical theory has been properly applied. The modern attack on the problem is less direct than the old method, which depended upon an all-embracing hypothesis. The new method is perhaps slower, but it is much more certain. By a direct study of the facts, we can specify, within an increasingly narrow range, the physical conditions under which the planets evolved. The manner of their origin must finally become apparent. . . .

It is an interesting commentary on modern science that the *age* of the Earth has been determined, although its origin remains a baffling problem. The oldest rocks in the Earth's crust solidified some two billion years ago. Radioactive substances within the rocks leave minute traces of lead and helium which constitute a measure of the time elapsed since the Earth cooled. Studies of meteorites show that none of these visitors from space have been solid for a much longer period than the crustal rocks. If the meteorites represent fragments of the solar system, we may conclude that the system is coeval with the Earth. The problem of the origin of the Earth is, therefore, synonymous with the problem of the origin of the entire system. Something happened about three billion years ago to generate the planetary bodies and to produce the order and regularity that we observe today.

Outstanding orderliness is apparent in the planetary motions. The members of the solar system move in the same direction along a common plane. Not only do the planets and a thousand or so asteroids follow this plane in their revolution about the Sun, but the great majority of the satellites move about their primaries in a similar fashion. The Sun, moreover, and all but one of the planets exhibit the same phenomenon in their axial rotation. Even Saturn's rings share in the common motion. We have noted the few exceptions, the Uranus system, Neptune's satellite, a few of the outer satellites of Jupiter and Saturn and notably the comets. Since the comets seem to share so few of the properties of the planets and asteroids, we may well exclude them from our main discussion; cometary evolution appears to constitute a separate and independent problem.

The common motion of so many bodies suggests an initial rotary action, as though the solar system were once sent spinning by some cosmic finger. There is, in fact, so much motion in the outer bounds of the system that the older evolutionary hypotheses have failed in one respect; they cannot explain the *angular momentum* of the major planets. The angular momentum of a planet moving in a circular orbit at a given distance from the Sun [1] is the product of the mass, distance and speed. Since the speed diminishes only as the square root of the distance, a given mass contributes more angular momentum at a greater distance from the Sun. For a planet moving in an elliptical orbit, Kepler's law of areas expresses the constancy of the angular momentum at all times. When the planet is near the Sun it moves more rapidly than when it is farther away. No force toward or away from the Sun can change the angular momentum of a planet. Only an external push or drag along the orbit can increase or diminish this fundamental quantity of motion.

Jupiter, with its great mass, carries about six tenths of the entire angular momentum of the solar system. The four giant planets contribute about ninety-eight per cent, and the terrestrial planets a fifth of a per cent. The Sun, with a thousand times the mass of Jupiter, rotates so slowly that its angular momentum is only two per cent of the whole. If all planets could be put into the Sun and could carry with them their present angular momentum, the augmented Sun would rotate in about twelve hours, rather than a month.

A satisfactory hypothesis for the origin of the solar system must first account for the existence of the planets, satellites and asteroids. It must then explain how they were set moving in the remarkable manner already noted, and must provide the system theoretically with the observed amount of angular momentum. Two types of hypotheses have been suggested. In

[1] Practically at the center of gravity of the solar system.

the first type, the system condensed from a gigantic cloud of glowing gases. In the second, the planets were torn from the Sun by an encounter with a passing star. Neither is satisfactory, but both have contributed greatly to astronomy by their impetus to thought.

The hypothesis that was believed for the longest time, excepting the Biblical account, was presented apologetically by the great French mathematician Laplace. According to his Nebular Hypothesis, a rotating and flattened nebula of diffuse material cooled slowly and contracted. In the plane of motion, successive rings of matter were supposed to have split off, to condense into the planets of our present solar system. Most of the matter finally contracted to form the Sun. Between the present orbits of Mars and Jupiter, the ring failed to "jell," and produced many asteroids instead of a planet. . . .

The Nebular Hypothesis is untenable for several reasons, particularly because a speed of rotation sufficient to leave nebular rings at the present distances of the planets would provide the nucleus with many times the angular momentum of the rings. The Sun, according to the Hypothesis should have *more* angular momentum than the planets, not one fiftieth as much. Furthermore, James Clerk Maxwell showed that a fluid ring could not coalesce into large planets but would be transformed into a ring of *planetoids*, such as Saturn's ring or the belt of asteroids.

The collision or encounter theories attempt to avoid the difficulties of angular momentum. If another star collided with the sun or passed very close to it, material would be ejected from its surface and might condense to form the planets. Several variations of the encounter theory have been propounded. In the Planetesimal Theory, proposed early this century by T. C. Chamberlin and F. R. Moulton, the passing star was supposed to have raised gigantic tides on the Sun. An appreciable quantity of matter, several times the present masses of the planets, was then ejected from the Sun's surface, and sent spiraling around it by the passing star. Most of the matter was lost or fell back into the Sun, but part remained, with a highly elliptical motion. The gases then condensed into small fragments, the planetesimals, and as time progressed the larger fragments swept up the smaller, to form the planets. The rapid motion of the passing star provided the angular momentum for the orbital motions of the planets, their rotations and the satellite systems. Within twenty million years after the encounter the formation of the planets would have been essentially complete.

Sir James Jeans and Harold Jeffreys have proposed an alternative version of such an encounter. They argue, in their Tidal Theory, that a long tidal filament was drawn out of the Sun by the passing star. The inner part of the filament returned to the Sun while the outer portion escaped into space. A central portion coalesced into a string of beadlike condensations, the embryo planets.

Jeffreys has more recently abandoned the Tidal Theory as untenable, and has substituted a collisional hypothesis in which the approaching star brushed by the Sun in actual contact. The subsequent phenomena of the filament and planet formation follow essentially the same plan as in the original Tidal Theory. R. A. Lyttleton of Cambridge, England has proposed that the Sun was a double star at the time of the collision. Its companion star was gravitationally torn away by a third star which closely approached the Sun. H. N. Russell had suggested previously that a companion star was struck, and that the planets evolved from its débris.

A number of serious objections have been raised against all of these encounter hypotheses. In particular, when mathematical analysis is applied, the observed distribution of angular momentum in the solar system has not yet been explained. A basic objection of another kind has more recently been presented.

Lyman Spitzer, while at the Harvard Observatory, proved by a physical and mathematical demonstration that the planets cannot be formed by a direct condensation of material taken forcibly from the Sun's surface or interior. Any star such as the Sun consists entirely of superheated gases. At a depth above which there is sufficient material to form the planets, either by a tidal or collisional process, the temperature is approximately 18,000,000° F. These tremendously hot gases would expand and escape except for the enormous pressure of the overlying layers, which are forced down by the Sun's great surface gravity. A tidal or collisional ejection, however, would remove the pressure and enable the gases to expand immediately. During a collision, two stars would remain in contact for only an hour or two, and the ejection would occur at velocities of hundreds of miles per second. Spitzer has shown that within a few minutes after their release, the gases would literally explode, long before they could cool by radiation. Even the internal gravitational attraction of a mass twice that of Jupiter would not hold the gases and permit them to condense. Hence planets cannot be formed directly out of matter that is removed catastrophically from the Sun.

We are left, apparently, with some form of the planetesimal hypothesis as the least objectionable explanation for the origin of the planetary system. Spitzer's arguments have not been applied mathematically to the formation of the small planetesimals, but certainly it is true that only a minute fraction of the gases ejected from the Sun would ever be available for forming the planets. Moreover, a stellar collision, rather than an encounter, is required. . . .

So far, our new approach to the problem of origin and evolution has not led to a complete solution. Nevertheless, considerable progress has been made. These conclusions are fairly certain. (1) The planets were once very hot, far above the temperature of melting rock. Even Pluto, now cold enough to hold helium and hydrogen, must have been sufficiently hot to lose the ordinary gases of the Earth's atmosphere. (2) The planets, therefore, grew from a fairly rapid condensation of material, not from a slow accretion process. (3) The planets developed probably from the Sun or possibly from another star. This third conclusion is based largely upon similitudes of chemical composition, but is strengthened by the first two conclusions. Interstellar material, the only alternative to stellar material for planet building, is, within our present knowledge, diffuse. Only an accretion process could produce the planets from diffuse material.

The problem of the possible existence of planets about other stars is still unsolved. If a stellar collision is required to produce planets, there will be only a few systems such as ours among millions of stars. If a single star, unaided, can generate a system of planets, then the number of planets may be enormous. . . .

1941

IS THERE LIFE ON OTHER WORLDS? *

SIR JAMES JEANS

So long as the earth was believed to be the center of the universe the question of life on other worlds could hardly arise; there were no other worlds in the astronomical sense, although a heaven above and a hell beneath might form adjuncts to this world. The cosmology of the *Divina Commedia* is typical of its period. In 1440 we find Nicholas of Cusa comparing our earth, as Pythagoras had done before him, to the other stars, although without expressing any opinion as to whether these other stars were inhabited or not. At the end of the next century Giordano Bruno wrote that "there are endless particular worlds similar to this of the earth." He plainly supposed these other worlds—"the moon, planets and other stars, which are infinite in number"—to be inhabited, since he regarded their creation as evidence of the Divine goodness. He was burned at the stake in 1600; had he lived only ten years longer, his convictions would have been strengthened by Galileo's discovery of mountains and supposed seas on the moon.

The arguments of Kepler and Newton led to a general recognition that the stars were not other worlds like our earth but other suns like our sun. When once this was accepted it became natural to imagine that they also were surrounded by planets and to picture each sun as showering life-sustaining light and heat on inhabitants more or less like ourselves. In 1829 a New York newspaper scored a great journalistic hit by giving a vivid, but wholly fictitious, account of the activities of the inhabitants of the

* An afternoon lecture of the Royal Institution of Great Britain, 1941. Reprinted by permission from the Royal Institution and from the author's estate.

moon as seen through the telescope recently erected by His Majesty's Government at the Cape.

It would be a long time before we could see what the New York paper claimed to see on the moon—batlike men flying through the air and inhabiting houses in trees—even if it were there to see. To see an object of human size on the moon in detail we should need a telescope of from 10,000 to a 100,000 inches aperture, and even then we should have to wait years, or more probably centuries, before the air was still and clear enough for us to see details of human size.

To detect general evidence of life on even the nearest of the planets would demand far larger telescopes than anything at present in existence, unless this evidence occupied an appreciable fraction of the planet's surface. The French astronomer Flammarion once suggested that if chains of light were placed on the Sahara on a sufficiently generous scale, they might be visible to Martian astronomers if any such there be. If this light were placed so as to form a mathematical pattern, intelligent Martians might conjecture that there was intelligent life on earth. Flammarion thought that the lights might suitably be arranged to illustrate the theorem of Pythagoras (Euclid, I. 47). Possibly a better scheme would be a group of searchlights which could emit successive flashes to represent a series of numbers. If, for instance, the numbers 3, 5, 7, 11, 13, 17, 19, 23 . . . (the sequence of primes) were transmitted, the Martians might surely infer the existence of intelligent Tellurians. But any visual communication between planets would need a combination of high telescopic power at one end and of engineering works on a colossal, although not impossible, scale at the other.

Some astronomers—mainly in the past—have thought that the so-called canals on Mars provided evidence of just this kind, although of course unintentionally on the part of the Martians. Two white patches which surround the two poles of Mars are observed to increase and decrease with the seasons, like our terrestrial polar ice. Over the surface of Mars some astronomers have claimed to see a geometrical network of straight lines, which they have interpreted as a system of irrigation canals, designed to bring melted ice from these polar caps to parched equatorial regions. Percival Lowell calculated that this could be done by a pumping system of 4,000 times the power of Niagara. It is fairly certain now that the polar caps are not of ice, but even if they were, the radiation of the summer sun on Mars is so feeble that it could not melt more than a very thin layer of ice before the winter cold came to freeze it solid again. Actually the caps are observed to change very rapidly and are most probably clouds consisting of some kind of solid particles.

The alleged canals cannot be seen at all in the largest telescopes nor can they be photographed, but there are technical reasons why neither of these considerations is conclusive against the existence of the canals. A variety of evidence suggests, however, that the canals are mere subjective illusions

—the result of overstraining the eyes in trying to see every detail of a never very brightly illuminated surface. Experiments with school children have shown that under such circumstances the strained eye tends to connect patches of color by straight lines. This will at least explain why various astronomers have claimed to see straight lines not only on Mars, where it is just conceivable that there might be canals, but also on Mercury and the largest satellite of Jupiter, where it seems beyond the bounds of possibility that canals could have been constructed, as well as on Venus, on which real canals could not possibly be seen since its solid surface is entirely hidden under clouds. It may be significant that E. E. Barnard, perhaps the most skilled observer that astronomy has ever known, was never able to see the canals at all, although he studied Mars for years through the largest telescopes.

A most promising line of approach to our problem is to examine which, if any, of the planets is physically suitable for life. But we are at once confronted with the difficulty that we do not know what precise conditions are necessary for life. A human being transferred to the surface of any one of the planets or of their satellites, would die at once, and this for several different reasons on each. On Jupiter he would be simultaneously frozen, asphyxiated, and poisoned, as well as doubly pressed to death by his own weight and by an atmospheric pressure of about a million terrestrial atmospheres. On Mercury he would be burned to death by the sun's heat, killed by its ultra-violet radiation, asphyxiated from want of oxygen, and desiccated from want of water. But this does not touch the question of whether other planets may not have developed species of life suited to their own physical conditions. When we think of the vast variety of conditions under which terrestrial life exists on earth—plankton, soil bacteria, stone bacteria, and the great variety of bacteria which are parasitic on the higher forms of life—it would seem rash to suggest that there are any physical conditions whatever to which life cannot adapt itself. Yet as the physical states of other planets are so different from that of our own, it seems safe to say that any life there may be on any of them must be very different from the life on earth.

The visible surface of Jupiter has a temperature of about −138° C., which represents about 248 degrees of frost on the Fahrenheit scale. The planet probably comprises an inner core of rock, with a surrounding layer of ice some 16,000 miles in thickness, and an atmosphere which again is several thousands of miles thick and exerts the pressure of a million terrestrial atmospheres which we have already mentioned. The only known constituents of this atmosphere are the poisonous gases methane and ammonia. It is certainly hard to imagine such a planet providing a home for life of any kind whatever. The planets Saturn, Uranus, Neptune, and Pluto, being farther from the sun, are almost certainly even colder than Jupiter and in all probability suffer from at least equal disabilities as abodes of life.

Turning sunward from these dismal planets, we come first to Mars, where we find conditions much more like those of our own planet. The average temperature is about —40° C., which is also —40° on the Fahrenheit scale, but the temperature rises above the freezing point on summer afternoons in the equatorial regions. The atmosphere contains at most only small amounts of oxygen and carbon dioxide, perhaps none at all, so that there can be no vegetation comparable with that of the earth. The surface, in so far as it can be tested by a study of its powers of reflection and polarization, appears to consist of lava and volcanic ash. To us it may not seem a promising or comfortable home for life, but life of some kind or other may be there nevertheless.

Being at the same average distance from the sun as the earth, the moon has about the same average temperature, but the variations around this average temperature are enormous, the equatorial temperature varying roughly from 120° C. to —80° C. The telescope shows high ranges of mountains, apparently volcanic, interspersed with flat plains of volcanic ash. The moon has no atmosphere and consequently no water; it shows no signs of life or change of any kind, unless perhaps for rare falls of rock such as might result from the impact of meteors falling in from outer space. A small town on the moon, perhaps even a large building, ought to be visible in our largest telescopes, but, needless to say, we see nothing of the kind.

Venus, the planet next to the earth, presents an interesting problem. It is similar to the earth in size but being nearer the sun is somewhat warmer. As it is blanketed in cloud we can only guess as to the nature of its surface. But its atmosphere can be studied and is found to contain little or no oxygen, so that the planet's surface can hardly be covered with vegetation as the surface of the earth is. Indeed, its surface is probably so hot that water would boil away. Yet no trace of water vapor is found in the atmosphere, so that the planet may well be devoid of water. There are reasons for thinking that its shroud of clouds may consist of solid particles, possibly hydrates of formaldehyde. Clearly any life that this planet may harbor must be very different from that of the earth.

The only planet that remains is Mercury. This always turns the same face to the sun and its temperature ranges from about 420° C. at the center of this face to unimaginable depths of cold in the eternal night of the face which never sees the sun. The planet is too feeble gravitationally to retain much of an atmosphere and its surface, in so far as this can be tested, appears to consist mainly of volcanic ash like the moon and Mars. Once again we have a planet which does not appear promising as an abode of life and any life that there may be must be very different from our own.

Thus our survey of the solar system forces us to the conclusion that it contains no place other than our earth which is at all suitable for life at all resembling that existing on earth. The other planets are ruled out largely by unsuitable temperatures. It used to be thought that Mars might have had a temperature more suited to life in some past epoch when the sun's radiation was more energetic than it now is, and that similarly Venus can perhaps look forward to a more temperate climate in some future age. But these possibilities hardly accord with modern views of stellar evolution. The sun is now thought to be a comparatively unchanging structure, which has radiated much as now through the greater part of its past life and will continue to do the same until it changes cataclysmically into a minute "white dwarf" star. When this happens there will be a fall of temperature too rapid for life to survive anywhere in the solar system and too great for new life ever to get a foothold. As regards suitability for life, the earth seems permanently to hold a unique position among the bodies surrounding our sun.

Our sun is, however, only one of myriads of stars in space. Our own galaxy alone contains about 100,000 million stars, and there are perhaps 10,000 million similar galaxies in space. Stars are about as numerous in space as grains of sand in the Sahara. What can we say about the possibilities of life on planets surrounding these other suns?

We want first to know whether these planets exist. Observational astronomy can tell us nothing; if every star in the sky were surrounded by a planetary system like that of our sun, no telescope on earth could reveal a single one of these planets. Theory can tell us a little more. While there is some doubt as to the exact manner in which the sun acquired its family of planets, all modern theories are at one in supposing that it was the result of the close approach of another star. Other stars in the sky must also experience similar approaches, although calculation shows that such events must be excessively rare. Under conditions like those which now prevail in the neighborhood of the sun, a star will experience an approach close enough to generate planets only about once in every million million million years. If we suppose the star to have lived under these conditions for about 2,000 million years, only one star in 500 million will have experienced the necessary close encounter, so that at most one star in 500 million will be surrounded by planets. This looks an absurdly minute fraction of the whole, yet when the whole consists of a thousand million million million stars, this minute fraction represents two million million stars. On this calculation, then two million million stars must already be surrounded by planets and a new solar system is born every few hours. The calculation probably needs many adjustments; for instance, conditions near our sun are not necessarily typical of conditions throughout space and the conditions of today are probably not typical of conditions in past ages. Indeed, on any reasonable view of stellar evolution, each star must have begun its life as a vast mass of nebulous gas, in which state it would present a far more vulnerable target than now for disruptive attacks by other stars. Detailed calculation shows that the chance of a star's producing planets in this early stage, although not large, would be quite considerable, and suggests, with a large margin to spare, that although planetary systems may be rare in space, their total number is far from insignificant. Out of the thousands or millions of millions of planets that there must surely be in space, a very great number must have physical conditions very similar to those prevailing on earth.

We cannot even guess whether these are inhabited by life like our own or by life of any kind whatever. The same chemical atoms exist there as exist here and must have the same properties, so that it is likely that the same inorganic compounds have formed there as have formed here. If so, we would like to know how far the chain of life has progressed, but present-day science can give no help. We can only wonder whether any life there may be elsewhere in the universe has succeeded in managing its affairs better than we have done in recent years.

1941

HOW THE STARS USE ATOMIC ENERGY *

GEORGE GAMOW

. . . Even before the discovery of atomic transformations and the hidden energy of the atom, it became clear that our sun, as well as all other stars in the sky, must conceal in their interiors some kind of unknown energy-sources which are immensely more powerful than any source of energy hitherto known to science. It was calculated that if the sun were using the ordinary energy of chemical transformations, being for example built of pure carbon and burning in the surrounding atmosphere of oxygen, it would have been turned into ashes in just a few thousand years. Even the short span of written human history is enough to reject such an assumption. In the middle of the last century the German physicist *Helmholtz,* and after him the British physicist *Lord Kelvin* formulated the so-called *contractive hypothesis* according to which the sun receives its continuous energy supply from a slow but steady shrinking of its giant body. The energy which can be liberated by such a contracting sun would be enough to support its radiation for the long period of about twenty million years, but even this number was not large enough to satisfy the geologists and paleontologists who require at least a billion years to explain the evolution of life on the surface of the earth.

Thus the problem of stellar energy-sources remained a deep mystery until the year 1896, when the discovery of radioactivity by *H. Becquerel* revealed the new and hitherto unsuspected sources of energy hidden inside the atom. However, although the importance of radioactivity for the

* From George Gamow: *Atomic Energy in Cosmic and Human Life.* Copyright 1946 by The Macmillan Company and used with their permission.

understanding of stellar energy-sources was realized almost from the very beginning, it was more than thirty years later that the relation between atomic transformations and the sources of stellar radiation was definitely established. The question had had to wait for the development of better knowledge concerning the physical conditions in the interior of stars, and the properties of nuclear-reactions.

During these years considerable progress in our understanding of the physics of stellar interiors was made, mainly due to the work of the British astronomer *Sir Arthur Eddington*, and the knowledge of atomic energy was largely expanded by the epoch-making experiments of *Lord Rutherford* on the artificial transformations of elements, and the mathematical theory of these phenomena developed by the author of the present book.

These developments made it possible for the two young physicists, *R. Atkinson* from England and *F. Houtermans* from Germany to show, in 1929, that under the conditions of high temperatures and densities existing in the central regions of stars, thermonuclear reactions of light elements could be expected to occur with a sufficiently high speed to supply all the energy necessary for stellar radiation. . . .

The first important point concerning stellar structures is that they represent large spheres of very hot gas. Direct measurements show that the temperature of the solar surface, which must be the coolest part of its giant body, is about 6,000° C. We know very well that at such temperatures even the most heat-resistant materials as tungsten will be completely turned into a gas. As we go deeper under the surface of the sun, the temperature steadily rises and, although we cannot make any direct measurements, we can surmise that the material near the solar center is many, many times hotter. But how hot? It would seem that any attempt to estimate the exact value of the central temperature of the sun and stars must necessarily lie in the region of pure speculation. Well, it is true, speculation it is, but as in so many instances presented by modern science, the results of such speculation can be considered to be just as certain as if we ourselves dived into the stellar interior with a thermometer in our hand. The point is that, as stated before, the stars are made entirely of gases, and the knowledge of the gaseous state of matter has progressed sufficiently far to permit us to make unambiguous predictions about the behavior of gases even at the most extreme conditions which can be expected near the center of a star. Thus, starting with the directly observed temperature and gas-pressure on the surface, we can proceed, step by step, deeper into the stellar body calculating from the well-established laws of gases, new temperatures and new pressures in each layer through which we pass in our mental journey.

In carrying through such calculations, we finally come to the values of central temperature and pressure which in the case of the sun turn out to be *20 million degrees centigrade*, and *160 billion atmospheres*. Although not obtained by direct measurements, these results can be considered to be just as certain as the estimates of the strength of a bridge, or the power of a hydroelectric installation made by a good engineer prior to the construction, on the basis of well-known laws of mechanics and hydrodynamics.

It is interesting to notice here that the exactness and certainty of the above quoted results is primarily due to the simplicity of gas laws governing the interior of stellar bodies. In fact we can be much more certain about the deep interior of the distant stars than about the state of solid matter forming the core of the Earth only a few hundred miles under our feet.

In making similar calculations in the case of various stars, *Eddington* came to the very interesting conclusion that, whereas the surface temperatures of stars can vary from only one or two thousand to over ten thousand degrees, and whereas their luminosities differ often by a factor of millions, their central temperatures remain always very close to the value of 20 million degrees obtained for the sun. Thus the central temperature of the giant star known as Y Cygni, which is about a thousand times brighter than the sun, is only 30 millions, whereas the very faint star Krüger 60 has in its interior a temperature of about 15 million degrees. It looks as if most of the stars maintain their interiors at about the same temperature—presumably necessary for some specific thermonuclear reaction, and vary it slightly to take care of the differences in their luminosities. In fact, small changes of the temperature will suffice to change the rate of energy-production in a thermonuclear reaction by a very large factor.

We have to find out now which, of all possible alchemical reactions, is *the* reaction which supplies the energy to our sun and other stars large and small. In order to answer this question we have apparently to apply the *Atkinson-Houtermans* formula for the rate of alchemic reactions to various possible alchemic transformations, and to see which of them has the appropriate rate of energy-liberation at temperatures of about 20 million degrees.

We can say, first of all, that this *stellar reaction* is certainly not the thermonuclear reaction in deuterium. In fact this reaction goes at full rate at temperatures of only a few hundred thousand degrees consuming all the material in just six hours at only three hundred thousand degrees. If there were some deuterium in the hot solar interior it would certainly be consumed in a negligible fraction of a second, and thus could not have been responsible for the long life of the sun. In Table I we give a list of various alchemical reactions between the light elements which could be considered as candidates for the honorable place of stellar, energy-producing reactions. For each of these reactions we give the time which is necessary for the reaction to run halfway under the conditions existing in stellar interiors.

In looking through the numbers given in Table I we notice at once that the alchemic reactions between lithium, beryllium and boron on one side and hydrogen on the other are excluded for exactly the same reason as the

TABLE I

The mean reaction times for various alchemical transformations under the conditions of the interior of the Sun. (Temp: 20,000,000° C, density 100 in respect to water.)

Alchemic reaction	*Mean reaction time*
${}_3Li^7 + {}_1H^1 \rightarrow 2\,{}_2He^4$	1 min.
${}_4Be^9 + {}_1H^1 \rightarrow {}_3Li^6 + {}_2He^4$	15 min.
${}_5B^{11} + {}_1H^1 \rightarrow 3\,{}_2He^4$	3 days
${}_6C^{12} + {}_1H^1 \rightarrow {}_7N^{13}$	$2.5 . 10^6$ years
${}_7N^{14} + {}_1H^1 \rightarrow {}_8O^{15}$	$5 . 10^7$ years
${}_8O^{16} + {}_1H^1 \rightarrow {}_9F^{17}$	10^{12} years
${}_{17}Cl^{37} + {}_1H^1 \rightarrow {}_{18}A^{38}$	$2 . 10^{25}$ years
${}_2He^4 + {}_2He^4 \rightarrow {}_4Be^8$	$1 . 10^{15}$ years
${}_3Li^7 + {}_2He^4 \rightarrow {}_5B^{11}$	$3 . 10^{13}$ years
${}_6C^{12} + {}_2He^4 \rightarrow {}_8O^{16}$	$2 . 10^{33}$ years

deuterium-reaction. They all would go *too fast*, and thus could not be responsible for the steady alchemical burning which supports the radiation of sun and stars. In fact, if there had been some of these light elements in the stellar interiors in the beginning of their evolutionary career, they would have been completely destroyed in the very first days of their life in a violent explosion.

On the other hand, such reactions as oxygen-hydrogen, chlorine-hydrogen, or the transformations involving helium (listed in the lower part of the table) are *too slow* and would not be able to supply the energy at the rate necessary for supporting the radiation of the sun and stars.

Thus we see that *the only alchemic transformations which can be made responsible for the stellar energy production are the reactions between carbon or nitrogen on one side and hydrogen on the other.*

Although the work of *Atkinson* and *Houtermans* proved definitely that the energy-production in the sun and other stars is due to thermonuclear reactions between light elements taking place in their hot interiors, the exact nature of that reaction was discovered only ten years later by the independent research of *H. Bethe* [1] in America and *C. v. Weizäcker* in Germany. The main point of their discovery lies in the fact that the nuclei of carbon and nitrogen which enter into an alchemic reaction with hydrogen do not vanish, but are regenerated again through a very peculiar process known as the *carbon-nitrogen-cycle*. In order to understand this process, we have to follow carefully the fate of the atoms of these two elements in the series of alchemic transformations taking place in the stellar interior.

[1] The series of reactions postulated by Bethe was

1. ${}_6C^{12} + {}_1H^1 \rightarrow {}_7N^{13}$
2. ${}_7N^{13} \rightarrow {}_6C^{13} + {}_1e^0$
3. ${}_6C^{13} + {}_1H^1 \rightarrow {}_7N^{14}$
4. ${}_7N^{14} + {}_1H^1 \rightarrow {}_8O^{15}$
5. ${}_8O^{15} \rightarrow {}_7N^{15} + {}_1e^0$
6. ${}_7N^{15} + {}_1H^1 \rightarrow {}_6C^{12} + {}_2He^4$.

Positrons are designated as ${}_1e^0$.—Eds.

When an atom of carbon fuses with a hydrogen atom according to the equation given in the table, we get as the result an atom of nitrogen-isotope with the atomic weight 13. This process can be directly observed in a laboratory, by subjecting a carbon-target to atomic bombardment by a beam of fast protons. Experiments show that the nucleus of nitrogen 13, formed as the result of proton-capture, is an unstable nucleus and, by emitting a positive electron, transforms itself into a nucleus of the stable but rare carbon-isotope: ${}_6C^{13}$. The mean time necessary for such a transformation is about ten minutes. Thus the capture of protons by the ordinary carbon nucleus in the stellar interior leads to the formation of the heavier carbon isotope, the nuclei of which will hang around until they are hit again by another proton. The capture of that proton, increasing both the weight and the charge of the nucleus by one unit, will turn it into a nucleus of ordinary nitrogen with the atomic weight 14. Still another proton comes in after a while and, being captured by nitrogen 14 nucleus, turns it over into the nucleus of oxygen 15. Here, as in the first case, the nucleus formed in the reaction is unstable and within two minutes turns into a stable nucleus of nitrogen 15 through the emission of another positive electron. The nuclei of nitrogen 15, being stable, move around through the interior of the star until they are hit again by a new proton.

Here a very interesting thing, also directly observed in laboratory experiments, takes place. If the fourth proton were captured by the nitrogen 15 nucleus as its three predecessors were, the result would be the nucleus of oxygen 16, i.e., the ordinary oxygen. But the energy liberated in the capture of that proton sets the compound nucleus of oxygen 16 in such a state of strong agitation,[1] that it immediately breaks up into two unequal parts. The smaller part is an alpha-particle, whereas the larger one represents the nucleus of ordinary carbon with which the entire process started.

Summarizing this somewhat lengthy description, we can say that *four protons, captured successively by a carbon nucleus (with two of the protons turning immediately into neutrons), are re-emitted again at the end of the cycle in the combined form of an alpha-particle.* The carbon-nucleus itself comes out of the reaction unchanged, like the Phoenix from the ashes, and its role consists only in helping, or *catalyzing*, as a chemist would say, the transformation of hydrogen into helium. The point is that, in order to unite into a helium nucleus without the help of a catalyzing agent, all four protons would have to meet together at some point of space, and it is easy to see that in the disorderly thermal motion the probability of such quadruple collision is incredibly small. The catalyzing nucleus catches the protons one after another, keeping them inside until all four

[1] The reason why the capture of the *fourth* proton results in particularly strong agitation of the nucleus lies in the fact that each four nuclear particles make a new nuclear subgroup (alpha-group), the formation of which inside the nucleus is connected with the liberation of considerable energy which set the entire nucleus into the state of strong vibrations.

are collected, and we have here, according to a witty remark of *Atkinson* and *Houtermans,* who first contemplated such a possibility, "a nuclear pot in which helium is being cooked from pure hydrogen. . . ." Instead of starting the cycle with a carbon-nucleus, we can just as well start it with a nucleus of nitrogen, or for that matter with any stable nucleus participating in the cycle. Since, in the final count, the stellar reaction reduces to the transformation of hydrogen into helium, the catalyzing nuclei of carbon and nitrogen remaining intact, it will last as long as there is any hydrogen left in the star. . . .

1946

THE MILKY WAY AND BEYOND *

SIR ARTHUR EDDINGTON

In one of Jules Verne's stories the astronomer begins his lecture with the words "Gentlemen, you have seen the moon—or at least heard tell of it." I think I may in the same way presume that you are acquainted with the Milky Way, which can be seen on any clear dark night as a faintly luminous band forming an arch from horizon to horizon. The telescopes show that it is composed of multitudes of stars. One is tempted to say "countless multitudes"; but it is part of the business of an astronomer to count them, and the number is not uncountable though it amounts to more than ten thousand milions. The number of stars in the Milky Way is considerably greater than the number of human beings on the earth. Each star, I may remind you, is an immense fiery globe of the same general nature as our sun.

There is no sharp division between the distant stars which form the Milky Way and the brighter stars which we see strewn over the sky. All these stars taken together form one system or galaxy; its extent is enormous but not unlimited. Since we are situated inside it we do not obtain a good view of its form; but we are able to see far away in space other galaxies which also consist of thousands of millions of stars, and presumably if we could see our own galaxy from outside, it would appear like one of them. These other galaxies are known as "spiral nebulae." We believe that our own Milky Way system is more or less like them. If so, the stars form a flat coil—rather like a watch-spring—except that the coil is double.

When we look out in directions perpendicular to the plane of the coil, we soon reach the limit of the system; but in the plane of the coil we see stars behind stars until they become indistinguishable and fade into the

* Lecture delivered at the University of Berlin, March 16, 1937. Reprinted in *Research and Progress*, Berlin, v. 3, Sept.–Oct. 1937. Reprinted by permission from the author's estate.

hazy light of the Milky Way. It has been ascertained that we are a very long way from the centre of our own galaxy, so that there are many more stars on one side of us than on the other.

Looking at one of these galaxies, it is impossible to resist the impression that it is whirling round—like a Catherine Wheel. It has, in fact, been possible to prove that some of the spiral nebulae are rotating, and to measure the rate of rotation. Also by studying the motions of the stars in our own galaxy, it has been found that it too is rotating about a centre. The centre is situated a long way from us in the constellation Ophiuchus near a particularly bright patch of the Milky Way; the actual centre is, however, hidden from us by a cloud of obscuring matter. My phrase, "whirling round," may possibly give you a wrong impression. With these vast systems we have to think in a different scale of space and time, and the whirling is slow according to our ordinary ideas. It takes about 300 million years for the Milky Way to turn round once. But after all that is not so very long. Geologists tell us that the older rocks in the earth's crust were formed 1,300 million years ago; so the sun, carrying with it the earth and planets, has made four or five complete revolutions round the centre of the galaxy within geological times.

The stars which form our Milky Way system show a very wide diversity. Some give out more than 10,000 times as much light and heat as the sun; others less than 1/100th. Some are extremely dense and compact; others are extremely tenuous. Some have a surface temperature as high as 20,000 or 30,000° C.; others not more than 3,000° C. Some are believed to be pulsating—swelling up and deflating within a period of a few days or weeks; these undergo great changes of light and heat accompanying the expansion and collapse. It would be awkward for us if our sun behaved that way. A considerable proportion (about 1/3 of the whole number) go about in pairs, forming "double stars"; the majority, however, are bachelors like the sun.

But in spite of this diversity, the stars have one comparatively uniform characteristic, namely their mass, that is, the amount of matter which goes to form them. A range from 1/5 to 5 times the sun's mass would cover all but the most exceptional stars; and the general run of the masses is within an even narrower range. Among a hundred stars picked at random the diversity of mass would not be greater proportionately than among a hundred men, women and children picked at random from a crowd.

Broadly speaking, a big star is big, not because it contains an excessive amount of material, but because it is puffed out like a balloon; and a small star is small because its material is highly compressed. Our sun, which is intermediate in this, as in most respects, has a density rather greater than that of water. (The sun is in every way a typical middle-class star.) The two extremes—the extremely rarefied and the extremely dense stars—are especially interesting. We find stars whose material is as tenuous as a gas. The well-known star Capella, for example, has an average density about equal to that of air; to be inside Capella would be like being surrounded by air, as we ordinarily are, except that the temperature (which is about 5,000,000° C) is hotter than we are accustomed to. Still more extreme are the red giant stars Betelgeuse in Orion and Antares in Scorpio. To obtain a star like Betelgeuse, we must imagine the sun swelling out until it has swallowed up Mercury, Venus and the Earth, and has a circumference almost equal to the orbit of Mars. The density of this vast globe is that of a gas in a rather highly exhausted vessel. Betelgeuse could be described as "a rather good vacuum."

At the other extreme are the "white dwarf" stars, which have extravagantly high density. I must say a little about the way in which this was discovered.

Between 1916 and 1924 I was very much occupied trying to understand the internal constitution of the stars, for example, finding the temperature in the deep interior, which is usually ten million degrees, and making out what sort of properties matter would have at such high temperatures. Physicists had recently been making great advances in our knowledge of atoms and radiation; and the problem was to apply this new knowledge to the study of what was taking place inside a star. In the end I obtained a formula by which, if you knew the mass of a star, you could calculate how bright it ought to be. An electrical engineer will tell you that to produce a certain amount of illumination you must have a dynamo of a size which he will specify; somewhat analogously I found that for a star to give a certain amount of illumination it must have a definite mass which the formula specified. This formula, however, was not intended to apply to all stars, but only to diffuse stars with densities corresponding to a gas, because the problem became too complicated if the material could not be treated as a perfect gas.

Having obtained the theoretical formula, the next thing was to compare it with observation. That is where the trouble often begins. And there was trouble in this case; only it was not of the usual kind. The observed masses and luminosities agreed with the formulae all right; the trouble was that they would not stop agreeing! The dense stars for which the formula was *not* intended agreed just as well as the diffuse stars for which the formula was intended. This surprising result could only mean that, although their densities were as great as that of water or iron, the stellar material was nevertheless behaving like a gas; in particular, it was compressible like an ordinary gas.

We had been rather blind not to have foreseen this. Why is it that we can compress air, but cannot appreciably compress water? It is because in air the ultimate particles (the molecules) are wide apart, with plenty of empty space between them. When we compress air we merely pack the molecules a bit closer, reducing the amount of vacant space. But in water the molecules are practically in contact and cannot be packed any closer.

In all substances the ordinary limit of compression is when the molecules jam in contact; after that we cannot appreciably increase the density. This limit corresponds approximately to the density of the solid or liquid state. We had been supposing that the same limit would apply in the interior of a star. We ought to have remembered that at the temperature of millions of degrees there prevailing the atoms are highly ionized, i.e. broken up. An atom has a heavy central nucleus surrounded by a widely extended but insubstantial structure of electrons—a sort of crinoline. At the high temperature in the stars this crinoline of electrons is broken up. If you are calculating how many dancers can be accommodated in a ball-room, it makes a difference whether the ladies wear crinolines or not. Judging by the crinolined terrestrial atoms we should reach the limit of compression at densities not much greater than water; but the uncrinolined stellar atoms can pack much more densely, and do not jam together until densities far beyond terrestrial experience are reached.

This suggested that there might exist stars of density greater than any material hitherto known, which called to mind a mystery concerning the Companion of Sirius. The dog-star Sirius has a faint companion close to it, visible in telescopes of moderate power. There is a method of finding densities of stars which I must not stop to explain. The method is rather tentative; and when it was found to give for the Companion of Sirius a density 50,000 times greater than water, it was naturally assumed that it had gone wrong in its application. But in the light of the foregoing discussion, it now seemed possible that the method had not failed, and that the extravagantly high density might be genuine. So astronomers endeavoured to check the determination of density by another method depending on Einstein's relativity theory. The second method confirmed the high density, and it is now generally accepted. The stuff of the Companion of Sirius is 2,000 times as dense as platinum. Imagine a match-box filled with this matter. It would need a crane to lift it—it would weigh a ton.

I am afraid that what I have to say about the stars is largely a matter of facts and figures. There is only one star near enough for us to study its surface, namely our sun. Ordinary photographs of the sun show few features, except the dark spots which appear at times. But much more interesting photographs are obtained by using a spectro-heliograph, which is an instrument blind to all light except that of one particular wave length—coming from one particular kind of atom.

Now let us turn to the rest of the universe which lies beyond the Milky Way. Our galaxy is, as it were, an oasis of matter in the desert of emptiness, an island in the boundless ocean of space. From our own island we see in the far distance other islands—in fact a whole archipelago of islands one beyond another till our vision fails. One of the nearest of them can actually be seen with the naked eye; it is in the constellation Andromeda, and looks like a faint, rather hazy, star. The light which we now see has taken 900,000 years to reach us. When we look at that faint object in Andromeda we are looking back 900,000 years into the past. Some of the telescopic spiral nebulae are much more distant. The most remote that has yet been examined is 300,000,000 light-years away.

These galaxies are very numerous. From sample counts it is found that more than a million of them are visible in our largest telescopes; and there must be many more fainter ones which we do not see. Our sun is just one star in a system of thousands of millions of stars; and that whole system is just one galaxy in a universe of thousands of millions of galaxies.

Let us pause to see where we have now got to in the scale of size. The following comparative table of distances will help to show us where we are:

	Kilometres
Distance of the sun..........................	150,000,000
Limit of the solar system (Orbit of Pluto)......	5,800,000,000
Distance of the nearest star....................	40,000,000,000,000
Distance of the nearest external galaxy..........	8,000,000,000,000,000,000
Distance of furthest galaxy yet observed........	3,000,000,000,000,000,000,000

Some people complain that they cannot realize these figures. Of course they cannot. But that is the last thing one wants to do with big numbers—to "realize" them. In a few weeks time our finance minister in England will be presenting his annual budget of about £900,000,000. Do you suppose that by way of preparation, he throws himself into a state of trance in which he can visualize the vast pile of coins or notes or commodities that it represents? I am quite sure he cannot "realize" £900,000,000. But he can spend it. It is a fallacious idea that these big numbers create a difficulty in comprehending astronomy; they can only do so if you are seeking the wrong sort of comprehension. They are not meant to be gaped at, but to be manipulated and used. It is as easy to use millions and billions and trillions for our counters as ones and twos and threes. What I want to call attention to in the above table is that since we are going out beyond the Milky Way we have taken a very big step up in the scale of distance.

The remarkable thing that has been discovered about these galaxies is that (except three or four of the nearest of them) they are running away from our own galaxy; and the further they are away, the faster they go. The distant ones have very high speeds. On the average the speed is proportional to the distance, so that a galaxy 10 million light-years away recedes at 1,500 kilometres per second, one 50 million light-years away recedes at 7,500 kilometres per second, and so on. The fastest yet discovered recedes at 42,000 kilometres per second.

Why are they all running away from us? If we think a little, we shall see that the aversion is not especially directed against us; they are running away from us, but they are also running away from each other. If this room were to expand 10 per cent in its dimensions, the seats all separating in proportion, you would at first think that everyone was moving away from you; the man 10 metres away has moved 1 metre further off; the man 20 metres away has moved 2 metres further off; and so on. Just as with the galaxies, the recession is proportional to the distance. This law of proportion is characteristic of a uniform expansion, not directed away from any one centre, but causing a general scattering apart. So we conclude that recession of the nebulae is an effect of uniform expansion.

The system of the galaxies is all the universe we know, and indeed we have strong reason to believe that it is the whole physical universe. The expansion of the system, or scattering apart of the galaxies, is therefore commonly referred to as the expansion of the universe; and the problem which it raises is the problem of the "expanding universe."

The expansion is proceeding so fast that, at the present rate, the nebulae will recede to double their present distances in 1,300 million years. Astronomers will have to double the apertures of their telescopes every 1,300 million years in order to keep pace with the recession. But seriously 1,300 million years is not a long period of cosmic history; I have already mentioned it as the age of terrestrial rocks. It comes as a surprise that the universe should have doubled its dimensions within geological times. It means that we cannot go back indefinitely in time; and indeed the enormous time-scale of billions [The English "billion" is equivalent to the American "trillion."] of years, which was fashionable ten years ago, must be drastically cut down. We are becoming reconciled to this speeding up of the time-scale of evolution, for various other lines of evidence have convinced us that it is essential. It seems clear now that we must take an upper limit to the age of the stars not greater than 10,000 million years; previously, an age of a thousand times longer was commonly adopted.

For reasons which I cannot discuss fully we believe that along with the expansion of the material universe there is an expansion of space itself. The idea is that the island galaxies are scattered throughout a "spherical space." Spherical space means that if you keep going straight on in any direction you will ultimately find yourself back at your starting point. This is analogous to what happens when you travel straight ahead on the earth; you reach your starting point again, having gone round the world. But here we apply the analogy to an extra dimension—to *space* instead of to a *surface*. I realize, of course, that this conception of a closed spherical space is very difficult to grasp, but really it is not worse than the older conception of infinite open space which no one can properly imagine. No one can conceive infinity; one just uses the term by habit without trying to grasp it. If I may refer to our English expression, "out of the frying-pan into the fire," I suggest that if you feel that in receiving this modern conception of space you are falling into the fire, please remember that you are at least escaping from the frying-pan.

Spherical space has many curious properties. I said that if you go straight ahead in any direction you will return to your starting point. So if you look far enough in any direction and there is nothing in the way, you ought to see—the back of your head. Well, not exactly—because light takes at least 6,000 million years to travel round the universe and your head was not there when it started. But you will understand the general idea. However, these curiosities do not concern us much. The main point is that if the galaxies are distributed over the spherical space more or less in the same way that human beings are distributed over the earth, they cannot form an expanding system—they cannot all be receding from one another—unless the space itself expands. So the expansion of the material system involves, and is an aspect of, an expansion of space.

This scattering apart of the galaxies was not unforeseen. As far back as 1917, Professor W. de Sitter showed that there was reason to expect this phenomenon and urged astronomers to look for it. But it is only recently that radial velocities of spiral nebulae have been measured in sufficient numbers to show conclusively that the scattering occurs. It is one of the deductions from relativity theory that there must exist a force, known as "cosmical repulsion," which tends to produce this kind of scattering in which every object recedes from every other object. You know the theory of relativity led to certain astronomical consequences—a bending of light near the sun detectable at eclipses, a motion of the perihelion of Mercury, a red-shift of spectral lines—which have been more or less satisfactorily verified. The existence of cosmical repulsion is an equally definite consequence of the theory, though this is not so widely known—partly because it comes from a more difficult branch of the theory and was not noticed so early, and perhaps partly because it is not so directly associated with the magic name of Einstein.

I can see no reason to doubt that the observed recession of the spiral nebulae is due to cosmical repulsion, and is the effect predicted by relativity theory which we were hoping to find. Many other explanations have been proposed—some of them rather fantastic—and there has been a great deal of discussion which seems to me rather pointless. In this, as in other developments of scientific exploration, we must recognize the limitations of our present knowledge and be prepared to consider revolutionary changes. But when, as in this case, observation agrees with what our existing knowledge had led us to expect, it is reasonable to feel encouraged to pursue the line of thought which has proved successful; and there seems little excuse for an outburst of unsupported speculation. . . .

1937

>>>><<<<

THE 200-INCH TELESCOPE *

SIR H. SPENCER JONES

INTRODUCTION

No instrument intended solely for scientific research has aroused greater interest amongst the general public than the 200-inch telescope. The progress of its construction has been closely followed, not merely in the United States but throughout the world. Though an attempt to do something that has not been done before, or to achieve something on a much larger scale than previously, is always likely to arouse interest, it is not mainly, I think, for this reason that the construction of the 200-inch telescope has captured the popular imagination. It is due rather to a realization of the immensity of the Universe and to the expectation that, by probing farther into its remote depths, an answer may be found to some of the still unsolved problems of the Universe.

The largest telescope previously built, the 100-inch reflector of the Mount Wilson Observatory, was completed in the darkest days of the last war. On the night in the year 1917, when the first trials of the completed instrument were being made, came the news of the disastrous Italian defeat at Caporetto. In the years that have since elapsed, our views of the Universe have been revolutionized. It is sufficient merely to recall that, at that time, it was still undecided whether the so-called spiral nebulae were constituent parts of our Milky Way or galactic system or whether they were island universes, remote in space, generally comparable to our own galactic system. Many astronomers were of the one opinion; many were of the other. The 100-inch telescope provided the answer to this and to many other problems. But for every question that it answered there were many others suggested, which it could not answer. The 100-inch telescope has photographed universes so distant that, even with its aid, the eye of man cannot see them; they are revealed as faint smudges on photographs with long exposures on sensitive plates. Light, ever more light, is the need before more can be learnt about these distant systems, and still larger telescopes the way to supply the need.

The importance of larger telescopes to make possible advances in astronomy in certain directions was fully realized by Dr. George Hale, Director of the Mount Wilson Observatory. When, in 1927, after ill-health had caused him to resign the directorship, the Editor of *Harper's Magazine* invited Hale to contribute an astronomical article, he chose as his subject "The Possibilities of Large Telescopes." In the course of this article he wrote:

* The twelfth Thomas Young Oration, delivered May 30, 1941. Reprinted from the *Proceedings of the Physical Society*, Vol. 53, 1941, with the permission of The Physical Society and the author.

"Like buried treasures, the outposts of the Universe have beckoned to the adventurous from immemorial times. Princes and potentates, political or industrial, equally with men of science, have felt the lure of the uncharted seas of space. If the cost of gathering celestial treasure exceeds that of searching for the buried chests of a Morgan or a Flint, the expectation of rich return is surely greater and the route no less attractive. . . . I believe that a 200-inch or even a 300-inch telescope could now be built and used to the greater advantage of astronomy. . . . Lick, Yerkes, Hooker and Carnegie have passed on, but the opportunity remains for some other donor to advance knowledge and to satisfy his own curiosity regarding the nature of the Universe and the problem of its unexplored depths."

A proof of this paper was sent to Dr. Wickliffe Rose, President of the Rockefeller General Education Board, and led within a few weeks to a gift of six million dollars to the California Institute of Technology for a 200-inch telescope, together with a complete astrophysical observatory, with laboratories, workshops and auxiliary equipment. Rarely can a magazine article have been so productive of result.

To have obtained the financial provision for the construction of a 200-inch telescope removed the first and the least of the difficulties. The many problems involved in proceeding in one step from a 100-inch telescope to one of double the aperture had then to be solved; the doubling of the aperture enormously increased the difficulties.

DESIGN OF THE MIRROR

The fundamental and the most difficult of the problems was the construction of a mirror of 200-inch diameter. The mirrors of the early reflecting telescopes were made of speculum metal, a hard and brittle alloy of copper and tin containing about one part by weight of tin to two of copper. Speculum metal will take a high degree of polish and has a moderately good reflecting power. It is difficult to cast and anneal, unless the copper content is increased, in which case the mirror is liable to develop a tarnish which can only be removed by repolishing and refiguring. The largest speculum mirror ever made was the 6-foot mirror of Lord Rosse's great reflector, completed in 1851. The discovery by Liebig of a simple chemical process by which a thin film of silver could be deposited on a glass surface made possible the silver-on-glass mirror. The application of Liebig's discovery to glass mirrors and the methods of making and testing such mirrors were due primarily to Foucault in the 'sixties of the last century, and since that time glass mirrors have entirely superseded speculum mirrors.

Glass has two important advantages as a material for mirrors: it can take a very high degree of polish and it is free from any liability to warp or distort with age. But it suffers from two great disadvantages, which make it far from an ideal material; it has a high coefficient of expansion and it is a poor conductor of heat. When a glass mirror is in use, changes and inequalities of temperature give rise to localized expansions and contractions which impair the figure of the mirror, change the focus and deform the images. Because the heat conductivity is low, temperature differences within the mirror persist for a long time.

For the same reasons, large glass mirrors are difficult to cast and to anneal. In order to obtain sufficient rigidity, it is customary for the thickness of the mirror to be about one-eighth of its diameter. The 100-inch mirror weighs about five tons. After casting, the mirror must be annealed, to relieve internal strains, by cooling at a rate so slow that at any stage the temperature throughout the mass must be practically uniform. A disk of 100-inch diameter requires several months' annealing, and even then there is a considerable risk that, when the annealing oven is opened, the disk will be found to be in fragments. There were, in fact, several failures to produce a satisfactory 100-inch disk, and, in the end, the one disk which had been successfully annealed, but which had been initially discarded because it contained many bubbles and imperfections, had to be used.

The 100-inch disk was made at the St. Gobain glassworks of ordinary plate glass. A 200-inch disk of similar glass, with the same ratio of thickness to diameter, would weigh 40 tons, and it was estimated that to avoid the risk of fracture during annealing, the annealing would need to be extended over nine years. It therefore became necessary to examine every possible alternative. One alternative was a built-up mirror instead of a solid disk, enabling a great saving in weight to be made without sacrifice of rigidity, and thereby simplifying considerably the problem of the annealing. The idea was not a new one. It had been tried nearly a century previously by Lord Rosse, who constructed a three-foot speculum mirror of cellular form, the reflecting surface being supported by a metal ring with radial and transverse stiffeners, dividing the back of the mirror into compartments, in which the air could circulate freely. The mirror was not a success: the images were not satisfactory, the supports at the back revealing themselves by defects in the optical surface. The idea was revived by Ritchey in 1924, who constructed a 60-inch disk of small plates of glass cemented, in the form of a honeycomb structure, to a top plate; the polished surface, however, showed the same defects. Pressure in polishing caused a flexure of the glass at the centre of each cell. For this reason, and because there were doubts whether such a mirror would keep its figure, this idea was not further entertained.

The possibilities of metal mirrors were considered, and many special alloys were suggested. A metal mirror, with a thin layer of glass of the same coefficient of expansion fused to its surface, was proposed by the Philips Lamp Works, of Eindhoven, Holland, and a small mirror of this type was tried. A mirror made of stainless steel was seriously considered, and several samples of stainless steel were examined. Stainless steel has the advantage of high heat conductivity, freedom from tarnishing and high reflectivity in the ultra-violet. The great drawback to a large mirror made of metal would be its weight; it is doubtful, moreover, whether permanence of figure could be guaranteed. Much experience would be necessary with smaller mirrors of so experimental a nature before it would be known whether they would meet the rigid requirements. It is possible that a light alloy might be found that would prove suitable for astronomical mirrors, and there is much scope for experiment in this direction; but it seemed unwise to hazard a 200-inch mirror in so untried a field and in default of long experience with mirrors of smaller size.

Two possibilities that were less in the nature of untried innovations were open. These were to make the mirror either of fused silica, which has a very low coefficient of expansion, or of the glass of high silica content, known as Pyrex, which has a coefficient of expansion about one-third that of plate glass. The prospect of a large mirror of fused silica was an inviting one; its insensitiveness to temperature changes would eliminate many troubles. Disks of small size had been successfully made of fused silica, and the General Electric Company was confident that a large mirror could be made. The services of the Company's research laboratory were offered on the basis of the cost of time and materials, without any additions for overhead charges. The contract for the work was placed on this basis.

The process consisted in melting the purest quartz sand obtainable, without any flux, in a circular electric furnace, which formed the mould. A temperature of 3,000° F. is needed to fuse the quartz. Fused quartz is very viscous and passes into vapour before it becomes thoroughly liquid, so that it is impossible to get rid of the large number of minute air bubbles that are trapped in it, even when vacuum pumps are continually pumping out the air above the quartz. The quartz disks thus obtained have a pearl-grey appearance, because of the air bubbles, and it is impossible to obtain a satisfactory optical surface from them. The disk to be made in this way was to be ground to the approximate curvature required; the second part of the process was to coat it to a sufficient thickness with a layer of transparent fused quartz, entirely free from air bubbles. The first method of producing the transparent layer was to cover the disk with slabs of clear quartz, a few inches square, and to weld them together with a blow-torch. The small slabs were made by welding pure quartz crystals in a special furnace; with great care it was possible to get them to run together into a single mass free from bubbles. It was found to be impossible to produce larger slabs free from the troublesome bubbles. Though by this method disks of small size, with a surface layer of clear quartz, were successfully made, the method failed when larger disks were attempted. The larger the surface, the more difficult it proved to weld the slabs evenly together, and it was evident that some different method would have to be devised for making a 200-inch disk.

Attempts were therefore made to produce the clear coating by spraying pure crystalline quartz, ground into a fine dust, on to the surface by means of an oxy-hydrogen flame. The rain of quartz droplets froze on the surface in a clear layer and disks up to two feet in diameter were successfully made. But the difficulties increased rapidly with the size of the disk. Much experimenting was carried out to ensure success; multiple nozzles, circling slowly round inside the furnace, were tried to ensure a uniform coating. There was no inherent reason why a 200-inch quartz disk should not ultimately have been successfully produced, but at a price. It was the price that put an end to the experiments; the cost would have been at least one million dollars, and probably much more. It seemed possible that the whole of the grant might be used up in making the mirror. The use of quartz was therefore reluctantly abandoned in favour of Pyrex glass.

The ordinary Pyrex glass, of which cooking utensils are made, has a coefficient of expansion about four times that of quartz but only one-third that of plate glass. Its use for domestic purposes shows that it can withstand large and rapid changes of temperature. With a larger percentage of silica, glass with a lower coefficient of expansion is possible, though the glass becomes more viscous, harder to melt and harder to cast as the silica content is increased. At the research laboratory of the Corning Glass Works, experiments were made to find to what extent the proportion of silica in the glass could be increased, without making the glass too difficult to use. The special low-expansion Pyrex glass, finally decided upon, had a coefficient of expansion one-quarter that of plate glass, three times that of quartz. The high silica content of this glass greatly reduces the time required for satisfactory annealing and thereby reduces the danger of devitrification, which is liable to occur when the annealing process is long.

A glass disk 200 inches in diameter and 30 inches in thickness would weigh about 40 tons. The problems involved in building a telescope sufficiently strong and rigid to carry such a weight and to be free from serious flexure effects were considerable. It was suggested by Dr. Day, of the Geophysical Institute, Washington, that the disk should be designed with a thin face supported on a ribbed back, the ribs being arranged to provide adequate stiffness. Not only would the weight be reduced and the mechanical problems of the design of the telescope be simplified, but the effects of changes of temperature would be reduced. The ribbed structure at the back of the disk would also simplify the design of the supports for the mirror. The mounting of the 100-inch mirror had recently been redesigned. The mirror rested in the telescope on a number of cast-iron pads, supported by counterpoised levers. These introduced friction when the mirror was turned from one position to another, causing strains and deterioration in the quality of the star-images. When the mirror was remounted with pads fitted to its back, which were supported by ball bearings on the counterpoised pads, the friction was eliminated and the quality of the images improved. The cells at the back of a ribbed mirror would be ideal for containing similar ball-bearing supports.

The ribbing was designed by Mr. Pease of the Mount Wilson Observatory. The main part of the disk was to be 5 inches thick; on the back of this there would be 36 cylindrical pockets, forming the corners of a network of equilateral triangles, whose sides formed the ribs. A ribbed coelostat mirror, made at the Corning Glass Works, was subjected to very severe tests in the Optical Shop in Pasadena and proved entirely satisfactory.

Meanwhile, investigations were being undertaken at the Research Laboratory of the Corning Glass Company to devise methods for casting and annealing large disks, and to find suitable materials for building the mould and cores and the best means of anchoring the cores. The high melting temperature of the special Pyrex glass caused difficulties that were absent at the lower melting temperature of plate glass. Fire bricks of high quality, from which satisfactory moulds for casting plate glass were made, proved useless because they absorbed moisture which turned to steam when the glass was poured in, filling the glass near the walls with bubbles. In the end, bricks of pure white silica were used. They were made from blocks of ground-up cork, sand and water mixed together; these blocks were fired in a kiln, when the cork burned out, leaving hard, porous bricks, which absorbed no moisture, were resistant to the high temperature of the molten Pyrex and enabled the glass to "breathe" by allowing any air or gas in it to escape through the pores.

The usual method of casting large mirrors had been to pour the molten glass into an open mould, the furnace being tapped and the glass running from it along a trough into the mould. The special Pyrex glass could not be poured in this way; it rapidly chilled sufficiently to stop the flow. It was therefore decided to fill the mould by ladling the glass into it from the furnace. Experiments soon showed that this alone was not sufficient. The molten glass running between the cores congealed before it properly filled the mould. Casting on the open floor had to be abandoned; the mould must be kept hot in a furnace of its own.

CASTING AND ANNEALING THE MIRROR

Before any attempt was made to cast the 200-inch disk, experience was gained with the disks for the smaller auxiliary mirrors for the telescope and for the mirrors to be used in the testing of the 200-inch. Disks progressively increasing in size were cast, the various causes of failure being eliminated in turn. Disks of 30, 60 and 120 inches diameter were cast before the 200-inch disk was attempted, the 120-inch disk being cast in the furnace designed and constructed for the 200-inch.

The cores were made of pieces of the special brick, cemented together, cut down to the correct size and then carefully shaped with a carborundum grinding-wheel. They were fastened down, at first, with a special furnace cement, but broke loose during the casting. The use of cement was therefore abandoned and the cores were anchored with dowels of silica brick. When the 60-inch disk was poured, many of the cores again came adrift; a second attempt was made, the greatest care being taken in the preparation and fixing of the cores. On this occasion one core only broke loose; it was ladled out, the pouring was completed, the disk was annealed for 69 days and a satisfactory disk was obtained, the missing hole where the core had come adrift being drilled out.

It was apparent that failure in the casting of the large disk would be liable to occur if a more secure method of anchoring the cores were not adopted. It was decided to use steel bolts with large heads, the cores being built round the bolts. This meant that the thickness of the cores would be reduced and more care in building them would be required. The 120-inch disk was successfully cast with the cores held down in this way, and a perfect disk was obtained after four months in the annealing oven. This disk had provided a good test of all the arrangements for dealing with the 200-inch disk.

The mould for the 200-inch disk was carried on a heavy circular steel table, to which was fitted a large number of electric heating coils, to keep the disk warm in the annealing oven. Around this was built a special domed or beehive casting oven, of silica brick and cement. The oven was provided with three swing doors to admit the ladles and a number of vents for the escape of the gases. It was maintained at a high temperature with special burners. The annealing oven was built nearby. This was in the form of an insulated steel tank, just large enough to fit closely over the disk. It was lined inside with a large number of electric heating elements, controlled from a special switchboard. The temperature inside the annealing oven could be maintained constant or lowered at any desired rate by suitable adjustment of the current in the heating coils. An automatic control by electric clocks enabled the temperature to be lowered at any desired rate.

On the floor below, a length of wide-gauge railroad was laid and a special truck with small double-flanged wheels, capable of carrying fifty tons, was constructed. It carried a skeleton girder platform, which could be raised or lowered by four powerful screw-jacks, operated by electric motors. After the casting was completed, the disk was to be lowered on to this truck, which was then to be run along the railroad until it was beneath the annealing oven; the disk would then be jacked up until it was safely in the annealer.

The mould for the 200-inch disk was constructed with 114 cores, each fastened to the bottom of the mould by bolts, passing through holes drilled in the steel table, each bolt being fixed in position by a nut working against a spring. Everything was ready for the casting in March 1934. The melting tank, 50 feet long by 15 feet wide, in a furnace heated by gas burners, could hold 65 tons of glass. For ten days before charging commenced, the furnace was heated, in order to raise its temperature to 2,700° F. The "batch" for the special Pyrex glass was fed in through a door at one end of the furnace at a rate of 4 tons a day. After it had all melted, it was heated for six days more to ensure uniformity and to allow gas bubbles to escape.

For the ladling process, three overhead monorail tracks were installed, running from the furnace to the three doors of the beehive oven. Each of the three ladles, capable of holding 700 lb. of glass, was suspended by a steel bar from a trolley running along one of the tracks, and was provided with a handle 20 feet long. By means of this arrangement, one ladleful could be taken from the melting furnace and poured into the mould every six minutes. As each ladle was removed from the furnace, the glass hanging round its edge was cleared away with a long bar, and during its transfer to the beehive oven, the outside was cooled by a water spray to prevent it from melting. About 400 pounds of glass were poured into the mould; the remainder, which had solidified on the inside of the ladle, was tipped out into a metal wheelbarrow and returned to the furnace. Ten hours of steady continuous ladling were required to fill the mould, but near the end an unfortunate mischance occurred. The high temperature was too much for some of the bolts and a few of the cores came adrift and floated to the surface of the melt. These were subsequently scooped out; by grinding at the back of the disk, where the cores were missing, the symmetry of the disk could be restored.

It was decided, however, that a second attempt should be made to cast a perfect disk; the imperfect disk would serve to check the conclusions about the length of time required for satisfactory annealing. From a special study in the laboratory of the annealing properties of the super-Pyrex glass, supplemented by theoretical investigations, it had been concluded that the disk could be perfectly annealed in somewhat less than a year. The imperfect disk was cooled at ten times the safe rate. After thirty days, it was removed from the annealing oven and found to be intact; careful examination by polarized light subsequently showed a slight degree of residual strain and confirmed that the original estimate was a safe one.

Before the second disk was cast, the method of anchoring the cores was modified. After various tests, it was decided to use bolts of chrome nickel steel, which satisfactorily passed a high-temperature test lasting for two weeks. But as an additional precaution against the risk of failure, the cores were made hollow and cool air was drawn through them by a suction fan throughout the process of pouring. The second disk was cast on 2 December 1934, and was completely successful, no hitch occurring during the process. The disk was placed in the annealer, to be maintained at a steady temperature for two months, and then cooled uniformly for eight months more.

But disaster nearly overtook it three months before the annealing was due to be completed. The Chemung River, which flows past the works and is subject to periodical flooding, overflowed its banks and the water rose higher and higher; for the first time in seventeen years it passed the highest safety mark. The annealing oven was out of danger on the second floor, but the transformer and the automatic temperature control equipment were on the ground floor. In spite of all efforts to protect the equipment with sandbags and concrete dykes the water steadily gained, and eventually the current had to be shut off, whilst the transformer and equipment were raised above the danger level. Three days passed before the current could be switched on again. But the dangers were not over, for shortly afterwards Corning was shaken by an earthquake. However, when the oven was opened at the allotted time, the disk was found to be perfect, and careful examination with a polariscope revealed no traces of strain. The disk weighed over 14½ tons. Its cost has not been made public, but the disk was insured by Lloyds of London for $100,000 for its journey across to California.

DELIVERY OF MIRROR TO PASADENA

The disk having been successfully completed, the packing and transport for 3,000 miles across the continent to California were not without their problems. The disk was cased in a box made of ½ inch steel plates, with a paddling all round of rubber sheeting, also ½-inch in thickness. The disk and casing together weighed 35 tons. It was necessary to transport the disk in the vertical position, as it diameter was too great for carriage by rail or road in the horizontal position. The route was carefully planned and checked, and the heights of all bridges and tunnels where the clearance was small were verified. In places there was not more than an inch or two to spare. A special well-hole car was made to carry the crated disk. Heavy cross-girders bolted to this car supported steel beams, which had been welded to the disk casing; gum rubber and hardwood blocks, counter-balanced with heavy springs, were placed between the beams on the case and the girders on the car to act as shock absorbers. Steel rods, two inches in thickness, from near the top of the crate to the four corners of the car, tightened by turnbuckles, held the casing firmly in position. Finally, as an additional protection, heavy steel plates were placed at an angle from near the top of the casing to the sides of the car. The speed of the train was limited to 25 miles an hour. The trans-continental journey was completed without incident and the disk arrived at Pasadena on 10 April 1936.

THE TELESCOPE AND MOUNTING

Whilst the investigations leading to the casting of the mirror had been under way, progress had been made with the mechanical design of the telescope and mounting. Two fundamental decisions had first to be made. What should be the ratio of the focal length of the mirror to its aperture and what type of mounting for the telescope tube should be adopted? The 100-inch telescope has an aperture ratio of f/5. If the same ratio were adopted for the 200-inch, the focal length would be 83 feet, requiring a very large dome. A shorter focal length would simplify the problems of design, would reduce the size of the dome and would at the same time appreciably reduce the cost. As, moreover, one of the principal applications of the telescope would be to the photography of the faintest and most remote galactic systems, the smaller ratio of focal length to aperture would be advantageous. It was therefore decided to adopt the ratio of f/3.3, giving a principal focal length of 55 feet and requiring a relatively short tube.

The next question to be decided was the type of mounting. A telescope must be provided with two degrees of freedom, so that it can be pointed to any desired part of the sky. Herschel's telescopes and Lord Rosse's 6-ft. reflector had been built so that the two motions were in altitude and azimuth. This type of mounting has the great inconvenience that during observations the telescope must be moved in both co-ordinates to follow the diurnal motion across the sky of the object under observation. More convenient is the equatorial type of mounting, in which the telescope can be turned about an axis (called the polar axis) parallel to the axis of the earth, and about a perpendicular axis (called the declination axis). The advantage of this type of mounting is that, when the telescope has been set on an object, it is only necessary to give it a motion around the polar axis in order to follow the diurnal motion; as, moreover, this rotation is at a uniform rate, it can be carried out mechanically, by clockwork or other suitable means. The invention of the equatorial mounting followed closely that of the telescope itself. Father Scheiner used an equatorial mounting for the heliotrope, with which he made his observations of sunspots, probably as early as 1616, and certainly before 1625, when his *Rosa Ursina,* containing a woodcut of the heliotrope, was published. He attributed the idea to Father Gruenberger. The application of a clockwork drive was first made by J. D. Cassini, at the Paris Observatory, somewhere about 1675. The great lengths of the early telescopes, necessitated by the chromatic aberrations of their single-lens objectives, caused the equatorial type of mounting to be abandoned for many years in favour of the altazimuth type. The equatorial mounting is now universally used for large instruments. . . .

THE DOME BUILDING

The building for housing the telescope has double walls of concrete, with a 12-inch air gap between them. The interior surface of the inner wall is covered with asbestos insulation. Around the top of the walls a circular track of two heavy rails was laid, the rails being welded together and ground smooth and level. The dome is supported by a massive ring-girder carried on 32 four-wheeled trucks, which run on this track. The trucks are fitted with heavy coiled springs. Horizontal wheels outside and clamps inside prevent the trucks from jumping off the rails. The outer wheels are larger than the inner, the outer track rail being correspondingly lower. The skeleton of the dome is formed by two massive box-girder arches, thirty feet apart, which on one side of the dome form the sides of the aperture for observations. The remainder of the framework is formed of relatively light beams. The outer covering is formed of steel plates of ¾-inch thickness, each weighing one ton, pressed into the correct spherical curvature and butt-welded together, forming a smooth hemispherical structure of great strength. An inner plating of aluminum panels is fitted, leaving a 12-inch thick air-space. Warm air between the two layers of the dome and the double walls of the building is pumped out from the top of the dome before observations are commenced, cool air being drawn in below. To minimize temperature variations within the dome, the aluminum panels, which form the inner plating, are in the form of hollow boxes of sheet aluminum each filled with crumpled aluminum foil. The dome building is 137 feet in diameter and 135 feet high, and is almost identical in size with the Pantheon at Rome.

The dome is turned by two pairs of 5-H.P. electric motors, with vertical shafts carrying rubber-tyred wheels. These wheels are pressed by springs, under a pressure of several tons, against a smooth welded steel band, a foot wide, laid on edge around the inside of the dome just above the trucks. The tension of the spring is adjusted so as to permit a certain amount of slip at starting while the motors are taking up the load. A smooth easy motion of the dome results and, when the dome is stationary, the pressure of the wheels acts as a brake against wind.

SELECTION OF SITE

The choice of a site for a very large telescope requires careful consideration. Unless a site is selected where the conditions are as favourable as can be obtained, the efficiency of the telescope would be greatly reduced and the advantages obtainable from its great light-grasp would in large measure be lost. The requirements are a clear transparent atmosphere, with a low percentage of cloudiness at all seasons of the year; a low daily range in temperature and a moderate annual range in temperature; a high percentage of nights, at all times of the year, when the "seeing" is good, which implies an absence of turbulence; a general freedom from strong winds and remoteness from towns or other sources of artificial light. In addition to these factors, a low latitude is desirable, because this permits observations to extend over the whole of one hemisphere of the sky together with a considerable belt of the other hemisphere; a low latitiude has the further advantage that the difference in the length of the nights in winter and summer is less and the duration of twilight is shorter than in a high latitude. There is no site in Great Britain that complies even approximately with these requirements, and the erection of a very large telescope in this country would not be justified. In the mountains of Southern California there are various regions where conditions are very favorable. They are generally good on Mount Wilson, but the scattered light from the artificial lights in the valley below the mountain is sufficient to be troublesome when giving long exposures with fast lenses on faint objects. The general conditions of the whole area were carefully studied; simultaneous tests of seeing were made at a number of selected sites by observers using similar instruments and methods, and measurements of the brightness of the sky were also made.

The site finally selected was on Mount Palomar, in the San Jacinto Mountains, at an altitude of 5,600 feet. The mountain is a solid granite block some 30 miles long and 10 miles wide, lying between two faults, and the risk of trouble from earthquakes is considered to be negligible. It is 125 miles southeast of Pasadena, in a sparsely populated area, where there is unlikely to be trouble from artificial light. On the mountain top a water supply, a Diesel electric power plant, a gas supply, living quarters for the permanent staff and for visiting staff, machine shops and garages have been provided. There are, in fact, all the amenities of life for a small township. Two-way radio communication on a wave-length of 7½ metres is maintained between Palomar and Pasadena. In addition to the 200-inch telescope building, other buildings to house auxiliary instruments have been erected, and an 18-inch Schmidt camera has already been in use for more than three years. A broad motor road with easy gradients up the mountain reaching to the Observatory has been constructed by San Diego County to provide access.

CONCLUSION

The 200-inch telescope is nearing completion in the midst of another great war. The optical figuring of the mirror is in an advanced stage, though it would be rash to predict when it will be completed. The final stages of the figuring of a large mirror are apt to be long drawn out, for the polishing heats the mirror, which must be left to acquire a uniform temperature before tests are made on it. As the work nears completion, the proportion of the time spent in waiting for the mirror to settle down and in making tests gets steadily greater. The low coefficient of expansion of the special Pyrex will here be of distinct advantage. When the mirror is completed, it is intended to coat it with a film of aluminum by the vacuum distillation process in order to secure the advantage of the high reflectivity of aluminum in the ultra-violet, where the reflectivity of silver is low. The construction of a steel chamber large enough to take the 200-inch mirror, and capable of holding a high vacuum of about 10^{-5} mm. of mercury, is one of the many tasks incidental to the completion of this project.

The 200-inch telescope is not only the largest but also the most expensive instrument ever constructed for scientific research. It was made possible by the vision of one man, George Ellery Hale, the greatest of American astronomers; but many have co-operated in working out the details, and its design embodies the ideas of astronomers, physicists, engineers and technicians of all sorts. Much thought and care and toil and skill have gone to its fashioning. The Observatory Council, which has been responsible for the final decision in all questions of design, has not hesitated to depart from hitherto established practice when there appeared to be valid reasons for so doing, and it is safe to assert that the 200-inch telescope will profoundly affect the design of large telescopes in the future. He who would venture to predict what will be discovered with its aid would be rash. But we can be sure that, because it will enable man to probe farther into space than he has yet done, new horizons will be opened up and the question will again be asked what lies beyond. The task of the astronomer will not be ended and the demand for a still larger telescope will once more arise.

1941

WORK FOR THE 200-INCH CAMERA *

IRA SPRAGUE BOWEN

Today a great astronomical instrument is nearing completion on Palomar Mountain in Southern California. It is commonly called the 200-inch telescope, but more accurately it should be named the 200-inch camera. Let me explain why I make this distinction.

The human eye has a limited sensitivity. No matter how long and intently we gaze at a faint object on a dark night we cannot bring to view any fainter details than were seen at first glance. In contrast, the photographic plate is quite different. It can build up an image through prolonged exposure. If you should try to photograph the starry heavens, for example, a few seconds exposure would get images of only a few stars. You could see more with the unaided eye. But prolong the exposure, and the photograph will record fainter and fainter stars, and in a few minutes its plate will have reached the sensitivity of the eye. By extending the exposure to many hours we may push far beyond anything the eye can see and record objects of almost any degree of faintness.

Because of this greater sensitivity of the photographic plate all large astronomical instruments are used almost exclusively as cameras rather than as visual telescopes. It is only by the use of the photographic plate that we have been able to obtain most of the knowledge we have of nebulae and other faint objects. No human eye has ever seen their details directly.

Let us therefore consider the Palomar Mountain instrument as a camera.

* From *The Scientists Speak*, edited by Warren Weaver. Reprinted by permission from Boni & Gaer, Inc. Copyright 1947 by Boni & Gaer, Inc.

The heart of any camera is its lens. The function of the lens is to collect the light coming from the object and bring it to a focus on the photographic plate. The quality of the photographs obtained depends to a large extent on the accuracy of design and perfection of workmanship of this vital part of every camera.

In the Palomar Mountain camera the role of the lens is taken by a great mirror. This mirror is in the form of a slightly concave disk 200 inches in diameter. It has been necessary to shape the surface of the mirror with the most extraordinary accuracy, for an error of more than a few millionths of an inch at any point on the suface would distort the image. This work of grinding and polishing is now in its final stages, and when completed some seven years will have been spent giving this surface the necessary perfection.

The mirror must not only have the right curvature, but it must be sufficiently stiff to maintain this accuracy of shape as the camera is pointed in various directions. To provide the necessary rigidity, the mirror is made of a huge ribbed block of pyrex glass. The glass is nearly 17 feet in diameter, 30 inches thick, and weighs nearly 15 tons.

The next essential, after the lens or mirror, is the camera body. The purpose of this structure is to support the lens and the photographic plate in their proper relative positions. Since the 200-inch mirror has a focal length of 55 feet, the mirror and photographic plate must be separated by this distance. To hold the mirror and plate with sufficient rigidity during the long exposures, requires a considerable structure. Actually, the body of the 200-inch camera is a framework of steel girders, weighing 125 tons.

The camera body is mounted in a huge steel cradle which permits the camera to be pointed at any point in the sky. The complete assembly—mirror, body, and cradle—weighs a total of over 500 tons, and the huge mechanism is precisely mounted on bearings and so adjusted that it can turn about an axis parallel to that of the earth. Its motion is controlled by a very precise clock. This arrangement is necessary since the camera must be kept pointed at a given star as the star moves from east to west in the sky.

A steel dome 135 feet in diameter and 135 feet high houses the telescope. To permit the camera to look out through a slot at any desired point in the sky, the dome can be rotated about a vertical axis, and it moves with great ease despite its weight of 1,000 tons.

In the construction of the 200-inch camera, the builders were faced, on the one hand, with most of the problems of heavy structural engineering. On the other hand, was the necessity of attaining high instrumental accuracy and smoothness of operation in these huge and massive mechanisms. It is no wonder that fifteen years have been required to build this instrument. The 200-inch camera on Palomar Mountain has probably cost more in both time and money than any other single instrument that has ever been constructed for peacetime scientific research.

At once a question presents itself. What is the justification for this huge expenditure of effort?

In answering, let us compare the 200-inch camera with the largest now in operation: namely, the 100-inch instrument on Mount Wilson. The mirror of the new camera has twice the diameter; therefore it has four times the area and, accordingly, four times the light-gathering power of the old one. Hence, the new camera should be able to photograph faint objects twice as far distant from our earth as was hitherto possible. But increasing the observable distance by a factor of two increases the volume of observable space by a factor of eight. In general, therefore, the Palomar Mountain camera should allow us to explore eight times as large a volume of the universe as has been possible in the past.

And now for some specific problems.

One of the outstanding accomplishments of the older 100-inch camera was the definite identification of the spiral nebulae as great systems of stars similar to our Milky Way. This was followed by measurements of the dimensions, the distances, and the velocities of these nebulae. For the first time we had a true picture of the structure and dimensions of the universe out to very distant limits.

However, despite this gain, many fundamental questions have remained unanswered. For example, are the stellar systems distributed through space uniformly and do they extend on indefinitely, or is a boundary finally reached beyond which there are fewer and fewer nebulae? Science also wants to know what is the true interpretation of the huge velocities with which all the stellar systems appear to be receding. Are these true velocities?

If so, are we to conclude that these stellar systems were thrown out by an enormous explosion involving the whole universe some billions of years ago? Or can these apparent velocities be interpreted as some strange pseudo-velocity caused by a curvature of space or by some little understood property of light? It is hoped that the answers to these questions will be found when we can observe a larger sample of our universe, such as the 200-inch camera will bring to view.

The possibility of changing one chemical element into another, with the release of enormous quantities of energy, was dramatically demonstrated at Hiroshima and Nagasaki. It had previously been shown that the energy which causes the sun and most of the stars to shine comes from a somewhat similar transformation in their substance, changing hydrogen into helium. We have reason to believe the chemical elements now on the earth and in the stars were formed from hydrogen by such a reaction in the past. Therefore, a study of the present chemical composition of these stars should provide important clues of conditions that existed in the earlier history of the universe—and we believe the 200-inch camera can assist those studies. With its fourfold increase in light-gathering power, the big mirror should open up many doors to this type of investigation—doors that were hitherto closed because of lack of light.

These are all important cosmic problems; the 200-inch camera on Palomar Mountain is a uniquely powerful instrument, and we have every reason to believe that it will make possible many major steps forward in our knowledge of the structure and history of the universe in which we live.

1947

ASTRONOMY AND SCIENTIFIC IDEAS *

HERBERT DINGLE

It is best not to try to visualise finite space. By exercising a strict abstemiousness of imagination we have hitherto accepted infinite space without question, although that too is beyond mental vision. It is scarcely logical to scorn finite space for a quality which its rival equally possesses, and it is not easy to see why there should be a universal instinctive tendency to do so. Possibly it is but one aspect of a general popular revolt against modern scientific concepts which, unlike their predecessors, are in general unpicturable by the imagination. Space, time, energy and the rest of them no longer correspond to the familiar notions we attach to those words, but are pure abstractions, having only a rational significance. We will not now labour this matter, but it is well to point out that if the modern scientist takes from the ordinary man (as well as from himself) the power to picture his concepts, he brings as substitute a far more precious gift—namely, the power to express them in terms of something which can be *done*. He displaces contemplation by action; he no longer says, "Look at this," but "Do this," and the new injunction removes the possibility of self-deception which was only too easily realised under the old.

The puzzled reader of modern astronomical paradoxes should therefore ask himself the question: "To what *operation* does this correspond?" and he can be perfectly sure that his question is capable of an intelligible and usually very simple answer. Let us ask it of finite space, and we shall get the following reply: What is meant by saying that space is finite is that if we travel about in it—taking, if we like, any compass we can devise to guide us always in a straight line—we shall find that if sufficient time is allowed we shall ultimately pass through familiar regions again. There will be a maximum distance to which we can travel from any specified body, such as the Earth, and when we are at that distance, no matter in what

* From *Science for a New World*, planned and arranged by Sir J. A. Thomson, edited by J. G. Crowther. Published by Harper & Brothers and reprinted with their permission.

direction we move we shall inevitably approach the body, just as any movement from the north pole of the Earth is toward the south pole. This statement of something which can be done is not a *consequence* of the conception of finite space; it *is* the conception of finite space. The question, "Why cannot we travel ever further from the body?" is meaningless for science, for science never asks, "Why?" in such an ultimate way as this. We might as well ask why apples fall to the ground and not away from it: it is not our business to inquire into such things, but merely to record that they do and how they do. The finitude of space, if actual, is a quality of nature, not a metaphysical doctrine.

Whether space is finite or infinite, however, its character is changing. If it is finite the change is accurately describable as "expansion": the sphere we spoke of is like a bladder undergoing inflation, so that points stationary on its surface are getting farther apart. This reveals itself to observation in one of the most remarkable facts of astronomy. It appears that the external galaxies—with very few exceptions, which can be satisfactorily accounted for—are receding from us at speeds proportional to their distances. Nebulae 43 million parsecs away are retreating at more than 12,000 miles a second, and greater distances, with correspondingly greater speeds, have recently been measured. The material universe is apparently being dissipated, and if the process continues unchecked, the time will come when, however greatly telescopic power may be improved, our own galaxy will be all that we can observe. We shall not lose that also, for the gravitational bond between its stars exceeds the effect of the scattering. It is only bodies at the enormous nebular distances that are bidding us farewell.

If our instinct is to ask, "How can space expand when there is nothing outside for it to expand into?" we must again remember that the idea must be interpreted in terms of operations only. Put somewhat graphically, it means this and nothing more: if we measure the greatest possible distance by which two bodies can be separated, we shall get a certain result; if we perform the same operation tomorrow we shall get a larger result. There is no need to court insanity by trying to imagine expansion into a vacuity which isn't there.

1934

ASTRONOMY

History and Bibliography

Armitage, A., *Sun, Stand Thou Still—The Life and Work of Copernicus the Astronomer* (New York, Henry Schuman, 1947).

Ball, Sir Robert, *Great Astronomers* (London, Isbister & Co., 1895).

Berry, Arthur, *A Short History of Astronomy* (New York, Charles Scribner's Sons, 1898).

Berry, Robert E., *Yankee Star-Gazer—Life of Nathaniel Bowditch* (New York, Whittlesey House, 1941).
Brashear, John A., *Autobiography*, edited by W. Lucien Scaife (New York, Am. Soc. Mech. Engineers, 1924).
Bryant, W. W., *A History of Astronomy* (New York, E. P. Dutton & Co., Inc., 1907).
Clerke, Mary A., *A Popular History of Astronomy During the Nineteenth Century* (London, A. & C. Black, 1905).
Dreyer, J. L. E., *History of the Planetary Systems from Thales to Kepler* (Cambridge, Cambridge University Press, 1906).
———, *Tycho Brahe, a Picture of Scientific Life and Work in the Sixteenth Century* (Edinburgh, A. & C. Black, 1890).
Ford, Edward, *David Rittenhouse, Astronomer-Patriot* (Philadelphia, University of Pennsylvania Press, 1946).
Gade, John Allyne, *The Life and Times of Tycho Brahe* (Princeton, Princeton University Press, 1947).
Harsanyi, Zsolt, *The Star-Gazer* (New York, G. P. Putnam's Sons, 1939).
Herschel, Sir John, *A Preliminary Discourse on the Study of Natural Philosophy* (London, Longmans, Green & Co., 1833).
Johnson, Francis R., *Astronomical Thought in Renaissance England* (Baltimore, The Johns Hopkins Press, 1937).
Lockyer, T. Mary, *Life and Work of Sir Norman Lockyer* (New York, The Macmillan Company, 1928).
Macpherson, Hector, *Modern Astronomy, Its Rise and Progress* (London, Oxford University Press, 1926).
Menon, C. P. S., *Early Astronomy and Cosmology* (London, Allen & Unwin, Ltd., 1932).
Newcomb, Simon, *The Reminiscences of an Astronomer* (Boston, Houghton Mifflin Company, 1903).
———, *Side Lights on Astronomy* (New York, Harper & Brothers, 1906).
Saile, Olaf, *Troubadour of the Stars: A Life of Kepler* (New York, O. Piest, 1940).
Shapley, Harlow, and Howarth, Helen, *Source Book in Astronomy* (New York, McGraw-Hill Book Company, Inc., 1929).
Williams, H. S., *The Great Astronomers* (New York, Simon & Schuster, Inc., 1930).

General

Baker, Robert H., *When the Stars Come Out* (New York, The Viking Press, 1934).
Bartky, Walter, *Highlights of Astronomy* (Chicago, University of Chicago Press, 1935).
Eddington, Sir A. S., *The Nature of the Physical World* (New York, The Macmillan Company, 1929).
Goldberg, Leo, and Aller, L. H., *Atoms, Stars and Nebulae* (Philadelphia, The Blakiston Company, 1943).
Jeans, Sir James, *Through Space and Time* (New York, The Macmillan Company, 1934).
———, *The Universe Around Us* (New York, The Macmillan Company, 1944).
Moulton, F. R., *Consider the Heavens* (New York, Doubleday & Co., 1935).
Noyes, Alfred, "Watchers of the Sky" (in *Torchbearers*, Vol. 1) (New York, Frederick A. Stokes Company, 1922).

ORCHARD, THOMAS N., *The Astronomy of Milton's Paradise Lost* (London, Longmans, Green & Co., 1896).

SERVISS, GARRETT P., *Astronomy with an Opera Glass* (New York, D. Appleton and Co., 1923).

The Solar System

DARWIN, G. H., *The Tides and Kindred Phenomena in the Solar System* (Boston, Houghton Mifflin Company, 1898).

FISHER, G. CLYDE, *The Story of the Moon* (New York, Doubleday & Co., Inc., 1943).

GAMOW, GEORGE, *The Birth and Death of the Sun* (New York, The Viking Press, 1940).

JONES, SIR H. S., *Life on Other Worlds* (New York, The Macmillan Company, 1940).

MITCHELL, S. A., *Eclipses of the Sun* (New York, Columbia University Press, 1935).

NININGER, H. H., *Our Stone-Pelted Planet* (Boston, Houghton Mifflin Company, 1933).

OLCOTT, WILLIAM T., *Sun-Lore of All Ages* (New York, G. P. Putnam's Sons, 1914).

OLIVIER, CHARLES P., *Comets* (Baltimore, The Williams & Wilkins Company, 1925).

———, *Meteors* (Baltimore, The Williams & Wilkins Company, 1925).

PROCTOR, MARY, *Romance of the Moon* (New York, Harper & Brothers, 1928).

RUSSELL, H. N., *The Solar System and Its Origin* (New York, The Macmillan Company, 1935).

STETSON, H. T., *Earth, Radio and the Stars* (New York, Whittlesey House, 1934).

———, *Sunspots in Action* (New York, The Ronald Press, 1947).

WATSON, F. G., *Between the Planets* (Philadelphia, The Blakiston Company, 1941).

WHIPPLE, FRED L., *Earth, Moon and Planets* (Philadelphia, The Blakiston Company, 1941).

The Stars

BARTON, S. G., and BARTON, W. H., JR., *A Guide to the Constellations* (New York, McGraw-Hill Book Company, Inc., 1943).

BOK, B. J., and BOK, P. F., *The Milky Way* (Philadelphia, The Blakiston Company, 1945).

CAMPBELL, LEON, and JACCHIA, LUIGI, *The Story of Variable Stars* (Philadelphia, The Blakiston Company, 1941).

DINGLE, HERBERT, *Modern Astrophysics* (New York, The Macmillan Company, 1927).

GAMOW, GEORGE, *Atomic Energy in Cosmic and Human Life* (New York, The Macmillan Company, 1946).

HALE, GEORGE E., *Signals from the Stars* (New York, Charles Scribner's Sons, 1931).

MERRILL, PAUL W., *The Nature of Variable Stars* (New York, The Macmillan Company, 1938).

OLCOTT, WILLIAM T., and PUTNAM, E. W., *Field Book of the Skies* (New York, G. P. Putnam's Sons, 1934).

OLCOTT, WILLIAM T., *Star Lore of all Ages* (New York, G. P. Putnam's Sons, 1911).

Nebulae

Eddington, Sir A. S., *The Expanding Universe* (New York, The Macmillan Company, 1933).

Hubble, Edwin P., *The Realm of the Nebulae* (New Haven, Yale University Press, 1936).

Shapley, Harlow, *Galaxies* (Philadelphia, The Blakiston Company, 1943).

Instruments and Applications

Bok, Bart J., and Wright, Frances W., *Basic Marine Navigation* (Boston, Houghton Mifflin Company, 1944).

Dimitroff, G. Z., and Baker, J. G., *Telescopes and Accessories* (Philadelphia, The Blakiston Company, 1945).

Ingalls, Albert G., editor, *Amateur Telescope Making* (New York, Munn & Co., 1935).

King, Edward S., *A Manual of Celestial Photography* (Boston, Eastern Science Supply Co., 1931).

Mixter, George W., *Primer of Navigation* (New York, D. Van Nostrand Company, Inc., 1944).

Pendray, George E., *Men, Mirrors and Stars* (New York, Harper & Brothers, 1946).

Wylie, Charles C., *Astronomy, Maps and Weather* (New York, Harper & Brothers, 1942).

III

GEOLOGY

In contrast to astronomy, geology is the youngest of the physical sciences. Historically it is the science of adventurers—of men like the one-armed Powell, who first made the perilous descent of the canyon of the Colorado; or Raphael Pumpelly, who explored in Japan, travelled up the Yangtse-Kiang and overland through Tartary and Siberia. The biographies of some of the early geologists make exciting reading.

But the actual foundations of geology were laid by a Scot, James Hutton, who was first a lawyer, then a physician, and finally a farmer. In 1785, he published his *Theory of the Earth* in which he showed that earth processes are still going on—mountains being uplifted, plateaus being eroded, sediment being laid down—and that through what goes on in the present, we have a clue to what went on in the past. No principle unfounded in observation was admitted. Earth history was removed from the realm of the miraculous. Another Scot, Sir Archibald Geikie, himself a great earth scientist, explains the importance of the theories of Hutton and his friend Playfair in "The Scottish Geologists." This doctrine of the evolution of the earth may be compared to Darwin's theory of the evolution of living things announced in the nineteenth century. Both bore the brunt of religious fanaticism which has had repercussions to this day. While few people nowadays believe that the earth is flat, the number who believe it was created literally in seven days is enormous. They refuse to believe the manifest proofs of an orderly design in the operations of nature.

Today geology is still the science of adventurers and explorers, but modern geologists have extended their operations to the laboratory. Three examples of their technique follow. In "Weighing the Earth," Paul R. Heyl, the man who performed the most recent work on the subject, tells how he applied mathematics and physics to the problem and why the results are important. In "X-Raying the Earth," Reginald A. Daly of Harvard also uses the principles of physics to determine the nature of a part of the earth which is forever hidden from direct observation. In "Earthquakes—What Are They?", Father Macelwane, an authority on the subject, explains how it would be impossible to understand these convulsions of the earth's crust without a knowledge of the nature and action of waves. Each of the three has depended for results on sciences other than his own specialty. And Claude E. ZoBell of the University of California has explained in "The Study of the Sea" how many sciences, physical and biological, are interrelated in oceanography.

As we turn to historical geology, W. O. Hotchkiss explains in "The Story of a Billion Years" how the theories of the Scottish geologists have been brought up to date. In his history of a Wisconsin mill pond, he makes graphic the whole story of sedimentation, tells us how fossils help give a connected picture of the past, and fixes chronologically the age of the dinosaurs and the days of prehistoric man.

What was the time scale of the events he describes? Geology has attempted an answer through measurement of strata of deposition. That attempt was incomplete. Now, through another science, a more elegant method of measuring geological time has been developed. Following on the work of Madame Curie, it has been discovered that the half-lives of the radioactive elements provide an accurate scale. Adolph Knopf of Yale reports how the computations are made in "The Geologic Records of Time."

As the earth cooled, mineral deposits were formed by fractional crystallization. Then, much later, as animal and vegetable life grew, died, and was deposited, coal and petroleum were formed under special conditions. C. C. Furnas gives us the outlines of the story in "The Formation of Mineral Deposits." Here is nature laying down the basic materials used in the great industries of the present.

So far, however, we have said little about how geologic conditions influence man and how he in turn influences them. Numerous books and articles have shown how man's wasteful treatment of his geologic heritage has destroyed past civilizations and may be in process of destroying our own. We have chosen to use a selection from one book which tells what, in at least one instance, is being done about it. In "TVA—Democracy on the March," David Lilienthal, formerly head of the Tennessee Valley Authority and now head of the American Atomic Energy Commission, explains how most of the sciences have been applied to reclaim the land we once destroyed. It is an illuminating study of the use of science for social ends.

Of the many individual sciences which comprise earth science, we explore one more in "What Makes the Weather," by Wolfgang Langewiesche. The science of meteorology has been revolutionized in recent times, and Langewiesche tells us of cold fronts and air masses, of the various airs that make American weather, and how the weather man analyzes them to give us results for our morning papers.

THE SCOTTISH GEOLOGISTS *

SIR ARCHIBALD GEIKIE

It was a fundamental doctrine of Hutton [James Hutton, 1726–1797] and his school that this globe has not always worn the aspect which it bears at present; that on the contrary, proofs may everywhere be culled that the land which we now see has been formed out of the wreck of an older land. Among these proofs, the most obvious are supplied by some of the more familiar kinds of rocks, which teach us that, though they are now portions of the dry land, they were originally sheets of gravel, sand, and mud, which had been worn from the face of long-vanished continents, and after being spread out over the floor of the sea were consolidated into compact stone, and were finally broken up and raised once more to form part of the dry land. This cycle of change involved two great systems of natural processes. On the one hand, men were taught that by the action of running water the materials of the solid land are in a state of continual decay and transport to the ocean. On the other hand, the ocean floor is liable from time to time to be upheaved by some stupendous internal force akin to that which gives rise to the volcano and the earthquake. Hutton further perceived that not only had the consolidated materials been disrupted and elevated, but that masses of molten rock had been thrust upward among them, and had cooled and crystallized in large bodies of granite and other eruptive rocks which form so prominent a feature on the earth's surface.

It was a special characteristic of this philosophical system that it sought in the changes now in progress on the earth's surface an explanation of those which occurred in older times. Its founder refused to invent causes or modes of operation, for those with which he was familiar seemed to him adequate to solve the problems with which he attempted to deal. Nowhere was the profoundness of his insight more astonishing than in the clear, definite way in which he proclaimed and reiterated his doctrine, that every part of the surface of the continents, from mountain top to seashore, is continually undergoing decay, and is thus slowly travelling to the sea. He saw that no sooner will the sea floor be elevated into new land than it must necessarily become a prey to this universal and unceasing degradation. He perceived that as the transport of disintegrated material is carried on chiefly by running water, rivers must slowly dig out for themselves the channels in which they flow, and thus that a system of valleys, radiating from the water parting of a country, must necessarily result from the descent of the streams from the mountain crests to the sea. He discerned that this ceaseless and wide-spread decay would eventually lead to the entire demolition of the dry land, but he contended that from time to time this

* Presidential Address before British Association for the Advancement of Science, 1892.

catastrophe is prevented by the operation of the under-ground forces, whereby new continents are upheaved from the bed of the ocean. And thus in his system a due proportion is maintained between land and water, and the condition of the earth as a habitable globe is preserved.

A theory of the earth so simple in outline, so bold in conception, so full of suggestion, and resting on so broad a base of observation and reflection, ought (we think) to have commanded at once the attention of men of science, even if it did not immediately awaken the interest of the outside world; but, as Playfair sorrowfully admitted, it attracted notice only very slowly, and several years elapsed before any one showed himself publicly concerned about it, either as an enemy or a friend. Some of its earliest critics assailed it for what they asserted to be its irreligious tendency,—an accusation which Hutton repudiated with much warmth. The sneer levelled by Cowper a few years earlier at all inquiries into the history of the universe was perfectly natural and intelligible from that poet's point of view. There was then a wide-spread belief that this world came into existence some six thousand years ago, and that any attempt greatly to increase that antiquity was meant as a blow to the authority of Holy Writ. So far, however, from aiming at the overthrow of orthodox beliefs, Hutton evidently regarded his "Theory" as an important contribution in aid of natural religion. He dwelt with unfeigned pleasure on the multitude of proofs which he was able to accumulate of an orderly design in the operations of Nature, decay and renovation being so nicely balanced as to maintain the habitable condition of the planet. But as he refused to admit the predominance of violent action in terrestrial changes, and on the contrary contended for the efficacy of the quiet, continuous processes which we can even now see at work around us, he was constrained to require an unlimited duration of past time for the production of those revolutions of which he perceived such clear and abundant proofs in the crust of the earth. The general public, however, failed to comprehend that the doctrine of the high antiquity of the globe was not inconsistent with the comparatively recent appearance of man,—a distinction which seems so obvious now.

Hutton died in 1797, beloved and regretted by the circle of friends who had learned to appreciate his estimable character and to admire his genius, but with little recognition from the world at large. Men knew not then that a great master had passed away from their midst, who had laid broad and deep the foundations of a new science; that his name would become a household word in after generations, and that pilgrims would come from distant lands to visit the scenes from which he drew his inspiration. . . .

Clear as was the insight and sagacious the inferences of the great masters [of the Edinburgh school] in regard to the history of the globe, their vision was necessarily limited by the comparatively narrow range of ascertained fact which up to their time had been established. They taught men to recognize that the present world is built of the ruins of an earlier one, and they explained with admirable perspicacity the operation of the processes whereby the degradation and renovation of land are brought about. But they never dreamed that a long and orderly series of such successive destructions and renewals had taken place and had left their records in the crust of the earth. They never imagined that from these records it would be possible to establish a determinate chronology that could be read everywhere and applied to the elucidation of the remotest quarter of the globe. It was by the memorable observations and generalizations of William Smith that this vast extension of our knowledge of the past history of the earth became possible. While the Scottish philosophers were building up their theory here, Smith was quietly ascertaining by extended journeys that the stratified rocks of the west of England occur in a definite sequence, and that each well-marked group of them can be discriminated from the others and identified across the country by means of its inclosed organic remains. It is nearly a hundred years since he made known his views, so that by a curious coincidence we may fitly celebrate on this occasion the centenary of William Smith as well as that of James Hutton. No single discovery has ever had a more momentous and far-reaching influence on the progress of a science than that law of organic succession which Smith established. At first it served merely to determine the order of the stratified rocks of England. But it soon proved to possess a world-wide value, for it was found to furnish the key to the structure of the whole stratified crust of the earth. It showed that within that crust lie the chronicles of a long history of plant and animal life upon this planet, it supplied the means of arranging the materials for this history in true chronological sequence, and it thus opened out a magnificent vista through a vast series of ages, each marked by its own distinctive types of organic life, which, in proportion to their antiquity, departed more and more from the aspect of the living world.

Thus a hundred years ago, by the brilliant theory of Hutton and the fruitful generalization of Smith, the study of the earth received in our country the impetus which has given birth to the modern science of geology. . . .

Fresh life was now breathed into the study of the earth. A new spirit seemed to animate the advance along every pathway of inquiry. Facts that had long been familiar came to possess a wider and deeper meaning when their connection with each other was recognized as parts of one great harmonious system of continuous change. In no department of Nature, for example, was this broader vision more remarkably displayed than in that wherein the circulation of water between land and sea plays the most conspicuous part. From the earliest times men had watched the coming of clouds, the fall of rain, the flow of rivers, and had recognized that on this nicely adjusted machinery the beauty and fertility of the land depend. But they now learned that this beauty and fertility involve a continual decay of the terrestrial surface; that the soil is a measure of this decay, and would cease to afford us maintenance were it not continually removed and renewed, that through the ceaseless transport of soil by rivers to the sea the face of the land is slowly lowered in level and carved into mountain and valley, and that the materials thus borne outwards to the floor of the ocean are not lost, but accumulate there to form rocks, which in the end will be upraised into new lands. Decay and renovation, in well-balanced proportions, were thus shown to be the system on which the existence of the earth as a habitable globe had been established. It was impossible to conceive that the economy of the planet could be maintained on any other basis. Without the circulation of water the life of plants and animals would be impossible, and with the circulation the decay of the surface of the land and the renovation of its disintegrated materials are necessarily involved.

As it is now, so must it have been in past time. Hutton and Playfair pointed to the stratified rocks of the earth's crust as demonstrations that the same processes which are at work to-day have been in operation from a remote antiquity. . . .

Obviously, however, human experience, in the few centuries during which attention has been turned to such subjects, has been too brief to warrant any dogmatic assumption that the various natural processes must have been carried on in the past with the same energy and at the same rate as they are carried on now. . . . It was an error to take for granted that no other kind of process or influence, nor any variation in the rate of activity save those of which man has had actual cognizance, has played a part in the terrestrial economy. The uniformitarian writers laid themselves open to the charge of maintaining a kind of perpetual motion in the machinery of Nature. They could find in the records of the earth's history no evidence of a beginning, no prospect of an end. . . .

The discoveries of William Smith, had they been adequately understood, would have been seen to offer a corrective to this rigidly uniformitarian conception, for they revealed that the crust of the earth contains the long record of an unmistakable order of progression in organic types. They proved that plants and animals have varied widely in successive periods of the earth's history; the present condition of organic life being only the latest phase of a long preceding series, each stage of which recedes further from the existing aspect of things as we trace it backward into the past. And though no relic had yet been found, or indeed was ever likely to be found, of the first living things that appeared upon the earth's surface, the manifest simplification of types in the older formations pointed irresistibly to some beginning from which the long procession has taken its start. If then it could thus be demonstrated that there had been upon the globe an orderly march of living forms from the lowliest grades in early times to man himself to-day, and thus that in one department of her domain, extending through the greater portion of the records of the earth's history, Nature had not been uniform, but had followed a vast and noble plan of evolution, surely it might have been expected that those who discovered and made known this plan would seek to ascertain whether some analogous physical progression from a definite beginning might not be discernible in the framework of the globe itself.

But the early masters of the science labored under two great disadvantages. In the first place, they found the oldest records of the earth's history so broken up and effaced as to be no longer legible. And in the second place, . . . they considered themselves bound to search for facts, not to build up theories; and as in the crust of the earth they could find no facts which threw any light upon the primeval constitution and subsequent development of our planet, they shut their ears to any theoretical interpretations that might be offered from other departments of science. . . .

What the more extreme members of the uniformitarian school failed to perceive was the absence of all evidence that terrestrial catastrophes even on a colossal scale might not be a part of the present economy of this globe. Such occurrences might never seriously affect the whole earth at one time, and might return at such wide intervals that no example of them has yet been chronicled by man. But that they have occurred again and again, and even within comparatively recent geological times, hardly admits of serious doubt. . . .

As the most recent and best known of these great transformations, the Ice Age stands out conspicuously before us. . . . There can not be any doubt that after man had become a denizen of the earth, a great physical change came over the Northern hemisphere. The climate, which had previously been so mild that evergreen trees flourished within ten or twelve degrees of the North Pole, now became so severe that vast sheets of snow and ice covered the north of Europe and crept southward beyond the south coast of Ireland, almost as far as the southern shores of England, and across the Baltic into France and Germany. This Arctic transformation was not an episode that lasted merely a few seasons, and left the land to resume thereafter its ancient aspect. With various successive fluctuations it must have endured for many thousands of years. When it began to disappear it probably faded away as slowly and imperceptibly as it had advanced, and when it finally vanished it left Europe and North America profoundly changed in the character alike of their scenery and of their inhabitants. The rugged rocky contours of earlier times were ground smooth and polished by the march of the ice across them, while the lower grounds were buried under wide and thick sheets of clay, gravel, and sand, left behind by the melting ice. The varied and abundant flora which had spread so far within the Arctic circle was driven away into more southern and less ungenial climes. But most memorable of all was the extirpation of the prominent large animals which, before the advent of the ice, had roamed over Europe. The lions, hyenas, wild horses, hippopotamuses, and other creatures either became entirely extinct or were driven into the Mediterranean basin and into Africa. In their place came northern forms—the reindeer, glutton, musk ox, wooly rhinoceros, and mammoth.

Such a marvellous transformation in climate, in scenery, in vegetation and in inhabitants, within what was after all but a brief portion of geological time, though it may have involved no sudden or violent convulsion, is surely entitled to rank as a catastrophe in the history of the globe. It was probably brought about mainly if not entirely by the operation of forces external to the earth. No similar calamity having befallen the continents within the time during which man has been recording his experience, the Ice Age might be cited as a contradiction to the doctrine of uniformity. And yet it manifestly arrived as part of the established order of Nature. Whether or not we grant that other ice ages preceded the last great one, we must admit that the conditions under which it arose, so far as we know them, might conceivably have occurred before and may occur again. The various agencies called into play by the extensive refrigeration of the Northern hemisphere were not different from those with which we are familiar. Snow fell and glaciers crept as they do to-day. Ice scored and polished rocks exactly as it still does among the Alps and in Norway. There was nothing abnormal in the phenomena, save the scale on which they were manifested. And thus, taking a broad view of the whole subject, we recognize the catastrophe, while at the same time we see in its progress the operation of those same natural processes which we know to be integral parts of the machinery whereby the surface of the earth is continually transformed.

Among the debts which science owes to the Huttonian school, not the least memorable is the promulgation of the first well-founded conceptions of the high antiquity of the globe. Some six thousand years had previously been believed to comprise the whole life of the planet, and indeed of the entire universe. When the curtain was then first raised that had veiled the history of the earth, and men, looking beyond the brief span within which they had supposed that history to have been transacted, beheld the records of a long vista of ages stretching far away into a dim illimitable past, the prospect vividly impressed their imagination. Astronomy had made known the immeasurable fields of space; the new science of geology seemed now to reveal boundless distances of time. . . .

The universal degradation of the land, so notable a characteristic of the earth's surface, has been regarded as an extremely slow process. Though it goes on without ceasing, yet from century to century it seems to leave hardly any perceptible trace on the landscapes of a country. Mountains and plains, hills and valleys appear to wear the same familiar aspect which is indicated in the oldest pages of history. This obvious slowness in one of the most important departments of geological activity doubtless contributed in large measure to form and foster a vague belief in the vastness of the antiquity required for the evolution of the earth.

But, as geologists eventually came to perceive, the rate of degradation of the land is capable of actual measurement. The amount of material worn away from the surface of any drainage basin and carried in the form of mud, sand, or gravel, by the main river into the sea represents the extent to which that surface has been lowered by waste in any given period of time. But denudation and deposition must be equivalent to each other. As much material must be laid down in sedimentary accumulations as has been mechanically removed, so that in measuring the annual bulk of sediment borne into the sea by a river, we obtain a clue not only to the rate of denudation of the land, but also to the rate at which the deposition of new sedimentary formations take place. . . .

But in actual fact the testimony in favor of the slow accumulation and high antiquity of the geological record is much stronger than might be inferred from the mere thickness of the stratified formations. These sedimentary deposits have not been laid down in one unbroken sequence, but have had their continuity interrupted again and again by upheaval and depression. So fragmentary are they in some regions that we can easily demonstrate the length of time represented there by still existing sedimentary strata to be vastly less than the time indicated by the gaps in the series.

There is yet a further and impressive body of evidence furnished by the successive races of plants and animals which have lived upon the earth and have left their remains sealed up within its rocky crust. No universal destructions of organic life are chronicled in the stratified rocks. It is everywhere admitted that, from the remotest times up to the present day, there has been an onward march of development, type succeeding type in one long continuous progression. As to the rate of this evolution precise data are wanting. There is, however, the important negative argument furnished by the absence of evidence of recognizable specific variations of organic forms since man began to observe and record. We know that within human experience a few species have become extinct, but there is no conclusive proof that a single new species have come into existence, nor are appreciable variations readily apparent in forms that live in a wild state. The seeds and plants found with Egyptian mummies, and the flowers and fruits depicted on Egyptian tombs, are easily identified with the vegetation of modern Egypt. The embalmed bodies of animals found in that country show no sensible divergence from the structure or proportions of the same animals at the present day. The human races of Northern Africa and Western Asia were already as distinct when portrayed by the ancient Egyptian artists as they are now, and they do not seem to have undergone any perceptible change since then. Thus a lapse of four or five thousand years has not been accompanied by any recognizable variation in such forms of plant and animal life as can be tendered in evidence. Absence of sensible change in these instances is, of course, no proof that considerable alteration may not have been accomplished in other forms more exposed to vicissitudes of climate and other external influences. But it furnishes at least a presumption in favor of the extremely tardy progress of organic variation.

If, however, we extend our vision beyond the narrow range of human history, and look at the remains of the plants and animals preserved in those younger formations which, though recent when regarded as parts of the whole geological record, must be many thousands of years older than the very oldest of human monuments, we encounter the most impressive proofs of the persistence of specific forms. Shells which lived in our seas before the coming of the Ice Age present the very same peculiarities of form, structure, and ornament which their descendants still possess. The lapse of so enormous an interval of time has not sufficed seriously to modify them. So too with the plants and the higher animals which still survive. Some forms have become extinct, but few or none which remain display any transitional gradations into new species. We must admit that such transitions have occurred, that indeed they have been in progress ever since organized existence began upon our planet, and are doubtless taking place now. But we can not detect them on the way, and we feel constrained to believe that their march must be excessively slow. . . .

If the many thousands of years which have elapsed since the Ice Age have produced no appreciable modification of surviving plants and animals, how vast a period must have been required for that marvellous scheme of organic development which is chronicled in the rocks! . . .

I have reserved for final consideration a branch of the history of the earth which, while it has become, within the lifetime of the present generation, one of the most interesting and fascinating departments of geological inquiry, owed its first impulse to the far-seeing intellects of Hutton and Playfair. With the penetration of genius these illustrious teachers perceived that if the broad masses of land and the great chains of mountains owe their origin to stupendous movements which from time to time have convulsed the earth, their details of contour must be mainly due to the eroding power of running water. They recognized that as the surface of the land is continually worn down, it is essentially by a process of sculpture that the physiognomy of every country has been developed, valleys being hollowed out and hills left standing, and that these inequalities in topographical detail are only varying and local accidents in the progress of the one great process of the degradation of the land.

From the broad and guiding outlines of theory thus sketched we have now advanced amid ever-widening multiplicity of detail into a fuller and nobler conception of the origin of scenery. The law of evolution is written as legibly on the landscapes of the earth as on any other page of the book of Nature. Not only do we recognize that the existing topography of the continents, instead of being primeval in origin, has gradually been developed after many precedent mutations, but we are enabled to trace these earlier revolutions in the structure of every hill and glen. Each mountain chain is thus found to be memorial of many successive stages in geographical evolution. Within certain limits land and sea have changed places again and again. Volcanoes have broken out and have become extinct in many countries long before the advent of man. Whole tribes of plants and animals have meanwhile come and gone, and in leaving their remains behind them as monuments at once of the slow development of organic types, and of the prolonged vicissitudes of the terrestrial surface, have furnished materials for a chronological arrangement of the earth's topographical features. Nor is it only from the organisms of former epochs that broad generalizations may be drawn regarding revolutions in geography. The living plants and animals of to-day have been discovered to be eloquent of ancient geographical features that have long since vanished. In their distribution they tell us that climates have changed; that islands have been disjoined from continents; that oceans once untied have been divided from each other, or once separate have now been joined; that some tracts of land have disappeared, while others for prolonged periods of time have remained in isolation. The present and the past are thus linked together, not merely by dead matter, but by the world of living things, into one vast system of continuous progression.

1892

WEIGHING THE EARTH *

PAUL R. HEYL

Have you ever wondered, when you have seen men excavating the cellar of a building and taking away the earth a ton at a time, how many tons there might be in the whole earth? Scientific men are the greatest wonderers to be found anywhere, and they have not only asked themselves this question (there was no one else to ask) but they have devised experiments to give the answer. It is, of course, a very large figure; about six thousand million million million tons; six followed by twenty-one ciphers. The number is really known a little more accurately than that; the first three figures are known, if any one should need them, and experiments are now in progress at the Bureau of Standards which, if all goes well, will give the fourth figure.

But why should any one need to know this number at all? Of what possible use can it be to anybody?

There are two answers to this question.

In the first place, a knowledge of the mass of the earth is of interest to

* Reprinted by permission of *The Scientific Monthly*. Copyright 1925 by The Science Press.

astronomers, for it is a starting point from which are obtained the masses of the moon and of the sun and of the other planets of the solar system. Our earth, therefore, is a natural standard of reference with which other quantities are compared; and it is the business of the Bureau of Standards to determine such fundamental reference quantities as accurately as possible.

In the second place, a knowledge of the earth's mass enables us to learn something about the interior of the earth, that region about which so much imaginative literature has been written, and which no one can ever hope to investigate directly. From the earth's mass we can calculate its density, that is, the number of times it is heavier than an equal globe of water; and this leads us to a rather remarkable conclusion.

The various rock materials which make up the outer layer of the earth, which are accessible to test and measure, turn out to have an average density between two and three times that of water, while, curiously enough, the figure for the earth as a whole comes out about twice this value. The inference is obvious: the core of the earth must be composed of something much heavier than the outer crust.

What can it be?

For this question, too, it is possible to find an answer. Several lines of argument, including the speed of travel of earthquake waves, the phenomena of terrestrial magnetism and some others, have led those who have given most attention to the subject to the strange conclusion that the core of the earth is a great ball of iron!

Occasionally there fall to the earth bodies called meteorites, which are often composed of metallic iron, sometimes with a stony admixture. These strange bodies seem to be floating about in space, and occasionally one of them comes near enough to the earth to be drawn in by its attraction. The idea is that the earth is like a great meteorite, or the result of the accretion or massing together of many such particles, in which process the heavier iron portions have gone to the center by virtue of their own weight, or attraction for each other, while the lighter stony portions formed the surface layers. The meteorites that fall to earth may thus be regarded as chips left over or unused portions of material.

So much comes out of an apparently dry and abstruse determination of a numerical constant of nature!

How is the earth weighed? Like many other scientific measurements, this operation is carried out by a roundabout process.

The first thing to do is to set up a miniature system representing the earth and a body near its surface, and determine by experiment the actual force of attraction between these bodies. This force depends on several things: in the first place, on the masses of the bodies, greater bodies attracting each other with more force than smaller ones; and second, on the distance between their centers, bodies attracting more strongly the closer they are together. All these quantities are measured in the miniature system: the masses of the two bodies, their distance from each other and the force of attraction between them.

In the actual case of the earth and a body on its surface, we can measure all but one of the quantities involved. We can weigh the small body and thus determine the force with which the earth attracts it. We can determine by the same operation the mass of the small body, and we know the distance from its center to the center of the earth. What we do not know is the mass of the earth. But by applying the results of our miniature experiment, in which every quantity was known, and solving a problem in proportion, we can calculate the mass of the earth.

The most difficult part of this experiment is to determine the force of attraction between the miniature earth and the small body attracted by it. Even with a mass of steel weighing 140 pounds (which is used in the arrangement employed in the experiment now in progress at the Bureau of Standards) and a ball of gold weighing an ounce and a half the force is measurable only in millionths of a grain, in metric units, about a thousandth of a milligram.

To determine this very small force with the necessary precision an arrangement called a torsion pendulum is used. A light rod of aluminum about eight inches long is hung by a very fine filament of tungsten at its center. This filament is such as is used in incandescent lamps. The rod hangs in a horizontal position and carries at each end a gold ball. The rod swings very slowly back and forth in a small arc, with a time of swing of about half an hour. So delicate is this arrangement that a very small force applied to the balls will perceptibly alter its time of swing.

The swinging system is enclosed in an airtight case from which the air is exhausted. This eliminates trouble from air currents which might disturb the swing and also allows the system to swing for a long time before coming to rest.

Outside this case the two large steel masses are placed, at first as close as possible to the gold balls inside. In this position the time of swing of the torsion pendulum is measured. The steel cylinders are now moved as far away as possible from the balls and the time of swing again measured. Due to the diminished attraction of the steel masses for the gold balls at the greater distance, the time of swing is now found to be about five minutes greater. From observations such as these the actual force of attraction between the steel cylinders and the gold balls can be calculated.

So delicate is a well-arranged torsion pendulum of this character that the presence of a person within ten feet of it will alter its time of swing because of the attraction of the person's body for the gold balls; or if a car is driven up outside the laboratory and parked the torsion pendulum will indicate its attraction. To avoid disturbances of this nature the apparatus is set up in a room thirty-five feet underground, where all moving masses are overhead, and have no effect on the pendulum.

This is not the first time the earth has been weighed. By the use of apparatus similar to that which has just been described this experiment has been conducted several times in the past century, with results of increasing precision as the technique of laboratory practice has gradually been perfected. No work of this kind has been done for a generation, and it has been thought that sufficient progress has been made in that time to warrant the attempt to obtain another figure of the weight of the earth.

About thirty years ago a piece of work of this kind was performed which has about it so much of human interest that it may be told here profitably.

As has often happened, two men worked on this experiment at the same time without knowing of each other's doings. One of them was a British scientific man, Professor Boys, who worked with the best facilities that London and Oxford University could furnish him. He spent several years at the task and obtained what was believed to be the most accurate figure obtained up to that time.

While he was doing this, another man, of whom Professor Boys had never heard, was working at the same problem hundreds of miles away in Bohemia. This man was Dr. Karl Braun, who had been a Jesuit teacher of physics all his life. At an advanced age he retired from teaching and was sent to a monastery in the mountains of Bohemia to end his days peacefully and quietly. But Dr. Braun could not content himself in inactivity, and for something to do set up an apparatus in his cell in the monastery and determined the weight of the earth. His result, when published, was almost exactly that obtained by Professor Boys.

Much of Dr. Braun's apparatus was made by himself. It is noteworthy that he was the first person to use a vacuum about his torsion pendulum with success. Professor Boys, in his published paper, said that he believed the use of a high vacuum to be impracticable.

Professor Boys could hardly credit Dr. Braun's achievement, and made the long trip to Bohemia to see him. He found Dr. Braun, at that time over eighty years old, planning a repetition of his work to eliminate some errors which he had recognized. Unfortunately, he did not live to do this.

A few years later, Dr. Burgess, the present director of the Bureau of Standards, carried out an experiment of this nature involving several novel features at the Sorbonne in Paris. He did not, however, succeed in improving upon the figure obtained by Boys and Braun. Since that date no work has been done on the question, until it was taken up again, under the auspices of Dr. Burgess, at the Bureau of Standards.

Nothing, it would seem, is too large or too small for men to attempt to weigh and measure. In this experiment that I have just described to you both extremes are to be found. The enormous mass of the earth is determined by measuring a force so small that only the most delicate pendulum known will detect it.

The enormous distances from the earth to the sun or to the stars do not appal the mind of man; neither do the inconceivably minute quantities involved in the study of the structure of atoms. Anything that exists is a fit object for study, no matter how large, no matter how small. Man may be but the merest speck in the universe, yet in his intelligent comprehension of it he is but little lower than the angels.

It is said that at one time an astronomer discovered a new star, which appeared to be approaching the earth with a great velocity. Night after night he studied it, finally becoming convinced that it was destined to strike the earth. He calculated that this would happen within a few years. Night after night he watched this approaching doom, fascinated by it. He did not announce his discovery, fearing to witness the orgy of lawlessness and despair into which it might plunge the world.

One night he spoke aloud and addressed the star as follows:

> I know that you will soon destroy me and all things living. I can calculate the day, nay, even the hour when this will happen. Yet you are but a blind, brute thing, and I would not change places with you!

1925

X-RAYING THE EARTH *

REGINALD A. DALY

Reality is never skin-deep. The true nature of the earth and its full wealth of hidden treasures cannot be argued from the visible rocks, the rocks upon which we live and out of which we make our living. The face of the earth, with its upstanding continents and depressed ocean-deeps, its vast ornament of plateau and mountain-chain, is molded by structure and process in hidden depths.

During the nineteenth century the geologists, a mere handful among the world's workers, studied the rocks at the surface, the accessible skin of the globe. They established many principal points in our planet's history. While with the astronomers space was deepening, a million years became for the rock-men the unit of time with which to outline earth's dramatic story. Thus, incidentally, the way was opened for the doctrine of organic evolution, demanding hundreds of millions of years, to become secured science rather than mere speculation. The first, main jobs of the geologist were to map the exposures of the rocks at the surface of the earth-skin or "crust," to distinguish the kinds and relative ages of the rocks, to gather the many facts that must be accounted for in the final explanation of continent, ocean, plateau, and mountain range. Yet the century closed without having dis-

* Reprinted by permission from *The Harvard Alumni Bulletin*, October 18, 1928, as corrected by the author, 1947.

closed clearly defined origins for these and of many another form and structure of the earth's surface and "crust." With increasing clearness geologists became convinced, however, that the main secret of highland and lowland, dry land and deep ocean, Himalaya and Mediterranean, barren rock and ore-bearing rock, must be sought in the invisible, the deep underground of the earth.

The nineteenth century bequeathed to the twentieth an outstanding responsibility—to invent and use new methods of exploring the earth's body far beyond the reach of direct penetration by the geologist's eye or by mine and bore-hole. What is the nature of the materials below the visible rocks? How are those materials arranged? What energies are stored in the globe, ready to do geological work when the occasion comes? Where is the earth's body strong, truly solid, able to bear loads indefinitely? Where is it weak, so weak as to permit movements of the material horizontally and vertically, under the urge of moderate internal pressures?

These questions represent fundamentals of the new earth-lore, already rapidly growing in our own century as investigators continue to employ new methods of research. The problems are largely matters for the physicist, but an unusual kind of physicist, one who makes experiments, like any of his fellows, but keeps thinking of a whole planet. He is an earth-physicist, a "geophysicist." The interpretation of messages from the earth's interior demands all the resources of ordinary physics and of extraordinary mathematics. The geophysicist is of a noble company, all of whom are reading messages from the untouchable reality of things. The inwardness of things —atoms, crystals, mountains, planets, stars, nebulas, universes—is the quarry of these hunters of genius and Promethean boldness. The unseen atom has been shown to be no less miraculous than the invisible interior of sun or star. And now, lately, the inner earth as a whole is the gripping subject of research for some of the intellectual giants of our time. To a considerable extent the methods used by all these students of the invisible, the essence of each problem, are in principle the same.

The feature common to most of the productive methods is the use of waves, vibrations, rhythmic motions. From the interior of star or nebula come light-waves, heat-waves, and whole troops of different unfelt waves. Each of these waves, whatever its nature, radiates through the "ether." With the speed of light, each rushes along lines that are always perpendicular to the front of the wave. These lines are the wave-paths or "rays" of the astrophysicist. In the exploration of the universe of stars, he uses light-rays, actinic rays, heat-rays, and cosmic rays of less familiar kinds. The exquisite internal architecture of crystals is being rapidly revealed with X-rays. The atom is becoming understood through its radiant effects and through experimental tests with external rays.

So it is with the new study of the earth; its profounder exploration is possible by means of waves, which may be of either natural or artificial origin. Waves extremely short, as measured from "crest" to "crest," are the X-rays, used in learning the atomic architecture of crystals. The somewhat longer waves of light tell us about the nature of stars. The still longer sound waves are now used to give the depths of the invisible ocean-floor. "Radio" waves, yet longer, are telling the aerologists much about the nature of the inaccessible upper atmosphere. For the study of the earth's skin, to the depths of a score of miles or so, the controlled shocks by artificial explosives, which give elastic waves longer than even "radio" waves, are used. Longest of all are the elastic waves set going when the hammer of the deadly earthquake strikes. Man is learning to harness for his inquiring use the very wrath of the earth; the tremblings of our vibrant globe are used to "X-ray" the deep interior.

When with his hands one bends a stick until it breaks, the sudden snap sends vibrations, often painful, along muscle, bone, and nerve of the arms. The "strain" of the stick is relieved by fracture, and the elastic energy accumulated in the stick during the bending is largely converted into the energy of wave-motion. In a somewhat similar way the rocks of the earth's crust have been, and now are being, strained; every day, somewhere, they are snapping and sending out elastic waves from one or more centers. The passage of these waves in the earth we call an earthquake, a seismic disturbance.

Each heavy shock creates waves of several kinds. The kind which travels fastest is like a sound wave: it is propagated by the alternation of compression and rarefaction in the rocks. The particles of the rocks here vibrate to and fro, in the direction of wave motion, that is, along the wave-path or wave "ray." Waves of this type, technically called longitudinal waves, can pass from rock into the fluid of ocean, lake, or atmosphere, and if the vibrations are frequent enough, are heard with the unaided ear. Somewhat slower is a second kind of wave which follows nearly the same path in the rocks, but is distinguished by the fact that now the rock-particles vibrate at right angles to the direction of propagation. Waves of the second type, called transverse waves, are analogous to waves of light. Unlike the latter, however, the transverse seismic waves are propagated in solids only and cannot pass through a liquid or gas.

These two kinds of waves, longitudinal and transverse, each radiating from the center of shock, correspond after a fashion to the X-rays used by the surgeon for exploring the deep inside of the human body. Similarly, the deep inside of the earth is being explored with the two kinds of seismic (earthquake) waves, waves whose diverging paths, or "rays," plunge right down into the vast interior of the globe and emerge, with their messages, thousands of miles from the center of shock. The longitudinal waves emerge even at the antipodes.

A major earthquake has enormous energy. At and near the center of shock it shatters the works of man and may rupture the very hills and mountain-sides. As each wave-front spreads into the earth, the intensity of the vibration falls very rapidly, so that a few hundreds of miles from the center the heaviest shock cannot be felt by a human being. Much less can he, at the "other side" of the globe, feel the impact of a wave which has plunged to a depth of a thousand miles or more and emerges under his feet.

In order to watch and time accurately each wave, as its ray emerges on the "other side," highly sensitive instruments are used. These wonderful instruments, called seismographs, magnify the motion of the vibrating rock and give a written record, or "graph," of that motion. They form the main equipment of seismographic stations. The mechanical or photographic record of a distant shock is the seismogram, a kind of hieroglyphic message from the mysterious heart of the planet. Each seismogram from a strong earthquake is a long, complex curve traced up and down on the registering paper of the seismograph. Usually the impulses of the longitudinal and transverse waves are evident to the expert seismologist, but in every case he finds represented much more than these two simple kinds of motion. He sees, in fact, a whole train of waves, which came racing out of the earth, often for much more than an hour after the first impulse was registered. A generation ago, most of the complex message could not be read. Then seismologists bethought themselves of a Rosetta stone.

Observation and theory soon showed that earthquake waves are closely analogous to the familiar waves of sound and light. Like these, the seismic rays are reflected and refracted at surfaces between different kinds of material. Seismic rays, during their passage through the earth, are broken up and dispersed, just as the sun's light is dispersed, in prism or rain drop, to make the glory of the rainbow. Seismic rays are diffracted, just as light rays are diffracted, at the interfaces of contrasted materials. As sound travels faster in water than in air, faster in rock than in either, so seismic waves travel faster in some kinds of rock than in other kinds. Long study of sound and light has led to the discovery of the laws of wave-motion, and these have made increasingly clear the meaning of seismograms. The analogy with sound and light is the Rosetta stone.

The discovery of the famous original enabled Napoleon's experts to begin the reading of Egypt's ancient literature. In like manner the seismologists, using the difficult but manageable Greek of modern physics, are beginning the task of making earthquakes tell the nature of the earth's interior and translating into significant speech the hieroglyphics written by the seismograph. It is a long task, requiring high intelligence and the patient accumulation of earthquake data from all parts of the globe, from ocean basin as well as from continent. The work is only just begun; yet the results already obtained are of supreme interest to the philosopher, to the geologist, and to the producer of petroleum, metals, and other materials from the rocks.

For here, too, the man of pure science, the seismologist, "fussing with experiments of no use to anyone," has proved to be another goose that has laid a golden egg. The methods developed by the worker in another "pure" science, seismology, are now, with the help of artificial earthquakes, locating structures that lead to hidden deposits of oil. So, millions are to be saved in the cost of bore-holes, and new oil, probably by the hundreds of millions of barrels, will be added to the world supply. With electrical, magnetic, and gravitational methods—all products of the "unpractical" man of "pure" science—valuable indications of hidden metal-bearing ores are secured, and the expense of exploration by bore-holes and shafts is greatly reduced. Seismological methods promise to be adaptable to this kind of detective work. Conquering the difficulties that still remain, future research should make this branch of geophysics, even in the search after metals, pay for its upkeep many times over.

The depths of the ocean are now being quickly and accurately measured by the echo of sound waves from the bottom of the sea. This method, incomparably more rapid and less expensive than the old one by sounding-line, is based on a principle fundamental in seismology. With variation of detail, "sonic" sounding, the use of waves reflected from underlying rock, is employed to measure the thickness of glaciers.

Thus, the Hintereisferner glacier of the Alps has recently been proved to be 830 feet thick in the middle. When, with the similar use of explosion-shocks and the seismograph, the thickness of the Antarctic and Greenland ice-caps are measured, we shall have precious data for guiding thought on the conditions of North America and Europe during the Glacial period. Furthermore, we could then estimate how far the sea-level was everywhere lowered when the water of these ice-caps was abstracted from the ocean and piled up, solid, on the land.

But from depths far greater than glacier-floor, ocean-floor, or mineral deposit come the messages from nature's earthquakes. A few illustrations of success in detecting the anatomy of a planet will show the real majesty of the questions and answers that already inspire the all-too-few workers in the new science of geophysics.

One of the outstanding seismological discoveries of recent years is the shelled character of our planet. At the center, and outwards to a little more than one-half of its radius, the earth is homogeneous in high degree. This so-called "core" is surrounded by successive shells or layers of material. Each shell, out to a level about thirty miles from the surface, is relatively homogeneous, and its material differs from that of the shell above or below, as well as from the material of the central core. The contacts between the shells and between the deepest shell and the core are technically called "discontinuities."

The discontinuity, or break of material, at the surface of the core is one of the most remarkable of all. It is located at a level about 1,800 miles below the earth's surface, nearly 2,200 miles from its center. A second principal break, found only under the continents and larger islands—and thus representing only parts of a complete earth-shell—is situated at the average depth of about 25 miles. Other discontinuities, limiting complete shells of the earth's body, have been reported at depths of about 75 miles, 250 miles, 750 miles, and 1,100 miles. All of these four breaks require further study. Their estimated depths may be somewhat changed, and other discontinuities may be discovered, but it is already clear in a general way how the earth is constituted—layer on layer. There is good evidence that the core and layers described are composed of matter which increases in density as the depth increases. Hence, so far as the great body of the earth is concerned, it is built stable.

The velocity of the longitudinal wave in the earth's core has been measured. The value obtained is appropriate to that of the metallic iron of the meteorites. However, the velocity is lower than that expected if the core iron were crystalline and solid, like the iron of our museum meteorites. The velocity of the longitudinal wave suggests, rather, that the core iron is fluid. In agreement with this conclusion, the slower, transverse wave seems not to be propagated through the core; we have learned that the transverse wave cannot persist in a fluid. If further research corroborates this tentative deduction by seismologists, a whole set of new, fascinating problems is opened up.

One question is that of temperature. The pressure on the core iron ranges from fifteen million to fifty million pounds to the square inch. Under such colossal pressures the iron can be fluid only on the condition that the temperature of the core is enormously high—at tens of thousands of degrees Centigrade. Both pressure and temperature are far beyond the range of the experimental laboratory. The physical state of the core iron cannot as yet be described. Is it a liquid, a gas, or iron in a "state" unknown to physics? The conditions of the earth's core are star-like. From their study can physicists of the future tell us something more of the true nature of the stars? If they can, they will be pretty sure, incidentally, to shed new light on the structure and life-story of the atoms; for the secret of the star and the secret of the atom are proving to be part of a single problem, the ultimate nature of matter.

Again, if the core is fluid, it is infinitely weak. It can offer no permanent resistance to forces which tend to distort the earth's body. Hence other questions for future research: Is this mobility of the earth's core important in the explanation of the slow upheavings and down-sinkings of great areas of the earth's "crust"? Is the sensitive core involved even in the tumult of mountain-building? No one can now tell, but speculate we must, for it is today's speculation which leads to tomorrow's science.

The exact nature of the earth-shells overlying the core and totalling fifteen hundred miles in thickness, is another problem for the future. Presumably, the deepest of these shells is a more rigid, because cooler, chemical equivalent of the "fluid" core, but it is not yet clear how thick this more rigid "iron" may be. The published conclusions as to the composition and precise thicknesses of the still higher shells are uncertain and demand further testing. Yet the principle that the earth is layered seems proved once for all and leads to an apparently inescapable and highly significant conclusion: The shell-structure of the earth seems to defy explanation unless it be assumed that our planet was formerly molten. It must have been fluid enough to stratify itself by gravity. The "heavier" materials sank toward the center, the "lighter" materials rose toward the surface, and the whole mass finally arranged itself as layers or shells, with the very dense iron in the central region. It seems necessary to assume primitive fluidity right to the surface, and, further, to assume that the earth was thus fluid after practically all of its substance had been collected in the planet-making process. This general deduction must control future research on the cosmogonic problem—the origin of the earth and its brothers and sisters of the solar system. The earth was born in fervent heat and in the beginning was fervently hot even at the surface.

While telling us much about the heart of the earth, the seismogram is still more authoritative and eloquent concerning the uppermost layers of the globe. By studying the instrumental records of the reflections, refractions, accelerations, and retardations of earthquake waves, seismologists have found that the continental rocks reach downwards about thirty miles. At that level there is a rather abrupt change to a world-circling shell of a quite different nature. The dominant rock of the continents is granite. According to the facts of geology, as of seismology, the underlying shell or substratum, is the heavier, dark-colored basalt, and is apparently the source of this commonest of lavas and the primary seat of all volcanic energies.

The depth of the continental rock, so determined from the writing of the longitudinal and transverse waves on seismographs, is confirmed by study of a different kind of vibrations which come pouring into the station still later than the transverse wave. This third division of a typical seismogram is written by a long train of oscillations, corresponding to what are called surface waves, because they faithfully follow the great curve of the earth's rocky skin. Surface waves are the strongest of all the vibrations recorded by distant earthquakes. They are caused by the reflection of the longitudinal and transverse waves as these, coming from the interior, impinge at low angles upon the contact of rock with ocean-water and of rock with the air. That contact acts like the wall of a gigantic whispering-gallery. From the character and velocities of the surface waves, expert seismologists have corroborated the evidence, won from the longitudinal and transverse waves, concerning the nature and depth of the continental rock.

But the surface waves inform us also about the kind of rock immediately beneath the deep oceans, whose waters hide from view about two-thirds of the solid surface of the whole earth. The measured velocities of the surface waves show that the earth's skin beneath the deep oceans is crystallized basalt. Thus the material forming an earth-shell directly beneath the continents is continuous with, and chemically identical with, the surface-rock under the deep sea.

Granite, the principal rock of the continents, is a relatively light rock. Basalt, the essential rock beneath the oceans, is relatively heavy. It is for this reason that the continents float high on the earth's body; they are pressed up by the surrounding, heavy, solid basalt, much as icebergs are pressed up by the denser water of the sea. This is why we have dry land, with its endless importance for man and organic life in general.

Seismology tells us why our home is stable, in spite of mighty forces which tend to level the earth's crust and drown us all. We may confidently expect also that this continued "X-raying" of the outer earth will furnish new information as to the reason why mountains stand so high and are able to keep their heads in the clouds, far above the general level of the continents. And to geophysics, especially to seismology, we look for new help in finding out the conditions for the earth's periodic revolutions when mountain chains were born and sea-bottoms became the pinnacles of the world.

1928;
revised 1947

EARTHQUAKES—WHAT ARE THEY? *

THE REVEREND JAMES B. MACELWANE, S.J.

Round about this earth of ours there run certain belts in which earthquakes occur more often than in other parts of the world. Why should this be the case? We read from time to time of destructive earthquakes in Japan. But many lesser shocks occur there of which we never hear. In fact, there is an earthquake, large or small, somewhere in Japan practically every day. Similarly, the Kurile Islands, the Aleutian Islands, Alaska and the Queen Charlotte Islands are subject to frequent earth shocks. Continuing around the Pacific circle, we meet with many earthquakes in California, Mexico, Central America, Venezuela, Colombia, Ecuador, Bolivia, Peru and Chile. And on the other side of the Pacific Ocean, the earthquake belt continues from Japan southward through

* Reprinted by permission from *The Scientific Monthly*. Copyright 1933 by The Science Press.

Formosa and the Phillipine Deep to New Zealand. Another somewhat less striking earthquake zone runs from Mexico and the Antilles through the northern Mediterranean countries and Asia Minor into the Pamirs, Turkestan, Assam and the Indian Ocean. In other parts of the earth, destructive earthquakes also occur, but as more or less isolated phenomena. Examples in this country are the Mississippi Valley earthquakes of 1811 and of the following year, and the Charleston earthquake of 1886.

Now why should destructive earthquakes occur more frequently in such a zone or belt as the border of the Pacific Ocean? What is an earthquake? Centuries ago, many people, and even scientific men, thought that earthquakes were caused by explosions down in the earth; and there have not been wanting men in our own time who held this view. Others, like Alexander von Humboldt, thought that earthquakes were connected with volcanoes; that the earth is a ball of molten lava covered by a thin shell of rock and that the volcanoes were a sort of safety valve. As long as the volcanoes are active, they said, the pressure within the molten lava of the earth is held down, but when the volcanoes cease their activity, thus closing the safety valves, so to speak, the increasing pressure eventually causes a fracture in the earth's crust. Another theory supposed that the lava occupied passageways in a more or less solid portion of the earth underneath the crust and that the movement of lava within these passages caused such pressure as to burst their walls, thus causing an earthquake.

Quite a different point of view was taken by those who held the theory that earthquakes occurred within the uppermost crust of the earth. This crust was supposed to be honeycombed with vast caves. Even the whole mountain chain of the Alps was thought to be an immense arch built up over a cavern. When the arch should break, thus allowing the overlying rocks to drop somewhat, we would have an earthquake. In many cases, those who held this theory believed that the entire roof would collapse and that earthquakes are generally due to the impact of the falling mass of rocks on the floor of the cavern.

But it has been shown, since the discovery of the passage of earthquake waves through the earth and their registration by means of seismographs, that the outer portion of the earth down to a depth of at least five-elevenths of the earth's radius is not only solid, but, with the exception of the outer layers, is more than twice as rigid as steel in the laboratory. It has also been shown that volcanoes are a purely surface phenomenon; that they have no connection with each other, even when they are but a few miles apart. Hence it is clear that earthquakes connected with volcanoes must be of very local character, if they are to be caused by the movement of lava. This is found to be actually the case. It is also clear that some other cause must operate in producing earthquakes, since destructive earthquakes often occur very far from volcanoes. In fact, some regions where there are frequent earthquakes have no volcanoes at all.

In the California earthquake of 1906, there occurred a fracture of the earth's crust which could be followed at the surface for a distance of more than 150 miles, extending from the Gualala River Valley on the northern coast of California southeastward through Tomales Bay and outside the Golden Gate to the old mission of San Juan Bautista. The rocks on the east side of this fracture moved southeastward relatively to those on the west side, so that every road, fence or other structure which had been built across the line of fracture was offset by varying amounts up to twenty-one feet. A study of this earthquake led scientific men to the conclusion that the mechanism of the earthquake was an elastic rebound. It was thought that the rocks in the portion of the earth's crust west of the fracture had been dragged northward until the ultimate strength of the rocks was reached along this zone of weakness. When the fracture occurred, the rocks, like bent springs, sprang back to an unstrained position. But this did not occur in one continuous throw, but in a series of jerks, each of which set up elastic vibrations in the rocks. These vibrations traveled out in all directions and constituted the earthquake proper. The zone of weakness in which the California earthquake occurred is a valley known as the San Andreas rift. It is usually quite straight and ignores entirely the physiography of the region, passing indifferently over lowlands and mountains and extending more than 300 miles beyond the end of the fracture of 1906 until it is lost in the Colorado desert east of San Bernardino. The entire floor of the valley has been broken up by earthquakes occurring through the ages into small blocks and ridges and even into rock flour.

The San Andreas rift is only one of the many features which parallel the Pacific Coast in California. There are other lesser rifts on which earthquakes have occurred. Similar to these rifts in some respects are the ocean deeps, along the walls of which occur some of the world's most violent earthquakes.

Why do these features parallel the Pacific shore? And why are earthquakes associated with them? Both seem to be connected in some way with the process of mountain-building, for many of the features in this circum-Pacific belt are geologically recent. Many have thought that mountain-building in general and the processes going on around the Pacific in particular are due to a shortening of the earth's crust caused by gradual cooling of the interior and the consequent shrinkage, but this is not evident. While the earth is surely losing heat by radiation into space, it is being heated by physical and chemical processes connected with radioactivity at such a rate that, unless the radioactive minerals are confined to the uppermost ten miles or so of the earth's crust, the earth must be getting hotter instead of cooler, because the amount of heat generated must exceed that which is conducted to the surface and radiated away.

Another suggested cause of earthquakes is isostatic compensation. If we take a column of rock extending downward from the top of a mountain chain to a given level within the earth's crust and compare it with another column extending to the same level under a plain, the mountain column will be considerably longer than the other and consequently will contain more rock. Hence it should weigh more, unless the rocks of which it is composed are lighter than those under the plain, but geodesists tell us that the two columns weigh the same. Hence the rocks under the plain must be the heavier of the two. But even if this is the case, we should expect the conditions to change; for rain and weather are continually removing rocks from the tops of the mountains and distributing the materials of which they are composed over the plain. Nevertheless, according to the geodesists, the columns continue to weigh the same. Hence we must conclude that compensation in some form must be taking place. There must be an inflow of rock into the mountain column and an outflow from the plain column. But the cold flow of a portion of a mass of rock must place enormous strain on the surrounding portions. When the stress reaches the ultimate strength of the rocks, there must be fracture and a relief of strain, thus causing an earthquake.

It has recently been found that earthquakes occur at considerable depth in the earth. Hence they can not be caused by purely surface strains. There are a few earthquakes which seem to have occurred at depths up to 300 miles. This is far below the depth of compensation of the geodesists. It is also below the zone of fracture of the geologists, and far down in what they call the zone of flow. Can an earthquake be generated by a simple regional flow? We do not know, but it would seem that sudden release of strain is necessary to cause the vibrations which we call an earthquake. It may be that a strain is produced and gradually grows in such a way as to produce planes of shear such as occur when a column is compressed lengthwise. These planes of maximum shear usually form an angle of about forty-five degrees with the direction of the force. Recent investigation into the failure of steel indicates that under certain conditions it will retain its full strength up to the moment of failure when the steel becomes as plastic as mud along the planes of maximum shear. The two portions of the column then glide over each other on the plastic zone until the strain is relieved, whereupon the steel within the zone becomes hard and rigid as before. It may be that a process somewhat similar to this may take place deep down in the earth, and that the sheared surface may be propagated upwards through the zone of flow to the zone of fracture and even to the surface of the earth. In that case, the plastic shear would give way to true fracture near the surface.

It is only by a careful study, not only of the waves produced by earthquakes and of the permanent displacements which occur in them, but of the actual movement along the planes of fracture, that we shall be able to discover what an earthquake really is. For the present, we must be satisfied with knowing that it is an elastic process; that it is usually destructive only within a very restricted belt, and that it is probably produced by the sudden release of a regional strain within the crust of the earth.

1933

>>>><<<<

THE STUDY OF THE SEA AND ITS RELATION TO MAN *

CLAUDE E. ZOBELL

. . . Considering that more than two-thirds of the earth is covered with water which influences the activities and well-being of man in many ways, it is surprising to learn that less than one-tenth of one per cent of the world's scientists are engaged in oceanographic research. Only about a score of colleges in the United States offer instruction in oceanography, and until recently there has been no satisfactory textbook on the subject. In some respects more is known of the topography of the moon than of the ocean floor, and more is known of the movements of certain distant stars than of ocean currents. Large areas of the earth are virtually unexplored, from an oceanographer's point of view.

Approximately 71 per cent, or more than 140,000,000 square miles, of the earth's surface is covered with water. The mean depth of the sea is about 12,500 feet. This may be contrasted with the mean elevation of the land above sea level, 2,300 feet. The greatest elevation in the world above sea level, Mount Everest in the Himalayas, is 29,000 feet, while the greatest known depression, the Mindanao Deep off the Philippines, is 35,400 feet in depth. If all the irregularities of the earth's surface were smoothed out, the resulting sphere would be covered with about 7,500 feet of water.

This great mass of sea water, 330,000,000 cubic miles, directly or indirectly influences the life of every inhabitant of the earth, regardless of whether he lives in the Sahara Desert or the South Sea Islands. World weather, climate, precipitation, and the carbon dioxide content of the atmosphere are all influenced by the ocean. The vertical and horizontal movements of large masses of water of different temperatures affect the humidity and temperature of the overlying atmosphere, thereby creating high or low pressure areas, world-wide air movements, precipitation, and other weather elements. That warm or cold ocean currents affect the climate of the adjacent land is well known. Transportation and communi-

* From *Science in the University*, University of California Press. Copyright 1944 by the Regents of the University of California.

cations are influenced by the oceans of the world, and the sea contains a great wealth of biological and mineral resources. Exclusive of insects, of which there are some 450,000 described species, four-fifths of all other species of animals known to man live in the sea, including 40,000 species of mollusks (oysters, clams, shellfish, etc.), nearly as many crustacea (lobsters, crabs, barnacles, etc.), and 15,000 species of marine fish. The plant kingdom is represented by 8,000 marine species. Many of these plants and animals are of commercial importance.

Vast stores of mineral wealth are to be found in the oceans of the world. Sea water contains an average of 3.5 per cent of mineral matter. About 85 per cent of the total is sodium chloride, or common table salt. Large quantities of salt are reclaimed from the sea, solar salterns at San Diego and San Francisco alone yielding more than two million barrels a year. The Pacific Ocean contains enough salt to cover the continental United States to a depth of nearly a mile. Incidentally, the salinity of the ocean is not perceptibly increasing in spite of the fact that the rivers of the world annually carry in five trillion tons of salt.

Nearly every known mineral element has been demonstrated in sea water, some in commercially procurable quantities. Magnesium, which is used in many alloys, is being extracted from sea water in large quantities. Also extracted from sea water are sodium and potassium. Like iodine, potassium cannot be extracted profitably except from certain seaweeds which concentrate these elements. Sea water itself contains only 0.037 per cent of potassium, while dried kelp contains from 10 to 14 per cent. Similarly, there is only 0.0000005 per cent of iodine in sea water, but certain seaweeds contain 0.2 to 0.5 per cent when dried. At current prices a cubic mile of sea water contains $60,000,000 worth of iodine.

Long before it was known that bromine would be useful in the preparation of lead tetraethyl, used in high-compression motor fuels, oceanographic research had demonstrated that sea water contains 0.0065 per cent of bromine. Today, bromine extracted from the sea is virtually indispensable to the operation of automobiles, planes, and similar mechanized equipment. However, we need have no apprehensions of a shortage so long as we have access to the sea, because a cubic mile of sea water contains 250,000 tons of bromine, and methods for its extraction are steadily being improved. As needs develop and chemical and metallurgical processes are perfected, more and more use will be made of the mineral resources of the sea.

Tremendous quantities of chlorine used in the chemical industries, manufacturing, and chemical warfare are being taken from the inexhaustible supply in the sea.

The much-heralded gold content, amounting to more than thirty trillion dollars' worth in the oceans of the world, or enough of this precious metal to give every one of the two billion inhabitants of the earth fifteen thousand dollars' worth each, is only a paper asset, because it costs more to extract it than it is worth.

However, the greatest wealth of the sea is not to be found in its mineral resources, but in its natural productivity, in plants as well as animals. Almost 200,000 species of animals are known to live in the sea and 8,000 species of plants grow there in abundance. In addition to their academic interest, many of these aquatic organisms are of commercial significance. Methods of conserving the plant and animal resources and methods of increasing or improving the biological productivity of the sea are practical problems meriting attention. The solution of such problems requires information on the food habits, cultural requirements, life histories, migrations, rates of growth, and a multiplicity of other factors which influence the organisms in the marine environment.

Accumulating evidence indicates that, acre for acre the world over, the sea is more productive than the land. The primary production (organic matter produced by photosynthetic organisms) of certain areas, such as the Gulf of California, for example, appears to compare favorably with that of fertile garden soil, and it is believed that there are far fewer barren acres in the sea than on the land. There is never any drought in the sea, even temperatures prevail, the altitude is virtually constant, and sea water is a perfectly balanced salt solution with only nitrates, phosphates, and possibly silicates sometimes becoming factors which limit plant growth. Moreover, whereas only the topmost few inches of the soil are productive, photosynthetic organisms grow throughout the water to a depth limited only by the penetration of sunlight, this being two hundred to eight hundred feet depending upon the latitude, season, water turbulence, atmospheric moisture, abundance of organisms in the water, and other factors. Then it is found that arctic and antarctic waters are quite productive in contradistinction to the barrenness of the land at high latitudes.

Many marine plants are of direct commercial importance. Kelp is extensively used for fertilizer, cattle feed, paper pulp, and insulating material, and from it are extracted potash, iodine, oils, solvents, tars, and alginic acid. The last-named product has become one of the most important products from seaweeds. Alginic acid is used for sizing, for improving the consistency of a variety of foods, as a dispersing agent in lacquers, in the manufacture of munitions, and for numerous other purposes. Nearly half a billion dollars' worth of kelp and allied seaweed is harvested from the sea each year. While vast forests of kelp are found growing in the ocean, the supply is not inexhaustible if the kelp is indiscriminately harvested. The best methods for its conservation and the effect of kelp cutting on marine fisheries and beach erosion are subjects receiving special attention at the Scripps Institution of Oceanography.

Agar, or vegetable gelatin, is extracted from certain red algae and widely used medicinally, as a constituent of bacteriological media, and in the preparation of several kinds of confections, desserts, and other foods. The entrance of the United States into World War II found us consuming an average of 600,000 pounds of agar a year, all of which except 35,000 pounds a year was imported from Japan. Consequently, all available supplies of agar have been frozen for military emergency use, and efforts are being made to increase our production from the agariferous seaweeds which occur in coastal waters.

Many seaweeds make palatable and nutritious foods for man. Seventy different species of marine plants are eaten in the Hawaiian Islands, and the Japanese as well as the Chinese make use of nearly as many. Irish moss, purple laver, dulse, seatron, kombu, amonori, kijiki, arame, or murlins harvested from the sea, make dishes which are really much more palatable than the term "seaweed" connotes. Students of oceanography from most maritime nations lament the fact that we make so little use of the countless tons of marine vegetation occurring along our coasts. Blessed as we are with a vast wealth of terrestrial resources, we have given far too little heed to the natural resources of the sea. The possibilities of exploitation are indicated by the fact that Japan obtains more than one-third of her raw resources from the sea.

Although many large, easily harvestible plants grow in the sea, it is principally the microscopic plants termed phytoplankton which are the primary producers, phytoplankton being tiny, free-floating chlorophyll-bearing photosynthetic organisms. It is upon these that most marine animals depend for food. The phytoplankton is to the grazing animals of the sea what grass is to those on the land, a fact which earns for it the name of "ocean pasturage." Sometimes there is so much phytoplankton in the water that it is literally soupy or colored by its presence.

In order to estimate its abundance, the phytoplankton is strained out of the water with extremely fine-meshed bolting silk. In certain regions where careful investigations have been made, such as the North Sea, for example, a relationship has been found between the amount of phytoplankton in the water and the abundance of fish. Consequently, the activities of some fishing fleets in their search for productive waters are guided by the abundance of phytoplankton, which the scientists have taught the fishermen to detect with simplified apparatus.

While many large animals, including certain whales, feed on the ocean pasturage, most of the phytoplankton is eaten by tiny drifting animals which are collectively termed zoöplankton. Because of their importance in the food cycles in the sea, the estimation of the abundance of zoöplankton organisms is also of practical significance. They are examined and enumerated after being caught in nets of somewhat larger mesh and capacity than those used for catching the phytoplankton.

Marine animal products of commerce aggregating over thirty billion dollars in value are annually harvested from the sea, and give employment to between fifteen and twenty million men in the Northern Hemisphere. Besides fish, which are used for food and fertilizer, these products include shellfish, crabs, lobsters, shrimps, sponges, furs, leather, liver oils, pearls, precious corals, and whale products—to mention just a few. Surely an industry of this magnitude deserves the most intelligent management possible. Although planned conservation and, to a less degree, cultivation of marine plant and animal life are practiced on a small scale by various maritime nations, for the most part man has been content simply to harvest that which is found in nature, exploiting the marine resources as he has exploited the forests.

A few thickly populated countries, notably Japan, Belgium, Holland, and the Scandinavian countries, are now profitably practicing aquiculture or the cultivation of shellfish and certain seaweeds. Aquiculture seems to hold almost unlimited possibilities for producing food and other products. Students of the subject aver that aquiculture is just as susceptible of scientific treatment as agriculture. This is a field in which scientists studying the sea have made, and can yet make, many important contributions.

Judging from the vast quantities of fish taken from the sea (more than a million tons annually along the coasts of the United States), it might seem that the marine resources are unlimited. However, past experiences should emphasize the desirability of international coöperation for conservation. At the turn of the century, the whaling industry gave employment to more than a hundred thousand men in the North Sea region, but ruthless "overfishing" has virtually exterminated these leviathans of the deep. The rapidly declining catches of albacore and abalone along the coast of California, of striped bass on the New England coast, and of lobster in both European and American waters calls for immediate research or remedial measures to prevent the extermination of these and other commercially valuable species. The indiscriminate activities of certain foreign fisheries almost within the shadow of our own coastline have threatened the permanence of the profitable fishing industry in California waters.

Even before the purchase of Alaska in 1867, it was recognized that the uncontrolled and piratical slaughter of Alaska fur seals threatened their extermination. After many international incidents and much negotiation, the Pelagic Treaty of 1911 with Russia, England, and Japan made provision for the protection of the seals and placed the control of the herd in the hands of the United States Government. Through a judicious plan of conservation, the herd which breeds exclusively on the Pribilof Islands now numbers nearly two million, and in the meantime more than a million sealskins of highest quality have been marketed.

Effective conservation measures are possible only when we have a thorough knowledge of the life histories of the animals concerned. At present the Scripps Institution of Oceanography is coöperating with the federal Fish and Wildlife Service and the California Division of Fish and Game in studying the spawning areas, early migration, life history, and food habits of the commercially valuable sardine. The objective of such studies is to gain information prerequisite to establishing effective conservation practices, and possibly information from which the abundance of sardines in a given area can be predicted.

Sometimes the rapid growth of plants and animals in the sea proves detrimental to the interests of man. This is true of the so-called "fouling" organisms which attach themselves tenaciously to submerged surfaces on which they grow. The accumulation of barnacles, hydroids, tunicates, shellfish, algae, and other organisms in sea water conduits often clogs them. Fouling organisms on ships' bottoms tend to retard the progress of a vessel through the water, thereby increasing fuel consumption, prolonging the voyage, and eventually necessitating drydocking, cleaning, and repainting.

After resting in the water for a few days, the pontoons of flying boats acquire an unwelcome load of fouling organisms which seriously interfere with the efficient operation of the boats. The fouling problem costs the United States Navy and merchant marine more than a hundred million dollars a year in peacetime, and inestimably more in time of war when maximum speed and continuous service on the seven seas are vitally important to naval strategy.

Ways and means of preventing the attachment and growth of fouling organisms have taxed the ingenuity of man ever since he first put to sea in a boat. Oceanographic research has contributed much relief, but an entirely satisfactory solution requires more information on the habits, life cycles, and associations of the troublemaking marine organisms.

Exploration of the ocean floor is another department of oceanographic research which has many practical applications. The study of cores of sedimentary material, collected from the bottom of the sea in long tubes attached to the end of a dredging cable, yields information of geological and paleontological significance. Most sedimentary rocks were formed in ancient seas, and the process is still going on in all its stages. Cores of stratified material a few feet in length provide a geological record of the part of the earth from which they came.

Numerous animals and myriads of bacteria live on the sea bottom, where they depend for a living upon the organic matter which falls to them through the water from the productive photosynthetic zone. Much of this organic matter undergoes decomposition on the ocean floor, probably for the most part by bacterial activity. Part of it is converted into plant nutrients which contribute to the fertility of the overlying water, and part of it is slowly buried by falling debris.

It is generally believed that the buried organic matter is the source of petroleum, although the exact nature of the transformation is not well understood. Since marine bottom deposits probably hold the secret of petroleum formation, geologists, chemists, and biologists alike are interested in them. Information on the conditions under which petroleum has been and is now being formed may facilitate the location of existing oil deposits and may possibly suggest ways in which organic matter may be used to produce oil under man-made conditions. For many years, oil geologists have made extensive use of oceanographic data in their quest for new oil fields. Foraminifera may be mentitoned as one example. These tiny shelled animals have earned for themselves the designation "master key to oil" because certain marine species are usually associated with petroleum deposits.

Contrary to popular conception, the topography of the ocean floor is more irregular than that of the better-known world above sea level. Towering mountains rise precipitously from the floor of the ocean, forming submarine ridges, reefs, banks, and islands. Between the mountains are abyssal basins, depressions, trenches, deeps, and canyons. The Mindanao and Ramapo deeps, which descend more than six miles below sea level, are just a few miles from land. Recent studies at the Scripps Institution of Oceanography have dealt with submarine canyons near La Jolla and Monterey where within a mile of the mainland the sea bottom drops off precipitously. The seaward extension of the Hudson River Valley is another example of a submarine canyon.

Except in the neighborhood of rivers, harbors, anchorages, bays, estuaries, and in close proximity to the land in general, relatively little is known concerning the extent and nature of the topographical features of the sea bottom because so few soundings have been made. As late as 1928 there was an area of two million square miles, one-half the area of the United States, in the southern Pacific in which only eight soundings had been made! In fact, the sea bottom is still a great unexplored wilderness for the most part. There are thousands of miles of uncharted waters along coasts where information on the bottom topography would be of great value in connection with military landing operations and the navigation of submarines.

The contour of the ocean floor affects oceanic circulation as well as the distribution of marine organisms. Different animal associations are found at different depths, and in certain regions the animal population on one side of a submarine ridge may be quite different from that on the other side. Shoals and banks provide some of the best fishing grounds.

Since the stability of the earth's crust is intimately associated with sedimentation in the sea and the physiography of the sea floor, fuller knowledge of the latter might disclose the locations where many great earthquakes originate. Some students of the subject believe that the high waves which occasionally devastate our shores have their origin in tremendous submarine rockslides—a subject for further research. Also, a detailed picture of the topographical features of the sea bottom would aid in the navigation of vessels, especially of submerged submarines equipped with appropriate echo depthfinders.

Hundreds of miles of expensive transoceanic communications cable have been saved, and still greater savings are possible, by knowing from a detailed picture of the ocean floor exactly how much cable must be paid out to insure its resting on the sea bottom and not suspended precariously from one submarine ridge to another where it will eventually break owing to its own weight. Lack of knowledge of the contour and character of the sea floor resulted in the failure of the first attempts to span the Atlantic with a cable. Now, two dozen transatlantic cables connect North America and Europe. Detailed soundings of the Atlantic crossings during the decade ending in 1930 have effected a saving of 8 to 10 per cent in the length of cable laid as compared with earlier projects.

The early mariner determined the depth of water under his vessel by lowering a weighted hemp line to the bottom and then measuring the length of the line in terms of fathoms, a fathom (six feet) being the length of line held by the outstretched arms of a man of average size. Later, greater depths were sounded by lowering a lead weight on the end of a steel piano wire and noting the revolutions of a pulley of known circumference over which the wire passed. Finally, the echo-sounding depthfinder was developed. With this device an oscillation or sound wave is directed from the vessel to the bottom of the sea, whence the oscillation is reflected or echoed upward again. The return oscillation is picked up by a microphone and amplified so that it can be detected in the pilot house. By knowing the rate at which the oscillation travels through water and the time required for it to go down and back again, the depth of the water can be calculated. Most modern vessels are equipped with echo depthfinders which aid them in finding their positions and especially in avoiding dangerous shoals. Similar devices aid the cutters of the International Ice Patrol in locating and charting the positions of icebergs in fog or in complete darkness. Also, supersonic echometers are used successfully by certain fishing fleets for detecting the presence of schools of fishes because the short waves are reflected by the fish in a recognizable pattern. These devices are being perfected to locate submarines even when their engines are not running. However, precise results require information on many characteristics of the water masses involved.

Every year, physical oceanographers are making important contributions to our knowledge of the circulatory movements of the water. It is commonly recognized that the horizontal movements of large masses of water have a pronounced effect upon local climatic conditions. This is exemplified by effects of the Labrador Current on the east coast as contrasted with that of the California Stream on the west coast. The vertical circulation or upwelling of large masses of cold water in temperate or tropical regions is equally or even more important in its effect upon oceanic as well as terrestrial conditions. Water from depths exceeding one thousand feet is almost invariably cold (30° to 38° F.), and it also differs in fertility, salinity, oxygen content, and in other respects, from surface water.

It will be appreciated at once that oceanic circulation influences the distribution of temperature, oxygen, salinity, and marine organisms. The temperature of the water influences the growth of plants and animals in the sea. The surface temperature of large masses of water also influences the evaporation of water and hence precipitation (rainfall) as well as atmospheric circulation (wind), not only over the sea, but over the land also. Thus world weather is influenced by the horizontal and vertical circulation of the sea. Many meteorologists believe that data on oceanic conditions may serve as a rational basis for forecasting, sometimes several weeks in advance, the general features of the weather for a given part of the world. However, the extension and improvement of these forecasts requires more data on oceanic circulation and the distribution of water temperatures.

On the east coast of the United States it has been found that the transport volumes, velocity, and width of the Gulf Stream fluctuate from year to year. Some years, this great stream of warm tropical water is a hundred miles closer to the coast than in other years, thereby materially altering climatic conditions in the New England States. Recent studies show that the velocity and width of the Gulf Stream can be forecast from data obtained in the Gulf of Mexico, and such forecasts are of inestimable value. In fact, there are some indications that the effects may be even more far-reaching, extending into the North Sea and the adjacent countries. Unfortunately, the present war has curtailed the studies which had been commenced on this problem by an international committee previously appointed for the purpose.

Knowledge of ocean currents expedites, cheapens, and safeguards navigation. Ignorance of the direction and velocity of the currents frequently results in discrepancies between the true position of the ship as determined by astronomical sights and that calculated for her by dead reckoning. The savings of time and fuel which result from charting the course of a vessel so that she goes with the current rather than against it, especially for slow freighters, is self-evident. While most of the major surface currents have been charted for many years, there are many systems of oceanic circulation about which little or nothing is known.

Mechanical effects of water movements may be noted along the coast. In many places the combined action of waves and currents is permitting the sea to encroach upon the land from a fraction of an inch to several feet each year. In other places, harbors and channels are being silted up and beaches altered. An example of the desirability of understanding ocean currents before planning coastal improvements is the million-dollar Santa Barbara yacht harbor. Though but few years have passed since the completion of this project, the harbor is silting up so that it continually requires expensive dredging, and the bathing beach for a considerable distance has been eroded by the altered currents.

Numerous devices have been proposed, patented, or tried for harnessing the seemingly limitless power of the waves and tides. The Passamaquoddy project is an outstanding example. Such potential sources of power must not be overlooked, but it is yet to be shown that they can compete with power from other sources.

Similarly, it is not economically feasible, by any process yet known, to make sea water fresh enough for irrigation purposes. Some promising small-scale experiments have been conducted on certain arid acres adjoining the ocean. Semipermeable pipes buried in the soil permit enough moisture to soak through and yet hold back the salt, thus providing for plant growth; but the cost is almost as prohibitive as that for the evaporation and condensation of sea water. Since the Colorado River constitutes the last important source of fresh water which can be made available for use in southern California, and since this is a supply which will be adequate only for another hundred years if the country continues to develop and population to increase at the same phenomenal rate as in the last hundred, the day may come when we shall look to the sea for water. While the development of aquiculture seems a more promising field of research for supplementing the productivity of the soil, the thought of utilizing sea water for irrigation is hardly more fantastic than the thought of bringing Colorado River water and power four hundred miles across deserts and mountains to Los Angeles was, a hundred years ago.

In conclusion it should be emphasized that while oceanographic research has done much to solve the mysteries of the deep, our knowledge of the sea is still woefully scant. For obvious reasons, scientists at the Scripps Institution of Oceanography, and others elsewhere, have with few exceptions concentrated their efforts upon a study of contiguous coastal waters and local problems. Consequently, in spite of the efforts of international committees charged with the responsibility of promoting the study of the sea on a world-wide basis, there are extensive unexplored areas and countless unsolved problems. It is becoming increasingly apparent that a complete understanding of oceanic phenomena and their effects on terrestrial conditions requires information about more distant deep-sea regions. Oceanographic research is international in scope and requires the unified efforts of chemists, physicists, meteorologists, mathematicians, geologists, and biologists having specialized training. However, in spite of the complexities and magnitude of the problems which challenge the ingenuity of marine scientists, progress is being made. The practical aspects of oceanographic research, together with the natural curiosity

TIME UNITS			DISTINCTIVE FEATURES	OROGENY	DATES
CENOZOIC ERA	CENOZOIC PERIOD	Recent epoch			
		Pleistocene epoch	The Stone Age of human history. Glaciation widespread, mountains attain present heights	Cascadian Rev.	1 000 000
		Pliocene epoch	Climate becomes cooler and drier. Man diverges from the apes.		
		Miocene epoch	Mammals reach climax; grazing types evolve as prairies spread. Elephants reach America.		
		Oligocene epoch	Mammals evolve rapidly. Great Apes arise in Eurasia.		
		Eocene epoch	Modern orders of mammals appear and evolve rapidly.		
		Paleocene epoch	Archaic mammals dominate. Valley glaciers appear locally.		
MESOZOIC ERA	CRETACEOUS PERIOD		Dinosaurs, pterodactyls, toothed birds reach climax and then die out. Small archaic mammals appear. Flowering plants and hardwood forests spread widely.	Laramide Rev.	60000000 To 70000000
	JURASSIC PERIOD		Dinosaurs and marine reptiles dominate. Toothed birds appear Ammonites reach climax.	Nevadian Dist.	
	TRIASSIC PERIOD		Small dinosaurs and the first mammals appear. Conifers and cycads dominate the forests. Ammonites evolve rapidly.	Palisade Dist.	
PALEOZOIC ERA	PERMIAN PERIOD		Continental uplift and orogeny widespread. Extremes of cold and aridity result in rapid evolution and many extinctions.	Appalachian Rev.	200 000 000
	PENNSYLVANIAN PERIOD	*Carboniferous*	Warm humid climate favors coal making. Reptiles and insects appear. Spore-bearing trees dominate swamp forests.		
	MISSISSIPPIAN PERIOD	*Carboniferous*	Shell-crushing sharks, crinoids, and lacy bryozoans attain climax.		
	DEVONIAN PERIOD		Lung-fishes evolve into air-breathing vertebrates (amphibians). First forests appear. Brachiopods reach climax.	Acadian Dist.	290 000 000
	SILURIAN PERIOD		Climate warm, locally arid. Corals form widespread reefs. First meagre evidence of land life recorded.		
	ORDOVICIAN PERIOD		Seas spread widely over low continents. Many groups of invertebrates make first appearance. Trilobites reach greatest differentiation.	Taconian Dist.	350 000 000
	CAMBRIAN PERIOD		Fossils abundant for the first time, representing marine life only. Trilobites and brachiopods dominate. Plants recorded only as lime-secreting algae		400 000 000
CRYPTOZOIC EON	KEWEENAWAN PERIOD		Vast lava flows and thick red sediments cover the Lake Superior region. A geo-syncline occupies the Rocky Mountain area	Killarney Rev	
	HURONIAN PERIOD		A geosyncline occupies the Great Lakes region. Glaciation is widespread in Canada Lake Superior iron ores are deposited		
	TIMISKAMIAN PERIOD		A long period of accumulation of sedi-mentary rocks is followed by great dis-turbances and then by profound erosion of the Canadian Shield	Algoman Rev.	1 050 000 000
	KEEWATIN PERIOD		Thick lava flows occupy the Lake Superior region, interfingering with the oldest known sedimentary rocks	Laurentian Rev.	

of man, should insure the continuation and expansion of the investigations of this last great unexplored frontier.

1944

THE STORY OF A BILLION YEARS *

W. O. HOTCHKISS

Geology . . . has found the year and the century too short to use as time units. It has grouped the past into larger units—into great cycles of similar events—so that our minds can picture them more readily.

To show you how these large group units are selected, I want to tell you the story of a Wisconsin mill pond that I once studied for a few interesting hours. This pocket edition of a geologic epoch began with an unusual event in the history of a stream—the building of a dam. It was ended by another unusual event—a flood that destroyed the dam, and cut a tiny canyon through the sediments deposited in the pond. Such epochs, on a vastly larger time scale, measured by the deposition of hundreds or thousands of feet of sediments, are used as units in the story of the billion years of the history of the earth. They begin with an unusual event, the depression of a large area below sea level. They endure millions or tens of millions of years, during which events are infallibly recorded in the sediments. They end with another unusual event—the elevation of the area above the sea and its subjection to the action of the wind, of the rain, and of the streams, which gradually wear it away.

As I looked at the vertical sides of the three foot "canyon" cut in the sediments in the Wisconsin mill pond, I could see the edges of thin horizontal layers of different kinds of mud. Closer examination showed that some of these layers were of coarse material and some of fine, that some were light colored and some dark. Some contained decayed leaves and other vegetable matter. By careful observation I could distinguish the layers that represented a year's deposit. Counting these annual layers told me that they had been accumulating for about seventy years. Information from neighboring farmers to the effect that the dam had been built seventy years before checked my observations most satisfactorily.

The alphabet of this story is simple. The little stream carried mud and sand, as all streams do. It carried fallen leaves in the autumn. It carried more mud and sand and more coarse material in flood times than in dry times. When it reached the still water of the pond, the sand and mud and even the leaves finally settled to the bottom, so that the water which

* From *The Story of a Billion Years* by W. O. Hotchkiss, The Century Company, 1932. Copyright 1932 by The Williams & Wilkins Company, and reprinted with their permission.

escaped over the dam was much clearer than that which came into the pond. The coarser sand and small pebbles settled much more quickly than the fine mud.

With these simple every-day facts as an alphabet I was prepared to read the story recorded in the mud layers behind the old dam. A thick layer of sand and fine pebbles told of a long-past flood stage in the little stream. When, over that layer, I found a layer of the finest mud, I knew that the flood had subsided. A layer which contained leaves in fair abundance enabled me to deduce with Sherlock Holmes certainty that it must have been deposited in the autumn. When I found these leaf-bearing layers separated by thin layers of fine mud, I knew that there had come a period of dry years without heavy rainfall and floods; and when I found the leaf-bearing layers separated by thick beds of coarser-grained material, I was certain that they represented a period of years of heavy rainfall during which the stream was more often in flood. In this way I could identify both the dry years and the rainy years. If I had desired, I could have checked my conclusions by the local weather records. I could have checked them also by cutting a large tree nearby and observing the layers of annual growth. Wet years would have been represented by thick layers and dry years by thin. By a similar study of the annular rings in the old trees of California and other places the weather records have been traced back beyond historical times. Thus, with satisfactory accuracy the climate of California in the time of Christ can be compared with that of the present.

DeGeer, studying the mud and sand deposits in ancient Swedish lakes, found that the climate had left a continuous record for the last eight thousand years, so that it is possible to tell with quite pleasing accuracy the various "spells of weather" which marked that long stretch of time.

The story of the mud layers in the Wisconsin mill pond illustrates perfectly three of the great fundamental principles of geology. The stream that flowed into the mill pond was typical of all streams, big and little. It carried mud and sand and pebbles with it in its flow. It deposited this material when its rapid flow was stopped in the mill pond. When the flood came that broke the dam, this deposit in the pond again started on its way toward the sea, to be redeposited in the next quiet water, and so by successive steps finally to be carried to the Gulf of Mexico and find a resting place in the sea.

The material carried into the mill pond had been washed from the adjacent hillsides into the stream by the rain, a process called "erosion." Any sand bank or rivulet shows this process at work. It is the process which carved the magnificent gorge of the Grand Canyon, but it is not different from the process you can see going on in your back yard during a shower or when the garden hose is at work.

The other fundamental principles learned from the study of the mill pond stream are known as "transportation" and "deposition." The stream transported the mud washed into it and, acting on the third fundamental principle, "deposition," deposited its load when it reached quiet water.

Erosion, transportation, and deposition are three fundamental geologic processes which we can see at work all about us. If with these processes in mind we look through the eyes of a billion years, the "everlasting hills" become only the uneroded remnants of hills once larger and different in shape. The pleasant valleys we love to look upon were once smaller and of different form.

Erosion and transportation are bit by bit continuously carving the face of the earth into new forms. Those who see and understand take delight not only in rebuilding in imagination the forms that have been worn away but also in picturing in the mind's eye those forms that natural processes will develop in the future.

In the story of the discoveries of the Scotch farmer, Hutton, it was indicated that successive beds of sand, lime mud, and clay had been deposited over large areas. In the story of the Wisconsin mill pond mention was made that some of the layers were found to contain the remains of leaves which had settled in the pond with the mud. During the deposition of the sands and clays and lime mud, which were hardened into rock to make the cliffs that Hutton examined, there were likewise deposited the remains of various living things—shells, skeletons of animals, pieces of vegetation, all sorts of things that might leave their imprints when these unconsolidated materials were later hardened into rocks. Such remains of living things have been of great value in helping us to unravel the story of the past from the study of these various rock beds.

As men studied these remains more and more, they noted that individual beds were characterized by certain types of animal and vegetable forms. Other beds above or below were characterized by different types. About one hundred years ago it began to be recognized that these remains, which are called fossils, are so definitely characteristic of the beds in which they occur that they make a most excellent means of identifying particular beds wherever they are found. When a certain group of fossils was found in a bed in eastern New York and the same group of fossils in the same kind of bed could be traced clear across the country from quarry to quarry, from hillside to hillside, it became apparent that this particular bed must have been deposited in a sea of that extent and that conditions in this sea were favorable to the existence of this kind of shell.

As lower, and therefore older, beds were examined it was found that in a general way the living forms were simpler as the age of the beds increased. As the overlying beds were examined, it was found that the forms of life usually became more complex, until in the more recent of these beds remains of higher animals and of man were found. As a result of these studies it was found that the whole series of beds laid down in the past could be divided into groups characterized by the forms of life which they contained. On the basis of this life history of the past the geologic eras have been named.

The oldest rocks found are those of the Proterozoic Era. They contain either no evidence of life or evidence that is very hazy and indefinite. Such fossils as exist are chiefly of microscopic simple forms, single-celled animals and plants like those we find in the waters of the sea and lakes today. Few of these earliest forms of life possessed hard parts that could be readily preserved.

After long ages, toward the end of the Proterozoic Era, and at the beginning of the next era, some living forms began to protect themselves with a hard shell or "exterior skeleton." Still later on larger and more complex organisms appeared, various kinds of shell fish and other small forms of life, much like those we find along our sea coasts and lake beaches today. About the middle of this era the first fishes began to appear, the earliest animals to possess a backbone. Toward the close of the era some of these developed the capacity to breathe and so to live on land as well as in water and thus became the first of what we call amphibians. This period of life development is given the name of the Paleozoic Era, which means "early life era."

The third great era was characterized by the development of enormous land animals and has been called the "Age of Reptiles." This era has been given the name of Mesozoic, meaning "middle forms of life." The great dinosaurs, which reached their highest development at this time, were among the largest land animals ever to inhabit the face of the globe. Most of them were animals that laid eggs, just as fish and turtles and alligators do at present. Most of them left their young to hatch out and care for themselves unaided from the day they were born. Their lives were easy, and they prospered and developed many different forms. Some were plant-eating and some were flesh-eating. Some of them found it easiest to get their food by swimming in the seas of those days and gradually developed the capacity to live in water. These reversed the experiences of their ancestors who had developed from fish that got tired of living in the water and developed lungs so that they could live on the land.

Toward the end of the Mesozoic Era a higher type of animal appeared which brought forth its young alive and cared for them and nursed them through a period of infancy. This great group of animals rules the earth today. They are known as mammals, a term which includes all animals which nurse their young. Just as some of the reptiles of the Mesozoic Era found an easier livelihood by returning to the sea to live, so in this later era some of the mammals found it desirable to live in the water. Thus were developed the whales, dolphins, and porpoises, inhabitants of our seas today, which bear living young and nurse them. This latest era of geologic time, which followed the Age of Reptiles, or Mesozoic Era, is given the name of the Age of Mammals, or Cenozoic Era.

The grand divisions of geologic time are known as Eras. These are divided into Periods which are in turn subdivided into Epochs. Epochs are further subdivided into Ages, but that is getting too far into technical detail. The division of the geologic past into epochs and ages has been by no means fully worked out. Much remains to be done before our knowledge is complete. Geology, like all other sciences, is a progressing, developing state of knowledge, no field of which will be completely known for long ages.

Each of the divisions of geologic time is, on a much grander scale, similar to the "epoch" of the deposits in the Wisconsin mill pond. As that began with the building of a dam which changed the conditions from those of an eroding valley to those of quiet water where the stream deposited its sediment, so each of them began with some event that changed the previous conditions. Nothing so insignificant as the building of a dam marked these eras, but some vaster thing, such as the slow submergence by the sea of half a continent, or the elevation of a great chain of mountains. The most important changes marked the close of one era and the beginning of another. Less important changes of this kind marked the ends of periods, epochs, and ages.

The close of the Paleozoic Era (early life) was marked by a great earth movement, estimated to have occurred about one hundred and eighty million years ago. This movement compressed and tilted the rocks that now make the Appalachian Mountains and raised them and the whole eastern part of the United States above sea level. How long a time this took we do not know, but we do know enough to feel quite sure that the process was too slow to be noticed by any casual observer, had there been one present. At the rate of one inch per year the highest peak in the Appalachians could have been elevated from sea level in seventy-five thousand years. In some parts of our country there are probably vertical movements of the earth's surface now going on at this rate, or even more rapid rates, which are entirely unnoticed by the people living there. Yet it is probable that the building of the Appalachian Mountains took place at a slower rate and occupied a much longer time.

The close of the Paleozoic and the beginning of the Mesozoic Eras, then, were marked by the mountain-building uplift that resulted in our Appalachian ranges. The end of the Mesozoic and the beginning of the Cenozoic Eras were similarly marked by the elevation and folding of the Rocky Mountains. This was approximately sixty million years ago. Our Rocky Mountains apparently are mere youths, only a third as old as their feeble grandfathers in the east.

The Sierra and Coast ranges along our west coast are mere infants, only about a third as old as the Rockies or perhaps even less.

The events marking the ends of geologic eras have been mentioned because of their bearing on the story of living things shown by the rocks. The elevation of vast areas above sea level, or depression below it, changed living conditions very greatly. Ocean currents were deflected into new courses. Where there had been warm water there was perhaps now cold, and vice versa. Organisms that had thrived before died under the changed conditions or underwent modifications that adapted them to the change. New types of organisms immigrated and ate up or drove out the old. So there were vast changes in the kinds of remains of life that were deposited in the sediments of the sea and shore. If you will consult a text book of geology and will turn first to the illustrations of the fossils found in Paleozoic rocks and then to those found in Mesozoic, you will find that even without knowing anything about their long specific names or attempting to qualify yourself as a paleontologist (one who studies fossils) you can see quite notable differences.

There are a number of epochs in each era and the average length of each of these epochs for the last 299 million years is more than twenty million years. In one of the epochs there was time for many changes in living forms to take place. When we consider the wide variety of kinds and sizes of dogs and cattle produced in a relatively few centuries by careful breeding, and then try to think of what might happen in only one geologic epoch of an average length of twenty million years, and then, if imagination is not already stretched to the breaking point, try to still further multiply this by fifty to get the record of a billion years, it is not difficult to see how living things in their struggles for existence have had ample time to develop from the simplest forms of one-celled beings to that exceedingly complex, little understood, but "inordinately proud" being that calls himself man.

One of the great steps toward dominating the earth was the development of life forms that were able to live upon and occupy the land. All the earlier forms were probably water-dwellers. In earliest times the land was barren of plants and animals. No living thing grew or crawled beyond the shore. If by accident it was left out of water, it promptly died. There is evidence that this condition prevailed in all the history of the earth up to a half-billion years ago. The landscape then consisted of bare rocks and sand and mud, deposits lying stark and naked as the rains and rivers of those ages left them. The landscape must have looked like a desert; yet in most of the world the rainfall was about as abundant as it is today.

Remains found in the rocks indicate that about five hundred million years ago, in the Cambrian Period, some few of the plants—which previously had all been sea plants—had found a way to live on land. They were the highest plant forms of their time, even though they were only algae and the simplest of mosses. They first found a precarious living along the rocks of the sea coast. Later on, after a hundred million years of progressive adjustment to their "new" surroundings, they began to look somewhat like some of the plants we see today.

About three hundred million years ago plants had developed swamp-living forms of moderate size, and in the Carboniferous Period, two hundred and fifty million years ago, great tree ferns and similar forms grew to a height of eighty feet. These forms and their associates accumulated in their swamp homes to considerable thickness, so that today they make one of our most valuable mineral resources. They used the sunlight of those days to transform water and carbon dioxide from the air into woody cellulose which was altered into the coal which we now use to drive our trains, run our factories, and light our homes. In fact, we might truly say that our present civilization is largely based on the sunshine that fell on the earth two hundred and fifty million years ago.

Plants continued to develop newer and better and more complex forms. About two hundred million years ago, in the Permian Epoch, the first cone-bearing trees appeared. About one hundred million years ago, in the Cretaceous Period, seed-bearing plants developed in abundance. Most plants up to that time had been spore-bearers like our ferns today. When the first seed-bearers appeared, they were so much better fitted to land conditions that they quickly became the dominant type of vegetation, a position which they hold today. They include all our grasses and grains and our fruit and nut-bearing trees. The spore-bearers have literally been relegated to the shade by the seed-bearers.

The development of animal life has a similar history. The earliest animal forms are concealed in the hazy and indistinct records of the very ancient rocks. At first all animals, like plants, were sea-dwellers and were long in developing hard parts, such as shells or bones, that would not be easily destroyed and "sunk without trace."

In the rocks of the Cambrian Period, which began more than five hundred million years ago, we find our first well-preserved evidence of an abundance of animal life. In older rocks, fossils are few in numbers not because living beings were scarce but because few of them had discovered how to utilize the lime in the water to build themselves stony protective armor. When this discovery was made, the rocks at once began to preserve the remains of an abundance of different forms of life, many of them quite complex in their organization. Those who have studied the long, slow evolution of living forms from the lowest to the highest have estimated that from sixty to ninety per cent of this evolution occurred before the Cambrian Period began. We find in these Cambrian rocks the remains of many hundreds of species of animals. Some are shellfish somewhat like our modern clams and oysters, others are similar to modern snails in having coiled shells, and still others are like corals in structure.

The next step in the evolution of animal life, the conquest of the land, required what to us seems a long period of time—perhaps 150 million years.

It could not be completed until plants had become land-dwellers. The earliest land animals found in the rocks are insects, spiders, and scorpions, which appeared about three hundred and sixty million years ago in the Silurian Period, and reached a high development in the Mesozoic Era, which covered the period of time from 180 million to 100 million years ago.

The first vertebrate skeleton was owned by an ancestral fish that lived perhaps four hundred million years ago in the Ordovician Period. He had found that he needed something to keep his head from being driven back into his body as he swam about in search of his prey, and so he grew a bony skeleton and discovered that life was easier. His predecessors all had "external skeletons," or shells, that were good armor against their enemies but were cumbersome and cut down the speed with which they could navigate and catch the other organisms on which they lived. This development of a backbone was an improvement of such great usefulness that all higher types of animals since that time have an internal jointed skeleton, the main feature of which is a flexible, jointed backbone. Nothing has been invented by nature thus far that is better for its purpose than this great device. It has been the prime factor that has enabled animals to attain to great size.

Since the first animal with a vertebrate skeleton appeared four hundred million years ago, there has been progress in size, until today we now have the largest animal that ever lived, the great blue whale, which is known to have attained a length of 106 feet. Progress was not rapid. One hundred million years had to pass after the invention of the backbone before animals ten feet long developed. It was not until the vertebrates took to living on the land that development to great size occurred. In the Age of Reptiles—the Mesozoic Era—when the dinosaurs and their kin were lords of creation, they so "quickly" added to their size that no more than thirty or forty million years of this era elapsed before they had attained to maximum lengths of seventy feet. This experiment of increasing the bulk of flesh inside one skin—or, to look at it from the inside out, the bulk of flesh surrounding a single backbone—was successful for about seventy-five million years, and the great animals of the period prospered for a time lasting from one hundred and fifty million years ago to seventy-five million years ago.

The development of these animals to greater size was not accompanied by corresponding brain development. The largest brain of those days was less than a quarter the size of yours or mine.

In the meantime nature was making a different kind of experiment. The great reptiles did not have any marked maternal instincts. Most of them continued the practice which characterized the poor fish and lower animals that had been left behind in the race. They laid eggs and left their young to hatch out and care for themselves. About one hundred and fifty million years ago there appeared some small animals that hatched their eggs inside their bodies and produced living young which they nursed and cared for through a period of helpless infancy. From this habit of nursing their young they have been given the name of mammals. With them the great quality of mother-love first began to be an important factor in the life of the earth. Through at least eight hundred and fifty million long years of the billion-year story living beings got along with little or none of the mother-love that is so powerful an influence in the lives of all of the higher animals today.

Mammals also gave up an old practice followed by all other living things, that of being cold-blooded. They found that to elevate the blood temperature gave them advantages over their cold-blooded associates. Warm blood and the habit of nursing their young were the most important new elements in life that distinguished the mammals. They had the same organs, muscles, nervous system, and brain as their cold-blooded, egg-laying neighbors, but they had in the two new improvements qualities that were to make them, after a hundred millions of years had elapsed, the dominant type of animals on the face of the globe. For the last sixty million years they have prospered more extensively than any other kind of animal life.

1932

THE GEOLOGIC RECORDS OF TIME *

ADOLPH KNOPF

. . . About at the turn of the last century came the revolutionary discoveries of radioactivity. Among these was the startling fact that the disintegration of the radioactive elements is accompanied by the spontaneous evolution of heat. Radioactive matter was soon found to be distributed universally throughout the rocks of the earth's outer shell; and the heat that is being continuously generated by the radioactive matter is in itself sufficient to account for most or all of the heat that is being lost by the earth. Thus the foundations on which the estimates of the physicists on the age of the earth had been based were destroyed. Unexpectedly, however, radioactivity supplied new and powerful means of measuring geologic time. The figures obtained were staggering in their immensity; the older estimates were multiplied at least ten-fold, and the formerly extravagant 100 million years became very modest indeed. Note now the reaction of the geologists: the new figures were so vast that they would not believe

* The tenth annual lecture on "Time and Its Mysteries," New York University, published in *The Sky*, July, 1941. Reprinted by permission of the New York University Press and of *The Sky*. Copyright 1941 by *The Sky*.

them. In the course of time, especially since 1930, the new estimates began to be generally accepted. Furthermore, the geologists have succeeded in popularizing them. We can hardly pick up a copy of a newspaper or magazine nowadays without being informed exactly how many million years ago some remarkable event in the history of the earth occurred. . . .

Soon after the discovery of radioactivity, it was found that the element uranium is disintegrating and is charging α-particles, and these α-particles after they have lost their electric charges become the gas helium. After the rate at which the helium is being generated had been determined, it occurred to Strutt, following the idea advanced by Rutherford in 1904, that if the helium formed by radioactive transformation is retained within the mineral in which it is generated, then the amount of the accumulated helium can be used to determine the ages of minerals. Various minerals of known geologic dates were examined and their ages in years were estimated.

Three surprises came out of these investigations: first, a very considerable amount of helium had accumulated in some of the minerals; second, great age was indicated for minerals that were already known to be extremely ancient; and third, the helium ages followed closely the geologic order. The oldest mineral had an indicated age of 700 million years—about seven times that of the then accepted age of the earth. Furthermore, these great ages were regarded as minimal figures, for part of the radiogenic helium had leaked away—as we now know, even the most tenacious of the highly radioactive minerals retains not more than half of the helium generated in it.

In 1905, Boltwood suggested that the ultimate product of the disintegration of uranium is lead. This suggestion, sensational in its day, was due to his recognition that lead is invariably present in all uranium minerals. Later, in 1907, by assembling the analyses of some 40 uranium minerals from a dozen localities, Boltwood showed that in minerals formed at the time and therefore of equal ages, a constant proportion exists between the amounts of the disintegration product—lead—and the parent substance—uranium.

Having thus shown with high probability that lead is the end product of the disintegration of uranium, he immediately proceeded to repay his debt to geology. If, said he, the quantity of lead occurring with a known amount of its radioactive parent, uranium, and the rate at which the uranium disintegrates are known, then the length of time required to produce the lead can be calculated, or in other words the mineral's age. Thus was born the *lead method* of determining the absolute age of uranium minerals—the best means we have for measuring geologic time in years. Boltwood computed the ages of 10 minerals, ranging from 410 million years for the uraninite from Portland, Conn., to 2,200 million years for thorianite from Ceylon. These were stupendous figures, and to accept them was not easy; it is therefore not surprising to find, almost 20 years later, the distinguished geochemist F. W. Clarke writing, "It is now plain that the uranium-lead ratio is of very questionable value in determining the age of minerals."

In his brilliant pioneer paper, Boltwood made a remarkable prediction. If lead is the end result of the disintegration of uranium, then the helium concurrently produced amounts to eight atoms of helium for every atom of uranium that disintegrates. The resulting lead should have an atomic weight of 206; its atomic weight is that of uranium, 238, minus 32, the weight of the eight expelled atoms of helium. This differs notably from the atomic weight of ordinary lead, which is 207.2.

In 1914, the prediction was put to the test. The atomic weight of lead of radioactive origin—lead obtained by Boltwood from a uraninite from North Carolina—was found to be substantially smaller than that of ordinary lead—a thrilling discovery to chemists, for never before in the history of science had the atomic weight of a chemical element been known to vary.

We now know that there are three principal radioactive series: the *uranium series*, in which the final stable product is lead of atomic weight 206 (Pb^{206}); the *actinium series*, ending in Pb^{207}; and the *thorium series*, ending in Pb^{208}. The relation of the actinium series has only recently been cleared up. The element uranium consists of two isotopes that disintegrate into lead at very different rates. The most abundant isotope is uranium I, which disintegrates to yield Pb^{206}, so slowly that at the end of 4.5 billion years only one half of it will have transformed to lead. The other isotope, constituting only $\frac{1}{140}$ part of the uranium, is actinouranium (U^{235}), and is the parent of the actinium series; it disintegrates about six times as rapidly as the uranium I and yields Pb^{207}. Thorium, the parent of the thorium series of radioactive elements, disintegrates at an extraordinarily slow rate; at the end of 13.9 billion years only one half of it will have been transformed to lead.

Most radioactive minerals that we use as time-clocks contain both uranium and thorium; consequently three kinds of radiogenic lead—Pb^{206}, Pb^{207}, and Pb^{208}—are being generated simultaneously within the same mineral. Only in pure thorium minerals is one single kind of lead (Pb^{208}) being produced.

How in practice do we actually use the lead method to determine the age of a mineral? The amounts of all three elements—uranium, thorium, and lead—in the mineral must be accurately determined by the chemist, and the atomic weight of the lead, or better still the amounts of the several isotopes present—Pb^{206}, Pb^{207}, and Pb^{208}—should be determined, now done by means of the mass-spectrograph. The rates of radioactive disintegration being known, it is easy to calculate the age of the mineral.

The lead method of measuring geologic time began to carry conviction even to the most doubting when it was shown that pure thorium minerals, associated in the same rocks with uranium minerals and therefore of the same geologic age, gave the same absolute ages. Moreover, all carefully determined lead ages invariably fell into their proper relative positions in the geologic time-scale.

In 1926, a uraninite from the Black Hills of South Dakota was shown to be 1,600 million years old. However, this uraninite occurred in a pegmatite dike, which is the very youngest member of a great assemblage of Pre-Cambrian rocks in which is plainly recorded a long antecedent history that extends much farther back in time. Therefore, in 1931, in reviewing the evidence, I suggested that the earth is in round numbers 2,000 million years old, and this estimate has become generally accepted during the past decade.

During the last few years the lead method has been greatly strengthened in two respects: first, by the development of very accurate means of determining the isotopic composition of lead; and second, by the recent discovery that ordinary lead contains a small proportion of an isotope of atomic weight 204 (Pb^{204}). This isotope of lead is not of radioactive origin; it occurs in all the ordinary lead (or lead of commerce) from all parts of the world; and is undoubtedly an inheritance along with the other chemical elements from the sun when the earth was born. The possibility that some common lead might have been deposited in a radioactive mineral during the time while the mineral was being formed has always been one of the difficulties of the lead method. Now, unexpectedly, we have a means of determining the amount of common lead that may occur mixed with the lead of radioactive origin.

Until recently it was held as absolutely necessary that only fresh, unoxidized minerals be used in determining ages by the lead method. The uranium minerals are readily susceptible to oxidation when exposed to weathering, and more uranium than lead is likely to be carried away by moving waters. On chemical analysis such oxidized minerals give high uranium-lead ratios, and this was the origin of some of the excessively great ages reported in early days.

It was pointed out only a few years ago that because radiogenic Pb^{206} and Pb^{207} are isotopes, and their chemical properties therefore identical, no amount of oxidation of the mineral in which they have formed can change the ratio between them. This ratio is characteristic of their age; in a young mineral, say 400 million years old, the ratio is 5.5 per cent, in a mineral 1,600 million years old it is 10 per cent. In the language of geology, the ratio between these two radiogenic leads is an *index fossil* of their age. The brilliant possibility of using this ratio to determine absolute ages was first tried out in 1936 by Rose and Stranathan, of New York University, and was found to work. The method requires extreme accuracy and has been especially developed by Alfred O. Nier during the past three years.

The most drastic test of the method so far has been on some of the highly oxidized uranium minerals from Katanga in the Belgian Congo, famous as the world's chief source of radium. The age of these deposits as found from the black unaltered pitchblende is 600 million years; the yellow oxidized pitchblende, when we apply the usual formulae for calculating the age of a mineral, yields the high figure of 1,000 million years, but the ratio of the radiogenic Pb^{207} to Pb^{208} gives the age as 600 million years.

The lead method, you can now see, has grown enormously in strength since it was first proposed by Boltwood. It can now employ minerals that contain common lead; it can utilize oxidized minerals; and in the case of an unoxidized mineral three completely independent determinations of age are afforded by one and the same specimen: first, by the lead derived from uranium I; second, by the lead derived from the thorium; and third, by the ratio between the amounts of lead derived from the two isotopes of uranium. The third is the most reliable. In a well-behaved mineral all three determinations of age agree closely.

There is the uraninite from Karelia on the polar circle in northwestern Russia, whose age is 1,800 million years. The most ancient radioactive minerals that have so far been found are in southeastern Manitoba, where, according to the ratio between Pb^{206} and Pb^{207}, a uraninite is 2,200 million years. This result is so stupendous that it requires further confirmation. Here again we have the tantalizing situation of radioactive minerals in pegmatites that cut through a rock formation which is therefore still older. Nowhere have we yet found radioactive evidence for the age of the oldest rocks of the earth. The conclusion at the present is that the earth is 2,000 million years old.

1941

THE FORMATION OF MINERAL DEPOSITS *

C. C. FURNAS

. . . No one can ever be certain that the stuff of which the earth is made has ever been entirely in a gaseous state, but it may have been. . . .

As long as this material was in the gaseous state, the composition was probably quite uniform throughout the mass. No concentration of particular elements or their compounds began until the second stage, when the bulk of the mass was liquid. After large amounts of liquid were present there may have been some separation of materials. There is evidence, by

* From *The Storehouse of Civilization* by C. C. Furnas, Bureau of Publications, Teachers College: Columbia University, reprinted by permission of the publishers. Copyright 1939 by Teachers College.

no means completely substantiated, that the original liquid separated into three liquid immiscible phases, a metallic melt, a sulfide melt, a silicate melt. The metallic melt would be in the center; the silicate melt on the outer crust.

After this preliminary rough separation (if there was such) came a number of natural processes which were instrumental in segregating elements and compounds to a sufficient extent to make ores which would be usable by man.

Geologists display a degree of agreement on theories which is greater than that shown by economists but still far from perfect; so no one explanation of the processes of ore formation can be expected to ring true to all ears. One generally accepted outline of the probable geo-actions involved includes seven processes. It is probably at least as good as any of the other available theories.

Only a few of the ninety-two elements of the earth's material occur in the pure state, that is, are not combined with some other element. The different chemical compounds which can be formed by the combinations of the elements number into the hundreds of thousands. Hence the molten blob of matter which once was the earth was made up of not a relatively few chemical elements but a host of chemical compounds of different melting points and densities. As the mass cooled, one compound after another would freeze out as a solid and become segregated and hence concentrated in the mass. This process of selective crystallization was the first important step in concentrating minerals. The study of the selective solidification of various components from a liquid phase is one of the fundamental tools of modern physical chemistry. The process always and inevitably follows the principles and implications of the phase rule which was first enunciated and explained by the American mathematician, Willard Gibbs.

There is no reason to go into any of the intricate details of the application of the phase rule to this phenomenon, but one or two examples will give an idea of the principles involved. Almost everyone knows that if sea water freezes, the salt in the sea water is squeezed out of the crystal of ice which is formed and thus is concentrated on the boundary of the crystal. The first solid phase which is formed from the liquid sea water is practically pure ice. Eventually, if the temperature is lowered, the concentration of salt at the crystal boundary will continue until the remaining water becomes "saturated" with salt and the salt itself begins to precipitate. Hence, when sea water is completely frozen, it consists of adjacent particles of practically pure water and practically pure salt. The size of the ice crystals will depend primarily upon the rate of cooling, for the slower the freezing process, the larger will be the crystals which are formed. Another important factor is the chance occurrence of nuclei of material in the mass of water which will aid in the formation of the first ice crystals. . . .

The two-component system of salt and water is much simpler than most of the systems which are important in the formation of mineral deposits. The phenomena involved in the freezing out of particular substances in a three-component system are essentially the same as those for the two-component system, but the picture is probably ten times as complex. It is safe to say that the crystallizations of material from a four-component system are certainly at least a hundred times as complicated as those from salt and water. When one considers that it is possible to have as many as a dozen chemical components in a molten magma in the earth's material, he can see that the formation of solid minerals from a fluid mixture is by no means a simple process.

Although there has been a great deal of investigation of the order and composition of the solid phases which separate from a complicated fluid mass, there is still a great deal to be learned in this field, particularly under conditions of high pressure. Suffice it to say that, though we do not have a quantitative understanding of all the phenomena, it is generally known that selective crystallization of particular mineral constituents from a molten mass has been one of the primary factors in building up the concentration of certain valuable components to the point where deposits may be dignified with the name of ores. This process probably performed no great service in the segregation of the minerals in the original crystallization of the earth's crust, but came into play in subsequent times when crystallization was being carried out on a smaller scale, chiefly in the intrusion of molten igneous material into overlying solid rock.

This process of selective crystallization is thought to be responsible for the formation of some deposits of iron, chromium, nickel, copper, gold, silver, platinum, palladium, and perhaps diamonds.

As earth liquids cool they begin to display mutual insolubilities even while all the material is still in the molten state. This means that one liquid separates from another, just as slag floats on top of molten iron in a ladle in a steel mill. In this same way molten feldspar and quartz tend to float to the top and separate in the upper part of a molten magma. These lighter liquids carry with them tin, tungsten, beryllium, columbium, rare earth metals, radium, uranium, phosphorus, fluorine, boron, and arsenic. The mass eventually solidifies and there may then be some further concentration by selective crystallization.

Strange as it may seem, molten rock in the depths of the earth often contains a great deal of water and light gases. Such volatile components are held in place only as long as there is a great deal of pressure on the molten mass. As soon as something happens to relieve the pressure, a volcanic eruption, or the movement of the magma into an area of intrusion, the water tends to leave with great rapidity. Along with the water, which may still be liquid even though it is very hot, go carbon dioxide, nitrogen, sulfur compounds, fluorides, chlorides, phosphates, arsenic and antimony compounds, selenides, and tellurides. The metals in the migrating compounds are gold, silver, iron, copper, lead, zinc, bismuth, tin, tungsten, mercury, manganese, nickel, cobalt, radium, and uranium. Minerals deposited by these volatile constituents appear as sublimates in volcanic areas and as deposits near igneous intrusions. A large number of valuable metal deposits have been formed in this way.

Water is continually moving about in some of the underground layers of our crust. It is constantly dissolving and reprecipitating materials. It may dissolve a substance while it is hot and precipitate it in a colder region. Conditions of acidity or alkalinity may change from place to place and cause solution or precipitation. The solvent action of underground waters has been responsible for the concentration of some deposits of iron, copper, lead, and zinc.

Water that is close to the surface often contains a considerable quantity of dissolved oxygen. The dissolving characteristics of such water may be entirely different from what they were when it was oxygen free. If it filters through a bed of rocky material containing iron minerals, it may dissolve out the other substances and leave the iron compounds behind. The result is that the iron is concentrated into a usable ore, the other materials being carried to other locations.

One of the major factors in bringing about the ultimate concentration of ores has been the formation of sediments. It must be remembered that the surface of the earth has been exposed to the selective action of the run-off of rain water for millions of years. Rainfall has always eroded the surface of the earth and will continue to do so. In some spots on the earth the total thickness of the deposits which have been laid down by sedimentation is approximately seventy miles. Such deposits can be storehouses for enormous quantities of ore, provided there has been some selective action in operation.

The iron deposits of the Lake Superior region occur as iron carbonate, oxide, or silicate, and are generally thought to be derived from marine sediments. The supposed course of events is that great quantities of molten rock, which was high in iron silicate because of previous selective crystallization, poured out on an ocean floor. These beds of molten rock were subsequently uplifted and exposed to the action of air and circulating water. The more soluble materials, including silica in a colloidal state, were leached out and carried away, leaving the highly insoluble iron oxide behind. Each step of the process was slow, but time is no barrier when millions of years are available. The rate of formation of the deposits was only an infinitesimal fraction of our present rate of depletion of them.

Aluminum is another metal that has been made available by the fortunate combination of the effects of sedimentation and weathering. The source of our common aluminum mineral, bauxite, seems to have been feldspar which was leached out with water containing carbon dioxide. The chemical action is idealized as follows:

$$\underset{\text{feldspar (orthoclase)}}{2KAlSi_3O_8} + CO_2 + 2H_2O \longrightarrow \underset{\text{potassium carbonate}}{K_2CO_3} + \underset{\text{kaolin}}{Al_2O_3 \cdot 2SiO_2 \cdot 2H_2O} + \underset{\text{silica}}{4SiO_2}$$

Further exposure to water removed the potassium carbonate and the silica, in solution or suspension, leaving relatively pure aluminum oxide behind. In some cases, when sulfur compounds happened to be present in leaching water, the silica was removed from the ore body; but the potassium compounds stayed behind to form the potassium-aluminum mineral, alunite,

$$K_2SO_4 \cdot Al_2(SO_4)_3 \cdot 4Al(OH)_3,$$

of which there are large deposits in Utah.

The geologists have some explanation for the formation of almost every known mineral. Most of the explanations seem plausible; others call for a liberal imagination. Investigations and explanations of this sort do more than satisfy curiosity; they are distinct aids in systematizing the knowledge of minerals, so that deposits of desired material may be searched for with some degree of assurance of success or may be detected by indirect means.

The last important process in mineral formation was that of biological activity. Living organisms are not ordinarily given the proper amount of credit for their part in forming the character of the earth's surface. We ordinarily think that the inconspicuous blobs of living matter, which we see everywhere we go, run through a certain life cycle, produce progeny, die, and leave the surroundings very much the same as they were before. This picture most decidedly is not correct. An individual coral polyp does not change the character of the earth very much, but polyps in numbers of astronomical size build reefs and islands of very pure limestone. To the casual observer it would seem that the polyp has built these great masses of land out of nothing; but, of course, it cannot do that any more than man can. It has taken the calcium compounds from a very dilute solution in sea water and built up a shell of calcium compounds to protect itself. In this process of following its preordained metabolic ritual, it has concentrated calcium by several thousandfold in the form of an insoluble compound. Insignificant as the coral polyp may appear, it is one of the most important creatures in changing the character of the earth's surface.

The simple organisms which make coral islands are only a few of the millions of species that exist on the earth. Practically all these species are imbued with the single purpose of living as long as possible and producing as many progeny as possible. But inevitably tied up with all of these processes of juggling organic compounds through a life cycle there are certain phenomena of mineral metabolism. No organism exists without some metal compounds in its structure; and in nearly all cases the concentration of the essential metal in the organism is considerably higher than that in the immediate environment. Thus there are a great many possibilities for the concentration of the metallic minerals.

If you think that the feeble efforts of plants and animals can hardly be significant in shaping the mineral character of the earth, you should recall that life in some form or another has been scattered over the crust for probably a billion years, that it has been concentrating metals all during that period. You may further visualize the magnitude of their work if you are reminded that there are probably 10^{13} tons of living matter (both plant and animal) on the surface of the earth today. If that same amount of living matter had existed on the earth for only half a billion years and if the average life cycle were one year, then the total amount of living matter which has been engaged in this concentrating process would amount to 5×10^{21} tons.

This figure is approximately equal to the entire weight of the earth and 170 times the weight of what is considered to be the earth's crust. Since the organisms have worked close to the surface, their total effect on concentrating minerals has been enormous. . . .

The mere presence of an enormous amount of organic matter would not, in itself, aid in the deposition of the minerals unless mineral concentration were going on in the organisms themselves. Investigations have shown that, in the cases of some metals, organisms have enormous powers of concentration. . . .

From the data on the quantity of matter going through the cycle of life each year and its ability to concentrate mineral elements, it is evident that plants and animals may very well have been major contributing factors in building up billions of tons of mineral deposits. Many deposits of phosphates, of silica in the form of diatomaceous earth, of copper, iron, zinc, sulfur, arsenic, iodine, and vanadium have been accumulated by living organisms.

It does not necessarily follow that, because an organism concentrates a metal within its own structure, this same concentration will carry over into the immediate earthy surroundings after the organism has died; but it usually happens that way. Either the metal is tied up as an insoluble compound in the animal's skeletal structure, as in the case of the coral, or the organisms themselves congregate in such dense communities that the mineral remains build up deposits of considerable magnitude. A great many of the low animals which live in the sea drop to the bottom of the ocean as sediment when they die. The organic part of their make-up is disposed of by the ever present scavengers or by simple oxidation, but the sediments usually remain on the ocean floor. Hence, after an ocean recedes or when the crust of the earth rises, the concentrated metal compounds on the ocean floor become mineral deposits on dry land. This means that the sediments of the ocean have been enriched in certain elements by the depletion of sea water in these same constituents. . . .

A few examples of the intensity of these concentrating processes will forestall the idea that they may be insignificant. Oysters commonly build up a concentration of copper two hundredfold greater than that of sea water. As a matter of fact, nearly all the lower marine organisms concentrate copper. This is because the respiratory fluid of their bodies, which corresponds to our blood, is hemocyanin. Hemocyanin is a close chemical relative of the hemoglobin of our blood, wherein copper is used instead of iron in the essential chemical compound. Ordinary kelp is known to build up relatively high concentrations of both potassium and iodine. The lobster has a concentration of iodine in its interior structure which is several hundred thousand times that of sea water. The unattractive sea cucumber contains up to 10 per cent of vanadium in its respiratory tract. This is a concentration of many thousandfold over that of sea water. . . .

Chile saltpeter (sodium nitrate) is considered to be of organic origin. It is generally thought to have been derived from guano, bacteria, or seaweed, though some contend that it is of volcanic origin. Quite likely it is a combination of all of these.

Some of the greatest iron ore deposits of the world are generally considered to be of organic origin. An important factor in the laying down of the Clinton hematite (the iron ores of Birmingham, Alabama, Chattanooga, Tennessee, and central New York) seems to have been the presence of certain iron bacteria. In the process of formation of this ore the leaching water contained iron in suspension or solution. These bacteria gargled iron water; it was essential to their life processes. The water passed on, but the skeletons of the organisms with their high iron content stayed behind.

The greatest mineral result of biological activity is seen in the formation of coal, petroleum, and oil shale. All three are derived from biological materials.

Perhaps a quarter of a billion years ago the earth was in the midst of the Carboniferous period. Plants grew with a rapidity and luxuriance not rivaled anywhere today, even in the tropics. Over 3,000 different plant species have been identified in the fossil remains of coal. More than 90 per cent of them were similar to plants we know today. The Lycopods, which are mainly small shrubs today, attained a height of a hundred feet and a diameter of three feet. Rushes were common and sometimes grew ninety feet tall. . . .

The heaviest growths occurred in extensive swamps, perhaps bordering on the flat shores of the sea. As the plants died the leaves and trunks sank into the miry ooze of the swamp out of contact with the air. The growing cycle went on above them, year after year, century after century, until the organic debris in the bottom of the swamps was sometimes hundreds of feet thick. Climate changed, no one knows why, sediment was washed in on top of the bogs, the organic detritus was buried deeper and deeper. No oxygen penetrated the mass, so the dead plants could not decay in the conventional manner. They lay there under the ground for millions of years. We now bore into those swamp beds of the past and find—coal.

At one time it was only possible to guess about what happened in the old swamp beds during the past quarter billion years; but the researches in organic chemistry and bacteriology have clarified the history of coal to a certain extent. It is quite evident that the principal feature of the formation of coal from plant materials consisted of the removal of oxygen from the plant structure by means of chemical or bacteriological action, or both.

The bulk of the dry substance of plants is cellulose and lignin, both of which have the generalized formula $C_6H_{10}O_5$. In such a substance the carbon is 44.4 per cent, the hydrogen 6.2 per cent, and the oxygen 49.4 per cent by weight. As plant material changed to coal it went through various stages of decomposition, giving products which are now roughly classified as those of peat, lignite, sub-bituminous coal, bituminous coal, semi-bituminous coal, semi-anthracite, and anthracite. . . .

If one follows the life line of coal as evidenced by the content of hydrogen, carbon, and oxygen, it is quite evident that oxygen was removed as the coal-forming process progressed. The oxygen removal probably was effected by the formation of carbon dioxide (CO_2) and water (H_2O). This, of course, required the removal of a certain amount of carbon and hydrogen as well. But each pound of oxygen leaving as carbon dioxide would remove only 0.375 pounds of carbon, and each pound of oxygen leaving as water would remove only 0.125 pounds of hydrogen. It is quite evident, then, that if the oxygen of the plant structure went into carbon dioxide and water and if these two substances were subsequently removed, the solid material left behind would display a net gain in the proportions of hydrogen and carbon. There is ample evidence that the gases, carbon monoxide (CO) and methane (CH_4), were also formed. Methane is evidently a common product of the decomposition of submerged vegetation. It is the common marsh gas which bubbles up from the bottom of swamps.

What caused these chemical reactions to take place in the forming of coal? There are various microorganisms that are anaerobic; they obtain the oxygen for their living processes from the oxygen in chemical compounds rather than from the free oxygen of the air. It is generally agreed that such microorganisms played a part in the formation of coal. Buried in the depth of the fibrous residues, they robbed the woody material of its oxygen to make water, carbon dioxide, and a few other gases. Along with, or subsequent to, the organisms' action there may have been inanimate chemical actions resulting in the breaking up of oxygen compounds. Such reactions have been carried out in the laboratory. High pressures and slightly elevated temperatures, such as would be found in the coal beds, may have aided the progress of such reactions. All the reactions were very slow; but a hundred million years is a long time, long enough to allow the slowest imaginable reactions to go to completion.

The origin of petroleum is much more a matter of dispute than the origin of coal. The opinion of the experts now tips the balance in favor of a vegetable origin for petroleum, though animal life may have contributed something. Petroleum deposits seem to be associated with salt water (coal deposits were usually laid down under fresh water). The petroleum-forming situation of the past would seem to call for an extensive array of shallow seashore areas where there was a heavy growth of seaweed, diatoms, and algae. The plants died and contributed their remains to the bottom ooze. There may have been considerable animal remains laid down in the same area. Some of these lower plants, such as the algae, have oil in their internal structure while they are still alive. If a great mass of these minute organisms were collected in one place and if the oil were squeezed out of each one, an oil accumulation would be started without any subsequent chemical or biological reaction.

Since it is well established that some organisms, such as the diatoms, produce oil in their own metabolic processes, it might seem sufficient to allow the matter of the explanation of the origin of petroleum to rest there; but the investigators have not been entirely satisfied with the sufficiency of that explanation. It is assumed, and with fairly good evidence, that after the plant and animal organisms had ceased to live, their bodies were worked on by anaerobic microorganisms (perhaps similar to those instrumental in the formation of coal) which removed the oxygen to form gases and water and left behind a hydrocarbon residue which is petroleum. There is also good laboratory evidence that some of the chemical changes may have taken place without the aid of organisms.

The process of deoxidation in the case of petroleum would have to be carried much further than in the case of bituminous coal. The analysis of a typical Pennsylvania crude oil is carbon 84.9 per cent, hydrogen 13.7 per cent, and oxygen 1.4 per cent by weight. There is no adequate explanation why the residual products should be oils instead of solids, such as coal.

The difference might be due to the fact that organisms other than those which made the coal decomposed the raw material of petroleum. It may be that the chemical character of the organic material which was the base of petroleum was different from that of the coals. There is some evidence for the latter hypothesis in the case of cannel coals. The cannel coals are free-burning and contain a great deal of oily materials. They were laid down under the same conditions as bituminous coal; but the raw material, instead of being the woody parts of plants, appears to have been vast accumulations of wind-borne spores and pollen grains. Thus the character of the original organic material probably has something to do with the final product.

There is considerable evidence that chemical changes divorced from living organisms have also made significant contributions to petroleum formation. If plant materials, such as cotton or algae or other marine organisms, are subjected to pressures of 100 to 200 atmospheres at temperatures of 300° C. in the presence of an alkaline material such as limestone, they produce gases such as carbon dioxide and hydrogen and an oily hydrocarbon residue.

Most of the experiments in making petroleum from carbohydrates have involved the use of a temperature of 300° C. or higher. There is good evidence that no temperatures as high as this were ever present in the beds of oil-forming materials. However, the processes might go on at the lower temperatures but at such slow rates that they could not be detected in the laboratory. Geological processes have time as an ally, for a million years in geology is an almost negligible interval. Hence, the necessity for high temperatures in the laboratory is no disproof of the low-temperature geochemical process of petroleum formation.

Whatever the process or combination of processes which entered into the making of petroleum, it is quite evident that the oily mass, after it was formed, migrated through the underground sand and silt to immense common reservoirs. The oil wells of today are merely the pockets in the earth's crust which happened to be most favorable physically for the accumulation of the oil and gas. Usually the reservoir of oil lies on top of dense rocky formations, in porous beds of sand. Gas is pocketed above the oil and water below it.

The organic residues of the past ages are not confined to coal and petroleum. Almost every large country in the world has more or less extensive deposits of sedimentary rock materials containing organic matter which will yield a satisfactory liquid fuel when subjected to destructive distillation. To these materials is given the name "oil shale," a generic term covering materials of various origins and compositions ranging from unusually dirty limestones, such as underlie the area around Chicago, Illinois, to low-grade coals. Oil shale apparently has had about the same geological history as coal—with a few details changed. The organic material is largely of plant origin. The plants grew, died, lay down, and started to decay in the conventional manner; but before decomposition by oxidation was complete they became imbedded with silt of various kinds and were buried under water or still more silt. The oxidation was halted and chemical reaction proceeded slowly along other lines, with the result that the organic matter was converted into hydrocarbons or something that gives oily hydrocarbons when heated. Even less is known about shale oil than about petroleum. The chemists have a name for it—kerogen—but that means nothing. Suffice it to say that the chemical make-up of the carboniferous constituents of oil shale are more closely related to coal than they are to liquid petroleum; but when heated the organic matter may be almost completely converted into liquid fuels. . . .

Nature's operations in laying down the world's mineral deposits have been proceeding over a span of probably two billion years. Now comes man digging into the storehouse. In one century of really active exploitation he has dug well down toward the bottom of some of the mineral bins of the two-billion-year-old storehouse. . . .

1939

TVA: DEMOCRACY ON THE MARCH *

DAVID E. LILIENTHAL

A new chapter in American public policy was written when Congress in May of 1933 passed the law creating the TVA. For the first time since the trees fell before the settlers' ax, America set out to command nature not by defying her, as in that wasteful past, but by understanding and acting upon her first law—the oneness of men and natural resources, the unity that binds together land, streams, forests, minerals, farming, industry, mankind. . . .

For fifteen years before TVA came into being Congressional and public debate centered largely on a single potential resource of the Tennessee River, hydro-electric power. . . .

How those power facilities were to be used, that was the major question which attracted public discussion down the years. That question was settled by the passage of the Act creating TVA. But it was not settled on the narrow issue of "public ownership" of power. The message of President Roosevelt urging approval of the Norris bill (which became a law

* From *TVA: Democracy on the March* by David E. Lilienthal, Harper & Brothers. Reprinted by permission from the publishers. Copyright 1944 by David E. Lilienthal.

with his signature on May 18, 1933) boldly proposed a new and fundamental change in the development of our country's resources. . . .

It is clear [the message read] that the Muscle Shoals development is but a small part of the potential public usefulness of the entire Tennessee River. Such use, if envisioned in its entirety, transcends mere power development: it enters the wide fields of flood control, soil erosion, afforestation, elimination from agricultural use of marginal lands, and distribution and diversification of industry. In short, this power development of war days leads logically to national planning for a complete river watershed involving many states and the future lives and welfare of millions. It touches and gives life to all forms of human concerns. . . .

The TVA Act was nothing inadvertent or impromptu. It was rather the deliberate and well-considered creation of a new national policy. For the first time in the history of the nation, the resources of a river were not only to be "envisioned in their entirety"; they were to be developed *in that unity with which nature herself regards her resources*—the waters, the land, and the forests together, a "seamless web"—just as Maitland saw "the unity of all history," of which one strand cannot be touched without affecting every other strand for good or ill. . . .

"Envisioned in its entirety" this river, like every river in the world, had many potential assets. It could yield hydro-electric power for the comfort of the people in their homes, could promote prosperity on their farms and foster the development of industry. But the same river by the very same dams, if they were wisely designed, could be made to provide a channel for navigation. The river could also be made to provide fun for fishermen and fish for food, pleasure from boating and swimming, a water supply for homes and factories. But the river also presented an account of liabilities. It threatened the welfare of the people by its recurrent floods; pollution from industrial wastes and public sewage diminished its value as a source of water supply and for recreation; its current carried to the sea the soil of the hills and fields to be lost there to men forever.

To a single agency, the TVA, these potentialities of the river for good and evil were entrusted. But the river was to be seen as part of the larger pattern of the region, one asset of the many that in nature are interwoven: the land, the minerals, the waters, the forests—and all of these as one—in their relation to the lives of the valley's people. It was the total benefit to all that was to be the common goal and the new agency's responsibility.

That is not the way public resource development had heretofore been undertaken in this country. Congress in creating TVA broke with the past. No single agency had in this way ever been assigned the unitary task of developing a river so as to release the total benefit from its waters for the people. Not far from where I write are other rivers developed by private interests or public agencies. They will serve to illustrate the contrast. On these rivers it is the common practice in public projects as well as private to build a single dam without first having fixed upon a general plan that will ultimately insure the full use of the whole river as a unit. There are dams built for the single purpose of power development. Such individual dams, in order to yield an immediate return in power, impair or destroy the river's full development of power at other sides, for they were not designed or built with the whole river thought of as it is in nature, a unit. These power dams are not built or operated to control floods, and do not provide a continuous navigable channel. The full usefulness of that river is lessened. Similarly, hundreds of millions of dollars in public funds have been expended for the single purpose of navigation on some of our rivers, but most of the dams constructed will not control the rivers' floods or create electric energy. They now stand as massive barriers against the erection of multi-purpose structures.

Over a long period of years scores of millions of dollars have been spent for levees to hold the waters back on the lower reaches of some of our rivers, but at the headwaters there were no reservoir dams that could make local levee protection effective.

And through the long years there has been a continuing disregard of nature's truth: that in any valley of the world what happens on the *river* is largely determined by what happens on the *land*—by the kind of crops that farmers plant and harvest, by the type of machines they use, by the number of trees they cut down. The full benefits of stream and of soil cannot be realized by the people if the water and the land are not developed in harmony.

If the soil is exposed, unprotected from the rains by cover and by roots, the people will be poor and the river will be muddy, heavy with the best soil of the fields. And as a consequence each year the farmers will be forced more and more to use their land in ways that speed up this cycle of ruin, until the cover and then the top soil itself are wholly gone. When that day comes, as in the great reaches of China's sorrowful Yellow River Valley, then the rains run off the land almost as rapidly as water runs from a pavement. Even a moderate rainfall forces the river from its banks, and every downpour brings disastrous floods, destroying crops and homes and bridges and highways, not only where the land is poor, but down the river's length, down in the areas where people are more prosperous, where the soil is still protected and factories have been built at the river's bend. Industries and railroads will be interrupted, farms flooded out, towns and villages destroyed, while heavy silt deposits fill the power reservoirs and stop up the channels of navigation.

It is otherwise where land is covered with sod or trees, and cultivated each season with the purpose of holding the rain where it falls. Such land literally serves as a water reservoir, a part of a system of flood control and river development, quite as directly as dams that stretch from bank to bank to hold the waters back. In many locations, after such proper land-use programs have been rather fully developed, the results should make it possible to reduce the magnitude and cost of engineering structures required for water control.

The farmers' new pastures and meadows themselves are reservoirs. If the changed farming practices now in use on many tens of thousands of Tennessee Valley farms were applied to all the agricultural area of our watershed (as some day I am confident they will be), the soil might absorb as much as half the customary twelve-inch surface run-off of rain each year; this storage of water on the farms would equal the capacity of two reservoirs as great as the one behind the Norris Dam, which stands 267 feet above the Clinch River.

This is of course nothing new, nothing discovered by the TVA. That a river could offer many benefits and a variety of hazards, that its improvement through engineering structures is inseparable from the development and use of the land of the watershed, has been recognized for many years by scientists and engineers. For over a generation a distinguished line of conservationists had seen this truth and written and spoken of it with great force. And as a matter of fact almost any farmer, standing in his barn door while he watches a torrential rain beat upon his land and fill his creek, could see that much. The point is that knowledge of this inseparability of land and streams has only once, here on this river, been carried into our national *action.* On every other watershed we turn our rivers over to engineers of one agency to develop while farm experts of other agencies concern themselves with the land. Thus far it is only in the Valley of the Tennessee that Congress has directed that these resources be dealt with as a whole, not separately.

The principles of unity whereby this valley has gone about the restoration of its land and the multiplication of the land's usefulness are, of course, the same as those that governed turning the river to man's account. The development of soil and its increased productivity are not simply problems of land, of farming, and of agricultural science, any more than the development of a river is only water control, dams, and engineering techniques. The restoration of land fertility, the healing of gullies, the reforestation of hillsides, these are no more ends in themselves than are flood control, navigation, and power. As the river is not separable from the land, so the land is inseparable from the forests and minerals, from the factories and shops, from the people making their living from their resources.

Here, too, the methods this valley has followed to achieve its purposes break sharply with those long prevailing. The methods differ because to think of resources as a unity compels the use of different ways. The idea of unity makes it inescapable that each man's farm must also be seen as one operating unit. The farm, too, is a "seamless web."

To the farmer on his land the problems do not fit into neat cubicles labeled "forestry" or "soil chemistry" or "mechanical engineering," nor to him is soil erosion or holding water on the land separate from the whole business of making a living on the land. And so in the way TVA goes about its responsibilities there are no "jurisdictional" lines, no excluding of the chemical engineer, say, because this is a "farm" problem, or of the businessman or the inventor because soil erosion is a "public issue," or of a county or state expert because agriculture is a "national" question. The invention by this valley's technicians of a new kind of machine and the decision of a businessman to produce and market it may be as important in land restoration as check dams in the gullies, if it thereby enables the farmer to make a living by raising soil-conserving crops. The invention here of a quick-freezing machine, a portable thresher, or a furrow seeder, all designed to overcome specific economic obstacles in the farmer's path toward land conservation, we see as just as real factors in land restoration as the terracing of the slopes.

Because they sinned against the unity of nature, because they developed some one resource without regard to its relation to every other resource in the life of man, ancient civilizations have fallen into decay and lie buried in oblivion. Everywhere in the world the trail of unbalanced resource development is marked by poverty, where prosperity seemed assured; by ugliness and desolation, with towns now dying that once were thriving; by land that once supported gracious living now eroded and bare, and over wide areas the chill of death to the ambitions of the enterprising young and to the security of the mature.

How industry came to Ducktown in the mountains of eastern Tennessee a generation ago is one such story. Copper ore was discovered; mining began; a smeltery was built. One of the resources of this remote region was being developed; it meant new jobs, income to supplement farming and forestry. But the developers had only copper in their plans. The magnificent hardwood forests to a distance of seven miles were cut and burned as fuel for the smelter's roasting ovens. The sulphur fumes from the stacks destroyed the thin cover that remained; not only the trees but every sign of living vegetation was killed and the soil became poison to life.

The dead land, shorn of its cover of grass and trees was torn mercilessly by the rains; and the once lovely and fruitful earth was cut into deep gullies that widened into desolate canyons twenty and more feet deep. No one can look upon this horror as it is today without a shudder. Silt, swept from unprotected slopes, filled the streams and destroyed fish life. The water was robbed of its value for men, for animals, and for industry, while farther down the stream a reservoir of a private power company was filling with silt. One of Ducktown's resources, copper, had been developed. But all its other resources had been destroyed in the process. The people and their institutions suffered in the end.

All this desolation caused as much pain to the officials of the copper company as it did to the lovers of nature. For balanced resource development is not, as the naïve appear to believe, a simple moral tale of "bad men" versus "good men." It is much more than that. It is the reflection of our national thinking. In fact, in this case, the early operators came to see the point better than most people, for they had to pay cash in damages for some of this destruction, after long and bitter lawsuits by the injured landowners. . . .

The "played-out" farmlands of the South, now in the process of rebuilding, were "mined" to grow a single crop of cotton: they are one more illustration of the remorseless arithmetic of nature. Here once lovely manor houses stand seedy and deserted because their foundation, the soil, has been exhausted, romantic monuments to a national tragedy of waste. And the great towers of Manhattan and Chicago, the modern business streets of Omaha on the prairies, all rest on the same foundations as the old plantation manor—the land, the waters, the minerals, and the forests. We are all in this together, cities and countryside.

There is no security or safety for us anywhere if nature's resources are exhausted. This day of machines and increasing populations multiplies our jeopardy. For this we must remember: Unless nature's laws of restoration are observed, modern technology can compress a once gradual process of resource exhaustion into the quick cycle of a generation or two. . . .

For when a people or a region rely almost exclusively for their living upon the extraction of raw materials—the cutting of lumber, the growing of wheat, the mining of coal or iron—and depend little upon the processing, by manufacture, of those raw materials, these natural resources are put under a severe drain to support a growing population. The income which comes to a region from cutting trees or growing cotton and bringing them to a point of transportation is only a small fraction of the income, the "value added," when those trees have been processed into paper or the cotton into overalls. If a region depends—as most "colonial" regions are forced to do—almost entirely upon the income from cutting the lumber or growing the cotton, and hardly at all upon making the paper, the textiles, the furniture, or any of the other articles manufactured from the raw resources, then the pressure to "mine" the fertility of the soil, to devastate the forests for lumber, to deplete the oil fields and coal reserves becomes very great indeed.

That pressure to deplete resources can be lessened by the growth of the industries which electric power encourages. But if the industry is only exploitative, if it does not *sustain* the productivity of the resources upon which all of us depend, industry can exhaust a region and hurt its people's chances of security and happiness. The "how" of industrial development, like the "how" of developing a river or the land or the forests, is the all-important point. . . .

Good will is not enough, nor speeches nor noble intentions. There will be those in abundance. There are principles and policies to develop and to observe if people are to benefit and democratic institutions are to flourish. The unity of nature's resources must not be disregarded, or the purpose for which such developments are undertaken will be betrayed as it has been betrayed before: by the way the job is done.

1944

»»-«««

WHAT MAKES THE WEATHER *

WOLFGANG LANGEWIESCHE

I

You wake up one morning and you are surprised: the weather, which had been gray and dreary for days and seemed as if it were going to stay that way forever, with no breaks in the clouds and no indication of a gradual clearing, is now all of a sudden clear and sunny and crisp, with a strong northwest wind blowing, and the whole world looks newly washed and newly painted.

"It" has become "fine." Why? How?

"Something" has cleared the air, you might say. But what? You might study out the weather news in the back of your newspaper, and you would get it explained to you in terms of barometric highs and lows; but just why a rise of barometric pressure should clear the air would still leave you puzzled. The honest truth is that the weather has never been explained. In school they told you about steam engines or electricity or even about really mysterious things, such as gravitation, and they could do it so that it made sense to a boy. They told you also about the weather, but their explanations failed to explain, and you knew it even then. The lows and highs, cyclones and anti-cyclones, the winds that blew around in circles—all these things were much more puzzling than the weather itself. That is why weather has always made only the dullest conversation: there simply was no rhyme nor reason to it.

But now there is. A revolutionary fresh view has uncovered the rhyme and reason in the weather. Applied to your particular surprise of that morning, it has this to say:

The air which was warm, moist, and gray last night is still warm, moist, and gray this morning; but it has been pushed fifty or one hundred miles to the south and east of where you live, and has been replaced by a mass of cold, clear, dry air coming from the north or west. It is as simple as that; there is no mysterious "It" in it; just plain physical sense. It is called Air Mass Analysis.

* Reprinted by permission from *Harper's Magazine* and from the author.

It is based upon the researches and experiments of a physicist named Vilhelm Bjerknes, of Norway, and though in this particular case it seems almost childishly simple, it is Norway's greatest contribution to world culture since Ibsen. Or perhaps because it is simple—the rare example of a science which in becoming more sophisticated also becomes more common sense and easier to understand. It is so new that it hasn't yet reached the newspapers, nor the high school curricula, much less the common knowledge of the public in general. But the weather bureaus of the airlines have worked by it for years, and pilots have to learn it. It is indispensable both in commercial flying and in air war; we could fly without gasoline, without aluminum, perhaps without radio, but we could never do without Bjerknes's Air Mass Analysis.

You might inquire next where that morning's new air came from, and just how it got to be cold, dry, and clear. And there you get close to the heart of the new weather science, where meteorology turns into honest, common-sense geography.

That air has come from Canada, where it has been quite literally air-conditioned. Not all parts of the world have the power to condition air, but Canada has. Especially in the fall and winter and early spring, the northern part of this continent becomes an almost perfectly designed mechanical refrigerator. The Rocky Mountains in the west keep currents of new air from flowing into the region. And for weeks the air lies still. The cool ground, much of it snow-covered; the ice of the frozen lakes; plus the perennial stored-up coldness of Hudson's Bay—all cool the layer of air immediately above them. This means a stabilizing and calming of the whole atmosphere all the way up; for cool air is heavy, and with a heavy layer bottommost, there is none of that upflowing of air, that up-welling of moisture-laden heat into the cooler, high altitude which is the mechanism that makes clouds. Thus there may be some low ground fogs there, but above them the long nights of those northern latitudes are clear and starry, wide open toward the black infinite spaces of the universe; and into that black infinity the air gradually radiates whatever warmth it may contain from its previous sojourns over other parts of the world. The result, after weeks of stagnation, is a huge mass of air that is uniformly ice-cold, dry, and clear. It stretches from the Rocky Mountains in the west to Labrador in the east, from the ice wastes of the Arctic to the prairies of Minnesota and North Dakota; and—the third dimension is the most important—it is ice-cold from the ground all the way up to the stratosphere. It is, in short, a veritable glacier of air.

That is an air mass. In the jargon of air-faring men, a mass of Polar Canadian air.

When a wave of good, fresh Polar Canadian air sweeps southward into the United States—it happens almost rhythmically every few days—you don't need a barometer to tell you so. There is nothing subtle, theoretical, or scientific about it. You can see and feel the air itself and even hear it. It comes surging out of a blue-green sky across the Dakotas, shaking the hangar doors, whistling in the grass, putting those red-checkered thick woolen jackets on the men, and lighting the stoves in the houses. It flows southward down the Mississippi Valley as a cold wave in winter, or as relief from a heat wave in summer, blowing as a northwest wind with small white hurrying clouds in it. In winter it may sweep southward as far as Tennessee and the Carolinas, bringing frosts with brilliantly clear skies, making the darkies shiver in their drafty cabins, and producing a wave of deaths by pneumonia. Sometimes it even reaches the Texas Gulf Coast; then it is locally called a norther, and the cows at night crowd for warmth around the gas flares in the oil fields. A duck hunter dies of exposure in the coastal swamps. A lively outbreak of Polar Canadian air may reach down into Florida, damage the orange crops, and embarrass local Chambers of Commerce. And deep outbreaks have been observed to drive all the way down to Central America, where they are feared as a fierce wind called the Tehuantepecer.

Polar Canadian is only one of many sorts of air. To put it in the unprecise language of the layman, the great Norwegian discovery is that air must always be of some distinct type: that it is never simply air but always conditioned and flavored. What we call weather is caused by gigantic waves in the air ocean which flood whole countries and continents for days at a stretch with one sort of air or another. And there is nothing theoretical about any of these various sorts of air.

Each kind is easily seen and felt and sniffed, and is, in fact, fairly familiar even to the city dweller, although he may not realize it. Each has its own peculiar characteristics, its own warmth or coolness, dampness or dryness, milkiness or clearness. Each has its own quality of light. In each, smoke behaves differently as it pours from the chimneys: in some kinds of air it creeps lazily, in some it bubbles away, in some it floats in layers. That is largely why the connoisseur can distinguish different types of air by smell.

Each type of air combines those qualities into an "atmosphere" of its own. Each makes an entirely different sort of day. In fact, what sort of day it is—raw, oppressive, balmy, dull, a "spring" day—depends almost entirely upon the sort of air that lies over your particular section of the country at that particular time.

And if you tried to describe the day in the old-fashioned terms—wind direction and velocity, humidity, state of the sky—you could never quite express its particular weather; but you can by naming the sort of air. An airplane pilot, once he is trained in the new weather thinking, can get quite impatient with the attempts of novelists, for instance, to describe weather. "Why don't you *say* it was Polar Canadian air and get on with your story?"

And if you are a connoisseur of airs just about the first thing you will note every morning is something like, "Ah, Caribbean air to-day"; or if you are really a judge you can make statements as detailed as, "Saskatchewan air, slightly flavored by the Great Lakes."

For just as wines do, the airs take their names and their flavors from the regions where they have matured. Of the seven airs that make up the American weather, one is quite rare and somewhat mysterious. It is known by the peculiarly wine-like name of Sec Superieur. It is believed to be of tropical origin, but it comes to this continent after spending weeks in the stratosphere somewhere above the Galápagos Islands. It is usually found only high aloft, and interests pilots more than farmers. But once in a while a tongue of it reaches the ground as hot, extremely dry, very clear weather; and wherever it licks there is a drought.

The other six airs all come from perfectly earthly places, though faraway ones. The easiest to recognize, the liveliest, is Polar Canadian. Its opposite number in the American sky is Tropical Gulf or Tropical Atlantic air—the steamy, warm air of the Eastern and Midwestern summer, the kind that comes as a southwest wind and starts people to talking about heat and humidity, the kind that is sometimes so steamy that it leaves you in doubt as to whether the sky means to be blue or overcast. This air is brewed of hot sun and warm sea water in the Caribbean region. The mechanism that does the air conditioning in this case is mostly the daily afternoon thunderstorm which carries moisture and heat high aloft in it.

Not quite so obvious is the origin of the moist, silvery, cool-in-summer, cool-in-winter air that dominates the weather of Seattle. It is called Polar Pacific, and it is a trick product. Its basic characteristics have been acquired over Siberia and it is cold and dry; but on its way across the Pacific its lower five to ten thousand feet have been warmed up and moistened. Sometimes such air comes straight across, reaching land in a couple of days. Sometimes it hangs over the water for a week, and it takes a good weatherman to predict just what sort of weather it will produce.

Its counterpart is a flavor known as Tropical Pacific. That is the air they sell to tourists in Southern California. It is really just plain South Seas air, though the story here too is not as clear-cut as it might be.

A clear-cut type is Polar Atlantic air. It sometimes blows down the New England coast as a nor'easter, cold, rainy, with low clouds. It is simply a chunk of the Grand Banks off Newfoundland gone traveling, and you can almost smell the sea.

And one air that every tourist notices in the Southwest is Tropical Continental. Its source region is the deserts of Arizona and Mexico. It is dry and hot and licks up moisture so greedily that it makes water feel on your skin as chilly as if it were gasoline. It is not an important one for America, though its European counterpart, Saharan air, is important for Europe.

Oklahoma, Colorado, and Kansas are as far as it ever gets; but even so, a few extra outbreaks of it per year, and we have a dust bowl.

II

The air mass idea is simple. As great ideas often do, the air mass idea makes you feel that you have known it right along. And in a vague way, you have. Take, for example, that half-brag, half-complaint of the Texans that there is nothing between Texas and the North Pole to keep out those northers but a barbed wire fence: it contains the kernel of the whole idea —the invading air mass—but only in a fooling way. Or take the manner in which the Mediterranean people have always given definite names to certain winds (boreas, sirocco, mistral) that blow hot or cold, dry or moist, across their roofs. They are names, however, without the larger view. In creative literature such things as a cold front passage—the sudden arrival of a cold air mass—have been described several times quite accurately, but always as a local spectacle, with the key thought missing.

Actually it took genius to see it. For air is a mercurial fluid, bubbly, changeable; it is as full of hidden energies as dynamite; it can assume the most unexpected appearances. There are days, to be sure, when the air virtually advertises its origin. Offhand, you might say that on perhaps half the days of the year it does. But there are also days when its appearance is altogether misleading.

Take, for example, the amazing metamorphosis that happens to Tropical Gulf air when it flows northward across the United States in winter. It starts out from among the Islands looking blue and sunny like an everlasting summer afternoon. When it arrives over the northern United States that same air appears as a dark-gray shapeless, drizzling overcast, and in the office buildings of New York and Chicago the electric lights are on throughout what is considered a shivery winter day. It *is* still the same air; if we could mix a pink dye into the air, as geographers sometimes mix dyes into rivers to trace the flow of water, a cloud of pink air would have traveled from Trinidad to New York. It has hardly changed at all its actual contents of heat and water; but as far as its appearance and its feel are concerned—its "weather" value—a few days of northward traveling have reversed it almost into a photographic negative of itself.

What happens in this particular case—and it accounts for half our winter days—is simply that the cool ground of the wintry continent chills this moist, warm air mass—chills it just a little, not enough to change its fundamental character, and not all the way up into its upper levels, but in its bottommost layer and that only just enough to make it condense out some of its abundant moisture in the form of visible clouds; it is quite similar to the effect of a cold window pane on the air of a well-heated, comfortable room—there is wetness and cooling right at the window, but the bulk of the room's air is not affected.

Perhaps the oddest example of this is the trick by which Polar Pacific air, striking the United States at Seattle, cool and moist, arrives in eastern Montana and the Dakotas as a chinook, a hot, dry, snow-melting wind.

As Polar Pacific air flows up the slopes of the Sierras and the Cascades it is lifted ten thousand feet into the thinner air of higher altitude. By one law of physics the lifting should chill the air through release of pressure. If you have ever bled excess pressure out of your tires you know this cooling by release of pressure—you know how ice-cold the air comes hissing out. But in this case, by a different law of physics, Polar Pacific reacts by cooling only moderately; then it starts condensing out its moisture and thereby protecting its warmth; hence the tremendous snowfalls of the sierras, the giant redwoods, the streams that irrigate California ranches.

Once across the Cascades and the Sierras, the air flows down the eastern slopes. In descending it comes under pressure and therefore heats up, just as air heats up in a tire pump. Warmed, the air increases its capacity to hold moisture; it becomes relatively drier—thus this air sucks back its own clouds into invisible form. When it arrives over the Columbia Basin, or the country round Reno, or Owens Valley, it is regular desert air—warm, very clear, and very dry. That is why the western deserts are where they are. Flowing on eastward, it comes against another hump, the Continental Divide and the Rockies. Here the whole process repeats itself. Again the air is lifted and *should* become ice-cold; again it merely cools moderately, clouds up, and drops its remaining moisture to protect its warmth; hence the lush greenery of Coeur d'Alene, the pine forests of New Mexico. Finally, as the air flows down the eastern slope of the Rockies, compression heats it once more, as in the bicycle pump. Twice on the way up it has dropped moisture and thus failed to cool; twice on the way down it has been heated: it is now extremely dry, and twenty degrees warmer than it was at Seattle. *That* is the chinook, a wind manufactured of exactly the sort of principles that work in air-conditioning machinery, and a good example of the trickery of air masses. But it is *still* a simple thing; it is still one actual physically identical mass of air that you are following. If you had put pink smoke into it at Seattle, pink smoke would have arrived in South Dakota.

That is how the air mass concept explains all sorts of weather detail: the various kinds of rain—showery or steady; the many types of cloud—low or high, solid or broken, layered or towering; thunderstorms; fog. An air mass, thus-and-thus conditioned, will react differently as it flows over the dry plains, the freshly plowed cotton fields, the cool lakes, the hot pavements, the Rocky Mountains of the United States.

An airplane pilot's weather sense consists largely of guessing the exact manner in which a given sort of air will behave along his route. Tropical

Gulf in summer over Alabama? Better not get caught in the middle afternoon with a low fuel reserve. We shall have to detour around many thunderstorms. The details are as multifarious as geography itself, but much of it has by now been put into the manuals, and the pilot memorizes such items as these:

Canadian air that passes over the Great Lakes in winter is moistened and warmed in its lower layers and becomes highly unstable. When such air hits the rolling country of western Pennsylvania and New York and the ridges of the Appalachians the hills have a sort of "trigger action" and cause snow flurries or rain squalls with very low ceilings and visibility.

In summer, Canadian air that flows into New England, dried, without passing over the Great Lakes, will be extremely clear and extremely bumpy.

Tropical Gulf over the South forms patchy ground fog just before sunrise that will persist for two or three hours.

As Polar Pacific air moves southward along the Pacific Coast it forms a layer of "high fog."

In Colorado and Nebraska fresh arriving Canadian air frequently shows as a dust storm.

Given two types of country underneath, one kind of air can produce two sorts of weather only a few miles apart. Tropical Atlantic air, for instance, appears over the hills of New England as hot and summery weather, slightly hazy, inclined toward afternoon thunderstorms. A few miles off the coast the same air appears as low banks of fog. That is because the granite and the woods are warmed all through, and actually a little warmer than Tropical Gulf air itself, at least during the day; while the ocean is much colder than the air, and cools it.

Again, one kind of country can have opposite effects on two different types of air. For example, the farms of the Middle West in the spring when the frost is just out of the ground: that sort of country feels cool to Tropical Gulf air that has flowed up the Mississippi Valley. The bottom layers of that warm moist air are chilled and thus the whole air mass is stabilized. It will stay nicely in layers; the clouds will form a flat, level overcast; smoke will spread and hover as a pall. But to a mass of freshly broken-out Canadian air that sort of country feels warm. The air in immediate contact with the ground is warmed, and the whole mass becomes bottom-light and unstable.

And that means action: a commotion much like the boiling of water on a huge scale and in slow motion. The warmed air floats away upward to the colder air aloft, forming bubbles of rising air, hundreds of feet in diameter, that are really hot-air balloons without a skin.

Those rising chunks of air are felt by fliers as bumps. When the ship flies into one it gets an upward jolt; when it flies out again it gets a downward jolt. They are what makes it possible to fly a glider, even over flat country; all you have to do is to find one of those bubbles, stay in it by circling in a tight turn, and let it carry you aloft.

The clear air, the tremendous visibility of such a day is itself the result of instability: the rising bubbles carry away the dust, the haze, the industrial smoke. The air is always roughest on one of those crisp, clear, newly washed days. If the rising air gets high enough it makes cumulus clouds, those characteristic, towering, puffy good-weather clouds. That sort of cloud is nothing but a puff of upward wind become visible. The rise has cooled the air and made its water vapor visible. Soaring pilots seek to get underneath a cumulus cloud—there is sure to be a lively upflow there. Sometimes, in really unstable air, the rising of the air reaches hurricane velocities. We call that a thunderstorm, but the lightning and thunder are only by-products of the thing. The thing itself is simply a vicious, explosive upsurging of air: the wind in thunderstorms blows sixty to one hundred miles per hour—straight up! The most daring of soaring pilots have flown into thunderstorms and have been sucked up almost to the stratosphere.

The weatherman, unlike the pilot, need not guess. He has got a slide rule; he has got the laws of gases, Charles's Law, Boyle's Law, Buys Ballot's Law at his fingertips. He has studied thermodynamics, and he has got a new device that is the biggest thing in weather science since Torricelli invented the barometer—the radio sonde with which he can take soundings of the upper air, find out just how moisture and temperature conditions are aloft, just how stable or unstable the air will be, at what level the clouds will form, and of what type they will be.

Radio sondes go up in the dead of night from a dozen airports all over the continent. The radio sonde looks like a box of candy, being a small carton wrapped in tinfoil; but it is actually a radio transmitter coupled to a thermometer and a moisture-meter. It is hung on a small parachute which is hitched to a balloon. It takes perhaps an hour for the balloon to reach the stratosphere, and all the time it signals its own readings in a strange, quacky voice, half Donald Duck, half voice from beyond. Then it stops. You know that the balloon has burst, the parachute is letting the instrument down gently.

The next morning some farm boy finds the shiny thing in a field, with a notice attached offering a reward for mailing it back to the weather bureau.

Also the next morning a man in Los Angeles paces up and down his office, scanning the wall where last night's upper-air soundings are tacked up. Emitting heavy cigar smoke and not even looking out of the window, he dictates a weather forecast for the transcontinental airway as far east as Salt Lake City, a forecast that goes into such detail that you sometimes think he is trying to show off.

III

With the air mass idea as a key, you can make more sense out of the weather than the professional weatherman could before Bjerknes; and even if you don't understand Boyle's Law and all the intricate physics of the atmosphere, you can do a quite respectable job of forecasting.

It goes like this: suppose you are deep in Caribbean air. You will have "air mass weather": a whole series of days of the typical sort that goes with that particular type of air when it overlies your particular section of the country in that particular season. There will be all sorts of minor changes; there will be a daily cycle of weather, clouds, perhaps thunderstorms, or showers; but essentially the weather will be the same day after day. Any *real* change in weather can come only as an incursion of a new air mass—probably Polar Canadian.

And when that air mass comes you will know it. New air rarely comes gently, gradually, by imperceptible degrees; almost always the new air mass advances into the old one with a clear-cut, sharply defined forward front. Where two air masses adjoin each other you may in half an hour's driving—in five minutes' flying—change your entire weather, travel from moist, muggy, cloudy weather into clear, cool, sunny weather. That clear-cut boundary is exactly what makes an air mass a distinct entity which you can plot on a map and say, "Here it begins; here it ends"; these sharp boundaries of the air masses are called "fronts" and are a discovery as important as the air mass itself.

You are watching, then, for a "cold front," the forward edge of an advancing mass of cold air. You will get almost no advance warning. You will see the cold air mass only when it is practically upon you. But you know that sooner or later it must come, and that it will come from the northwest. Thus, an occasional long-distance call will be enough. Suppose you are in Pittsburgh, with a moist, warm southwest wind: the bare news that Chicago has a northerly wind might be enough of a clue. If you knew also that Chicago was twenty degrees cooler you would be certain that a cold air mass had swamped Chicago and was now presumably on its way to Pittsburgh, traveling presumably at something like 30 m.p.h. You could guess the time of arrival of its forward front within a few hours. That is why the most innocent weather reports are now so secret; why the British censor suppresses snow flurries in Scotland; why a submarine in the Atlantic would love to know merely the wind direction and temperature at, say, Columbus, Ohio; why the Gestapo had that weather station in Greenland.

Knowing that a cold front is coming, you know what kind of weather to expect; though some cold fronts are extremely fierce, and others quite gentle (noticeable only if you watch for them), the type is always the same. It is all in the book—Bjerknes described it and even drew pictures of it. It was the advance of such a cold front which occurred while you slept that night before you awoke to find the world fresh and newly painted.

Cold air is heavy; as polar air plows into a region occupied by tropical air it underruns; it gets underneath the warm air and lifts it up even as it pushes it back. A cold front acts physically like a cowcatcher.

Seen from the ground, the sequence of events is this: an hour or two before the cold front arrives the clouds in the sky become confused, somewhat like a herd of cattle that smells the coyotes; but you observe that by intuition rather than by measurable signs. Apart from that, there are no advance signs. The wind will be southerly to the last, and the air warm and moist.

Big cumulus clouds build up all around, some of them with dark bases, showers, and in summer thunder and lightning—that is the warm moist air going aloft. A dark bank of solid cloud appears in the northwest, and though the wind is still southerly, this bank keeps building up and coming nearer: it is the actual forward edge of the advancing cold air. When it arrives there is a cloudburst. Then the cold air comes sweeping in from the northwest with vicious gusts. This is the squall that capsizes sailboats and uproots trees, flattens forests and unroofs houses.

The whole commotion probably is over in half an hour. The wind eases up, though it is still cool and northwesterly, the rain ceases, the clouds break and new sky shows: the front has passed, the cold air mass has arrived.

The weatherman can calculate these things too. He has watched and sounded out each of the two air masses for days or even weeks, ever since it moved into his ken somewhere on the outskirts of the American world. Thus an airline weatherman may look at a temperature-moisture graph and say, "This is dynamite. This air will be stable enough as long as it isn't disturbed. But wait till some cold air gets underneath this and starts lifting it. This stuff is going to go crazy."

In making your own guess you would take the same chance that the weatherman takes every morning—that you might be right and yet get an error chalked up against you. Suppose the Chicago weatherman, seeing a cold front approach, forecasts thunderstorms. One thunderstorm passes north of the city, disturbing the 30,000 inhabitants of Waukegan. Another big one passes south of Chicago, across farms just south of Hammond, Ind., affecting another 30,000 people. None happens to hit Chicago itself, with its 3 million people. On a per capita basis, the weatherman was 98 per cent wrong! Actually he was right.

Now you are in the cold air mass, and you can reasonably expect "air mass weather" for a while rather than "frontal" weather; *i.e.*, a whole series of whatever sort of day goes with Canadian air in your particular section of the country at that particular season.

Any real change in the weather *now* can again come only with an incursion of a new and different air mass—and now that will probably mean tropical maritime air of the Gulf kind. To forecast that invasion is no trick at all: you can see the forward front of the warm air mass in the sky several days before it sweeps in on the ground. Warm air is light. As Caribbean air advances into a region occupied by Canadian air it produces a pattern that is the exact opposite of the cold front. The warm front overhangs forward, overruns the cold air; the warm air mass may appear high above Boston when at ground level it is just invading Richmond, Va.

Again the sequence of events is predictable—Bjerknes drew the picture. It is the approaching warm front that makes for "bad" weather, for rain of the steady, rather than the showery kind, for low ceilings.

Consider a warm front on the morning when its foot is near Richmond and its top over Boston. Boston that morning sees streaks of cirrus in its sky—"mares' tails," the white, feathery, diaphanous cloud arranged in filaments and bands, that is so unsubstantial that the sun shines clear through it and you are hardly conscious of it as a cloud—and actually it doesn't consist of water droplets, as do most clouds, but of ice crystals. New Haven the same morning has the same kind of cloud, but slightly thicker, more nearly as a solid, milky layer. New York that same morning sees the warm air as a gray solid overcast at 8,000 feet. Philadelphia has the same sort of cloud at 5,000, with steady rain. Washington has 1,500 feet, rain. Quantico and Richmond report fog, and all airplanes are grounded. Raleigh, N.C., has clearing weather, the wind has shifted that morning to the southwest, and it is getting hot and humid there. Raleigh would be definitely behind the front, well in the warm air mass itself.

By nightfall Boston has the weather that was New Haven's in the morning. The moon, seen through a milky sheet of cirrus clouds, has a halo: "There is going to be rain." New Haven that night has New York's weather of that morning; New York has Philadelphia's; and so on down the line—the whole front has advanced one hundred miles. In forecasting the weather for Boston it is safe to guess that Boston will get in succession New Haven weather, New York weather, Philadelphia, Washington, Richmond weather—and finally Raleigh weather—in a sequence that should take two or three days: steady lowering clouds, rainy periods, some fog—followed finally by a wind shift to the southwest, and rapid breaking of clouds, and much warmer, very humid weather.

And then the cycle begins all over. You are then deep in Caribbean air again. You will have Caribbean air mass weather, and your weather eye had better be cocked northwest to watch for the first signs of polar air.

IV

There *is* a rhythm, then, in the weather, or at least a sort of rhyme, a repetitive sequence. All those folk rules that attribute weather changes to the phases of the moon, or to some other simple periodicity ("If the weather is O.K. on Friday, it is sure to rain over the week-end") are not so far from the mark after all. The rhythm does not work in terms of rain or shine; but it does work in terms of air masses; and thus, indirectly and loosely, through the tricky physics of the air, it governs also the actual weather.

What makes the air masses move, and what makes them move rhythmically—that is the crowning one of the great Norwegian discoveries. Some of it had long been known. It was understood that the motive power is the sun. By heating the tropics and leaving the polar region cold, it sets up a worldwide circulation of air, poleward at high altitude, equatorward at lower levels. It was understood that this simple circulation is complicated by many other factors such as the monsoon effect: continents heat up in summer and draw air in from over the ocean, in winter they cool and air flows out over the ocean; there was the baffling Coriolis Force that makes all moving things (on the Northern Hemisphere) curve to the right. In everyday life we don't notice it, but some geographers hold that it affects the flow of rivers, and artillerymen make allowance for it: a long-range gun is always aimed at a spot hundreds of yards to the left of the target. The monsoons and the Coriolis Force between them break up the simple pole-to-equator-to-pole flow of the air into a worldwide complicated system of interlocking "wheels"—huge eddies that show variously as tradewinds, calm belts, prevailing westerlies. Charts have been drawn of the air ocean's currents showing how air is piled up over some parts of the world, rushed away from others.

But it remained for the Norwegians to discover the polar front—perhaps the last-discovered geographical thing on this earth. Bjerknes himself first saw it—that the worldwide air circulation keeps piling up new masses of polar air in the north and pressing them southward; it keeps piling up new masses of tropical air in the south, pressing them northward; and thus forever keeps forcing tropical and polar air masses against each other along a front; that the demarcation line between tropical air masses, pressing northward, and polar air masses, pressing southward, runs clear around the world: through North America and across the Atlantic, through Europe and across Siberia, through Japan and across the Pacific. The polar front is clear-cut in some places, tends to wash out in others; but it always reëstablishes itself.

In summer, the polar front runs across North America north of the Great Lakes; in winter, it takes up a position across the United States. Wherever it is, it keeps advancing southward, retreating northward, much like a battlefront. And all the cold fronts and warm fronts are but sections of this greater front.

The rhythmical flowing of the air masses, the Norwegians discovered, is simply this wave action along the polar front. Like all the rest of the modern weather concepts, this one becomes common sense, almost self-evident—the moment you realize that air is stuff, a real fluid that has density and weight. Except that it occurs on a scale of unhuman magnitude, wave action along the polar front is almost exactly the same thing as waves on a lake.

In a lake, a dense, heavy fluid—the water—lies underneath a thin, light fluid—the air—and the result is that rhythmical welling up and down of the lake-surface that we call waves. Along the polar front, a dense, heavy fluid, the polar air, lies to the north of a thin, lighter fluid, the tropical air; the result is a rhythmical welling southward and northward of the two kinds of air. When a water wave rolls across a lake its first manifestation is a downward bulging of the water, then an upward surging. When a wave occurs in the polar front it appears first as a northward surging of warm air, and that means all the phenomena of a warm front. Then, in the rhythmical backswing, comes the southward surging of cold air, and that means all the phenomena of a cold front.

These waves are bigger than the imagination can easily encompass. They measure 500 to 1,000 miles from crest to crest. When tropical air surges northward it will wash to the edge of the Arctic; when polar air surges southward it reaches down into the tropics. Such a wave will travel along the polar front all the way from somewhere out in the Pacific, across the United States and out to the Atlantic; that is the meteorological action which underlies the recent novel *Storm* by George Stewart: the progress of a wave along the polar front.

So similar are these air waves to the air-water waves of a lake that there are even whitecaps and breakers. What we call a whitecap or a breaker is a whirling together of air and water into a white foam. In the great waves along the polar front the same toppling-over can occur: warm and cold air sometimes wheel around each other, underrun and overrun each other, in a complicated, spiral pattern.

And that is where the old papery weather science of the schoolbooks merges with the realistic observations of the Norwegians. You remember about those Lows that were traveling across the weather map and brought with them bad weather. You know how a dropping barometer has always indicated the coming of bad weather—though we have never quite known why.

Now it turns out that the barometric low is nothing but one of those toppling-over waves in the polar front—or rather, it is the way in which the spiral surging of the air masses affects the barometers. Look at the Middle West when it is being swept by one of those waves, take a reading of everybody's barometer, and you get the typical low. Look at it when a low is centered, watch the kinds of air that are flowing there, the wind directions, the temperatures and humidities and you find that a low has a definite internal structure: the typical wave pattern, with a warm air mass going north and a cold air mass going south, both phases of the same wave.

Barometric pressures turn out to be not the cause of the weather, but simply a result, a rather unimportant secondary symptom of it. What weather actually is the Norwegians have made clear. It is the wave action of the air ocean.

1942

GEOLOGY

History and Biography

ADAMS, FRANK D., *The Birth and Development of the Geological Sciences* (Baltimore, The Williams and Wilkins Company, 1938).

AGAR, FLINT and LONGWELL, *Geology from Original Sources* (New York, Henry Holt and Company, Inc., 1929).

AGASSIZ, LOUIS, *Geological Sketches* (Boston, Ticknor and Fields, 1866).

———, *A Journey to Brazil* (Boston, Ticknor and Fields, 1865).

GEIKIE, SIR ARCHIBALD, *The Founders of Geology* (New York, The Macmillan Company, 1905).

———, *Geological Sketches at Home and Abroad* (New York, The Macmillan Company, 1892).

LYELL, SIR CHARLES, *Principles of Geology* (New York, D. Appleton and Co., 1889).

MATHER, KIRTLEY F., and MASON, SHIRLEY L., *A Source Book in Geology* (New York, McGraw-Hill Book Company, Inc., 1939).

MERRILL, GEORGE P., *The First One Hundred Years of American Geology* (New Haven, Yale University Press, 1924).

PLAYFAIR, JOHN, *Biographical Account of the late Dr. James Hutton* in *Works*, Vol. IV (Edinburgh, Archibald Constable & Co., 1822).

PUMPELLY, RAPHAEL, *My Reminiscences* (New York, Henry Holt and Company, Inc., 1918).

STEFANSSON, VILHJALMUR, *The Friendly Arctic* (New York, The Macmillan Company, 1943).

WILLIS, BAILEY, *Living Africa* (New York, Whittlesey House, 1930).

WOLFE, LINNIE MARSH, *Son of the Wilderness* (*Life of John Muir*) (New York, Alfred A. Knopf, Inc., 1945).

Method

GILBERT, G. K., "The Inculcation of Scientific Method by Example" (New Haven, *Am. Jour. Science*, 1886), pp. 284–299.

JOHNSON, DOUGLAS, *The Mysterious Craters of the Carolina Coast* in *Science in Progress*, 2nd Series (New Haven, Yale University Press, 1940).

General, Physiographic

ATWOOD, WALLACE W., *The Rocky Mountains* (New York, The Vanguard Press, 1945).

BRETZ, J. HARLAN, *Earth Sciences: Meteorology, Oceanography, Geology* (New York, John Wiley & Sons, Inc., 1940).

CHASE, STUART, *Rich Land, Poor Land* (New York, McGraw-Hill Book Company, Inc., 1936).

CRONEIS, C. G., and KRUMBEIN, W. C., *Down to Earth: An Introduction to Geology* (Chicago, University of Chicago Press, 1936).

DALY, REGINALD A., *Architecture of the Earth* (New York, D. Appleton-Century Company, Inc., 1938).

DAVIS, W. M., and SNYDER, W. H., *Physical Geography* (Boston, Ginn & Co., 1898).

FENNEMAN, N. M., *Physiography of Eastern United States* (New York, McGraw-Hill Book Company, Inc., 1938).

———, *Physiography of Western United States* (New York, McGraw-Hill Book Company, Inc., 1931).

GAMOW, GEORGE, *Biography of the Earth* (New York, The Viking Press, 1941).

HOBBS, W. H., *Earth Features and Their Meaning* (New York, The Macmillan Company, 1931).

HOLMES, A., *The Age of the Earth* (New York, Harper & Brothers, 1937).

LILIENTHAL, DAVID, *TVA—Democracy on the March* (New York, Harper & Brothers, 1944; also Pocket Books).

LOBECK, ARMIN K., *Geomorphology: an Introduction to the Study of Landscapes* (New York, McGraw-Hill Book Company, Inc., 1939).

MATHER, KIRTLEY, *Enough and to Spare* (New York, Harper & Brothers, 1944).

MUIR, JOHN, *Steep Trails* (Boston, Houghton Mifflin Company, 1918).

POWELL, JOHN, *Report of Explorations in 1873 of the Colorado of the West* (Washington Government Printing Office, 1874).

SCHUCHERT, CHARLES, and LEVENE, CLARA, *The Earth and Its Rhythms* (New York, D. Appleton and Co., 1927).

SEARS, PAUL B., *Deserts on the March* (Norman, University of Oklahoma Press, 1935).

TARR, WILLIAM A., *Introductory Economic Geology* (New York, McGraw-Hill Book Company, Inc., 1938).

TYNDALL, JOHN, *Forms of Water* (New York, D. Appleton and Co., 1899).

———, *Hours of Exercise in the Alps* (London, Longmans, Green & Co., 1899).

Minerals

DANA, JAMES D., *Manual of Mineralogy,* revised by C. S. Hurlbut (New York, John Wiley & Sons, 1941).

ENGLISH, GEORGE L., *Getting Acquainted with Minerals* (New York, McGraw-Hill Book Company, Inc., 1934).

FITZHUGH, EDWARD F., *Treasures in the Earth* (Caldwell, Idaho, Caxton Press, 1936).

KEMP, JAMES F., *A Handbook of Rocks,* revised by F. F. Grout (New York, D. Van Nostrand Company, Inc., 1940).

KRAUS, E. H., and HOLDEN, E. I., *Gems and Gem Materials* (New York, McGraw-Hill Book Company, Inc., 1925).

Lord, Eliot, *Comstock Mining and Mines* (Washington, U.S. Geological Survey Monographs, V. 4, 1883).

Lovering, Thomas, *Minerals in World Affairs* (New York, Prentice-Hall, Inc., 1943).

Moore, Elwood S., *Coal, Its Properties, Analysis, Classification, Geology, Extraction, Uses and Distribution* (New York, John Wiley & Sons, Inc., 1940).

Pirsson, L. V., and Knopf, Adolph, *Rocks and Rock Minerals* (New York, John Wiley & Sons, Inc., 1947).

Rickard, T. A., *Man and Metals: a History of Mining in Relation to the Development of Civilization* (New York, Whittlesey House, 1932).

Fossils

Hotchkiss, W. O., *The Story of a Billion Years* (New York, The Century Co., 1932).

Lull, Richard S., *Fossils* (New York, The University Society, 1931).

Merriam, John C., *The Living Past* (New York, Charles Scribner's Sons, 1930).

Miller, Hugh, *The Old Red Sandstone* (New York, E. P. Dutton & Co., Inc., 1907).

Raymond, Percy, *Prehistoric Life* (Cambridge, Harvard University Press, 1939).

Shimer, Hervey W., *An Introduction to Earth History* (Boston, Ginn & Co., 1925).

Wilder, H. H., *Man's Prehistoric Past* (New York, The Macmillan Company, 1923).

Earthquakes and Volcanoes

Dutton, Clarence E., *The Charleston Earthquake* (Washington, U.S. Geol. Survey, 9th Ann. Report, 1887–88).

Griggs, Robert F., *The Valley of Ten Thousand Smokes* (Washington, National Geographic Society, 1922).

Heck, Nicholas H., *Earthquakes* (Princeton, Princeton University Press, 1936).

Lynch, John J., *Our Trembling Earth* (New York, Dodd, Mead & Company, 1940).

Macelwane, J. B., *Earthquakes* (Milwaukee, Bruce Publishing Company, 1947).

Glaciers and Oceans

Coker, R. E., *The Great and Wide Sea* (Chapel Hill, University of North Carolina Press, 1947).

Coleman, Arthur P., *Ice Ages, Recent and Ancient* (New York, The Macmillan Company, 1926).

Daly, Reginald A., *The Floor of the Ocean* (Chapel Hill, University of North Carolina Press, 1942).

Lane, Ferdinand C., *The Mysterious Sea* (New York, Doubleday & Co., Inc., 1947).

Sverdrup, H. U., Johnson, M. W., and Fleming, R. H., *The Oceans, their Physics, Chemistry and General Biology* (New York, Prentice-Hall, Inc., 1942).

The Weather

BROOKS, CHARLES F., *Why the Weather?* (New York, Harcourt, Brace and Company, Inc., 1935).
HUMPHREYS, WILLIAM J., *Fogs, Clouds and Aviation* (Baltimore, The Williams and Wilkins Company, 1943).
———, *Ways of the Weather* (Lancaster, Pa., Jacques Cattell Press, 1942).
PETTERSSEN, SVERRE, *Introduction to Meteorology* (New York, McGraw-Hill Book Company, Inc., 1941).
SHAW, SIR NAPIER, *The Drama of Weather* (Cambridge, Cambridge University Press, 1939).
STEWART, GEORGE R., *Storm* (New York, Random House, Inc., 1941).
TANNEHILL, IVAN R., *Hurricanes* (Princeton, Princeton University Press, 1938).
———, *Weather Around the World* (Princeton, Princeton University Press, 1943).

IV

MATHEMATICS

As Eric Temple Bell has emphasized, mathematics is both the queen and the handmaiden of the sciences. The study of mathematics requires the use of logic in its most rigid and exact form. And without mathematics it is likely that nine-tenths of the work described in this book would have been impossible. Only in its early stages is a science purely observational. It can never be truly exact until it is expressed in mathematical form. Astronomy, the oldest, is also the most exact of the sciences. Biology, still in large part unable to express itself mathematically, remains a young science. From Plato to Whitehead, some of the greatest minds have been awed by the beauty and power of mathematics. Some of their thoughts are expressed in the opening selection in this section.

To the layman, higher mathematics appears austere and removed from practical experience. Yet the mathematician himself is a creator in much the same manner as other artists and scientists. In "Mathematical Creation," Henri Poincaré, the great French mathematician, gives you a portrait of himself at work which is not soon forgotten. The flashes of insight he records, the sudden recognition of order amid a chaos of seemingly unconnected facts, have resulted in additions of permanent value to the fund of knowledge of the subject.

In "The Study of Mathematics," composed of selections from two of his essays, Bertrand Russell writes glowingly of its usefulness. With Alfred North Whitehead he is the author of *Principia Mathematica*, one of the important works of contemporary times. Whitehead himself is the author of *An Introduction to Mathematics*, perhaps the best book on the subject ever written for non-specialists. In the selection from it here given, Whitehead leads us by easy steps into the subject, divorces it from the dull pedantry with which it is usually associated, and makes it an adventure of the mind. It has been emphasized many times that mathematical creation and arithmetical exercise have nothing whatever in common. These selections make it obvious why this is true.

Lastly, in another selection which emphasizes the relation between the sciences, we present "From Cyzicus to Neptune" by Eric Temple Bell. He describes some of the most exciting of all astronomical discoveries, made possible by mathematics. The selection is taken from

Professor Bell's book *The Handmaiden of the Sciences*, which is recommended to those who would learn how mathematics has performed services in many scientific fields.

THOUGHTS ON MATHEMATICS: PLATO TO WHITEHEAD

Let no one ignorant of geometry enter my door.

PLATO

For without mathematics, nothing worth knowing in philosophy can be attained.

For he who knows not mathematics cannot know any other science; what is more, he cannot discover his own ignorance, or find its proper remedy.

ROGER BACON

The Universe is the grand book of philosophy. The book lies continually open to man's gaze, yet none can hope to comprehend it who has not first mastered the language and the characters in which it has been written. This language is mathematics; these characters are triangles, circles and other geometrical figures.

GALILEO GALILEI

If one be bird-witted, that is easily distracted and unable to keep his attention as long as he should, mathematics provides a remedy: for in them, if the mind be caught away but a moment, the demonstration has to be commenced anew.

LORD BACON

Numbers are so much the measure of everything that is valuable that it is not possible to demonstrate the success of any action or the prudence of any undertaking without them.

RICHARD STEELE

The possession of precise information about a person's ability, character, intentions, psychological disposition and even moral integrity may be indicated by a succinct and expressive colloquialism, redolent of Pythagoras, namely, "I've got your number."

R. D. CARMICHAEL

There is an astonishing imagination, even in the science of mathematics. . . . We repeat, there was far more imagination in the head of Archimedes than in that of Homer.

VOLTAIRE

It may well be doubted whether, in all the range of science, there is any field so fascinating to the explorer—so rich in hidden treasures—so fruitful in delightful surprises—as that of Pure Mathematics. The charm lies chiefly . . . in the absolute certainty of its results; for that is what, beyond all mental treasures, the human intellect craves for. Let us only be sure of *something!* More light, more light!

"And if our fate be death, give light and let us die!" This is the cry that, through all the ages, is going up from perplexed Humanity, and Science has little else to offer, that will really meet the demands of its votaries, than the conclusions of pure mathematics.

C. L. DODGSON

When he had a few moments for diversion, he (Napoleon) not infrequently employed them over a book of logarithms, in which he always found recreation.

J. S. C. ABBOTT

In every case the awakening touch has been the mathematical spirit, the attempt to count, to measure, or to calculate. What to the poet or the seer may appear to be the very death of all his poetry and all his visions —the cold touch of the calculating mind—this has proved to be the spell by which knowledge has been born, by which new sciences have been created, and hundreds of definite problems put before the minds and into the hands of diligent students. It is the geometrical figure, the dry algebraical formula, which transforms the vague reasoning of the philosopher into a tangible and manageable conception; which represents, though it does not explain, the things and processes of nature; this clothes the fruitful, but otherwise indefinite, ideas in such a form that the strict logical methods of thought can be applied, that the human mind can in its inner chamber explore a train of reasoning the result of which corresponds to the phenomena of the outer world.

J. T. MERZ

Behind the artisan is the chemist, behind the chemist a physicist, behind the physicist a mathematician.

W. F. WHITE

Mathematics is no more the art of reckoning and computation than architecture is the art of making bricks or hewing wood, no more than painting is the art of mixing colors on a palate, no more than the science of geology is the art of breaking rocks, or the science of anatomy the art of butchering.

C. J. KEYSER

I will not go so far as to say that to contract a history of thought without profound study of the mathematical ideas of successive epochs is like omitting Hamlet from the play which is named after him. That would be claiming too much. But it is certainly analagous to cutting out the part of Ophelia. This simile is singularly exact. For Ophelia is quite essential to the play, she is very charming,—and a little mad. Let us grant that the pursuit of mathematics is a divine madness of the human spirit, a refuge from the goading urgency of contingent happenings.

ALFRED NORTH WHITEHEAD

MATHEMATICAL CREATION *

HENRI POINCARÉ

The genesis of mathematical creation is a problem which should intensely interest the psychologist. It is the activity in which the human mind seems to take least from the outside world, in which it acts or seems to act only of itself and on itself, so that in studying the procedure of geometric thought we may hope to reach what is most essential in man's mind. . . .

A first fact should surprise us, or rather would surprise us if we were not so used to it. How does it happen there are people who do not understand mathematics? If mathematics invokes only the rules of logic, such as are accepted by all normal minds; if its evidence is based on principles common to all men, and that none could deny without being mad, how does it come about that so many persons are here refractory? . . .

And further: how is error possible in mathematics? A sane mind should not be guilty of a logical fallacy, and yet there are very fine minds who do not trip in brief reasoning such as occurs in the ordinary doings of life, and who are incapable of following or repeating without error the mathematical demonstrations which are longer, but which after all are only an accumulation of brief reasonings wholly analogous to those they make so easily. Need we add that mathematicians themselves are not infallible?

The answer seems to me evident. Imagine a long series of syllogisms,

* From *The Foundations of Science*, The Science Press. Reprinted by permission of the publishers. Copyright 1913 by The Science Press. Translated by George Bruce Halsted.

and that the conclusions of the first serve as premises of the following: we shall be able to catch each of these syllogisms, and it is not in passing from premises to conclusion that we are in danger of deceiving ourselves. But between the moment in which we first meet a proposition as conclusion of one syllogism and that in which we re-encounter it as premise of another syllogism occasionally some time will elapse, several links of the chain will have unrolled; so it may happen that we have forgotten it, or, worse, that we have forgotten its meaning. So it may happen that we replace it by a slightly different proposition, or that, while retaining the same enunciation, we attribute to it a slightly different meaning, and thus it is that we are exposed to error.

Often the mathematician uses a rule. Naturally he begins by demonstrating this rule; and at the time when this proof is fresh in his memory he understands perfectly its meaning and its bearing, and he is in no danger of changing it. But subsequently he trusts his memory and afterward only applies it in a mechanical way; and then if his memory fails him, he may apply it all wrong. Thus it is, to take a simple example, that we sometimes make slips in calculation because we have forgotten our multiplication table.

According to this, the special aptitude for mathematics would be due only to a very sure memory or to a prodigious force of attention. It would be a power like that of the whist player who remembers the cards played; or, to go up a step, like that of the chess player who can visualize a great number of combinations and hold them in his memory. Every good mathematician ought to be a good chess player, and inversely; likewise he should be a good computer. Of course that sometimes happens; thus Gauss was at the same time a geometer of genius and a very precocious and accurate computer.

But there are exceptions; or rather I err; I cannot call them exceptions without the exceptions being more than the rule. Gauss it is, on the contrary, who was an exception. As for myself, I must confess, I am absolutely incapable even of adding without mistakes. In the same way I should be but a poor chess player; I would perceive that by a certain play I should expose myself to a certain danger; I would pass in review several other plays, rejecting them for other reasons, and then finally I should make the move first examined, having meantime forgotten the danger I had foreseen.

In a word, my memory is not bad, but it would be insufficient to make me a good chess player. Why, then, does it not fail me in a difficult piece of mathematical reasoning where most chess players would lose themselves? Evidently because it is guided by the general march of the reasoning. A mathematical demonstration is not a simple juxtaposition of syllogisms, it is syllogisms *placed in a certain order*, and the order in which these elements are placed is much more important than the elements themselves. If I have the feeling, the intuition, so to speak, of this order, so as to perceive at a glance the reasoning as a whole, I need no longer fear lest I forget one of the elements, for each of them will take its allotted place in the array, and that without any effort of memory on my part.

It seems to me then, in repeating a reasoning learned, that I could have invented it. This is often only an illusion; but even then, even if I am not so gifted as to create it by myself, I myself reinvent it in so far as I repeat it.

We know that this feeling, this intuition of mathematical order, that makes us divine hidden harmonies and relations, cannot be possessed by everyone. Some will not have either this delicate feeling so difficult to define, or a strength of memory and attention beyond the ordinary, and then they will be absolutely incapable of understanding higher mathematics. Such are the majority. Others will have this feeling only in a slight degree, but they will be gifted with an uncommon memory and a great power of attention. They will learn by heart the details one after another; they can understand mathematics and sometimes make applications, but they cannot create. Others, finally, will possess in a less or greater degree the special intuition referred to, and then not only can they understand mathematics even if their memory is nothing extraordinary, but they may become creators and try to invent with more or less success according as this intuition is more or less developed in them.

In fact, what is mathematical creation? It does not consist in making new combinations with mathematical entities already known. Anyone could do that, but the combinations so made would be infinite in number and most of them absolutely without interest. To create consists precisely in not making useless combinations and in making those which are useful and which are only a small minority. Invention is discernment, choice.

How to make this choice I have before explained; the mathematical facts worthy of being studied are those which, by their analogy with other facts, are capable of leading us to the knowledge of a mathematical law just as experimental facts lead us to the knowledge of a physical law. They are those which reveal to us unsuspected kinship between other facts, long known, but wrongly believed to be strangers to one another. . . .

It is time to penetrate deeper and to see what goes on in the very soul of the mathematician. For this, I believe, I can do best by recalling memories of my own. But I shall limit myself to telling how I wrote my first memoir on Fuchsian functions. I beg the reader's pardon; I am about to use some technical expressions, but they need not frighten him, for he is not obliged to understand them. I shall say, for example, that I have found the demonstration of such a theorem under such circumstances. This theorem will have a barbarous name, unfamiliar to many, but that is unimportant; what is of interest for the psychologist is not the theorem but the circumstances.

For fifteen days I strove to prove that there could not be any functions like those I have since called Fuchsian functions. I was then very ignorant; every day I seated myself at my worktable, stayed an hour or two, tried a great number of combinations, and reached no results. One evening, contrary to my custom, I drank black coffee and could not sleep. Ideas rose in crowds; I felt them collide until pairs interlocked, so to speak, making a stable combination. By the next morning I had established the existence of a class of Fuchsian functions, those which come from the hypergeometric series; I had only to write out the results, which took but a few hours. . . .

Most striking at first is this appearance of sudden illumination, a manifest sign of long, unconscious prior work. The role of this unconscious work in mathematical invention appears to me incontestable, and traces of it would be found in other cases where it is less evident. Often when one works at a hard question, nothing good is accomplished at the first attack. Then one takes a rest, longer or shorter, and sits down anew to the work. During the first half-hour, as before, nothing is found, and then all of a sudden the decisive idea presents itself to the mind. It might be said that the conscious work has been more fruitful because it has been interrupted and the rest has given back to the mind its force and freshness. But it is more probably that this rest has been filled out with unconscious work and that the result of this work has afterward revealed itself to the geometer just as in the cases I have cited; only the revelation, instead of coming during a walk or journey, has happened during a period of conscious work, but independently of this work which plays at most a role of excitant, as if it were the goad stimulating the results already reached during rest, but remaining unconscious, to assume the conscious form.

There is another remark to be made about the conditions of this unconscious work: it is possible, and of a certainty it is only fruitful, if it is on the one hand preceded and on the other hand followed by a period of conscious work. These sudden inspirations (and the examples already cited sufficiently prove this) never happen except after some days of voluntary effort which has appeared absolutely fruitless and whence nothing good seems to have come, where the way taken seems totally astray. These efforts then have not been as sterile as one thinks; they have set agoing the unconscious machine and without them it would not have moved and would have produced nothing.

1913

THE STUDY OF MATHEMATICS *

BERTRAND RUSSELL

In regard to every form of human activity it is necessary that the question should be asked from time to time, What is its purpose and ideal? In what way does it contribute to the beauty of human existence? As respects those pursuits which contribute only remotely, by providing the mechanism of life, it is well to be reminded that not the mere fact of living is to be desired, but the art of living in the contemplation of great things. Still more in regard to those avocations which have no end outside themselves, which are to be justified, if at all, as actually adding to the sum of the world's permanent possessions, it is necessary to keep alive a knowledge of their aims, a clear prefiguring vision of the temple in which creative imagination is to be embodied. . . .

Although tradition has decreed that the great bulk of educated men shall know at least the elements of the subject [of mathematics], the reasons for which the tradition arose are forgotten, buried beneath a great rubbish-heap of pedantries and trivialities. To those who inquire as to the purpose of mathematics, the usual answer will be that it facilitates the making of machines, the travelling from place to place, and the victory over foreign nations, whether in war or commerce. If it be objected that these ends—all of which are of doubtful value—are not furthered by the merely elementary study imposed upon those who do not become expert mathematicians, the reply, it is true, will probably be that mathematics trains the reasoning faculties. Yet the very men who make this reply are, for the most part, unwilling to abandon the teaching of definite fallacies, known to be such, and instinctively rejected by the unsophisticated mind of every intelligent learner. And the reasoning faculty itself is generally conceived, by those who urge its cultivation, as merely a means for the avoidance of pitfalls and a help in the discovery of rules for the guidance of practical life. All these are undeniably important achievements to the credit of mathematics; yet it is none of these that entitles mathematics to a place in every liberal education. . . .

Mathematics, rightly viewed, possesses not only truth, but supreme beauty—a beauty cold and austere, like that of sculpture, without appeal to any part of our weaker nature, without the gorgeous trappings of painting or music, yet sublimely pure, and capable of a stern perfection such as only the greatest art can show. The true spirit of delight, the exaltation, the sense of being more than man, which is the touchstone of the highest excellence, is to be found in mathematics as surely as in poetry. What is best in mathematics deserves not merely to be learnt as a task,

* Reprinted from *Mysticism and Logic* by Bertrand Russell, by permission of W. W. Norton & Company, Inc., New York. Copyright 1929 by the publishers.

but to be assimilated as a part of daily thought, and brought again and again before the mind with ever-renewed encouragement. Real life is, to most men, a long second-best, a perpetual compromise between the ideal and the possible; but the world of pure reason knows no compromise, no practical limitations, no barrier to the creative activity embodying in splendid edifices the passionate aspiration after the perfect from which all great work springs. Remote from human passions, remote even from the pitiful facts of nature, the generations have gradually created an ordered cosmos, where pure thought can dwell as in its natural home, and where one, at least, of our nobler impulses can escape from the dreary exile of the actual world.

So little, however, have mathematicians aimed at beauty, that hardly anything in their work has had this conscious purpose. Much, owing to irrepressible instincts, which were better than avowed beliefs, has been moulded by an unconscious taste; but much also has been spoilt by false notions of what was fitting. The characteristic excellence of mathematics is only to be found where the reasoning is rigidly logical: the rules of logic are to mathematics what those of structure are to architecture. In the most beautiful work, a chain of argument is presented in which every link is important on its own account, in which there is an air of ease and lucidity throughout, and the premises achieve more than would have been thought possible, by means which appear natural and inevitable. Literature embodies what is general in particular circumstances whose universal significance shines through their individual dress; but mathematics endeavours to present whatever is most general in its purity, without any irrelevant trappings. . . .

. . . The nineteenth century, which prided itself upon the invention of steam and evolution, might have derived a more legitimate title to fame from the discovery of pure mathematics. This science, like most others, was baptised long before it was born; and thus we find writers before the nineteenth century alluding to what they called pure mathematics. But if they had been asked what this subject was, they would only have been able to say that it consisted of Arithmetic, Algebra, Geometry, and so on. As to what these studies had in common, and as to what distinguished them from applied mathematics, our ancestors were completely in the dark.

Pure mathematics was discovered by Boole, in a work which he called the *Laws of Thought* (1854). This work abounds in asseverations that it is not mathematical, the fact being that Boole was too modest to suppose his book the first ever written on mathematics. He was also mistaken in supposing that he was dealing with the laws of thought: the question how people actually think was quite irrelevant to him, and if his book had really contained the laws of thought, it was curious that no one should ever have thought in such a way before. His book was in fact concerned with formal logic, and this is the same thing as mathematics.

Pure mathematics consists entirely of assertions to the effect that, if such and such a proposition is true of *anything*, then such and such another proposition is true of that thing. It is essential not to discuss whether the first proposition is really true, and not to mention what the anything is, of which it is supposed to be true. Both these points would belong to applied mathematics. We start, in pure mathematics, from certain rules of inference, by which we can infer that *if* one proposition is true, then so is some other proposition. These rules of inference constitute the major part of the principles of formal logic. We then take any hypothesis that seems amusing, and deduce its consequences. *If* our hypothesis is about *anything*, and not about some one or more particular things, then our deductions constitute mathematics. Thus mathematics may be defined as the subject in which we never know what we are talking about, nor whether what we are saying is true. People who have been puzzled by the beginnings of mathematics will, I hope, find comfort in this definition, and will probably agree that it is accurate. . . .

1929 edition

AN INTRODUCTION TO MATHEMATICS *

ALFRED NORTH WHITEHEAD

THE ABSTRACT NATURE OF MATHEMATICS

The study of mathematics is apt to commence in disappointment. The important applications of the science, the theoretical interest of its ideas, and the logical rigour of its methods, all generate the expectation of a speedy introduction to processes of interest. We are told that by its aid the stars are weighed and the billions of molecules in a drop of water are counted. Yet, like the ghost of Hamlet's father, this great science eludes the efforts of our mental weapons to grasp it—" 'Tis here, 'tis there, 'tis gone"—and what we do see does not suggest the same excuse for illusiveness as sufficed for the ghost, that it is too noble for our gross methods. "A show of violence," if ever excusable, may surely be "offered" to the trivial results which occupy the pages of some elementary mathematical treatises.

The reason for this failure of the science to live up to its reputation is

* From *An Introduction to Mathematics* by Alfred North Whitehead, The Home University Library. Reprinted by permission from the Oxford University Press. Copyright 1911 by Henry Holt and Company, Inc.; copyright 1948 by Oxford University Press.

that its fundamental ideas are not explained to the student disentangled from the technical procedure which has been invented to facilitate their exact presentation in particular instances. Accordingly, the unfortunate learner finds himself struggling to acquire a knowledge of a mass of details which are not illuminated by any general conception. Without a doubt, technical facility is a first requisite for valuable mental activity: we shall fail to appreciate the rhythm of Milton, or the passion of Shelley, so long as we find it necessary to spell the words and are not quite certain of the forms of the individual letters. In this sense there is no royal road to learning. But it is equally an error to confine attention to technical processes, excluding consideration of general ideas. Here lies the road to pedantry. . . .

The first acquaintance which most people have with mathematics is through arithmetic. That two and two make four is usually taken as the type of a simple mathematical proposition which everyone will have heard of. Arithmetic, therefore, will be a good subject to consider in order to discover, if possible, the most obvious characteristic of the science. Now, the first noticeable fact about arithmetic is that it applies to everything, to tastes and to sounds, to apples and to angels, to the ideas of the mind and to the bones of the body. The nature of the things is perfectly indifferent, of all things it is true that two and two make four. Thus we write down as the leading characteristic of mathematics that it deals with properties and ideas which are applicable to things just because they are things, and apart from any particular feelings, or emotions, or sensations, in any way connected with them. This is what is meant by calling mathematics an abstract science.

The result which we have reached deserves attention. It is natural to think that an abstract science cannot be of much importance in the affairs of human life, because it has omitted from its consideration everything of real interest. It will be remembered that Swift, in his description of Gulliver's voyage to Laputa, is of two minds on this point. He describes the mathematicians of that country as silly and useless dreamers, whose attention has to be awakened by flappers. Also, the mathematical tailor measures his height by a quadrant, and deduces his other dimensions by a rule and compasses, producing a suit of very ill-fitting clothes. On the other hand, the mathematicians of Laputa, by their marvellous invention of the magnetic island floating in the air, ruled the country and maintained their ascendency over their subjects. Swift, indeed, lived at a time peculiarly unsuited for gibes at contemporary mathematicians. Newton's *Principia* had just been written, one of the great forces which have transformed the modern world. Swift might just as well have laughed at an earthquake.

But a mere list of the achievements of mathematics is an unsatisfactory way of arriving at an idea of its importance. It is worth while to spend a little thought in getting at the root reason why mathematics, because of its very abstractness, must always remain one of the most important topics for thought. Let us try to make clear to ourselves why explanations of the order of events necessarily tend to become mathematical.

Consider how all events are interconnected. When we see the lightning, we listen for the thunder; when we hear the wind, we look for the waves on the sea; in the chill autumn, the leaves fall. Everywhere order reigns, so that when some circumstances have been noted we can foresee that others will also be present. The progress of science consists in observing these interconnections and in showing with a patient ingenuity that the events of this evershifting world are but examples of a few general connections or relations called laws. To see what is general in what is particular and what is permanent in what is transitory is the aim of scientific thought. In the eye of science, the fall of an apple, the motion of a planet round a sun, and the clinging of the atmosphere to the earth are all seen as examples of the law of gravity. This possibility of disentangling the most complex evanescent circumstances into various examples of permanent laws is the controlling idea of modern thought.

Now let us think of the sort of laws which we want in order completely to realize this scientific ideal. Our knowledge of the particular facts of the world around us is gained from our sensations. We see, and hear, and taste, and smell, and feel hot and cold, and push, and rub, and ache, and tingle. These are just our own personal sensations: my toothache cannot be your toothache, and my sight cannot be your sight. But we ascribe the origin of these sensations to relations between the things which form the external world. Thus the dentist extracts not the toothache but the tooth. And not only so, we also endeavour to imagine the world as one connected set of things which underlies all the perceptions of all people. There is not one world of things for my sensations and another for yours, but one world in which we both exist. It is the same tooth both for dentist and patient. Also we hear and we touch the same world as we see.

It is easy, therefore, to understand that we want to describe the connections between these external things in some way which does not depend on any particular sensations, nor even on all the sensations of any particular person. The laws satisfied by the course of events in the world of external things are to be described, if possible, in a neutral universal fashion, the same for blind men as for deaf men, and the same for beings with faculties beyond our ken as for normal human beings.

But when we have put aside our immediate sensations, the most serviceable part—from its clearness, definiteness, and universality—of what is left is composed of our general ideas of the abstract formal properties of things; in fact, the abstract mathematical ideas mentioned above. Thus it comes about that, step by step, and not realizing the full meaning of the process, mankind has been led to search for a mathematical description of the properties of the universe, because in this way only can a general idea of the course of events be formed, freed from reference to particular persons or to particular types of sensation. For example, it might be asked at dinner: "What was it which underlay my sensation of sight, yours of touch, and his of taste and smell?" the answer being "an apple." But in its final analysis, science seeks to describe an apple in terms of the positions and motions of molecules, a description which ignores me and you and him, and also ignores sight and touch and taste and smell. Thus mathematical ideas, because they are abstract, supply just what is wanted for a scientific description of the course of events.

This point has usually been misunderstood, from being thought of in too narrow a way. Pythagoras had a glimpse of it when he proclaimed that number was the source of all things. In modern times the belief that the ultimate explanation of all things was to be found in Newtonian mechanics was an adumbration of the truth that all science as it grows towards perfection becomes mathematical in its ideas.

VARIABLES

Mathematics as a science commenced when first someone, probably a Greek, proved propositions about *any* things or about *some* things, without specification of definite particular things. These propositions were first enunciated by the Greeks for geometry; and, accordingly, geometry was the great Greek mathematical science. After the rise of geometry centuries passed away before algebra made a really effective start, despite some faint anticipations by the later Greek mathematicians.

The ideas of *any* and of *some* are introduced into algebra by the use of letters, instead of the definite numbers of arithmetic. Thus, instead of saying that $2 + 3 = 3 + 2$, in algebra we generalize and say that, if x and y stand for *any* two numbers, then $x + y = y + x$. Again, in the place of saying that $3 > 2$, we generalize and say that if x be *any* number there exists *some* number (or numbers) y such that $y > x$. We may remark in passing that this latter assumption—for when put in its strict ultimate form it is an assumption—is of vital importance, both to philosophy and to mathematics; for by it the notion of infinity is introduced. Perhaps it required the introduction of the arabic numerals, by which the use of letters as standing for definite numbers has been completely discarded in mathematics, in order to suggest to mathematicians the technical convenience of the use of letters for the ideas of *any* number and *some* number. The Romans would have stated the number of the year in which this is written in the form MDCCCCX., whereas we write it 1910, thus leaving the letters for the other usage. But this is merely a speculation. After the rise of algebra the differential calculus was invented by Newton and Leibniz, and then a pause in the progress of the philosophy of mathematical thought occurred so far as these notions are concerned; and it was not till within the last few years that it has been realized how fundamental *any* and *some* are to the very nature of mathematics, with the result of opening out still further subjects for mathematical exploration.

Let us now make some simple algebraic statements, with the object of understanding exactly how these fundamental ideas occur.

(1) For *any* number x, $x + 2 = 2 + x$;
(2) For *some* number x, $x + 2 = 3$;
(3) For *some* number x, $x + 2 > 3$.

The first point to notice is the possibilities contained in the meaning of *some*, as here used. Since $x + 2 = 2 + x$ for any number x, it is true for *some* number x. Thus, as here used, *any* implies *some* and *some* does not exclude *any*. Again, in the second example, there is, in fact, only one number x, such that $x + 2 = 3$, namely only the number 1. Thus the *some* may be one number only. But in the third example, any number x which is greater than 1 gives $x + 2 > 3$. Hence there are an infinite number of numbers which answer to the *some* number in this case. Thus *some* may be anything between *any* and *one only*, including both these limiting cases.

It is natural to supersede the statements (2) and (3) by the questions:

(2′) For what number x is $x + 2 = 3$;
(3′) For what numbers x is $x + 2 > 3$.

Considering (2′), $x + 2 = 3$ is an equation, and it is easy to see that its solution is $x = 3 - 2 = 1$. When we have asked the question implied in the statement of the equation $x + 2 = 3$, x is called the unknown. The object of the solution of the equation is the determination of the unknown. Equations are of great importance in mathematics, and it seems as though (2′) exemplified a much more thoroughgoing and fundamental idea than the original statement (2). This, however, is a complete mistake. The idea of the undetermined "variable" as occurring in the use of "some" or "any" is the really important one in mathematics; that of the "unknown" in an equation, which is to be solved as quickly as possible, is only of subordinate use, though of course it is very important. One of the causes of the apparent triviality of much of elementary algebra is the preoccupation of the text-books with the solution of equations. The same remark applies to the solution of the inequality (3′) as compared to the original statement (3).

But the majority of interesting formulæ, especially when the idea of *some* is present, involve more than one variable. For example, the consideration of the pairs of numbers x and y (fractional or integral) which satisfy $x + y = 1$ involves the idea of two correlated variables, x and y. When two variables are present the same two main types of statement occur. For example, (1) for *any* pair of numbers, x and y, $x + y = y + x$, and (2) for *some* pairs of numbers, x and y, $x + y = 1$.

The second type of statement invites consideration of the aggregate of pairs of numbers which are bound together by some fixed relation—in the case given, by the relation $x + y = 1$. One use of formulæ of the first type, true for *any* pair of numbers, is that by them formulæ of the second type can be thrown into an indefinite number of equivalent forms. For example, the relation $x + y = 1$ is equivalent to the relations

$$y + x = 1, \quad (x - y) + 2y = 1, \quad 6x + 6y = 6,$$

and so on. Thus a skilful mathematician uses that equivalent form of the relation under consideration which is most convenient for his immediate purpose.

It is not in general true that, when a pair of terms satisfy some fixed relation, if one of the terms is given the other is also definitely determined. For example, when x and y satisfy $y^2 = x$, if $x = 4$, y can be ± 2, thus, for any positive value of x there are alternative values for y. Also in the relation $x + y > 1$, when either x or y is given, an indefinite number of values remain open for the other.

Again there is another important point to be noticed. If we restrict ourselves to positive numbers, integral or fractional, in considering the relation $x + y = 1$, then, if either x or y be greater than 1, there is no positive number which the other can assume so as to satisfy the relation. Thus the "field" of the relation for x is restricted to numbers less than 1, and similarly for the "field" open to y. Again, consider integral numbers only, positive or negative, and take the relation $y^2 = x$, satisfied by pairs of such numbers. Then whatever integral value is given to y, x can assume one corresponding integral value. So the "field" for y is unrestricted among these positive or negative integers. But the "field" for x is restricted in two ways. In the first place x must be positive, and in the second place, since y is to be integral, x must be a perfect square. Accordingly, the "field" of x is restricted to the set of integers 1^2, 2^2, 3^2, 4^2, and so on, *i.e.*, to 1, 4, 9, 16, and so on. . . .

Another example of a relation between two variables is afforded by considering the variations in the pressure and volume of a given mass of some gaseous substance—such as air or coal-gas or steam—at a constant temperature. Let v be the number of cubic feet in its volume and p its pressure in lb. weight per square inch. Then the law, known as Boyle's law, expressing the relation between p and v as both vary, is that the product pv is constant, always supposing that the temperature does not alter. . . .

METHODS OF APPLICATION

The way in which the idea of variables satisfying a relation occurs in the applications of mathematics is worth thought, and by devoting some time to it we shall clear up our thoughts on the whole subject.

Let us start with the simplest of examples:—Suppose that building costs

1s. per cubic foot and that *20s.* make £1. Then in all the complex circumstances which attend the building of a new house, amid all the various sensations and emotions of the owner, the architect, the builder, the workmen, and the onlookers as the house has grown to completion, this fixed correlation is by the law assumed to hold between the cubic content and the cost to the owner, namely that if x be the number of cubic feet, and £y the cost, then $20y = x$. This correlation of x and y is assumed to be true for the building of any house by any owner. Also, the volume of the house and the cost are not supposed to have been perceived or apprehended by any particular sensation or faculty, or by any particular man. They are stated in an abstract general way, with complete indifference to the owner's state of mind when he has to pay the bill.

Now think a bit further as to what all this means. The building of a house is a complicated set of circumstances. It is impossible to begin to apply the law, or to test it, unless amid the general course of events it is possible to recognize a definite set of occurrences as forming a particular instance of the building of a house. In short, we must know a house when we see it, and must recognize the events which belong to its building. Then amidst these events, thus isolated in idea from the rest of nature, the two elements of the cost and cubic content must be determinable; and when they are both determined, if the law be true, they satisfy the general formula

$$20y = x.$$

But is the law true? Anyone who has had much to do with building will know that we have here put the cost rather high. It is only for an expensive type of house that it will work out at this price. This brings out another point which must be made clear. While we are making mathematical calculations connected with the formula $20y = x$, it is indifferent to us whether the law be true or false. In fact, the very meanings assigned to x and y, as being a number of cubic feet and a number of pounds sterling, are indifferent. During the mathematical investigation we are, in fact, merely considering the properties of this correlation between a pair of variable numbers x and y. Our results will apply equally well, if we interpret y to mean a number of fishermen and x the number of fish caught, so that the assumed law is that on the average each fisherman catches twenty fish. The mathematical certainty of the investigation only attaches to the results considered as giving properties of the correlation $20y = x$ between the variable pair of numbers x and y. There is no mathematical certainty whatever about the cost of the actual building of any house. The law is not quite true and the result it gives will not be quite accurate. In fact, it may well be hopelessly wrong.

Now all this no doubt seems very obvious. But in truth with more complicated instances there is no more common error than to assume that, because prolonged and accurate mathematical calculations have been made, the application of the result to some fact of nature is absolutely certain. The conclusion of no argument can be more certain than the assumptions from which it starts. All mathematical calculations about the course of nature must start from some assumed law of nature, such, for instance, as the assumed law of the cost of building stated above. Accordingly, however accurately we have calculated that some event must occur, the doubt always remains—Is the law true? If the law states a precise result, almost certainly it is not precisely accurate; and thus even at the best the result, precisely as calculated, is not likely to occur. But then we have no faculty capable of observation with ideal precision, so, after all, our inaccurate laws may be good enough.

We will now turn to an actual case, that of Newton and the Law of Gravity. This law states that any two bodies attract one another with a force proportional to the product of their masses, and inversely proportional to the square of the distance between them. Thus if m and M are the masses of the two bodies, reckoned in lbs. say, and d miles is the distance between them, the force on either body, due to the attraction of the other and directed towards it, is proportional to $\frac{mM}{d^2}$; thus this force can be written as equal to $\frac{kmM}{d^2}$, where k is a definite number depending on the absolute magnitude of this attraction and also on the scale by which we choose to measure forces. It is easy to see that, if we wish to reckon in terms of forces such as the weight of a mass of 1 lb., the number which k represents must be extremely small; for when m and M and d are each put equal to 1, $\frac{kmM}{d^2}$ becomes the gravitational attraction of two equal masses of 1 lb. at the distance of one mile, and this is quite inappreciable.

However, we have now got our formula for the force of attraction. If we call this force F, it is $F = k\frac{mM}{d^2}$, giving the correlation between the variables F, m, M, and d. We all know the story of how it was found out. Newton, it states, was sitting in an orchard and watched the fall of an apple, and then the law of universal gravitation burst upon his mind. It may be that the final formulation of the law occurred to him in an orchard, as well as elsewhere—and he must have been somewhere. But for our purposes it is more instructive to dwell upon the vast amount of preparatory thought, the product of many minds and many centuries, which was necessary before this exact law could be formulated. In the first place, the mathematical habit of mind and the mathematical procedure explained in the previous two chapters had to be generated; otherwise Newton could never have thought of a formula representing the force between *any* two masses at *any* distance. Again, what are the meanings of the terms employed,

Force, Mass, Distance? Take the easiest of these terms, Distance. It seems very obvious to us to conceive all material things as forming a definite geometrical whole, such that the distances of the various parts are measurable in terms of some unit length, such as a mile or a yard. This is almost the first aspect of a material structure which occurs to us. It is the gradual outcome of the study of geometry and of the theory of measurement. Even now, in certain cases, other modes of thought are convenient. In a mountainous country distances are often reckoned in hours. But leaving distance, the other terms, Force and Mass, are much more obscure. The exact comprehension of the ideas which Newton meant to convey by these words was of slow growth, and, indeed, Newton himself was the first man who had thoroughly mastered the true general principles of Dynamics.

Throughout the middle ages, under the influence of Aristotle, the science was entirely misconceived. Newton had the advantage of coming after a series of great men, notably Galileo, in Italy, who in the previous two centuries had reconstructed the science and had invented the right way of thinking about it. He completed their work. Then, finally, having the ideas of force, mass, and distance, clear and distinct in his mind, and realising their importance and their relevance to the fall of an apple and the motions of the planets, he hit upon the law of gravitation and proved it to be the formula always satisfied in these various motions.

The vital point in the application of mathematical formulæ is to have clear ideas and a correct estimate of their relevance to the phenomena under observation. No less than ourselves, our remote ancestors were impressed with the importance of natural phenomena and with the desirability of taking energetic measures to regulate the sequence of events. Under the influence of irrelevant ideas they executed elaborate religious ceremonies to aid the birth of the new moon, and performed sacrifices to save the sun during the crisis of an eclipse. There is no reason to believe that they were more stupid than we are. But at that epoch there had not been opportunity for the slow accumulation of clear and relevant ideas.

The sort of way in which physical sciences grow into a form capable of treatment by mathematical methods is illustrated by the history of the gradual growth of the science of electromagnetism. Thunderstorms are events on a grand scale, arousing terror in men and even animals. From the earliest times they must have been objects of wild and fantastic hypotheses, though it may be doubted whether our modern scientific discoveries in connection with electricity are not more astonishing than any of the magical explanations of savages. The Greeks knew that amber (Greek, electron) when rubbed would attract light and dry bodies. In 1600 A.D., Dr. Gilbert, of Colchester, published the first work on the subject in which any scientific method is followed. He made a list of substances possessing properties similar to those of amber; he must also have the credit of connecting, however vaguely, electric and magnetic phenomena. At the end of the seventeenth and throughout the eighteenth century knowledge advanced. Electrical machines were made, sparks were obtained from them; and the Leyden Jar was invented, by which these effects could be intensified. Some organised knowledge was being obtained; but still no relevant mathematical ideas had been found out. Franklin, in the year 1752, sent a kite into the clouds and proved that thunderstorms were electrical.

Meanwhile from the earliest epoch (2634 B.C.) the Chinese had utilized the characteristic property of the compass needle, but do not seem to have connected it with any theoretical ideas. The really profound changes in human life all have their ultimate origin in knowledge pursued for its own sake. The use of the compass was not introduced into Europe till the end of the twelfth century A.D., more than 3,000 years after its first use in China. The importance which the science of electromagnetism has since assumed in every department of human life is not due to the superior practical bias of Europeans, but to the fact that in the West electrical and magnetic phenomena were studied by men who were dominated by abstract theoretic interests.

The discovery of the electric current is due to two Italians, Galvani in 1780, and Volta in 1792. This great invention opened a new series of phenomena for investigation. The scentific world had now three separate, though allied, groups of occurrences on hand—the effects of "statical" electricity arising from frictional electrical machines, the magnetic phenomena, and the effects due to electric currents. From the end of the eighteenth century onwards, these three lines of investigation were quickly inter-connected and the modern science of electromagnetism was constructed, which now threatens to transform human life.

Mathematical ideas now appear. During the decade 1780 to 1789, Coulomb, a Frenchman, proved that magnetic poles attract or repel each other, in proportion to the inverse square of their distances, and also that the same law holds for electric charges—laws curiously analogous to that of gravitation. In 1820, Öersted, a Dane, discovered that electric currents exert a force on magnets, and almost immediately afterwards the mathematical law of the force was correctly formulated by Ampère, a Frenchman, who also proved that two electric currents exerted forces on each other. "The experimental investigation by which Ampère established the law of the mechanical action between electric currents is one of the most brilliant achievements in science. The whole, theory and experiment, seems as if it had leaped, full grown and full armed, from the brain of the 'Newton of Electricity.' It is perfect in form, and unassailable in accuracy, and it is summed up in a formula from which all the phenomena may be deduced, and which must always remain the cardinal formula of electro-dynamics." [1]

The momentous laws of induction between currents and between currents and magnets were discovered by Michael Faraday in 1831–32. Fara-

[1] *Electricity and Magnetism*, Clerk Maxwell, Vol. II., ch. iii.

day was asked: "What is the use of this discovery?" He answered: "What is the use of a child—it grows to be a man." Faraday's child has grown to be a man and is now the basis of all the modern applications of electricity. Faraday also reorganized the whole theoretical conception of the science. His ideas, which had not been fully understood by the scientific world, were extended and put into a directly mathematical form by Clerk Maxwell in 1873. As a result of his mathematical investigations, Maxwell recognized that, under certain conditions, electrical vibrations ought to be propagated. He at once suggested that the vibrations which form light are electrical. This suggestion has since been verified, so that now the whole theory of light is nothing but a branch of the great science of electricity. Also Hertz, a German, in 1888, following on Maxwell's ideas, succeeded in producing electric vibrations by direct electrical methods. His experiments are the basis of our wireless telegraphy.

In more recent years even more fundamental discoveries have been made, and the science continues to grow in theoretic importance and in practical interest. This rapid sketch of its progress illustrates how, by the gradual introduction of the relevant theoretic ideas, suggested by experiment and themselves suggesting fresh experiments, a whole mass of isolated and even trivial phenomena are welded together into one coherent science, in which the results of abstract mathematical deductions, starting from a few simple assumed laws, supply the explanation to the complex tangle of the course of events.

Finally, passing beyond the particular sciences of electromagnetism and light, we can generalize our point of view still further, and direct our attention to the growth of mathematical physics considered as one great chapter of scientific thought. In the first place, what in the barest outlines is the story of its growth?

It did not begin as one science, or as the product of one band of men. The Chaldean shepherds watched the skies, the agents of Government in Mesopotamia and Egypt measured the land, priests and philosophers brooded on the general nature of all things. The vast mass of the operations of nature appeared due to mysterious unfathomable forces. "The wind bloweth where it listeth" expresses accurately the blank ignorance then existing of any stable rules followed in detail by the succession of phenomena. In broad outline, then as now, a regularity of events was patent. But no minute tracing of their interconnection was possible, and there was no knowledge how even to set about to construct such a science.

Detached speculations, a few happy or unhappy shots at the nature of things, formed the utmost which could be produced.

Meanwhile land-surveys had produced geometry, and the observations of the heavens disclosed the exact regularity of the solar system. Some of the later Greeks, such as Archimedes, had just views on the elementary phenomena of hydrostatics and optics. Indeed, Archimedes, who combined a genius for mathematics with a physical insight, must rank with Newton, who lived nearly two thousand years later, as one of the founders of mathematical physics. He lived at Syracuse, the great Greek city of Sicily. When the Romans besieged the town (in 212 to 210 B.C.), he is said to have burned their ships by concentrating on them, by means of mirrors, the sun's rays. The story is highly improbable, but is good evidence of the reputation which he had gained among his contemporaries for his knowledge of optics. At the end of this siege he was killed. According to one account given by Plutarch, in his life of Marcellus, he was found by a Roman soldier absorbed in the study of a geometrical diagram which he had traced on the sandy floor of his room. He did not immediately obey the orders of his captor, and so was killed. For the credit of the Roman generals it must be said that the soldiers had orders to spare him. . . .

DYNAMICS

The world had to wait for eighteen hundred years till the Greek mathematical physicists found successors. In the sixteenth and seventeenth centuries of our era great Italians, in particular Leonardo da Vinci, the artist (born 1452, died 1519), and Galileo (born 1564, died 1642), rediscovered the secret, known to Archimedes, of relating abstract mathematical ideas with the experimental investigation of natural phenomena. Meanwhile the slow advance of mathematics and the accumulation of accurate astronomical knowledge had placed natural philosophers in a much more advantageous position for research. Also the very egoistic self-assertion of that age, its greediness for personal experience, led its thinkers to want to see for themselves what happened; and the secret of the relation of mathematical theory and experiment in inductive reasoning was practically discovered. It was an act eminently characteristic of the age that Galileo, a philosopher, should have dropped the weights from the leaning tower of Pisa. There are always men of thought and men of action; mathematical physics is the product of an age which combined in the same men impulses to thought with impulses to action.

This matter of the dropping of weights from the tower marks picturesquely an essential step in knowledge, no less a step than the first attainment of correct ideas on the science of dynamics, the basal science of the whole subject. The particular point in dispute was as to whether bodies of different weights would fall from the same height in the same time. According to a dictum of Aristotle, universally followed up to that epoch, the heavier weight would fall the quicker. Galileo affirmed that they would fall in the same time, and proved his point by dropping weights from the top of the leaning tower. The apparent exceptions to the rule all arise when, for some reason, such as extreme lightness or great speed, the air resistance is important. But neglecting the air the law is exact.

Galileo's successful experiment was not the result of a mere lucky guess.

It arose from his correct ideas in connection with inertia and mass. The first law of motion, as following Newton we now enunciate it, is—Every body continues in its state of rest or of uniform motion in a straight line, except so far as it is compelled by impressed force to change that state. This law is more than a dry formula: it is also a pæan of triumph over defeated heretics. The point at issue can be understood by deleting from the law the phrase "or of uniform motion in a straight line." We there obtain what might be taken as the Aristotelian opposition formula: "Every body continues in its state of rest except so far as it is compelled by impressed force to change that state."

In this last false formula it is asserted that, apart from force, a body continues in a state of rest; and accordingly that, if a body is moving, a force is required to sustain the motion; so that when the force ceases, the motion ceases. The true Newtonian law takes diametrically the opposite point of view. The state of a body unacted on by force is that of uniform motion in a straight line, and no external force or influence is to be looked for as the cause, or, if you like to put it so, as the invariable accompaniment of this uniform rectilinear motion. Rest is merely a particular case of such motion, merely when the velocity is and remains zero. Thus, when a body is moving, we do not seek for any external influence except to explain changes in the rate of the velocity or changes in its direction. So long as the body is moving at the same rate and in the same direction there is no need to invoke the aid of any forces.

The difference between the two points of view is well seen by reference to the theory of the motion of the planets. Copernicus, a Pole, born at Thorn in West Prussia (born 1473, died 1543), showed how much simpler it was to conceive the planets, including the earth, as revolving round the sun in orbits which are nearly circular; and later, Kepler, a German mathematician, in the year 1609 proved that, in fact, the orbits are practically ellipses, that is, a special sort of oval curves. . . . Immediately the question arose as to what are the forces which preserve the planets in this motion. According to the old false view, held by Kepler, the actual velocity itself required preservation by force. Thus he looked for tangential forces. But according to the Newtonian law, apart from some force the planet would move for ever with its existing velocity in a straight line, and thus depart entirely from the sun. Newton, therefore, had to search for a force which would bend the motion round into its elliptical orbit. This he showed must be a force directed towards the sun. In fact, the force is the gravitational attraction of the sun acting according to the law of the inverse square of the distance, which has been stated above.

The science of mechanics rose among the Greeks from a consideration of the theory of the mechanical advantage obtained by the use of a lever, and also from a consideration of various problems connected with the weights of bodies. It was finally put on its true basis at the end of the sixteenth and during the seventeenth centuries, as the preceding account shows, partly with the view of explaining the theory of falling bodies, but chiefly in order to give a scientific theory of planetary motions. But since those days dynamics has taken upon itself a more ambitious task, and now claims to be the ultimate science of which the others are but branches. The claim amounts to this: namely, that the various qualities of things perceptible to the senses are merely our peculiar mode of appreciating changes in position on the part of things existing in space. For example, suppose we look at Westminster Abbey. It has been standing there, grey and immovable, for centuries past. But, according to modern scientific theory, that greyness, which so heightens our sense of the immobility of the building, is itself nothing but our way of appreciating the rapid motions of the ultimate molecules, which form the outer surface of the building and communicate vibrations to a substance called the ether. Again we lay our hands on its stones and note their cool, even temperature, so symbolic of the quiet repose of the building. But this feeling of temperature simply marks our sense of the transfer of heat from the hand to the stone, or from the stone to the hand; and, according to modern science, heat is nothing but the agitation of the molecules of a body. Finally, the organ begins playing, and again sound is nothing but the result of motions of the air striking on the drum of the ear.

Thus the endeavour to give a dynamical explanation of phenomena is the attempt to explain them by statements of the general form, that such and such a substance or body was in this place and is now in that place. Thus we arrive at the great basal idea of modern science, that all our sensations are the result of comparisons of the changed configurations of things in space at various times. It follows therefore, that the laws of motion, that is, the laws of the changes of configurations of things, are the ultimate laws of physical science.

In the application of mathematics to the investigation of natural philosophy, science does systematically what ordinary thought does casually. When we talk of a chair, we usually mean something which we have been seeing or feeling in some way; though most of our language will presuppose that there is something which exists independently of our sight or feeling. Now in mathematical physics the opposite course is taken. The chair is conceived without any reference to anyone in particular, or to any special modes of perception. The result is that the chair becomes in thought a set of molecules in space, or a group of electrons, a portion of the ether in motion, or however the current scientific ideas describe it. But the point is that science reduces the chair to things moving in space and influencing each other's motions. Then the various elements or factors which enter into a set of circumstances, as thus conceived, are merely the things, like lengths of lines, sizes of angles, areas, and volumes, by which the positions of bodies in space can be settled. Of course, in addition to these geometrical elements the fact of motion and change necessitates the introduction of the rates of changes of such elements, that is to say, velocities, angular velocities, accelerations, and suchlike things. Accordingly, mathematical physics deals with correlations between variable numbers which are supposed to represent the correlations which exist in nature between the measures of these geometrical elements and of their rates of change. But always the mathematical laws deal with variables, and it is only in the occasional testing of the laws by reference to experiments, or in the use of the laws for special predictions that definite numbers are substituted. . . .

1911

FROM CYZICUS TO NEPTUNE *

ERIC TEMPLE BELL

A ROYAL ROAD

To one of Alexander the Great's tutors, the Greek mathematician Menaechmus, is attributed the discouraging remark "There is no royal road to geometry." Alexander had impatiently ordered Menaechmus to abridge his proofs. Unable to oblige his impetuous pupil, Menaechmus nevertheless, perhaps in spite of himself, did succeed in leveling another royal road. This was the straight highway to the true beginning of mathematical astronomy and therefore also of analytical mechanics and mathematical physics. Without the purely mathematical inventions of this somewhat obscure Greek geometer it is inconceivable that the course of the physical sciences, in particular mathematical physics and theoretical astronomy, could have followed even remotely any such direction as they actually have.

Of the life of Menaechmus little is known beyond his problematical dates, 375–325 B. C., and the uncertified tradition that he succeeded the incomparable Eudoxus (408–355 B. C.), precursor of the integral calculus, as director of the mathematical seminar at Cyzicus. Far more important for science than all the trivialities of Menaechmus' forgotten life is the memorable fact that he invented the conic sections. It was the simple geometry of these curves that led to the beginning of modern astronomy. The conics are easily visualized.

Imagine a cone standing on a circular base B. The surface of the cone is to be extended (as in the figure) indefinitely in both directions through the vertex V. The two parts of this extended cone issuing from V (one up, the other down), are called nappes; the straight line AVA' through V perpen-

* From *The Handmaiden of the Sciences* by Eric Temple Bell, The Williams and Wilkins Company, reprinted by permission from the publishers. Copyright 1937 by The Williams and Wilkins Company.

dicular to B is the *axis*, and any straight line, such as G, which passes through V and lies on the surface is a *generator* (see figure). The curve of intersection of a plane with either or both nappes is a *conic section*, or briefly, a *conic*. According to this definition it is easily seen that there are precisely seven species of conics.

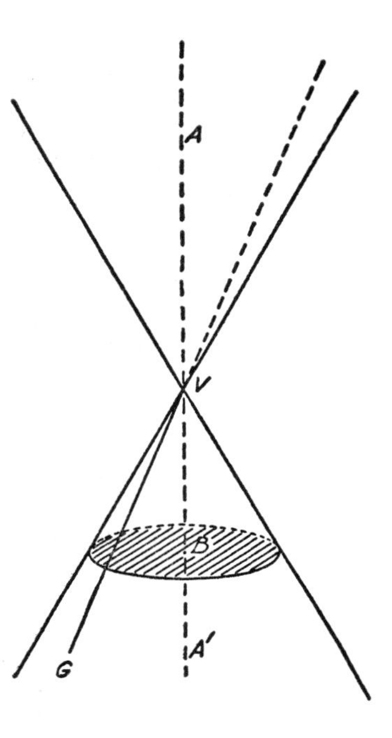

In 1, 2, 3 the plane passes through V.

1. If the plane passes through V and does not cut the surface elsewhere, the conic is a *point*.

2. If the plane passes through V and touches the surface, the conic is a *straight line* (or pair of coincident straight lines).

3. If the plane passes through V and also intersects B in distinct points, the conic is *a pair of intersecting straight lines:*

In 4, 5, 6, 7 the plane does not pass through V.

4. If the plane cuts the axis at right angles, the conic is a *circle.*

5. If the plane is not parallel to the axis or to a generator, the conic is an *ellipse.*

6. If the plane is parallel to a generator, the conic is a *parabola.*

7. If the plane is parallel to the axis, the conic is a hyperbola, consisting of two branches.

The first two of these are of no interest. Note however that the point conic can be considered as a circle with radius zero, and that the straight line conic is a degenerate case of the pair of intersecting straight lines—when the lines coincide. For what is to follow, the ellipse is the most interesting of the conics, although the parabola also has useful properties, two of which may be noted in passing.

A parabola is approximately the path of a ball, a bullet, or a shell in the air. If the air offered no resistance the path would be exactly a parabola. Thus if warfare were conducted in a vacuum, as it should be, the calculations of ballistics would be much simpler than they actually are, and it would cost considerably less than the $25,000 or so of taxes which it is now necessary to shoot away in order to slaughter one patriot.

Parabolic mirrors offer a somewhat less bloody application of the conics, such mirrors being used in some automobile headlights. Suppose we were required to construct a mirror which would reflect the light from a point-source in a beam of parallel rays. Trial and error might grope for centuries to discover what mathematics reveals with a turn of the hand: there is exactly one type of mirror which will do what is wanted, namely the parabolic. Moreover the calculation prescribes the unique point at which the light must be placed in front of the mirror to produce the parallel rays. This point is called the *focus* of the parabola.

Passing to the ellipse, which will shortly assume the rôle of guide in mathematical astronomy, we must define its *foci*. First, to draw an ellipse, we tie a thread to two pins stuck in the drawing board, say at F and F', and keep the thread taut with the point P of the pencil; P then traces out the curve—an ellipse—permitted by this restraint (see figure).

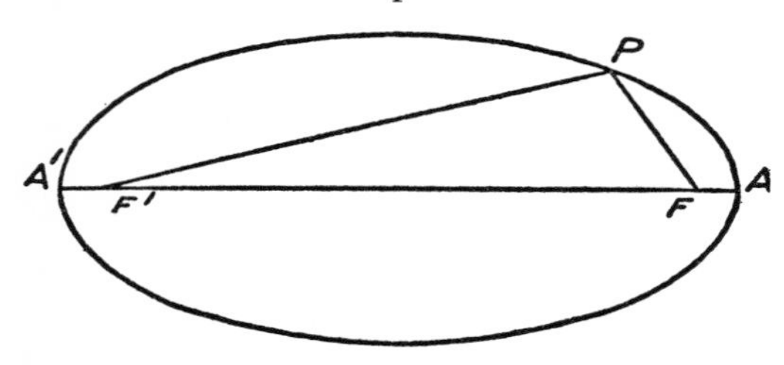

Let the line joining F, F' cut the ellipse in the points A, A'. Then the segment AA' is called the *major axis* of the ellipse, and each of F, F' is a *focus* of the ellipse. From the manner in which the curve was drawn it is clear that the sum of the distances, PF, PF' is *constant*—the same—for all positions of the point P on the ellipse; this sum is equal to AA'.

If the foci F, F' move into coincidence the ellipse degenerates to a circle. Thus, in a sense, an ellipse is a *generalization* of a circle. This is of some importance as the earlier Greek astronomers chose the too obvious circle as the key to the geometry of the heavens, whereas the ellipse would have fitted more refined observations better. . . .

All the conics are unified from the algebraic point of view of analytic geometry. The several species of conics correspond to the essentially distinct types of equations of the second degree in two variables.

KEPLER'S FAITH

Through the labors of a host of Greek mathematicians, of whom Apollonius (c. 260–200 B. C.) towers up as one of the greatest geometers of all time, the geometry of the conic sections was minutely elaborated long before the decline of Greek learning. There is no evidence that any of the Greek mathematicians suspected that conics would some day prove of paramount importance in the dynamics of the solar system. The contrary appears to be the case. Otherwise Ptolemy (2nd Century A. D.) might have been tempted to try ellipses instead of circles as a clue to the geometry of planetary orbits—the Copernican picture of the solar system with all the planets revolving round the Sun is sometimes said to have been imagined (and forgotten) by the Greeks. The Greeks, by the way, seem to have done everything in modern science but never to have done much with it. Possibly they were too vague, too philosophical, to state clearly what, if anything, they really meant.

In devoting the hard labor they did to conic sections the Greek geometers set a fashion followed in modern times by the majority of professional mathematicians. Disregarding any practical or scientific use their creations might have then or later, the pioneers developed mathematics for its own interest. Even from the standpoint of the crassest practicality this austere fashion seems to have been profitable enough. It can be argued, of course, that strict attention to the immediately useful might have proved more profitable, even for mathematics. That, however, is not how science has actually developed, and speculations on how mathematics might have evolved certainly cannot affect the past, although they may inspire educational reformers to new and more frightful excesses.

After the decline of Greece as a leader in geometrical research, knowledge of the conics was fostered and transmitted to Christian Europeans by sagacious infidels, notably the Arabs. All through this protracted nightmare the Ptolemaic description of the solar system, with the intolerable complexity of its cycles upon cycles, epicycles upon epicycles, brooded like a god. We need not describe Ptolemy's masterpiece. Except for its historical interest this massive work is now happily ignored. The Ptolemaic theory was one of humanity's major blunders in its gropings to touch what it cannot see.

Unfortunately for the progress of knowledge the Ptolemaic theory, with the Earth at the centre of everything, was fully competent to account for the observed motions of the planets. This was its damnatory excellence. And more, with sufficient ingenuity the theory could be modified to accommodate certain new observations. Had not the simpler heliocentric picture of the solar system disclosed itself to Copernicus we might still be admiring the Ptolemaic description of the Solar System as one of the sublimest achievements of the human mind. Possibly it was; the Copernican revolution swept it into limbo.

Familiar as we are now with the rapid obsolescence of physical theories, it is difficult for us to imagine the terrific uproar occasioned by Copernicus' fundamental remark that all the planets revolve round the Sun. Nor perhaps did Copernicus himself foresee the full fury of the row his work was to precipitate when, in 1543, he touched on his deathbed the first printed copy of his treatise on the motions of the heavenly bodies. More prudent than his successor Galileo (1564–1642), Copernicus saved himself considerable embarrassment by resigning from life in the nick of time.

The bigoted intelligentsia of all colors, from humanists and theologians to astronomers and mathematicians, rallied to the flag of authority. Unlike the sophisticates of our own generation the sages of the Sixteenth Century seem to have preferred complexity to simplicity. They would have none of the beautifully direct heliocentric theory. The Chinese involution of the Ptolemaic system, which should have been buried the day Copernicus died, was embalmed and fitted with new gears to preserve it in a ghastly semblance of life for decades after it was dead. Not so many years ago we witnessed a similar brainless rush to the banner of tradition when Einstein amended (and abolished) the Newtonian law of gravitation. Einstein escaped the concentration camps, it is true; yet—we are assured by his former associates and compatriots—his theory is as trivial as was that of Copernicus.

After Copernicus the next long stride toward a rational celestial mechanics was taken by the astronomer Tycho Brahe (1546–1601). Either the laborious Tycho was too absorbed in his observations to have time for mathematics, or he lacked the right type of mind to synthesize his masses of data into a simple geometrical picture. What he had recorded of the motions of the planets, with an accuracy seldom approached before his time, ached for a mathematical interpreter. Did the planets revolve around the Sun in circles, or was some less banal curve demanded to portray their orbits? Johann Kepler (1571–1630), at one time Tycho's assistant, was to find the solution.

A highly gifted mathematician, a terrific worker, a first rate astronomer, and a man of undeviating intellectual honesty, Kepler was the ideal candidate to sift the accumulated data, to calculate endlessly, and to be satisfied with nothing short of the completest accuracy attainable at the time. Undeterred by poverty, failure, domestic tragedy, and persecution, but sustained by his mystical belief in an attainable mathematical harmony and perfection of nature, Kepler persisted for fifteen years before finding the simple regularity he sought.

What Kepler accomplished is one of the most astounding feats of arithmetical divination in the history of science. His labors were rewarded by three of the grandest empirical discoveries ever made, *Kepler's laws:* all the planets describe ellipses round the Sun, which is at one focus of these ellipses; the line joining the Sun to any planet sweeps over equal areas in equal times; the squares of the periodic times of the planets are proportional to the cubes of the major axes of their orbits. All this he inferred by what was little better than common arithmetic abbreviated by logarithms.

The story of Kepler's epochal discoveries is so familiar that we need not dwell on it here, except to note the curious inconsequence of it all. This applies with equal force to every mathematical formulation of natural 'laws' which we shall notice later.

What stimulated Kepler to keep slaving all those fifteen years? An utter absurdity. In addition to his faith in the mathematical perfectibility of astronomy, Kepler also believed wholeheartedly in astrology. This was nothing against him. For a scientist of Kepler's generation astrology was as respectable scientifically and mathematically as the quantum theory or relativity is to theoretical physicists today. Nonsense now, astrology was not nonsense in the Sixteenth Century. . . .

CALCULATION PLUS INSIGHT

The full power of the mathematical method is not displayed in any such laborious cut-and-try as Kepler sweated over to find his three laws. The hidden strength of mathematics partly reveals itself at the next and far more difficult encounter with the unknown.

Before Kepler's laws could be deduced from something simpler a mathematics of continuous change had to be invented. This was the differential calculus (described in a later chapter), brought to a usable state of perfection in the Seventeenth Century by Newton (1642–1727) and Leibniz (1646–1716). In addition the empirical laws of motion had to be discovered and stated in a form adapted to mathematical reasoning. Galileo (1564–1642) and Newton between them accomplished this. Finally, although it may not have been logically required (as will be seen when we consider Einstein's work), the concept of *force* had to be clarified, in particular the notion of a *force of attraction* between material bodies such as the Sun and the planets. This was accomplished in Newton's law of universal gravitation. With these partly empirical preliminaries disposed of the solar system was ready for idealization into a map of reality of sufficient abstractness to be explored mathematically.

The laws mentioned above may be recalled. First, the three laws of motion:

1. Every body will continue in its state of rest or of uniform motion in a straight line unless it is compelled to change that state by impressed force.
2. Rate of change of motion is proportional to the impressed force, and takes place in the direction in which the force acts.
3. Action and reaction are equal and opposite.

The first of these defines inertia; the second (in which 'motion' means *momentum*, or 'mass times velocity,' both mass and velocity being measured in the appropriate units), introduces the intuitive notion of a *rate*. The last is probably the most important contribution of mathematics to science. . . .

Newton's law of universal gravitation has a more audible mathematical ring:

4. Any two particles of matter in the universe attract one another with a force which is proportional to the product of the masses of the particles, and inversely proportional to the square of the distance between them.

Thus, if m, M are numbers measuring the masses of the particles, and d measures the distance between the particles, the force of attraction is measured by

$$k \times \frac{m \times M}{d^2},$$

in which k is some constant number depending only on the units in terms of which mass, distance, and force are measured. If the distance is *doubled*, the attractive force is only *one-fourth* of what it was before; if the distance is *trebled*, the force is diminished to *one-ninth*, and so on.

It should appear reasonable even to one who remembers no mathematics beyond arithmetic that the path of one particle being attracted by another will depend upon the law of attraction between the two particles. If the attraction is according to the Newtonian law of the inverse square (square = second power) of the distance the path will bear but little resemblance to that compelled by a law of the inverse third, or fourth, or fifth . . . power of the distance. It should also be fairly obvious that the following question admits a definite answer: If a body, say a comet, is observed to trace a certain definitely known path, characterized geometrically, in its approach to the Sun, what law of attraction between the Sun and the comet will account for the observed path?

A similar problem was proposed in August, 1684 to Newton. For some months the astronomer Halley and other friends of Newton had been discussing the problem in the following precise form: What is the path of a body attracted by a force directed toward a fixed point, the force varying in intensity as the inverse square of the distance? Newton answered instantly, "An ellipse." "How do you know?" he was asked. "Why, I have calculated it." Thus originated the imperishable *Principia,* which Newton later wrote out for Halley. It contained a complete treatise on motion.

When solved fully by Newton this problem answered both the direct and inverse forms of the question proposed, and accounted at one stroke for Kepler's three laws. The laws were deduced from the simple law of universal gravitation. The 'inverse' answer showed that if the path is an ellipse the law of attraction is the Newtonian.

It is definitely known that the almost Greek methods of the *Principia,* with their rigid geometrical deductions, are not those by which Newton reached his results, but that he used the calculus as an immeasurably more penetrating instrument of exploration. The calculus being a strange and prickly novelty at the time, Newton wisely recast his findings in the classical geometry familiar to his contemporaries. Today the deduction of Kepler's laws from the Newtonian law of gravitation is accomplished by means of the calculus in a page or two in the textbooks on dynamics. In Newton's day it was a task for a titan. We do seem to progress in some things.

Newton's law contained vastly more than Kepler's too smooth laws. Combined with the calculus it made possible an attack on the observed irregularities of the supposedly perfect elliptical orbits. It is clear that if Newton's law is indeed universal, then every planet in the solar system must perturb every other and cause it to depart from the true ellipse which it would follow if it were the only planet in the system and if both it and the Sun were perfect homogeneous spheres. As the mass of the Sun greatly exceeds that of the planets, the observed irregularities will be slight. But they will be none the less important. We shall see next a spectacular example of the importance of attending to slight though awkward discrepancies between oversimplified mathematical perfection and obstinate facts of observation. Newton himself initiated the study of perturbations which was to enlarge our knowledge of the solar system and prove useful in our own day in the yet more difficult field of atomic structure.

MATHEMATICAL PROPHECY

The next episode in this brief story of the royal road opens with Newton in his great prime and closes with a young man in his early twenties. As only one main road is being followed from the Cyzicus of Menaechmus to the Cambridge of John Couch Adams, we must pass by unexplored the many alluring highways branching off to other great empires of mathematical reasoning, and condense the boundless work of a century to one fleeting glimpse. At the end of the road we shall see a typical example—also one of the most famous—of the prophetic power of mathematics when applied to a masterly abstraction of nature. Newton's law of universal gravitation was such an abstraction; the methods of mathematical analysis developed from the calculus elicited from Newton's law what it implicitly concealed.

Even today we look in vain for any generalization of physical science which has unified any such vast mass of diverse phenomena as was reduced to a coherent unity by Newton's law. At a first glance we may think that some of the recent generalizations have a scope as wide as Newton's had in its heyday, but a little consideration shows that this is an illusion. Not only did universal gravitation as mathematicized in Newton's law sweep together, sift, and simplify the scattered astronomical knowledge of twenty centuries or more; it subjected the mysterious tides to mathematical rule, and for over two centuries served as a suggestive guide in all fields of physical science where there was any glimmer of hope that a mechanical philosophy could simplify and unify the data of the senses. The extreme simplicity of the law itself is equalled only by one other powerful generalization of modern science, the law of the conservation of energy, which asserts that the total amount of energy in the universe remains constant. Electric energy, for instance, may be transformed into heat and light, and seem to be dissipated, but actually nothing has been lost. This great generalization (now radically modified since the advent of relativity) may justly claim to have been a descendant of Newton's.

In the century following Newton a host of powerful mathematicians, including Euler (1702–1783), Lagrange (1736–1813), and Laplace (1749–1827), explored the heavens with Newton's universal law as their sole guide, finding almost everywhere measurably complete accord between theory and observation. The mathematical methods used by Newton's successors were not those of the *Principia*, but the more flexible analysis which evolved from the first rather crudely stated forms of the differential and integral calculus.

Not all of these great mathematicians believed in the Newtonian law as a truly universal principle. Euler, for one, doubted whether anything so elementary could possibly account for even so simple a situation as that posed by the motion of the Moon. By 'simple' here we mean simple only to uninstructed intuition. The motion of the Moon offers one of the most complicated problems in the whole range of dynamical astronomy. So great are the mathematical difficulties that any analyst of Euler's time might well have believed the Newtonian hypothesis of the inverse square law to be inadequate. The Newtonian law solves the problem of two attracting bodies completely and with a Keplerian simplicity. When more than two bodies attract one another according to the Newtonian law of universal gravitation, no exact solution of the problem of completely describing their motions exists even today. The method of successive approximations is applied to yield progressively more accurate descriptions of the motion sufficient for all practical purposes, such as those demanded by the computation of the nautical almanac. The motion of the Moon is a 'three-body problem,' the bodies being the Earth, the Sun, and the Moon.

Among those who doubted the universality and adequacy of the Newtonian law was G. B. Airy (1801–1892), for long Astronomer Royal of Newton's own England. Airy's doubt was perfectly legitimate, and indeed highly creditable to a man of science, even if based on a total misconception of the nature of the real difficulties involved. But no skeptic has a right to impose the inertia of his disbelief on young men ardently pushing forward to what they believe are attainable discoveries. To Airy more than to any other relic of academic conservatism is due the official indifference with which the calculations of young Adams—recounted in a moment—were received, when he ventured to sustain Newton by one of the most brilliant mathematical predictions in all the brilliant history of mathematical science. We have not space to go into the record of the official lethargy which robbed Adams of a unique 'first'; so with this brief (but on the whole adequate) obituary of his chief obstructor we shall pass on to what Adams did.

On March 13, 1781 William Herschel discovered with his telescope a new member of the Sun's family, the planet subsequently known as Uranus (after a happily abortive attempt to name it for King George of England). The newcomer offered a superb opportunity for testing the Newtonian law.

Before long discrepancies between calculation and observation appeared in the orbit of Uranus that could not be explained away by postulating faulty arithmetic or defective telescopes. Newton's hypothesis simply did not fit the observed facts.

But man is a theorizing animal, and the erratic irregularities of Uranus' motion were attributed to the perturbations of some more distant planet, as yet undiscovered. This hypothetical planet, attracting Uranus according to the Newtonian law of the inverse square, would account for everything provided only it existed, and its mass and orbit were of the right mathematical specifications to produce exactly those irregularities in the orbit of Uranus which had actually been observed.

Mathematically the problem was an inverse one of extreme difficulty. It would be laborious but comparatively easy to calculate the effect of a *known* planet on the motion of Uranus. But given the erratic motion it was much more difficult to reach out with mathematical analysis into the vague of ultra-planetary space and discover how massive, and where, the *unobserved* perturber was at any particular date.

By the early 1840's many astronomers believed that such an ultra-Uranian planet existed. In a historic prophecy Herschel stated on September 10, 1846, "We see it [the hypothetical planet] as Columbus saw America from the coast of Spain. Its movements have been felt, trembling along the far-reaching line of our analysis with a certainty hardly inferior to that of ocular demonstration."

The analysis to which Herschel referred was modern mathematics, as it then existed, applied to the Newtonian law. Mathematically the problem of Uranus was this: given the perturbations, to discover the mass and the orbit of the unknown planet producing them—in short, to discover the unobserved member of the Sun's family responsible for the indisputable disharmony in the otherwise harmonious Newtonian symphony of the solar system.

No simile can convey the difficulty of such a problem to anyone who has not seen something similar attempted. 'A needle in a haystack' might be suggested, but here we do not know whether the haystack exists or, if it did exist, in what country it might be, or whether, after all, there is a needle to be found.

About eleven months before Herschel prophesied, young Adams (1819–1892) had sent to the Astronomer Royal numerical estimates of the mass and orbit of the undiscovered planet. Moreover Adams had calculated where and when the hypothetical planet perturbing Uranus could be observed in telescopes. Subsequent events proved his calculations correct within a reasonable margin of accuracy. Had a patch of sky no larger than three and a half Moons been searched when Adams told the Astronomer Royal to look, the planet would have been found. But Adams at the time was only an unknown quantity of twenty-four. As an undergraduate at Trinity College, Cambridge, he had resolved to attack the Uranian problem the moment he was quit of his examinations. On taking his degree in January 1843 with the highest honors, he immediately set about his self-imposed task.

In the meantime a seasoned mathematical astronomer in France, U. J. J. Leverrier (1811–1877), had also attacked the perturbations of Uranus in an attempt to locate and estimate the unknown perturber. He also succeeded. Both Adams and Leverrier worked in complete ignorance of what the other was doing.

Leverrier was the luckiest in his friends. The policy of 'wait and don't see' delayed search for the planet by the English astronomers until Leverrier's livelier continental friends had already located the suspect in the heavens—very approximately where both Adams and Leverrier had instructed practical astronomers to direct their telescopes.

Thus was Neptune discovered by pure mathematical analysis applied to a great physical hypothesis, and thus ended one glorious canto of the epic begun by Menaechmus, carried on by Kepler, and sped well on to its climax —as yet unpredictable—by Newton.

1937

MATHEMATICS

History and Biography

BALL, W. W. R., *A Short Account of the History of Mathematics* (New York, The Macmillan Company, 1915).

BELL, ERIC T., *The Development of Mathematics* (New York, McGraw-Hill Book Company, Inc., 1940).

———, *Men of Mathematics* (New York, Simon & Schuster, Inc., 1937).

CAJORI, FLORIAN, *The Early Mathematical Sciences in North and South America* (Boston, Richard G. Badger, 1928).

———, *A History of Mathematics* (New York, The Macmillan Company, 1919).

HEATH, T. L., *A History of Greek Mathematics* (Oxford, Clarendon Press, 1921).

SARTON, GEORGE, *The Study of the History of Mathematics* (Cambridge, Harvard University Press, 1936).

SMITH, DAVID E., *A Source Book of Mathematics* (New York, McGraw-Hill Book Company, Inc., 1929).

SULLIVAN, J. W. N., *The History of Mathematics in Europe from the Fall of Greek Science to the Rise of the Conception of Mathematical Rigour* (London, Oxford University Press, 1925).

Nature and Applications

ABBOTT, EDWIN, *Flatland: A Romance of Many Dimensions* (Boston, Roberts Bros., 1885).

BAKST, AARON, *Mathematics: Its Magic and Mastery* (New York, D. Van Nostrand Company, Inc., 1941).

BELL, ERIC T., *The Handmaiden of the Sciences* (Baltimore, The Williams and Wilkins Company, 1937).

———, *The Queen of the Sciences* (Baltimore, The Williams and Wilkins Company, 1931).

DANTZIG, TOBIAS, *Number, the Language of Science* (New York, The Macmillan Company, 1939).

DRESDEN, ARNOLD, *An Invitation to Mathematics* (New York, Henry Holt and Company, Inc., 1936).

Encyclopaedia Britannica, *Calculating Machines* (Chicago, Encyclopaedia Britannica, edition of 1947).

HOGBEN, LANCELOT, *Mathematics for the Millions* (New York, W. W. Norton & Company, 1940).

KASNER, EDWARD, and NEWMAN, JAMES, *Mathematics and the Imagination* (New York, Simon & Schuster, 1940).

KRAITCHIK, MAURICE, *Mathematical Recreations* (New York, W. W. Norton & Company, 1942).

LOGSDON, MAYME, *A Mathematician Explains* (Chicago, The University of Chicago Press, 1936).

MERRIMAN, GAYLORD, *To Discover Mathematics* (New York, John Wiley & Sons, Inc., 1942).

POLYA, G., *How to Solve It* (Princeton, Princeton University Press, 1945).

WHITEHEAD, ALFRED N., *An Introduction to Mathematics* (New York, Henry Holt and Company, Inc., 1911).

PHYSICS

THE lives and characters of scientists have exhibited extraordinary diversity, and in this section you will observe some of the most unusual at work. Newton in his early days was the complete eccentric, as you will gather from the description of him by his assistant Humphrey Newton; but in later years, as Director of the Mint, he became a man of the world. Franklin was a wit, a statesman, a brilliant writer, as well as an important scientific thinker. The unworldly Einstein, the genius in mathematical physics, is said to have difficulty with simple arithmetic. Faraday was a bottle washer who rose from obscurity. Marie Curie spent her early days in poverty. Lord Kelvin made a fortune by adapting his discoveries to the uses of transportation and communication.

Many like these play their parts in Professor Bumstead's extraordinary brief "History of Physics" which is our opening article. Here in shortest space are described the really great advances on which rests the massive structure of modern physics. Following this bird's-eye view, we turn back for all-too-brief glimpses of the work of the man whom Lagrange described as "the greatest genius who ever existed." Born the son of a farmer, Newton was to discover the law of gravitation, the laws of motion, the principles of optics, and the composite nature of light, and simultaneously with Leibnitz was to invent the calculus. Any one of these achievements would have marked him as a genius of the first rank. Together they place him on a summit which to this day has never been approached.

Matter and energy have been two fundamental concepts which have engaged the attention of physicists. Originally their various forms were conceived to have little connection with one another. Gradually a process of unification has taken place until now, as explained below, even the two fundamentals are considered merely different manifestations of the same thing. This monism, this tendency to refer many phenomena to a single ultimate constituent, is a way in which science is considered to "explain" the problems it attacks.

One pioneer on these lines was von Helmholtz, who showed in "On the Sensation of Sound in General" that sound is a kind of motion and thus of energy. Franklin, in his "Electrical Experiments," showed that lightning and electricity were the same. Meanwhile, other experimenters, like Count Rumford in his work on heat as a mode of motion, were further unifying our concept of energy. Bumstead has given us the outlines of the subject, showing the continuity of the historical line with Faraday's work on fields of energy, Maxwell's mathematical formulation of Faraday's hypotheses, and the experimental verification which came with the discovery of the Hertzian waves which Marconi was to harness in his wireless telegraphy.

The theme is further developed in "Concepts and Forms of Energy" by C. C. Furnas, who here shows how the progress of civilization is primarily a matter of the control of energy in its different manifestations. Just one of these manifestations is discussed briefly in "Microwaves" by Lee Alvin DuBridge, President of the California Institute of Technology. Hundreds and thousands of other aspects and applications, for peace and war, are of course under intensive investigation.

In an earlier section, W. F. Durand, the pioneer in aerodynamics, discusses the relation between pure and applied science. This relation is now shown in action in Durand's own specialty. In "Trial by Wind Tunnel," George W. Gray shows modern airplane design being developed in the laboratory. In "Jets Power Future Flying," Watson Davis, Director of Science Service, the well-known organization for dissemination of scientific information, throws light on the latest developments which will have profound effects on the commercial and military aviation of the future.

We previously mentioned the view that energy and matter are manifestations of a single fundamental concept. As we know, Einstein's famous formula $E = Mc^2$ expresses this view mathematically. When E is the amount of energy, M the mass, and c the velocity of light, the formula obviously states the equivalence of the two forms. The history of this relation has its climax in atomic fission, but its beginnings were in the speculation on the nature of matter of Democritus and Lucretius. Sir James Jeans, one of the most appealing of modern writers on science, first tells us something of the historical background. Then he shows how our conception of the atom as an indestructible building block has been entirely changed. The change was presaged by Henri Becquerel's observation of the fogging of a carefully wrapped photographic plate which was left near some rare minerals. It continued with Marie Curie's isolation of radium, charmingly described in her non-technical paper "The Discovery of Radium." Jeans discusses briefly our theoretical advances up to recent years.

Again, in a long selection from Professor Smyth's "Atomic Energy for Military Purposes," we turn from theory to practice, from pure science to technology. Much of the material in this selection is difficult for the untrained reader to understand, but the attempt has been made to present excerpts which give a running account of the project. Even a cursory reading cannot fail to inflame the imagination with its picture of five years of feverish effort, its solution of "insoluble" technical problems, its overwhelmingly dramatic illustration of how a "long-haired" mathematical equation, properly applied, can alter the course of history.

The section closes with articles on two concepts which have had a great effect on the progress of physical theory. Gilbert N. Lewis, the physical chemist, discusses some aspects of thermodynamics in "The Scientific Meaning of Chance." Paul R. Heyl, the man who weighed the earth, writes with clarity and distinction about the most publicized theory of modern times. It is impossible really to understand relativity without mathematics. It is worth-while pointing out also that, as Dingle explains in "Astronomy and Scientific Ideas," much modern theory simply does not lend itself to "common sense" exposition. Heyl, however, has succeeded as well as anyone else in presenting in brief space some of the implications of relativity theory for the reader who is not an expert.

THE HISTORY OF PHYSICS *

HENRY ANDREWS BUMSTEAD

The beginnings of anything like a connected history of the science which is now called physics may be placed with considerable definiteness about the beginning of the 17th century and associated with the great name of Galileo. It is of course true that innumerable isolated facts had been known for many centuries which are now included among the data of this science; and many tools and simple machines which are now regarded as applications of physical principles had been devised and used. Even prehistoric man knew some of these—to his very great advantage. But, with one important exception which will be mentioned later, there was, in the ancient world, no connected body of knowledge in this field which can properly be called scientific. In this respect physics differs radically from mathe-

* A lecture delivered at Yale University, October 21, 1920, the fourth of a series on the History of Science under the auspices of the Yale Chapter of the Gamma Alpha Graduate Scientific Fraternity. Reprinted by permission from *The Scientific Monthly*.

matics, or astronomy, natural history, or medicine, each of which began its modern career with a store of scientific knowledge that had been obtained and put in order before the Renaissance.

The reason for this difference is doubtless to be found in the fact that the progress of physics is dependent, almost from the first step, on the method of experiment as distinguished from the method of observation. For some unknown psychological reason, the appreciation of the possibilities of experiment as an intellectual tool and the ability to make use of its technique appear very late in the history of human development. A few individuals like Archimedes understood and practiced it, and it is difficult to understand why the seed which they sowed proved sterile. Certain inhibitions, common (despite their very different temperaments) to the Greeks, the Romans and the men of the Middle Ages, seem to have prevented the infection from spreading from its original foci. I have no theory to offer as to the cause of the removal of these inhibitions during the 16th and 17th centuries; but whatever the cause we must, I think, recognize that about that time a new factor made its appearance in the intellectual world which has survived and grown and has produced momentous results.

Some of you no doubt will be disposed to question the novelty which I have attributed to the methods used by Galileo and his successors. You will say with truth that men have been experimenting since long before the dawn of history; that by this means they improved their weapons, food, clothing, shelter and means of transport so that the enormous advantage in material surroundings which the Roman of the Augustan Age had over the prehistoric cave dweller may properly be said to be the result of a long course of progressive experimentation. But what I have, for the sake of making a distinction, called the experimental method in science is a very different thing from the slow empirical improvement of tools and appliances which went on before the beginnings of the modern era. The two kinds of activity differ fundamentally in the objects which they seek to attain and in the means they adopt for the accomplishment of their purposes. . . .

The experiment itself is an observation made under highly artificial and carefully prearranged conditions, and it is this which gives the method its greatest advantage over simple observation of natural phenomena. This is well illustrated by Galileo's work upon the principles of mechanics and in their application to the particular case of the motion of falling bodies. Centuries of inescapable observation of moving bodies had led to no correct idea of the simple laws underlying their behavior, because these laws had been obscured by the effect of friction—a secondary condition of the problem. Galileo's experiments consisted in reducing these effects until the true nature of the phenomena could be observed. The famous experiment at the Leaning Tower of Pisa was a spectacular demonstration of one point of his theory designed to confute his Aristotelian critics; but the really important and fertile experiments were quite simply arranged with the help of iron balls, inclined tracks, boards, nails and bits of string. With the simplest material means he laid the foundations of dynamics and, with it, those of physical science as a whole. Lagrange remarks that Galileo's contributions to mechanics "did not bring him in his lifetime as much celebrity as those discoveries which he made about the system of the world, but they are today the most enduring and real part of the glory of this great man. The discoveries of Jupiter's satellites, of the phases of Venus, of sun spots, etc., needed only telescopes and assiduity; but extraordinary genius was needed to disentangle the laws of nature from phenomena which are always going on under our eyes, but of which the explanation had always eluded the search of philosophers." [1]

The world was ready for the structure which was to be erected upon the foundations laid by Galileo. In the next generation, Torricelli in Italy and Pascal in France showed by bold reasoning and experimentation that Nature's *horror vacui* was due to the weight of the atmosphere; while Guericke in Germany and Boyle in England discovered other important properties of gases. In dynamics, the direct succession fell to Christian Huygens of Amsterdam, a natural philosopher of very high rank and a worthy successor of Galileo. He completed the theory of the pendulum and by its use determined the acceleration of gravity; invented and constructed the pendulum clock and escapement, discovered the theorems of centrifugal force, and was the first to use what is now called the principle of *vis viva* or kinetic energy. His investigations in optics are also of great importance and he was one of the first proponents of the wave theory of light.

To try to give in a small fraction of a single lecture any adequate account of the mighty deeds of Newton is, of course, to attempt the impossible. Fortunately the main features of his achievements are so familiarly known that a brief recapitulation is all that is necessary. Born in 1642, the year of Galileo's death, his genius developed with extraordinary rapidity. It appears to be quite certain that the essential parts of all his great discoveries were made before he was twenty-five years old, although most of them were published much later. The delay was due partly to lack of facilities for publication but mainly to Newton's carefulness in verification and in working out all possible consequences of his hypotheses. His first great discovery (made in the year in which he received the bachelor's degree at

[1] The necessary brevity of this lecture may result in giving the impression that Galileo had no forerunners. This is of course not the case. Archimedes has already been mentioned—a lonely genius who laid firmly the foundations of the statics of solids and liquids. Stevinus, sixteen years older than Galileo, made notable additions to the Archimedean statics. And a century earlier Leonardo da Vinci (a miracle of versatility) had made important discoveries in statics, and had found the true law of the refraction of light. Most of Leonardo's scientific work, however, remained buried in his manuscript notes and has only recently been revealed to the world.

Cambridge) was the "direct and inverse methods of fluxions" which are in all essentials identical with the differential and integral calculus, but with a less convenient and fertile notation. This discovery belongs of course primarily to the history of mathematics; but both physics and astronomy may proudly claim it as belonging partly to them for two reasons; first, because it was the exigencies of their problems which led directly to it; and second, because it was an absolutely indispensable tool for the mechanical and astronomical discoveries of Newton and his successors. In the same year (1665) Newton "began to think of gravity extending to the orb of the moon"; he soon found from one of Kepler's laws that the forces which keep the planets in their orbits must vary inversely as the square of their distances from the sun. He applied this rule to the earth and moon and found an approximate agreement between the force necessary to keep the moon in her orbit and the force of gravity at the surface of the earth. "All this," says Newton in later life, "was in the two plague years of 1665 and 1666, for in those days I was in the prime of my age for invention, and minded mathematics and philosophy more than at any time since."

During the twenty-one years which elapsed before the publication of the *Principia* in 1687, Newton, in the midst of other duties and of investigations on other subjects, recurred again and again to the astronomical and dynamical problems which had engaged his youthful attention. It was only after ten or twelve years that he cleared up the difficulties of centrifugal force (Huygens' previous work being then unknown to him) and thus discovered that the two remaining laws of Kepler were consequences of his gravitational law. In the last three or four years of the period under consideration he appears to have worked steadily at the development of the subject and to have discovered the large number of important theorems and relations which make the *Principia* the most stupendous and overwhelming publication in the history of science.

In all this work there are three streams of discovery which may be separated by logical analysis, but which are so closely intermingled that it is difficult to see how any one of them could have gone on without the other two. Nobody has ever been able to believe that Newton could have extended the Galilean dynamics to the intricate motion of the planets except by the aid of the method of fluxions or its equivalent; and certainly nothing could have been done without a knowledge of the law of gravitation. On the other hand, the solution of astronomical problems required and facilitated a more exact formulation of the principles of mechanics than Galileo had been able to give; although mathematically intricate, they are dynamically simpler than terrestrial problems since no appreciable frictional or dissipative forces are present; and they furnish tests and verifications of dynamical laws of far greater accuracy than can be obtained in any other way.

Under such conditions it seems futile to attempt to decide whether physics is most indebted to Newton for the formulation of the laws of motion, for the discovery of the law of inverse squares, or for the invention of the fluxional calculus. Any one of the three (if it could have been produced alone) would have made his name immortal; the fact that we owe all three to one person places him upon a pinnacle of greatness which has not even been approached by any other man of science.

I must not neglect to mention also Newton's contributions to optics which, while not of the fundamental importance of those we have just been discussing, were nevertheless worthy of their author. I need only to recall to your memory that he investigated the composition of white light, the colors of thin films, diffraction, and the possibilities of achromatism in refracting telescopes. He was not infallible; for he decided that it was impossible to make an achromatic refractor, and he supported the corpuscular theory of light against the undulatory theory of Huygens. In both cases, however, the evidence obtainable in his time strongly supported his position; and I think it was this, rather than the mere authority of his name, which caused the corpuscular theory to prevail during the following century.

In the eighteenth century the development of mechanics and of gravitational theory was carried on by the three Bernoullis, Euler, Clairaut, d'Alembert and others. This development reached its culmination near the end of the century in the publication of Lagrange's "Mécanique Analytique" and of the "Mécanique Céleste" of Laplace—works which for completeness and finish have seldom if ever been excelled. The period was not characterized by new discoveries of the first magnitude but by the careful working out of the theories founded by Galileo and Newton and the perfection of mathematical methods for dealing with complicated problems. This was an admirable preparation for the great outburst of discovery which began toward the end of the eighteenth century and was continued still more conspicuously in the first years of the nineteenth.

In other branches of physics and in chemistry, the ground was also being prepared in a different way by the accumulation of experimental facts and relations which formed the raw material for the generalizations of the period which was to come, and served as starting points for notable advances. It is necessary therefore to go back and to trace briefly the course of the tributary streams of discovery which were soon to join the main current. We shall have to consider what had been learned about magnetism, electricity, light and heat.

The ancients were acquainted with the curious property possessed by the lode-stone of Magnesia of attracting iron, and also knew that when amber was rubbed it attracted bits of straw and other light bodies. Nothing came of this knowledge for centuries; but at some unknown time prior to the Crusades, the north-seeking property of the magnetized needle was discovered and the mariner's compass was invented. The science of magnetism was indeed almost the only part of physics that made any progress during the Middle Ages. In the thirteenth century Petrus Peregrinus of Picardy, experimenting with a spherical lode stone and a needle, found that the stone possessed two "poles" which appeared to be the seat of the magnetic power.

The true founder of both magnetic and electric science, however, was William Gilbert of Colchester, physician to Queen Elizabeth. Twenty-four years older than Galileo, Gilbert must be regarded as one of the pioneers of the experimental method. His work had not the scope and depth which characterized that of the great Italian, nor were its consequences so immediate and so revolutionary; but he was nevertheless a truly scientific experimenter and, considering the time in which he lived, we must regard him as a prodigy of originality. He showed quite conclusively that the behavior of the compass was due to the fact that the earth itself was a great magnet. For two thousand years it had been supposed that amber alone was capable of being excited by friction to attract other bodies; Gilbert found that many bodies could be thus excited and that among them were such commonplace substances as glass, sulphur and resin. His experiments and his reasoning were sound, and he devised a hypothesis of "electric effluvia" which was helpful to electrical science for a long time.

During the eighteenth century the experimental knowledge of both electricity and magnetism progressed rapidly. The conduction of the electrified state by metals was discovered by Stephen Gray; the Leyden jar was invented; du Fay found that there existed two opposite states of electrification which he called vitreous and resinous and that these behaved, as to attractions and repulsions, like the two poles of a magnet. America made her first contribution to physics in the very important work of Benjamin Franklin. Toward the close of this period of activity the doctrines of electric effluvia and of Cartesian vortices had been definitely replaced by the theory that the forces observed were due to action at a distance between charges of a single electric fluid and matter (Franklin) or to a similar action between two fluids (Coulomb). Eventually the law of variation of this force with the distance was experimentally determined by Coulomb and found to be the familiar inverse square relation of Newton. The same law was shown by Coulomb to hold for the forces between magnetic poles also; and either one, or two, magnetic fluids had to be predicated to account for the variation in the strength of magnets. Indeed the application of gravitational theory to these forces rendered inevitable the introduction of such imponderable fluids to take the place of the material masses which play the same rôle in the case of gravitation.

I have already mentioned briefly Newton's researches in optics and his adherence to the corpuscular theory in which he was followed by most philosophers. This introduced another "imponderable" which was however supposed to consist of excessively minute discrete corpuscles instead of a continuous fluid. Many important optical phenomena had been discovered. Descartes had published the mathematical law of refraction which however was not his own discovery but was apparently communicated to him by Snell of Leyden; Newton had discovered and properly interpreted the composite nature of white light and had investigated the simpler cases of diffraction and of what is now called interference; Huygens had observed double refraction in Iceland spar and had given the proximate explanation of it (on the wave theory) which is still current; and he observed that the two beams which had passed through the spar differed from each other and from ordinary light in the peculiar way which we now indicate by calling them polarized. Time is lacking for any discussion of the ingenious arguments by which the two rival theories of light were supported.

The quantitative study of heat begins with Galileo's construction of the first thermometer—an air-thermometer of considerable sensitiveness but of inconvenient design. Improvements of one kind or another were made by many men and the fixity of certain temperatures (such as that of melting ice) was established. The first really reliable thermometers were made by Fahrenheit in the first quarter of the eighteenth century. All of the early thermal experiments and theories were confused by the failure to distinguish clearly between temperature and quantity of heat, and by the great and apparently capricious differences between the heat capacities, or specific heats, of different substances. All these difficulties were finally cleared up in a masterly manner by Joseph Black near the end of the period we are considering. He established calorimetric measurements on a firm basis, and showed quite clearly that in all such experiments heat behaves like a substance which passes from one body to another and sometimes becomes "latent" for a time (as when ice melts) but which is never created or destroyed. All these conclusions are true within the range of Black's experiments; and it was only at a later date that the exceptions were seen to be of great importance and not explicable by appealing to latency or to a variation in heat capacity. What was known at that time thoroughly justified a substantial theory of heat as the most convenient hypothesis available; and thus another imponderable fluid took its place as a respectable and useful article in the physicist's creed. Many unavailing attempts were made to show the identity of two or more of these hypothetical substances. Thus, on account of the phenomena of radiant heat, it was proposed to identify caloric with the light corpuscles; but the fact that light passed through glass while radiant heat did not, was an insuperable obstacle to this view. There was always in the background the possibility that both heat and light were forms of motion, but at the period now under consideration the substantial theories undoubtedly held the field. This state of things led to very sharp boundaries between the different fields of physics and discouraged the natural inclination to apply the principles of dynamics (which by this time had come to seem almost intuitive) to other physical phenomena. There was no great encouragement to apply the principles of mechanics to the imponderables; so far as experiment showed they lacked not only the conspicuous property of weight but also the most essential dynamical characteristic of ordinary matter, inertia. The natural and fertile method of dealing with them was to take as postulates for the mathematical development of the subject certain empirical relations as simple and fundamental as possible. It was not until the establishment of the conservation of energy in the late forties of the nineteenth century that the barriers between the different "physical forces" were broken down.

The intervening period however was one of brilliant discovery in both mathematical and experimental physics. In the theory of heat two works of this period must at least be mentioned. In 1822 Joseph Fourier published his *Théorie Analytique de la Chaleur*, a work of genius which has had a profound effect in almost all branches of theoretical physics and upon pure mathematics as well. A still more momentous event in the history of science was the publication in 1824 of Carnot's *Réflections sur le Puissance Motrice du Feu*. His primary purpose was the investigation of the efficiency of heat engines which had recently become a matter of interest owing to the increasing use of the steam engine invented by Newcomen and Watt. In this paper Carnot makes use of an analogy; he saw that the production of work by an engine might be regarded as due to the fall of caloric from a higher to a lower temperature just as the work of a water mill is a consequence of the fall of water from a higher to a lower level. He follows a course of reasoning so simple yet so effective that it seems inspired; it is based upon the denial of the possibility of perpetual motion which even at that time was a pretty firmly established empirical fact owing to the consistent failure of all attempts to produce such motion. He thus establishes the general principle which is now called "the second law of thermodynamics" and which is of far wider application than could have been imagined by Carnot or any of his contemporaries. For it happens that nearly every phenomenon in the physical universe is attended by an evolution or absorption of heat and is therefore subject to the second law. It governs every chemical reaction as was shown by Willard Gibbs fifty years later, and the physical and chemical processes of life. It sets bounds to cosmological speculations and to forecasts of the future of the human race. Not the slightest deviation from it has ever been observed and the probability of such deviation is so minute that it must be regarded as one of the most firmly established of scientific facts.

In electrostatics and magnetism this period was marked by the development of the mathematical consequences of Coulomb's discovery that the inverse square law applies to these forces. Much of the gravitational theory could be taken over directly while the special applications to electricity were made by Poisson, Green, and others. In the meanwhile however another set of electrical phenomena had appeared. In 1791 Galvani, professor of anatomy at Bologna, gave an account of his experiments on the contraction of frogs' legs when touched with two different metals in series and, with much ability, supported the view that it was an electrical manifestation. He naturally supposed that the origin of the electrical disturbance was in the animal tissues. This was combatted a year later by Volta who referred the seat of the forces involved to the point of contact between the dissimilar metals, and gave good evidence that they were electrical. The effects however were very small, and interest flagged until 1800 when Volta invented the "pile" by means of which very appreciable results could be obtained. This at once excited much attention; and in the same year Nicholson and Carlisle in England in experimenting with the Voltaic pile observed the decomposition of water by electrolysis and shortly afterward Humphrey Davy advanced the chemical theory of the pile, which, after many years of struggle, eventually superseded the contact theory of Volta. There was a rapid advance in the knowledge of the electric current, of batteries, and of the electrolytic process. These experiments produced a profound effect upon chemistry through the electrochemical theory of Berzelius; and although this has long been given up, the most modern theories have, in a different form, reverted to the view that chemical forces are of electrical origin.

Many attempts had been made to discover some connection between the phenomena of electricity and those of magnetism but all had failed until 1820 when Oersted of Copenhagen observed and correctly described the action of an electric current upon a magnet brought near it. As soon as the news of this observation reached Paris, Ampère began the series of investigations which was to render his name immortal in electrical science. Within a week he had demonstrated to the Academy the attractions and repulsions of parallel currents; and during the ensuing three years his brilliant experimental and mathematical researches laid a sure and firm foundation for all the subsequent developments in electrodynamics. As was to be expected, he based his investigations on the Newtonian model, by using current-elements acting upon each other by forces in the line joining them. Again the law proved to be that of the inverse square; but the fact that the attracting elements were directed quantities added many difficulties which, in the state of mathematical science at that time, gave ample scope to the "Newton of electricity" for the display of his genius. The vector relations involved in the statement of his problem caused an indeterminateness which later gave rise to many rivals to Ampère's expression for the force between current elements. These all gave the same result when integrated around closed circuits which alone were amenable to experiment; and no one could succeed in devising experiments which would discriminate between them. One of these rival theories, that of Weber, is interesting as being in some respects similar to the modern theory of electrons.

Great as is the debt which electrical science owes to Ampère, it is exceeded by its obligation to Faraday whose marvellous experimental skill and instinctive perception of the inner nature of phenomena are still the wonder and admiration of all men of science. At twenty-one years of age he was a journeyman book-binder who had educated himself in some degree by reading the books which he was given to bind. The Encyclopaedia Britannica aroused his interest in science and he applied to Davy for employment in the Royal Institution. For a number of years, as Davy's assistant, his chief work was in chemistry; but Oersted's discovery turned his thoughts toward electricity and thereafter it was his principal field of work. In 1831 he made the capital discovery of the induction of currents which is not only of the most fundamental consequence to the theory of electromagnetism but is the foundation of the innumerable practical applications of electricity to the uses of man. Of his many other discoveries I shall mention only two; the quantitative laws of electrolysis which bear his name and which gave the first suggestions of an atomic theory of electricity, and the specific inductive capacity of dielectrics.

Because of the deficiencies of his early education, Faraday never acquired the technique of the mathematician. But, as Maxwell has pointed out, his mind was admirably fitted for dealing with quantitative relations. He overcame the handicap under which he suffered by devising his own methods of representing the quantitative side of phenomena—methods which not only enabled him to achieve his unparalleled success as a discoverer but which are so useful to others that they have held the field in elementary instruction in electromagnetism as well as in the most complicated problems of modern electrical engineering. His lines of force were to him real entities and he conceived of all forces as being transmitted from point to point in a continuous medium. The idea of action at a distance was repugnant to him. It is indeed to most physicists but Faraday was not tempted as most of us are to use distance forces because of their mathematical convenience and thus to escape the prodigious difficulties of imagining a medium with the necessary properties to account for the forces. Faraday's prejudices were to have important consequences in the next generation as we shall see when we come to speak of Maxwell.

The year 1800 is an important date in the history of optics as it is in that of electricity; for in that year Thomas Young took up the cudgels for the wave theory of light which had been almost completely neglected since the time of Huygens. In the following year he explained the colors of thin films (Newton's rings) by means of the "interference" of waves; and in 1803 he applied the same idea to certain problems of diffraction, but in a way which was afterward proved to be wrong. He was drawn into a controversy with the great Laplace who had worked out a theory of double refraction on the corpuscular basis; and for a dozen years or more Young found little sympathy and support for his views among scientific men of established reputation. Indeed he was far from having a good case; the explanation of diffraction was not satisfactory; there was no explanation of polarization since waves in the tenuous and fluid ether were quite naturally supposed to be compressional like sound waves in air; and, for the same reason, no satisfactory explanation of double refraction appeared to be possible.

The first defect was remedied by the work of Fresnel, presented to the Paris Academy in 1816, in which the author began that brilliant series of experimental and mathematical investigations which left the wave theory completely victorious over its rival. He gave the true theory of diffraction by a slit and a wire and showed that it agreed with the results of his experimental measurements. Poisson, who was one of the referees of his paper, noted the fatal objection that Fresnel's theory would require a bright spot in the exact center of the shadow of a circular object. When, however, the matter was put to the test of experiment under suitable conditions, the bright spot was found and this naturally produced a reaction in favor of Fresnel's theory. It appears to have been Young who took the bold step of suggesting that the vibrations in light waves were transverse and that thus polarization could be explained. Fresnel at once took up this suggestion and succeeded in bringing into line all the intricacies of crystalline refraction, including that in biaxial crystals which had been discovered a few years before by Brewster and had been a stumbling block to all other theories. Later he took up the theory of reflection and refraction by ordinary transparent bodies with equal success; and since the completion of his series of memoirs there has never been a doubt in the mind of any competent person that light has the kinematical properties of transverse wave motion.

On the dynamical side, however, matters were not so clear. Only a solid can transmit tranverse elastic waves and it was difficult to believe that the ether could be a solid and yet allow the free motion of material bodies through it without the slightest detectable resistance. This was the origin of the great problem of the existence and properties of the ether—a problem which has excited the most eager interest of physicists for a hundred years and is still with us. Many of the most important discoveries, mathematical and experimental, have arisen from attempts at its solution. It at once stimulated the mathematical study of the theory of elastic solids and of the applicability of this theory to the phenomena of light. The work of Gauchy, Green, McCullagh, Stokes and Kelvin in this field may be said to have created a new era in mathematical physics and even in mathematics itself; for the treatment of continuous media required methods which differed in many ways from those appropriate to distance forces of the Newtonian type. It was also the first attempt to apply in all strictness the principles of dynamics to natural phenomena outside the restricted field of mechanics proper. It was never perfectly successful, but so nearly that there was constant encouragement to persevere. We shall have occasion to look at a second phase of this gallant attack upon the mysteries of Nature when we come to deal with the work of Clerk Maxwell.

About the middle of the century occurred the epoch-making discovery of the conservation of energy which brought all kinds of physical and chemical phenomena into much more intimate relation with each other than had previously been suspected. Incidentally, it greatly strengthened the tendency, of which I have just spoken, to seek for a strictly dynamical foundation for all such phenomena.

The discovery arose primarily in a reconsideration of the nature of heat, and its history is so curious and interesting that it is with regret that I recognize the impossibility of giving an adequate account of it within the limits of this lecture. As we have seen, the belief that heat was a substantial fluid had prevailed for many years and had proved useful; but there had always been a suspicion (extending back to the time of Hooke and Newton) that it might be an effect of motion—either of the fine particles of which ordinary matter was made up, or of light-corpuscles within matter. At the end of the eighteenth century, Count Rumford had made experiments which ought to have started things in the right direction, but were disregarded. Carnot himself, in some posthumous notes which were not published until 1878, gave so clear an outline of the true theory that we cannot doubt that the course of science would have been greatly altered, as Mach remarks, if Carnot had not died of cholera in 1832. The caloric theory was finally overthrown by the labors of two men, Mayer and Joule, quite independently and neither having in the beginning any knowledge of the work of the other. Mayer, a Jewish physician of Heilbronn, began his process of reasoning with the observation that venous blood is a brighter red in tropical than in temperate climates. He was so ignorant of the terminology of physics that he could not make himself understood at first and suffered many rebuffs in consequence. His persistence however was sublime; he learned to write so that physicists could understand him, unearthed forgotten experiments, and eventually, without any experiments of his own, gave conclusive evidence for his theory and obtained a good value of the mechanical equivalent of heat. There could scarcely be a greater contrast than that between him and his fellow discoverer. Joule was a Manchester brewer and amateur of science, a skilful and accurate experimenter who year after year turned out unimpeachable quantitative evidence of the equivalence between mechanical work and heat in all sorts of transformations. A third collaborator in placing the new theory on a firm foundation was Helmholtz, whose celebrated memoir of 1847 showed clearly the generality of the new principle and its applicability to all branches of science; he gave it suitable mathematical formulation and demonstrated its great power in finding relations between phenomena of apparently different kinds.

The next step was the reconciliation of the new principle with that of Carnot, and it proved to be a difficult one. It puzzled Kelvin for several years and delayed his complete adherence to Joule's theory; ultimately he saw his way clearly and as a result of his work and that of Clausius the modern theory was established upon the two principles which stand side by side as the first and second laws of thermodynamics. These two empirical principles are probably the most firmly established and most thoroughly verified of all the so-called laws of nature. In the classical treatment of the subject they are regarded as axioms, and deductions are made from them so that, in form, the science is like geometry. As I have previously intimated, the results obtained are of great generality and of far-reaching consequence in practical applications as well as in philosophical implications. It is one of the great triumphs of theoretical physics.

Side by side with this theory there grew up another method of dealing with the subject which was less general and more hypothetical but has proved to be an invaluable aid to research. As soon as it was recognized that heat and mechanical energy are mutually convertible, it became inevitable that physicists should seek for a detailed mechanical theory of heat. The obvious hypothesis was that heat consisted of the energy of motion of the small particles, or molecules, of matter whose existence had been more or less generally accepted since Dalton's introduction of the atomic theory to account for the chemical laws of definite and multiple proportion. In order to develop this theory, the laws of mechanics had to be applied statistically to enormous aggregates of molecules reacting upon each other in various ways. The simplest state of matter from this point of view is the gaseous one; and in the hands of Clausius and Maxwell the kinetic theory of gases made great progress in a few years. Atomic and molecular theory became at once definite and quantitative. One of Dalton's atoms might be of any size so long as it was small enough to escape individual observation and had the correct ratio of mass to other atoms; but the atoms and molecules of the physical theory had definite and calculable mass, size, velocity and free-path. They became very real to physicists and were constantly used in reasoning and in planning experiments.

About twenty-five years ago a determined attack upon all atomic theories was made by Ostwald and his followers among the physical chemists—largely through ignorance of the real evidence upon which they were based. They ridiculed such theories as metaphysical figments of the imagination and attacked them as obstacles to real advance in the philosophy of nature. The faith of physicists however was not for a moment shaken; and it has been justified by the progress of discovery in the intervening years. The last doubting Thomas has been convinced and only those who deny the objectivity of matter itself can now question the real, physical existence of atoms and molecules.

Through the labors of Boltzmann, Gibbs and others, the application of statistical mechanics to molecular problems was developed and generalized so as to be applicable to other states of matter than the gaseous one; and attempts were made to reduce the whole of thermodynamics to a mechanical basis. The subject is a very difficult one with many pitfalls for even the most wary; and we must conclude, I think, that the attempt has met with a defeat that is probably final. It has, however, led directly to the quantum theory of Planck, a great generalization which is the most puzzling and the most promising treasure in the possession of the physicist of today.

The next great landmark of which we must take note is the unification of the theories of electrodynamics and of optics by Clerk Maxwell. He himself tells us that, impressed by the value and fertility of Faraday's ideas, he decided, in beginning his serious study of electricity, to read no mathematics on the subject until he had mastered Faraday's "Experimental Researches." Maxwell was a highly trained and original mathematician and his first papers on electrodynamics were devoted to the expression in clear mathematical form of some of Faraday's hypotheses and modes of thought. Like his chosen master he rejected action at a distance and concentrated his attention upon the hypothetical medium by means of which electromagnetic forces might be transmitted. In several memoirs published during the sixties he gave details of mechanical models which were adapted to this end. By gradual steps these auxiliaries were done away with and at the same time the theory far outgrew its original purpose of translating Faraday into mathematical language. Maxwell showed clearly that all the known facts of electrodynamics could be attributed to the action of a medium and by strict mathematical reasoning he deducted the properties which this medium must have. These turned out to be identical in all details with those which we must attribute to the luminiferous ether in order to account for the phenomena of light. Thus was born the electromagnetic theory of light and two great domains of physics were brought together under a single system of hypotheses clearly expressed in the form of differential equations.

The publication of Maxwell's "Treatise on Electricity and Magnetism" in 1873 was an event of the first importance in the history of science. The new theory was slow in making its way, especially on the continent of Europe, and Maxwell himself died in 1879. His work was taken up, however, by a group of devoted adherents among whom we may mention Heaviside, Lodge, Rowland, Poynting, Gibbs, J. J. Thomson, and Larmor. In 1886 Hertz, whose attention had been some years before directed to Maxwell's theory by Helmholtz, made an accidental observation which to his acute mind offered the possibility of a direct test of the finite speed of propogation of electromagnetic action. His brilliant series of experiments demonstrated the existence, speed, and properties of electromagnetic waves and served as a complete verification of Maxwell's theory. All of you know that the wonders of wireless are a direct consequence of the experiments of Hertz; but to the physicist this is less interesting and significant than the steady growth in scope and authority of Maxwell's equations, which come nearer to the ideal of a "world formula" than anything else known to the modern man of science.

For something like ten years it was generally supposed that the main outlines of the science of physics had been drawn in fairly satisfactory, and perhaps final, form. There was still much to be done but it would be concerned with details—with perfecting theories and increasing the accuracy of measurements. A great deal of very valuable work of this kind was done in many fields; as an example I may refer briefly to the development of accurate measurement in spectroscopy.

The use of the spectroscope as a method of chemical analysis was placed on a sound basis about 1860, by Bunsen and Kirchhoff, and the application of this method was extended, by the brilliant discovery of Kirchhoff, to the atmospheres of the sun and stars. You all know something of the wonderful results which have followed the application of the spectroscope to astronomical problems and of the growth of the borderland science which is called astrophysics. Great improvements in spectroscopic apparatus were made by Rowland, Michelson, and others, and there grew up a body of skilful spectroscopists, who devoted themselves to the accurate measurement of the wave lengths of the innumerable spectral lines given out by the different chemical elements and to the discovery of empirical relations between the numerical values of these wave lengths. It was hoped that such observations would throw light upon the structure of atoms but for many years no progress was made in this direction. Indeed it is only recently that the results of a generation of spectroscopists are beginning to be useful for this purpose and only after the clue to a theory of atomic structure had been given by investigations in other fields. Spectroscopy is almost the only part of physics in which a large mass of data was accumulated before the existence of a guiding hypothesis or theory to direct the work. The method of simple induction and classification which has played so large a part in some other sciences seems to be unsuited to the problems of physics.

Accurate measurements, however, do sometimes produce brilliant discoveries—when they fall into the right hands. A classical example of this is the discovery of argon by Lord Rayleigh as the result of a quite prosaic undertaking to redetermine with great accuracy the density of nitrogen. As a sequel to Rayleigh's work, a whole family of chemical elements, whose existence had been entirely unsuspected by chemists, was discovered by

Ramsay. But it is only in rare instances that this sort of thing occurs; usually an accurate measurement leads to no exciting result, but takes its place among the solid foundation stones of the science. And for perhaps a decade there was fairly widespread opinion among physicists that this was what they must look forward to, and that the future of physics lay "in the last place of decimals."

These anticipations of a useful, if somewhat dull, old age for the science were happily disappointed in the last years of the century by the remarkable outburst of unexpected discoveries among which the Röntgen rays came first in point of time. This was followed almost at once by Becquerel's discovery of radioactivity, the identification of the subatomic "corpuscle" or electron by J. J. Thomson, and the investigations of the ionization of gases which have led to many important results. No physicist who has reached middle age can forget the romantic interest of the ten years following 1895, when startling discoveries followed each other in rapid succession and the physical journals were awaited with an impatience not unlike the desire for newspapers in wartime. But the news was all good news, and recorded an almost unbroken series of victories.

These discoveries were, as I have said, unexpected but they were not in any real sense accidental. They came as the result of a careful and prolonged study of the electrical discharge through rarefied gases—a complicated set of phenomena very difficult to put in order. Twenty years earlier, Maxwell had predicted that the next great step in our knowledge of the relations between electricity and matter would come from a study of the discharge through gases; and it had been prosecuted in that spirit by many men though the clue which they sought eluded them for twenty years. When it did come at last, it was in a form which was, so far as I know, entirely unpredicted and unexpected. This was so much the case that it took us more than fifteen years to find out quite certainly just what the X-rays were. It was not until 1912 that Laue's discovery of the diffraction of X-rays by crystals and the subsequent work of W. H. and W. L. Bragg made it quite certain that these rays were of the same nature as light but with wave lengths only about 1/5000 of those in the visible spectrum. This had indeed been for some time the prevailing hypothesis as to their nature but there was little quantitative evidence to support it; and only a year or two previous to the discovery of crystalline diffraction W. H. Bragg himself had brought forward many reasons for thinking that X-rays might be corpuscular. The study of these very short waves has already given us invaluable knowledge of the nature of the atoms of different elements and promises still greater advances in the future; it has provided a new and powerful method of studying crystal structure and has revolutionized our conception of the nature of chemical combination in crystalline bodies; and it promises to have practical applications as useful in industry as ordinary spectroscopy.

The discovery of the radioactivity by Becquerel followed almost immediately upon Röntgen's discovery of the X-rays, and was in a sense a direct consequence of it; they are alike too in that they have both had important medical applications which have drawn much public attention. Madame Curie's sensational discovery of radium was an early incident in the history of this subject. But by far the most important development in this field was the establishment by Rutherford and his pupils of the cause and source of energy of these radiations. He has shown in the most conclusive way that they are due to the disintegration of the atoms of the radioactive elements—uranium, thorium, radium, etc.—and that a spontaneous transmutation of these elements is going on constantly. The genealogy of the radioactive elements is known more accurately than that of most royal families; and the birth and mortality statistics of the various kinds of atoms are in all the text books. Thus a part of the dream of the alchemists has come true, but only a part; for up to the present all attempts to produce artificially the transmutation of the heavy elements have failed. In fact we have not been able to affect in the slightest way the spontaneous transmutation of the radioactive elements; it can neither be retarded nor accelerated by any agency at our command. We do know, however, that vast stores of energy are locked up in the atoms of the heavier elements and if the time should ever come when this can be released and controlled by man it will doubtless cause a revolution in industrial processes more fundamental than that which followed upon the introduction of steam and electricity. One small step in this direction has been taken within the past two years. Rutherford has obtained evidence that the nitrogen atom may be broken up by bombardment with alpha rays, and that one of the products of this process is hydrogen. It is perhaps too early to regard this as being definitely established; and, even if it be true, the amount of matter transmuted in this way is excessively minute while the quantity of energy released in the process (if any) is far below what could possibly be measured experimentally. We have however become accustomed to small beginnings which ultimately produce great results; and a modern physicist would be rash indeed who should attempt to set bounds to the possibilities of future discovery in this direction.

The discovery of the electron was also an event of the first importance in the history of our science. It is the ultimate atom of negative electricity and is a constituent of all material atoms. It can also exist in the free or "disembodied" state, as for example in the cathode rays, the beta rays from radium, and in the electronic stream from incandescent bodies. In the last of these forms it has proved to be of great practical use to telephony and wireless telegraphy in the audion or thermionic tube which is the cause of most of the remarkable advances in these fields during the past five or six years. To the physicist and chemist of today the electron is an indispensable concept in both theoretical and experimental investigations; and its reality can be questioned only on those philosophical grounds which may put in doubt the existence of matter itself.

The nature of positive electricity is not so definitely known; but evidence is accumulating that it too exists in an atomic form as the "nucleus" of the atom of hydrogen—the residue left when the hydrogen atom is deprived of its single negative electron. It is becoming probable that the "nuclei" of other atoms are built up out of these and of negative electrons. If this group of hypotheses should stand the test of time we shall have to conclude that matter and electricity are different aspects of the same stuff—that the atoms of matter are formed by different collocations of the atoms of positive and negative electricity.

Another line of physical inquiry which has proved to be of deep and fundamental significance is the so-called quantum theory of Planck. It originated in the study (both experimental and theoretical) of the intensity and quality of the radiation from a "black body," or perfect radiator, when held at a definite temperature. The total intensity of such radiations were deduced theoretically by Stefan from the principles of thermodynamics and the predicted results have been amply verified by experiment. When however the attempt is made to predict the way in which the energy is distributed in the spectrum, so as to be able to tell what fraction of the total intensity is carried by any particular wave length, the problem becomes much more difficult. It is necessary to have recourse to statistical methods analogous to those used by Maxwell, Boltzmann and Gibbs in accounting for the thermodynamic properties of material bodies. First steps in this direction were taken by W. Wien but the deductions from his theory were not altogether in accord with experimental results. Planck succeeded in obtaining a formula which agreed with experiment, but only by making certain very daring hypotheses; the most conspicuous of these is that the emission, or the absorption of radiation, or both, takes place not steadily and continuously as we had always supposed but by finite, discrete "quanta." From one point of view this hypothesis of Planck may be regarded as extending the field of the atomic theory, hitherto restricted to matter, to energy as well. I can not hope to suggest even remotely in the brief time at my disposal how revolutionary Planck's assumptions really are; they are still very imperfectly understood and it has not yet been possible to reconcile them wholly with other facts and general laws which appear to rest upon very solid foundations. Indeed, if the results of Planck's speculations had been confined to the deduction of a formula for the radiation of a black body they would not, I think, have long engaged the serious attention of physicists. But they began to turn up unmistakably in many other fields of investigation—for example, in connection with the photoelectric effect, with X-rays, and in all theories of atomic structure. At present no one doubts that most of our fundamental ideas in mechanics and electrodynamics must be revised in the light of the quantum theory which however is itself still in a very immature state. The problem thus arising of bringing together under one system apparently discrepant bodies of phenomena is an exceedingly difficult one and we may have to wait for another Newton to solve it. But it possesses the greatest fascination for all theoretical physicists; they are able to congratulate themselves upon the possession of an unsolved problem of the first magnitude and of great difficulty and they know that as long as it lasts, life will not be dull for them.

I should be in despair if it were necessary to give, at the end of a lecture already too long, an account of Einstein, relativity and gravitation. Fortunately any need that you may feel for instruction on these subjects has doubtless been satisfied by the newspapers, the magazines, and by innumerable books, popular and otherwise. Let me say in all seriousness however, that the more one knows of the history and recent developments of physics the more sincere and ardent is one's admiration for the individuality and brilliant originality of Einstein's genius. It does not seem probable at present that his discoveries will have as great an effect upon the immediate future of physics as some of the others which I have just discussed. But the ultimate result of his work upon *methods* used in the theoretical side of physical science may well prove to be revolutionary; and it seems highly probable that it will change to some extent our philosophical views of the nature of the external world and of our relation to it. . . .

1921

SIR ISAAC NEWTON *

HUMPHREY NEWTON

"His carriage was very meek, sedate and humble, never seemingly angry, of profound thought, his countenance mild, pleasant and comely. I cannot say I ever saw him laugh but once, which put me in mind of the Ephesian philosopher, who laughed only once in his lifetime, to see an ass eating thistles when plenty of grass was by. He always kept close to his studies, very rarely went visiting and had few visitors. I never knew him to take any recreation or pastime either in riding out to take the air, walking, bowling, or any other exercise whatever, thinking all hours lost that were not spent in his studies, to which he kept so close that he seldom left his chamber except at term time, when he read in the schools as Lucasianus Professor, where so few went to hear him, and fewer that understood him, that ofttimes he did in a manner, for want

* "Letters to John Conduitt," quoted in *Memoirs of Sir Isaac Newton* by Sir David Brewster, Edinburgh, Thomas Constable and Co., 1855.

of hearers read to the walls. Foreigners he received with a great deal of freedom, candour, and respect. When invited to a treat, which was very seldom, he used to return it very handsomely, and with much satisfaction to himself. So intent, so serious upon his studies, that he ate very sparingly, nay, ofttimes he has forgot to eat at all, so that, going into his chamber, I have found his mess untouched, of which, when I have reminded him, he would reply—'Have I?' and then making to the table would eat a bite or two standing, for I cannot say I ever saw him sit at table by himself. He very rarely went to bed till two or three of the clock, sometimes not until five or six, lying about four or five hours, especially at spring and fall of the leaf, at which times he used to employ about six weeks in his elaboratory, the fires scarcely going out either night or day; he sitting up one night and I another till he had finished his chemical experiments, in the performance of which he was the most accurate, strict, exact. What his aim might be I was not able to penetrate into, but his pains, his diligence at these set times made me think he aimed at something beyond the reach of human art and industry. I cannot say I ever saw him drink either wine, ale or beer, excepting at meals and then but very sparingly. He very rarely went to dine in the hall, except on some public days, and then if he has not been minded, would go very carelessly, with shoes down at heels, stockings untied, surplice on, and his head scarcely combed.

His elaboratory was well furnished with chemical materials, as bodies, receivers, heads, crucibles, etc. which was made very little use of, the crucibles excepted, in which he fused his metals; he would sometimes, tho' very seldom, look into an old mouldy book which lay in his elaboratory, I think it was titled Agricola de Metallis, the transmuting of metals being his chief design, for which purpose antimony was a great ingredient. He has sometimes taken a turn or two, has made a sudden stand, turn'd himself about, run up the stairs like another Archimedes, with an Eureka fall to write on his desk standing without giving himself the leisure to draw a chair to sit down on. He would with great acuteness answer a question, but would very seldom start one. Dr. Boerhave, in some of his writings, speaking of Sir Isaac: 'That man,' says he, 'comprehends as much as all mankind besides.'

1727/8

DISCOVERIES

SIR ISAAC NEWTON

CONCERNING THE LAW OF GRAVITATION*

Hitherto we have explained the phaenomena of the heavens and of our sea by the power of gravity, but have not yet assigned the cause of this power. This is certain, that it must proceed from a cause that penetrates to the very centres of the sun and planets, without suffering the least diminution of its force; that operates not according to the quantity of the surfaces of the particles upon which it acts (as mechanical causes used to do), but according to the quantity of the solid matter which they contain, and propagates its virtue on all sides to immense distances, decreasing always in the duplicate proportions of the distances. Gravitation towards the sun is made up out of the gravitations towards the several particles of which the body of the sun is composed; and in receding from the sun decreases accurately in the duplicate proportion of the distances as far as the orb of Saturn, as evidently appears from the quiescence of the aphelions of the planets; nay, and even to the remotest aphelions of the comets, if these aphelions are also quiescent. But hitherto I have not been able to discover the cause of those properties of gravity from phaenomena, and I frame no hypotheses; for whatever is not deduced from the phaenomena is to be called an hypothesis; and hypotheses, whether metaphysical or physical, whether of occult qualities or mechanical, have no place in experimental philosophy. In this philosophy particular propositions are inferred from the phaenomena, and afterwards rendered general by induction. Thus it was that the impenetrability, the mobility, and the impulsive force of bodies, and the laws of motion and gravitation were discovered. And to us it is enough that gravity does really exist, and act according to the laws which we have explained, and abundantly serves to account for all the motions of the celestial bodies, and of our sea.

LAWS OF MOTIONS*

Law I. *Every body perseveres in its state of rest, or of uniform motion in a right line, unless it is compelled to change that state by force impressed thereon.*

Projectiles persevere in their motions, so far as they are not retarded by the resistance of the air, or impelled downwards by the force of gravity. A top, whose parts by their cohesion are perpetually drawn aside from rectilinear motions, does not cease its rotation, otherwise than as it is retarded by the air. The greater bodies of the planets and comets, meeting

* From Newton's *Principia*, third edition, 1726. Translated by Andrew Motte, 1729. First American edition, 1848.

with less resistance in more free spaces, preserve their motions both progressive and circular for a much longer time.

Law II. *The alteration of motion is ever proportional to the motive force impressed; and is made in the direction of the right line in which that force is impressed.*

If any force generates a motion, a double force will generate double the motion, a triple force triple the motion, whether that force be impressed altogether and at once, or gradually and successively. And this motion (being always directed the same way with the generating force), if the body moved before, is added to or subducted from the former motion, according as they directly conspire with or are directly contrary to each other; or obliquely joined, when they are oblique, so as to produce a new motion compounded from the determination of both.

Law III. *To every action there is always opposed an equal reaction; or the mutual actions of two bodies upon each other are always equal, and directed to contrary parts.*

Whatever draws or presses another is as much drawn or pressed by that other. If you press a stone with your finger, the finger is also pressed by the stone. If a horse draws a stone tied to a rope, the horse (if I may so say) will be equally drawn back towards the stone; for the distended rope, by the same endeavor to relax or unbend itself, will draw the horse as much towards the stone, as it does the stone towards the horse, and will obstruct the progress of the one as much as it advances that of the other. If a body impinge upon another, and by its force change the motion of the other, that body also (because of the equality of the mutual pressure) will undergo an equal change, in its own motion, towards the contrary part. The changes made by these actions are equal, not in the velocities but in the motions of bodies; that is to say, if the bodies are not hindered by any other impediments. For, because the motions are equally changed, the changes of the velocities made towards contrary parts are reciprocally proportional to the bodies.

THE DISPERSION OF LIGHT*

In the year 1666 (at which time I applied myself to the grinding of optick glasses of other figures than spherical) I procured me a triangular glass prism, to try therewith the celebrated phaenomena of colours. And in order thereto, having darkened my chamber, and made a small hole in my window-shuts, to let in a convenient quantity of the sun's light, I placed my prism at its entrance, that it might be thereby refracted to the opposite wall. It was at first a very pleasing divertissement, to view the vivid and intense colours produced thereby; but after a while applying myself to consider them more circumspectly, I became surprised, to see them in an oblong form; which, according to the received laws of re-

* From Newton's "A New Theory About Light and Colours." A letter communicated to the editor of the Transactions of the Royal Society, February, 1672.

fraction, I expected should have been circular. They were terminated at the sides with straight lines, but at the ends, the decay of light was so gradual that it was difficult to determine justly, what was their figure; yet they seemed semicircular.

Comparing the length of this colour'd Spectrum with its breadth, I found it about five times greater, a disproportion so extravagant, that it excited me to a more than ordinary curiosity to examining from whence it might proceed. I could scarce think, that the various thicknesses of the glass, or the termination with shadow or darkness, could have any influence on light to produce such an effect; yet I thought it not amiss, first to examine those circumstances, and so try'd what would happen by transmitting light through parts of the glass of divers thicknesses, or through holes in the window of divers bignesses, or by setting the prism without, so that the light might pass through it, and be refracted, before it was terminated by the hole: But I found none of these circumstances material. The fashion of the colours was in all these cases the same. . . .

The gradual removal of these suspicions led me to the Experimentum Crucis, which was this: I took two boards, and placed one of them close behind the prism at the window, so that the light might pass through a small hole, made in it for the purpose, and fall on the other board, which I placed at about 12 feet distance, having first made a small hole in it also, for some of the incident light to pass through. Then I placed another prism behind this second board, so that the light trajected through both the boards might pass through that also, and be again refracted before it arrived at the wall. This done, I took the first prism in my hand, and turned it to and fro slowly about its axis, so much as to make the several parts of the image cast, on the second board, successively pass through the hole in it, that I might observe to what places on the wall the second prism would refract them. And I saw by the variation of those places, that the light, tending to that end of the image, towards which the refraction of the first prism was made, did in the second prism suffer a refraction considerably greater than the light tending to the other end. And so the true cause of the length of that image was detected to be no other, than that light is not similar or homogenial, but consists of *Difform Rays, some of which are more Refrangible than others;* so that without any difference in their incidence on the same medium, some shall be more Refracted than others; and therefore that, according to their *particular Degrees of Refrangibility*, they were transmitted through the prism to divers parts of the opposite wall. . . .

ON THE ORIGIN OF COLOURS*

The colours of all natural bodies have no other origin than this, that they are variously qualified, to reflect one sort of light in greater plenty than an-

* From Newton's "A New Theory About Light and Colours." A letter communicated to the editor of the Transactions of the Royal Society, February, 1672.

other. And this I have experimented in a dark room, by illuminating those bodies with uncompounded light of divers colours. For by that means any body may be made to appear of any colour. They have there no appropriate colour, but ever appear of the colour of the light cast upon them, but yet with this difference, that they are most brisk and vivid in the light of their own daylight colour. Minimum appeareth there of any colour indifferently, with which it is illustrated, but yet most luminous in red, and so bise appeareth indifferently of any colour, but yet most luminous in blue. And therefore minimum reflecteth rays of any colour, but most copiously those endowed with red, that is, with all sorts of rays promiscuously blended, those qualified with red shall abound most in that reflected light, and by their prevalence cause it to appear of that colour. And for the same reason bise, reflecting blue most copiously, shall appear blue by the excess of those rays in its reflected light; and the like of other bodies. And that this is the entire and adequate cause of their colours, is manifest, because they have no power to change or alter the colours of any sort of rays incident apart, but put on all colours indifferently, with which they are enlightened.

These things being so, it can be no longer disputed, whether there be colours in the dark, or whether they be the qualities of the objects we see, no nor perhaps, whether light be a body. For, since colours are the quality of light, having its rays for their entire and immediate subject, how can we think those rays qualities also, unless one quality may be the subject of, and sustain another; which in effect is to call it substance. We should not know bodies for substances; were it not for their sensible qualities, and the principle of those being now found due to something else, we have as good reason to believe that to be a substance also.

Besides, whoever thought any quality to be a heterogeneous aggregate, such as light is discovered to be? But to determine more absolutely what light is, after what manner refracted, and by what modes or actions it produceth in our minds the phantasms of colours, is not so easie; and I shall not mingle conjectures with certainties.

ON THE SENSATION OF SOUND IN GENERAL *

HERMANN VON HELMHOLTZ

Sensations result from the action of an external stimulus on the sensitive apparatus of our nerves. Sensations differ in kind, partly with the organ of sense excited, and partly with the nature of the stimulus employed. Each organ of sense produces peculiar sensations which cannot be ex-

* From *The Sensations of Tone as a Physiological Basis for the Theory of Music.* Translated by Alexander J. Ellis in 1885 from the fourth German edition, 1877.

cited by means of any other; the eye gives sensations of light, the ear sensations of sound, the skin sensations of touch. Even when the same sunbeams which excite in the eye sensations of light impinge on the skin and excite its nerves, they are felt only as heat, not as light. In the same way the vibration of elastic bodies heard by the ear can also be felt by the skin, but in that case produce only a whirring, fluttering sensation, not sound. The sensation of sound is therefore a species of reaction against external stimulus, peculiar to the ear and excitable in no other organ of the body, and is completely distinct from the sensation of any other sense.

As our problem is to study the laws of the sensation of hearing, our first business will be to examine how many kinds of sensation the ear can generate and what differences in the external means of excitement or sound correspond to these differences of sensation.

The first and principal difference between various sounds experienced by our ear is that between noises and musical tones. The soughing, howling, and whistling of the wind, the splashing of water, the rolling and rumbling of carriages, are examples of the first kind, and the tones of all musical instruments of the second. Noises and musical tones may certainly intermingle in very various degrees and pass insensibly into one another, but their extremes are widely separated.

The nature of the difference between musical tones and noises can generally be determined by attentive aural observation without artificial assistance. We perceive that generally a noise is accompanied by a rapid alternation of different kinds of sensations of sound. Think, for example, of the rattling of a carriage over granite paving stones, the splashing or seething of a waterfall or of the waves of the sea, the rustling of leaves in a wood. In all these cases we have rapid, irregular, but distinctly perceptible alternations of various kinds of sounds, which crop up fitfully. When the wind howls the alternation is slow, the sound slowly and gradually rises and then falls again. It is also more or less possible to separate restlessly alternating sounds in case of the greater number of other noises. We shall hereafter become acquainted with an instrument, called a resonator, which will materially assist the ear in making this separation. On the other hand, a musical tone strikes the ear as a perfectly undisturbed, uniform sound which remains unaltered as long as it exists, and it presents no alternation of various kinds of constituents. To this, then, corresponds a simple, regular kind of sensation, whereas in a noise many various sensations of musical tone are irregularly mixed up and as it were tumbled about in confusion. We can easily compound noises out of musical tones, as, for example, by simultaneously striking all the keys contained in one or two octaves of a pianoforte. This shows us that musical tones are the simpler and more regular elements of the sensations of hearing, and that we have consequently first to study the laws and peculiarities of this class of sensations.

Then comes the further question: On what difference in the external means of excitement does the difference between noise and musical tone depend? The normal and usual means of excitement for the human ear is atmospheric vibration. The irregularly alternating sensation of the ear in the case of noises leads us to conclude that for these the vibration of the air must also change irregularly. For musical tones, on the other hand, we anticipate a regular motion of the air, continuing uniformly, and in its turn excited by an equally regular motion of the sonorous body, whose impulses were conducted to the ear by the air.

Those regular motions which produce musical tones have been exactly investigated by physicists. They are *oscillations*, *vibrations*, or *swings*, that is, up-and-down, or to-and-fro motions of sonorous bodies, and it is necessary that these oscillations should be regularly periodic. By a *periodic motion* we mean one which constantly returns to the same condition after exactly equal intervals of time. The length of the equal intervals of time between one state of the motion and its next exact repetition we call the *length of the oscillation*, vibration, or swing, or the *period* of the motion. In what manner the moving body actually moves during one period is perfectly indifferent. As illustrations of periodical motion, take the motion of a clock pendulum, of a stone attached to a string and whirled round in a circle with uniform velocity, of a hammer made to rise and fall uniformly by its connection with a water wheel. All these motions, however different be their form, are periodic in the sense here explained. The length of their periods, which in the cases adduced is generally from one to several seconds, is relatively long in comparison with the much shorter periods of the vibrations producing musical tones, the lowest or deepest of which makes at least thirty in a second, while in other cases their number may increase to several thousand in a second.

Our definition of periodic motion then enables us to answer the question proposed as follows. The sensation of a musical tone is due to a rapid periodic motion of the sonorous body; the sensation of a noise to non-periodic motions.

The musical vibrations of solid bodies are often visible. Although they may be too rapid for the eye to follow them singly, we easily recognize that a sounding string, or tuning fork, or the tongue of a reed pipe, is rapidly vibrating between two fixed limits, and the regular, apparently immovable image that we see, notwithstanding the real motion of the body, leads us to conclude that the backward and forward motions are quite regular. In other cases we can feel the swinging motions of sonorous solids. Thus the player feels the trembling of the reed in the mouthpiece of a clarinet, oboe, or bassoon, or of his own lips in the mouthpieces of trumpets and trombones.

The motions proceeding from the sounding bodies are usually conducted to our ear by means of the atmosphere. The particles of air must also execute periodically recurrent vibrations, in order to excite the sensation of a musical tone in our ear. This is actually the case, although in daily experience sound at first seems to be some agent, which is constantly advancing through the air and propagating itself further and further. We must, however, here distinguish between the motion of the individual particles of air—which takes place periodically backward and forward within very narrow limits—and the propagation of the sonorous tremor. The latter is constantly advancing by the constant attraction of fresh particles into its sphere of tremor.

This is a peculiarity of all so-called *undulatory motions*. Suppose a stone to be thrown into a piece of calm water. Round the spot struck there forms a little ring of wave which, advancing equally in all directions, expands to a constantly increasing circle. Corresponding to this ring of wave, sound also proceeds in the air from the excited point and advances in all directions as far as the limits of the mass of air extend. The process in the air is essentially identical with that on the surface of the water. The principal difference consists in the spherical propagation of sound in all directions through the atmosphere which fills all surrounding space, whereas the waves of the water can only advance in rings or circles on its surface. The crests of the waves of water correspond in the waves of sound to spherical shells where the air is condensed, and the troughs to shells where it is rarefied. On the free surface of the water the mass when compressed can slip upward and so form ridges, but in the interior of the sea of air the mass must be condensed, as there is no unoccupied spot for its escape.

The waves of water, therefore, continually advance without returning. But we must not suppose that the particles of water of which the waves are composed advance in a similar manner to the waves themselves. The motion of the particles of water on the surface can easily be rendered visible by floating a chip of wood upon it. This will exactly share the motion of the adjacent particles. Now such a chip is not carried on by the rings of wave. It only bobs up and down and finally rests on its original spot. The adjacent particles of water move in the same manner. When the ring of wave reaches them they are set bobbing; when it has passed over them they are still in their old place and remain there at rest while the ring of wave continues to advance toward fresh spots on the surface of the water and sets new particles of water in motion. Hence the waves which pass over the surface of the water are constantly built up of fresh particles of water. What really advances as a wave is only the tremor, the altered form of the surface, while the individual particles of water themselves merely move up and down transiently and never depart far from their original position. . . .

Now let us return to the surface of the water. We have supposed that one of its points has been struck by a stone and set in motion. This motion has spread out in the form of a ring of wave over the surface of the water and, having reached the chip of wood, has set it bobbing up and down. Hence by means of the wave the motion which the stone first excited in one point of the surface of the water has been communicated to the chip which was at another point of the same surface. The process which goes on in the atmospheric ocean about us is of a precisely similar nature. For the stone substitute a sounding body, which shakes the air; for the chip of wood substitute the human ear, on which impinge the waves of air excited by the shock, setting its movable parts in vibration. The waves of air proceeding from a sounding body transport the tremor to the human ear exactly in the same way as the water transports the tremor produced by the stone to the floating chip.

In this way also it is easy to see how a body which itself makes periodical oscillations will necessarily set the particles of air in periodical motion. A falling stone gives the surface of the water a single shock. Now replace the stone by a regular series of drops falling from a vessel with a small orifice. Every separate drop will excite a ring of wave, each ring of wave will advance over the surface of the water precisely like its predecessor, and will be in the same way followed by its successors. In this manner a regular series of concentric rings will be formed and propagated over the surface of the water. The number of drops which fall into the water in a second will be the number of waves which reach our floating chip in a second, and the number of times that this chip will therefore bob up and down in a second, thus executing a periodical motion, the period of which is equal to the interval of time between the falling of consecutive drops. In the same way for the atmosphere, a periodically oscillating sonorous body produces a similar periodical motion, first in the mass of air, and then in the drum skin of our ear, and the period of these vibrations must be the same as that of the vibration in the sonorous body. . . .

1877

ELECTRICAL EXPERIMENTS *

BENJAMIN FRANKLIN

THE KITE

As frequent mention is made in public papers from Europe of the success of the Philadelphia experiment for drawing the electric fire from clouds by means of pointed rods of iron erected on high buildings, &, it may be agreeable to the curious to be informed, that the same experiment

* From *The Ingenious Dr. Franklin,* edited by Nathan Goodman, University of Pennsylvania Press. Copyright 1931 by the University of Pennsylvania Press.

has succeeded in Philadelphia, though made in a different and more easy manner, which is as follows:

Make a small cross of two light strips of cedar, the arms so long as to reach to the four corners of a large thin silk handkerchief when extended; tie the corners of the handkerchief to the extremities of the cross, so you have the body of a kite; which being properly accommodated with a tail, loop, and string, will rise in the air, like those made of paper; but this being of silk, is fitter to bear the wet and wind of a thunder-gust without tearing. To the top of the upright stick of the cross is to be fixed a very sharp pointed wire, rising a foot or more above the wood. To the end of the twine, next the hand, is to be tied a silk ribbon, and where the silk and twine join, a key may be fastened. This kite is to be raised when a thunder-gust appears to be coming on, and the person who holds the string must stand within a door or window or under some cover, so that the silk ribbon may not be wet; and care must be taken that the twine does not touch the frame of the door or window. As soon as any of the thunder-clouds come over the kite, the pointed wire will draw the electric fire from them, and the kite, with all the twine, will be electrified, and the loose filaments of the twine will stand out every way, and be attracted by an approaching finger. And when the rain has wet the kite and twine, so that it can conduct the electric fire freely, you will find it stream out plentifully from the key on the approach of your knuckle. At this key the phial may be charged; and from electric fire thus obtained, spirits may be kindled, and all the other electric experiments be performed, which are usually done by the help of a rubbed glass globe or tube, and thereby the sameness of the electric matter with that of lightning completely demonstrated.

Letter to Peter Collinson, 1752

ELECTRICAL EXPERIMENTS AND ELECTROCUTION

Your question, how I came first to think of proposing the experiment of drawing down the lightning, in order to ascertain its sameness with the electric fluid, I cannot answer better than by giving you an extract from the minutes I used to keep of the experiments I made, with memorandums of such as I purposed to make, the reasons for making them, and the observations that arose upon them, from which minutes my letters were afterwards drawn. By this extract you will see, that the thought was not so much "an out-of-the-way one," but that it might have occurred to any electrician.

"*November* 7, 1749. Electrical fluid agrees with lightning in these particulars. 1. Giving light. 2. Colour of the light. 3. Crooked direction. 4. Swift motion. 5. Being conducted by metals. 6. Crack or noise in exploding. 7. Subsisting in water or ice. 8. Rending bodies it passes through. 9. Destroying animals. 10. Melting metals. 11. Firing inflammable substances. 12. Sulphureous smell. The electric fluid is attracted by points. We do not know whether this property is in lightning. But since they agree in all particulars wherein we can already compare them, is it not probable they agree likewise in this? Let the experiment be made." . . .

The knocking down of the six men was performed with two of my large jarrs not fully charged. I laid one end of my discharging rod upon the head of the first, he laid his hand on the head of the second; the second his hand on the head of the third, and so to the last, who held, in his hand, the chain that was connected with the outside of the jarrs. When they were thus placed, I applied the other end of my rod to the prime-conductor, and they all dropt together. When they got up, they all declared they had not felt any stroke, and wondered how they came to fall; nor did any of them either hear the crack, or see the light of it. You suppose it a dangerous experiment; but I had once suffered the same myself, receiving, by accident, an equal stroke through my head, that struck me down, without hurting me: And I had seen a young woman, that was about to be electrified through the feet, (for some indisposition) receive a greater charge through the head, by inadvertently stooping forward to look at the placing of her feet, till her forhead (as she was very tall) came too near my prime-conductor: she dropt, but instantly got up again, complaining of nothing. A person so struck, sinks down doubled, or folded together as it were, the joints losing their strength and stiffness at once, so that he drops on the spot where he stood, instantly, and there is no previous staggering, nor does he ever fall lengthwise. Too great a charge might, indeed, kill a man, but I have not yet seen any hurt done by it. It would certainly, as you observe, be the easiest of all deaths. . . .

Letter to John Lining, 1755

CONCEPTS AND FORMS OF ENERGY *

C. C. FURNAS

Energy is the ability of a system to do work. Power, in the technical sense, is the time-rate of doing work. Hence, the word *power* as it is often employed is somewhat of a misnomer, a term with indefinite meaning. But the discussion need not be clouded by dictionary quibbling. It is only necessary to present a brief discussion of the concepts of energy and work in the technical sense.

There are two very important fundamentals that the early Greek scien-

* From *The Storehouse of Civilization* by C. C. Furnas, Bureau of Publications, Teachers College: Columbia University, reprinted by permission of the publishers. Copyright 1939 by Teachers College.

tists never grasped. They had no clear idea of the concept of energy, nor did they develop the concept of mass as divorced from the weight of an object. Had it not been for the snobbish attitude of the intellectuals of that time, they probably would have engaged in considerable experimental work and formulated some clear ideas on the subject. If that had happened, it would be fairly safe to assume that the development of modern science would have begun some 2,000 years ago. If experimental science had really gotten under way at that time, the whole course of history undoubtedly would have been changed.

In order that we may start in where the Greeks left off, it is first necessary to study, in considerable detail, the modern concepts of energy. Since we are dependent on our commonly acknowledged five senses for our knowledge of the physical world, energy does not always make itself directly evident, for it cannot always be seen, felt, heard, tasted, or smelled. A high-voltage transmission line looks innocent enough and gives no evidence of the energy coursing through its strands; only by transmission into other forms is energy made evident in any one of a variety of ways.

The most familiar and important forms of energy that we know of are gravitational potential energy, electrical energy, radiant energy, kinetic energy, and heat. Heat is to be regarded as the kinetic energy involved in the rapid and random motions of the individual molecules of which matter is composed.

GRAVITATION

Gravitational force is evidenced by the attractive force one body has for another by virtue of its mass. No one knows why this force should exist, but it follows very definite laws apparently applicable and unchanging throughout the entire universe. When an object falls to earth, for instance the traditional apple of Newton's observation, the action is due to the gravitational attraction between that object and the large mass of the earth. If the earth attracted the apple, the apple must have attracted the earth, and hence according to Newton's second law of motion, it would seem as if the falling apple should have pulled the earth out of its orbit. It undoubtedly did, but the effect was so slight as to be immeasurable. However, the mutual effects of gravitation are evidenced in the course of the bodies of the solar universe; that is, the large mass of the earth keeps pulling the moon toward it and thus causes the moon to progress in an elliptical orbit around the earth. The moon also pulls the earth, and hence the path of our planet through space has a distinct wobble. The sun in turn pulls both the moon and the earth—and all the other planetary bodies—out of the straight-line path which they would like to pursue, so that the members of the planetary family revolve around the sun in orbits shaped roughly as ellipses. This ever present and all-pervading force of attraction between material bodies is very useful in man's utilization of energy, as we shall see later.

ELECTRICAL ENERGY

The person who asks for an exact definition of electricity is in line for a disappointment. We say that the electric current is a stream of electrons flowing through a wire or some other conductor; but no one knows exactly what an electron is. To satisfy our desire to define things, we say that an electron is a concentrated bundle of electrical energy. It has a measurable, though minute, mass and a number of properties of an infinitesimal bit of solid matter; many of its physical characteristics are well known. But one might study all the published information on the electron, and when he had finished he would still ask: What really is an electron?

RADIANT ENERGY

The best known form of radiant energy is light. Newton, who is ordinarily thought of as the father of our modern ideas of gravitation, also did a great deal of pioneer work on the fundamental character of light. He found that white sunlight could be separated into its different constituent wave lengths (i.e., its colors) by the simple expedient of passing it through a triangular prism. He speculated at great length upon the fundamental character of light. He thought of a ray of light as being made up of tiny corpuscles, which traveled through space at infinite, or at least very high, speed and which could pass through certain forms of matter, such as water or glass. The physicists after Newton, however, decided that this hypothesis did not fit the facts. They found by some simple experiments that light acts as if it were energy propagated in the form of a transverse wave motion, qualitatively similar to waves on the surface of water. Hence Newton's hypothesis fell into disuse and Christian Huygens' transverse-wave theory of light held the field for a couple of centuries. But there were some discouraging shortcomings to the theory despite the fact that nearly everyone accepted it. In the first place, if one were to have waves as we ordinarily conceive them, he must have something to do the waving. Hence the physicists piled on another hypothesis, namely, the "ether." The ether was supposed to pervade all the universe and have the properties of rigid matter; yet it couldn't be matter as we know it, for interstellar space is practically devoid of matter. Hence the absurdity was used to justify a theory which appeared to be good, but which was inadequate.

Shortly after 1900 the German physicist, Max Planck, threw tradition to the winds when he was trying to derive some satisfactory equations to correlate the distribution of radiant energy leaving a hot body. The old transverse-wave theory with its attendant ether was inadequate. As a sheer stroke of genius he hypothesized that energy came from a radiating body in minute bundles or quanta. The amount of energy in each of these bundles was assumed to be proportional to the frequency of vibration of the radiation. Expressed as a simple equation,

$$E = hv$$

where E is the energy per quantum,
h is a universal constant $= 6.613 \times 10^{-27}$ erg seconds,
v is the frequency, vibrations per second.

The idea, which was nothing but a hypothesis to start with, has since been proved to be essentially correct. The standing of the hypothesis was greatly enhanced in 1905 when Albert Einstein showed that, in order to account for the results of experiments on the photoelectric effect, it was necessary to assume that light itself consists of corpuscles or photons, and that each photon has an energy content equal to the product of Planck's constant and the frequency of light.

Planck's constant, h, has become famous and fundamental to modern physics. The work arising from this minute postulated constant has changed all of our concepts of radiant energy. You will see that the idea harkens back to Newton's old corpuscular theory. One picture of radiation is that of minute bundles of energy wriggling through space in some snake-wise fashion. This is not exact, nor really correct, but it gives something to visualize. These little bundles have a very definite wave length, that is, a definite distance between the crests of the wriggles, but they are not matter in any sense of the word. No all-pervading ether is required for the propagation of such radiation, so the ether is now obsolete. All radiant energy travels at a constant speed, approximately 186,000 miles per second in vacuum; hence the shorter the wave length, the greater the frequency of oscillation in those bundles. Expressed in the form of an equation, frequency $= \frac{\text{speed}}{\text{wave length}}$; hence, from Planck's equation, the shorter the wave length, the greater the energy in each bundle, or quantum. The amount of energy in each quantum of red light of a certain wave length is definite, reproducible, and measurable. Blue light has a shorter wave length than the red, hence each quantum or bundle of blue light has more energy than the red. As we come to waves shorter than the visible, we enter the ultraviolet region. Each quantum there has more energy than one in the visible region. Hence the ultraviolet light is much more effective than the visible in performing tasks where a large amount of energy is required, for instance, in promoting the chemical reactions which take place when a photographic film is exposed to light.

As we come on up in the spectrum of radiant energy to shorter and shorter wave lengths, that is, to higher frequencies, we encounter the X rays. These rays have so much energy in each quantum that they are very penetrating. Their wave lengths are much shorter than atomic dimensions, so they can pass through matter which we ordinarily consider to be opaque. Moreover, their high energy makes them very effective in promoting the chemical reactions on a photographic plate. The well-known use of X rays for photographing the bones or the other interior parts of an animal body is possible because of the high energy content of each quantum.

Still shorter than the X rays are the very penetrating gamma rays which are spontaneously given off by the disintegration of radium or other radioactive materials. Gamma rays can pass through heavy blocks of steel. Hence gamma radiation is frequently used for photographing the interior of heavy steel castings to detect blow holes or other faults.

The most penetrating radiation known to exist is in the form of the cosmic rays which are showered down on us from interstellar space. The place or manner of their origin is very much a matter of dispute, and all of their properties have not yet been determined. It is by no means certain that they are actually radiation in the sense that visible light is radiation. They make themselves evident on earth by knocking electrons loose from atoms of matter and causing them to travel with very high speed. Are the "rays" that come from space actually particles themselves, such as electrons, traveling at very high speed? They may be. There is good evidence that they are. The best analysis of the data now available indicates that the bulk of the cosmic rays entering our atmosphere are charged particles, and that these particles are both positive and negative electrons, with the positives predominating.

In the last analysis, the disputes on the origin and nature of cosmic rays are only of academic interest, for charged particles traveling at high speed have some of the characteristics of light rays. The experiment leading to this discovery is one of the monuments of modern physics and represents one of America's major contributions to scientific knowledge. Whatever the exact nature of cosmic rays, they act as if they were made up of radiation of extremely short wave length, the most concentrated bits of energy yet detected. Perhaps there are even more powerful radiations than cosmic rays, but no one has any evidence of them.

If we observe the radiation of wave lengths *longer* than the visible, we come first to the infrared rays. These are commonly called the heat rays and you are well aware of their existence when you stand in front of, but at some distance from, a hot radiator. If the room is perfectly dark you cannot see the radiator, hence the rays are invisible, but your skin is warmed by them, nevertheless.

As we progress down to the longer wave lengths, that is, to lower frequencies of vibration, we find the longer infrared and eventually come to the very short radio waves. These radio waves are, of course, invisible. They have but a slight heating effect because the amount of energy in each quantum is very small. The shortest known radio waves are a few centimeters in length and the longest ones are several miles in length.

Nearly all of the wave lengths of radiation, from the shortest cosmic rays (10^{-12} cm.) to the longest radio waves (2.5×10^6 cm.), are known to exist and have been studied.

It must be emphasized that in our dealings with energy we are, for the most part, simply transforming one form of energy into another. We do not make energy, nor do we take it away. We simply move it from one place to another and change its form.

POTENTIAL AND KINETIC ENERGY

There is another idea which must come into this energy discussion. We frequently speak of energy as being potential or kinetic. This is a rather unfortunate division, and frequently it gives rise to a confusion of concepts due to the confusion of terms. The terminology rose from a consideration of the effects of gravitation. We might think of the energy of a system as the ability to do mechanical work. Then we can say that when a certain system has the ability to do mechanical work but is not performing the task, all of its energy is "potential." However, if the system is performing mechanical work its energy is "kinetic." The usual illustration is that of a rock resting on the top of a high hill. The rock possesses the potential ability to do work in the valley below, but it does none of this work so long as it is resting on the hilltop. However, if someone opens the door of this storehouse of energy by starting the rock rolling down the hillside, the potential energy is converted into kinetic energy, as evidenced by the speed of travel of the rock. If you are so unfortunate as to be in the path of the missile as it reaches the valley, you have very effective and perhaps devastating evidence of the amount of kinetic energy which this rock has acquired.

The more practical illustration is that of the hydroelectric plant. Water in a lake or reservoir on the top of a mountain or plateau produces no power; but if this water is led down the hill through a conduit and into the body of a turbine, the potential energy of the water on the hilltop is converted into the kinetic energy of the stream of water moving at high speed through the turbine and this kinetic energy can, by means of a generator, be converted into electrical energy.

Another familiar illustration of potential energy is that of gasoline in the fuel tank of an automobile. In this case the potentiality of the energy has nothing to do with gravity. The gasoline has ability to go through with certain chemical reactions. When it is introduced with a certain amount of air into a cylinder of the automobile motor, it explodes. The gases of combustion expand, because of the heat produced, and the kinetic energy produced by this action makes itself evident in the downward motion of the piston, which in turn drives the wheels of the car.

Perhaps this whole picture will be clearer if we follow a familiar and apparently simple process through the intricacies of its energy history.

Consider the electric light. Millions of years ago certain quanta of energy came down to the surface of the earth and there struck the leaves of a luxuriant plant growing in the Carboniferous swamp. The plant, by chemical processes not yet clearly understood, used this radiant energy to transform carbon dioxide and water into the complicated chemical compounds of its structure. After its brief season of living, this plant died and was gradually buried under other plants and silt. Then by further chemical reactions (as yet not completely known) this plant was transformed into material which we call coal. This material lay in the coal seams for millions of years and was dug up by enterprising technicians. It contained considerable potential energy in the form of compounds of carbon and hydrogen, so it was taken to a power plant where this potential energy might be transformed into a profit. In the power plant, the coal, perhaps as lumps, perhaps as fine powder, was introduced into the hot combustion space of a boiler furnace. There it was burned or allowed to combine with the oxygen of the air. The potential energy of the chemical compounds of the coal was thus transformed into heat. This heat, being simply the violent random movement of the molecules of the products of combustion, might be considered kinetic energy. But all the energy did not stay in the form of invisible heat of the molecules, for part of this energy of molecular movement was converted into radiant energy. This radiant energy passed through the combustion space and struck the metal walls, or tubes, of the steam boiler, and was absorbed. When it was absorbed, the radiant energy was converted back into heat in this thin sheet of steel. Here again this heat energy may be potential or it may be kinetic, depending on the point of view. By the processes of conduction and convection, this heat energy was transmitted to the water on the inside of the boiler. The water, under the stress of the violent molecular agitation, vaporized into steam under high pressure. This steam was conducted to a steam engine (usually a turbine) where it expanded to do mechanical work. The mechanical work in this case consisted of turning the rotor of an electric generator. The function of this generator was to transform the potential energy of the steam into "electrical pressure" which could make electrons move along a conductor if a complete return circuit were provided. This stream of electrons was conducted by copper wires to the consumer who was interested in having a bit of illumination. When the consumer turned on the switch which connected his light bulb to the electric circuit, the pressure caused electrons to be circulated through the tungsten filament of the light bulb. Tungsten is a material which has a high electrical resistance, hence the electrons encountered considerable difficulty in getting through the filament. They registered their protest to this resistance by heating the filament, hence the energy of a stream of electrons was converted into heat. Then again, as always, the laws of radiation became effective and the hot tungsten filament glowed;

that is, it gave off radiant energy. A small part of this radiant energy which was given off lay between the wave lengths of 0.0004 and 0.0008 millimeters and hence was visible radiation. The bulk of the radiation, however, had a longer wave length than the visible and was evidenced only as heat. A long and tedious process is involved in harnessing energy to our needs. Small wonder that the Greeks, who had never acquired the fundamental concepts of energy, were unable to go far in its utilization.

This process of harnessing the energy of the coal to produce light is so long and involved that it must seem very inefficient. As a matter of fact, it is. Less than 2 per cent of the potential energy which was present in the chemical compounds of the coal was transformed into possible radiation at the light bulb. Probably less than 2 per cent of the radiation from the sun which fell on the leaf of the tree fern in the Carboniferous swamp was transformed into the potential energy of the compounds of that plant. Hence, our net efficiency in transforming sunlight into the visible light from the incandescent bulb is less than 0.04 per cent. It would seem as if man's ingenuity still has a long way to go and that he should be able to harness sunlight more efficiently than by this extremely roundabout process. Simplicity and efficiency may rise together in the future, but the long way around had to come first, bit by bit.

The statement that we merely change energy from one form to another may well bear further illustration. A large lathe for cutting metal from a cylindrical shaft may be driven by a twenty-five horsepower motor. It might seem on first thought that all of this energy from the motor is merely passing out of existence. Actually, no energy passes out of existence; in this case it is being transformed into heat energy; i.e., the tool in cutting through the metal encounters resistance in tearing the chips of metal away from the main body. The energy of the work of cutting is immediately transformed into heat in the metal being cut. Any lathe operator knows by experience how hot these chips can be.

THE EQUIVALENTS OF ENERGY

If all these manipulations with energy simply transform it from one form to another, and if the convenient rules of correlation which we call the "laws of nature" are universal, there should be some unchanging equivalents between the forms of energy. The great advances in physics began as soon as the early experimenters realized that this must be true. The classic experiment along this line came with James Prescott Joule's determination of the mechanical equivalent of heat. As in the case of many great experiments, the essential idea back of his work was very simple. He merely determined how much the temperature of a small body of water would rise if one performed a certain amount of work on the water by agitating it with a small paddle wheel. He found that a given quantity of work measured in ergs always produced the same amount of heat energy measured in calories. (One calorie is equal to 4.185×10^7 ergs. The erg is the quantity of energy equal to the work done by a force acting for one second which gives a mass of one gram an acceleration of one centimeter per second.) It might be thought, then, that one calorie could be transformed into 4.185×10^7 ergs of mechanical energy; but this process of transforming heat into mechanical work cannot be done with 100 per cent efficiency for reasons which will be shown later. There is always some energy left over, not transformed from heat to mechanical energy.

The constants which define the relation between the units employed to measure the different forms of energy have now been determined with a high degree of accuracy. These equivalences of the transformation of one form of energy into another seem to be universal and unchanging. Hence, the constants which we use are fundamental entities of nature. The further experimental work along these lines has progressed, and the more exact the experimenters have become, the greater has been the evidence that energy is never made, only transformed. There have been estimates of the total amount of energy which is in existence in the universe. Obviously it must be a figure of astronomical magnitude. The law of the conservation of energy is the most firmly established of all the laws of physics, provided one considers that mass may be transformed into energy, and vice versa. . . .

HEAT AND WORK

It was mentioned that Joule transformed all of the mechanical energy used in the agitation of a small body of water into the heat energy evidenced by the rise in temperature of the water; but neither Joule nor anyone else could take this heat energy and transform all of it back into mechanical energy. Even the most efficient modern power plants are unable to transform more than 25 or 30 per cent of the heat energy released in a firebox into the mechanical energy of the steam engine or turbine. This inconvenient phenomenon calls for a brief discussion of the "availability" of energy. All of a given quantity of mechanical or electrical energy can easily be transformed into heat energy, but the reverse is not true; heat energy is the resultant of the random motion of molecules of matter, whereas mechanical energy is the evidence of an ordered motion of matter, that is, motion in one direction only rather than in all directions. In effect, then, the steam engine selects those molecules which are going in the desired direction—in the direction of the moving piston—and utilizes their energies. Those molecules which are not moving in the direction of the piston cannot do any mechanical work against the piston and, hence, their energies are not utilizable. The concept which is used to measure this availability of energy is called *entropy*, a decidedly elusive but necessary abstraction. To grasp fully the concept of entropy means making a study of the science of thermodynamics which is beyond the scope of this work, but perhaps a qualitative picture may be developed.

In general, it may be said that the greater the entropy, the less the availability of heat for doing work. The classic expression of this idea is "The energy of the universe is constant but the entropy tends to become a maximum." As far as observation can show, all the energy of the universe is gradually being dissipated to lower and lower states of availability (i.e., its entropy is increasing) and, hence, it is steadily becoming less available for utilization. If this is true the energy-life of the universe is obviously finite and no one has any evidence to the contrary. The astronomers may eventually discover some reversal of this second law of thermodynamics, but they have no definite evidence of it as yet.

The complexity of the idea of entropy is increased by the fact that the concept is also used as a measure of the extensive factor of heat. Electrical energy dissipated in a unit of time is the product of the extensive factor, current (amperes), and the intensive factor, potential drop (volts). Analogously, heat (calories) is the product of the intensive factor (absolute temperature) and the extensive factor (entropy). Consider a block of iron heated to 1,000° C. absolute (727° on the Centigrade scale). Then the entropy of each 1,000 calories in this block is $^{1000}/_{1000}$, or 1 entropy unit. If this block of iron is then brought in contact with another that is at a lower temperature, heat will flow from the hotter to the colder block until the two are at the same temperature. Assume that the second block is of such a size that, after the heat transfer has taken place, both blocks are at a temperature of 500° C. absolute (227° on the Centigrade scale). Then the entropy of each 1,000 calories at this lower temperature is $^{1000}/_{500}$, or 2 entropy units. In other words, each 1,000 calories of energy in the form of heat doubles its entropy whenever its absolute temperature is cut in half. The analogy comes back again to the electrical circuit. A 1,000-watt electric heater with a 1,000-volt potential drop across it draws a current of 1 ampere. If the potential drop is reduced to 500 volts, the current must be 2 amperes in order to give a rate of dissipation of energy of 1,000 watts. If the potential drop is cut to 100 volts, then the current must be 10 amperes to give the same rate of dissipation of energy.

Most householders are familiar with watts of power because they pay money for them. Every elementary experimenter in physics is familiar with volts of potential difference and amperes of current because meters are available to measure them. If one can measure an entity by observing the position of a needle on a graduated scale, he acquires a familiarity with it and perhaps can understand it. But there are no entropy meters, so the quantity remains unfamiliar and always a bit abstruse. We cannot measure entropy directly so we evaluate it in a roundabout way by dividing quantity of heat by the absolute temperature of the system. In other words, as far as our sensory experience is concerned, entropy is an artificiality. But it is a necessary artificiality for the quantitative considerations of the availability of heat. A quantity of heat in an object at 500° C. will not flow to an object of temperature 600° C.; it will flow only to a place where the temperature is less than 500° C. Energy in the form of heat cannot be transformed into mechanical work unless it flows to a place of lower temperature. The concept of entropy is necessary for computing the amount of heat that can be transformed into work (as in a steam engine) when heat flows between points having different temperatures.

Considerations such as these led to the development of the science of thermodynamics, a product of several great minds among the French, German, English, and American scientists of the past century. The development and mastery of the subject has been one of the chief instruments not only in the improved utilization of power devices but in the understanding and utilization of the fundamentals of chemical reactions.

One of the first accomplishments of the science of thermodynamics was to show that for a heat engine

$$\text{Efficiency} = \frac{T_1 - T_2}{T_1},$$

where T_1 refers to the absolute temperature at the place where the heat is being released for use in the engine and T_2 refers to the temperature of the material exhausted from the engine. Hence, the only way to convert heat energy with 100 per cent efficiency into mechanical energy is to have the temperature of the place where the energy is released for use infinitely high (an impossibility) or to maintain the temperature of the engine exhaust itself at absolute zero (practically an impossibility). No matter how adept we may become in mechanical matters, we can never convert more than a fraction of heat energy into mechanical energy. Great advances have been made in increasing efficiency by going to higher pressures, and to higher values of T_1 in both steam and internal combustion engines. The limit of this increased efficiency has not yet been reached; but it will never approach 100 per cent. If we want to utilize our energy supply with all possible efficiency, we must utilize something other than heat engines. Whether or not it will ever be possible to do away with the inherently inefficient heat engine, only future scientists and technologists can decide.

It might seem that nineteenth-century scientists muttering in their beards about entropy at abominably dry gatherings could have nothing to do with the welfare of the race, but the beneficial effect has been swift and startling. The early steam power plants were not more than 5 per cent efficient. At the time of Watt's invention they were even poorer than that. In 1837 a learned Dr. Lardner proved that a steam voyage across the Atlantic was beyond the realm of possibility because so much coal would be required for the voyage that there would be no room left for passengers or other heavy load. But the thermodynamicists went to work and, with the aid of clever mechanics, they increased efficiency of steam power plants many fold. It is a poor power plant now that cannot transform at least 20 per cent of the potential heat energy of coal into electrical energy. Some of the really up-to-date plants operate with an efficiency of 30 per cent or better. Airplane motors operate with an efficiency better than 40 per cent. Most of the improvement has been brought about through higher pressures and temperatures. James Watt's engines used boiler pressures of only seven pounds per square inch. Today 1,000 pounds per square inch is widely used, and 1,400 pounds is not uncommon. Boiler pressures of 2,500 pounds per square inch seem to be just around the corner. Had the scientists and engineers not improved efficiency, long ocean voyages and airplane flights would be impossible; but what is more important, the power plants on land would have depleted the coal supply much more rapidly than they have. The best way to conserve the supply of our fossil energy is to increase the efficiency of its use. The pure scientist has been back of the great improvements of the past; he still has much work to do along these lines in the future.

1939

MICROWAVES *

LEE ALVIN DUBRIDGE

Microwaves are radio waves, similar to those used in ordinary broadcasting, only of much shorter wave length and of higher frequency. There is a direct relationship, it will be remembered, between wave length and frequency. As the wave length is shortened, the frequency of the vibrations becomes correspondingly higher.

The length of the radio waves which brings broadcast programs into your homes is probably between 200 and 600 meters. That is, these broadcasting waves are from one-tenth to one-third of a mile long. And their frequency ranges from about one-half million cycles or vibrations per second for the third-of-a-mile waves to about one and one-half million cycles for the tenth-of-a-mile waves. If your radio set can be tuned to the short-wave band, such as is used for communication with Europe, you may receive wave lengths as short as twenty-five meters, about seventy-five feet. Before the war the shortest waves in practical use measured about one and a half meters, or five feet. This one-and-a-half meter wave has a frequency of two hundred million cycles, or 200 megacycles. Radio waves of higher frequency were, in those days, only laboratory curiosities.

* From *The Scientists Speak*, edited by Warren Weaver. Reprinted by permission from Boni & Gaer, Inc. Copyright 1947 by Boni & Gaer, Inc.

Today the situation is very different. As a result of years of intensive war research, radio waves of only ten centimeters, or four inches long, have become common. Waves as short as one centimeter, or less than half an inch, are now a practical possibility. The frequency of these one-centimeter waves is thirty thousand million vibrations per second.

It is these very short radio waves that are called microwaves—specifically, those of wave lengths shorter than about 20 centimeters. During the war these high-frequency radiations were not only brought out of the laboratory, but nearly two billion dollars worth of radar equipment using microwaves had been produced or was on order at the end of the war. For five years this huge development and manufacturing effort was carried on behind closed doors, guarded by military security.

Microwaves in themselves are not particularly new or revolutionary. Physicists and engineers had been experimenting with them in the laboratory for many years. What happened under the spur of war is that microwaves have been made available for practical use.

Two things made this possible. One was a small metal vacuum tube developed by the British physicists Oliphant and Randall at the University of Birmingham in 1940. The second influence was something quite different—the organization of a huge international scientific and manufacturing enterprise which concentrated on the problem for five years.

Let us look first at the little vacuum tube. It was brought to this country by the British more than a year before we entered the war. It is known as a resonant cavity magnetron. Magnetron is the general name for a vacuum tube that operates in a magnetic field. Many magnetrons of different kinds had been developed and used long before the war. The resonant cavity magnetron is one in which the oscillating circuits are in the form of cavities or holes drilled within the body of the tube. The British physicists had invented an arrangement of these cavities and other features which enabled the tube to produce very high power at very high efficiency at extremely short wave lengths.

Previous microwave tubes generated such small outputs of power that ultrasensitive instruments were necessary to detect it. This new tube generated so much power that a piece of steel wool held near the tube burst into flame. It is difficult to describe the amazement of physicists and engineers when they first witnessed this tube in operation. Such a power at a frequency of three thousand million cycles had never been thought possible. But now, five years later, we look back on that tube and realize that, miraculous as it was, it was only a crude beginning. Present-day magnetrons are 100 times more powerful. They can produce pulses of high-frequency power up to 1,000 kilowatts.

But one vacuum tube does not make a radar set. A large scientific, engineering, and manufacturing effort was called for to produce the microwave radar that was so urgently needed in the war.

In the summer of 1940 the National Defense Research Committee, later to become part of the Office of Scientific Research and Development, undertook to organize this scientific effort. Being assured of cooperation from the British authorities, the United States Army, Navy, and American industry, the National Defense Research Committee established a microwave laboratory at the Massachusetts Institute of Technology. This Radiation Laboratory eventually grew to nearly 4,000 employees and served as a focus for the large international cooperative research program. As a result of this effort, microwave radar was made available for use on every battle front.

Microwaves are fascinating to work with. They are just like ordinary radio waves except for wave length. But the short wave length causes them to exhibit many properties normally associated with light. A microwave antenna, for example, often resembles a searchlight. By combining the techniques of dipoles, horns, and parabolic reflectors, one can produce and project into space a microwave beam of almost any desired shape and sharpness. Turned around, as a receiver, the antenna will receive energy only from certain areas, ignoring others.

The energy within a beam of microwaves can be sharply concentrated. It may well turn out to be more economical to carry radio and television programs or even telephone conversations from point to point across the country on such beams rather than through telephone cables. However, microwave beams travel through space in straight lines only and are not bounced back from the ionosphere. Hence, in a transmission across the country, the beam would have to be projected from tower to tower, 30 to 50 miles apart.

For transmission over short distances—a few yards or so—microwave beams can be still further concentrated by passing them through hollow metal pipes called wave guides. This remarkable behavior of the waves was discovered before the war and extensively studied at the Bell Telephone Laboratories, at the Massachusetts Institute of Technology, and other places. The pipe may be circular or rectangular, but its dimensions must be properly related to the wave length. The longer the wave length, the larger must be the pipe.

The pipe may have bends and twists, and, if properly designed, the waves follow them without loss. Even flexible metal pipes have been developed and are used like a water hose. The microwaves, like the water, do not care whether the hose is bent or straight. One can even provide a sort of nozzle at the exit end of the pipe and direct the waves into a narrow stream or a wide spray. In this particular, however, the waves behave just the way water would not. If the nozzle is a wide-mouthed horn, the microwaves will contract into a slender stream. If the nozzle is narrowed, the stream will flare into a wider cone.

It was the attainment of narrow microwave beams that gave radar the sharpness of vision which proved so important for many military applications, such as the control of bombing and of gunfire.

The next great field for microwaves may be in communications. At these superhigh-frequencies, atmospheric static does not exist. Directional radio communication from point to point, from ship to ship, or from ground to aircraft, is a practicable possibility. With a sharp beam one may have almost the advantage of a private wire telephone. In the microwave region there are thousands of radio channels available, so it would even be possible to assign to each airplane its own private frequency channel.

There are other possible applications—to induction heating, to industrial control, and in physical research. It is an interesting fact that these microwaves, indeed all radio waves, are vibrations of the same nature as light rays, infrared, ultraviolet, and X rays, differing only in wave lengths and frequencies. They are all electromagnetic radiations. And when a new part of the electromagnetic spectrum becomes available for practical use—as here—no one can predict its future. We only know that a new area of applied science has been opened. Experience tells us that whenever this happens, the new area yields dividends in all sorts of unexpected ways for years to come.

1947

>>>-<<<

TRIAL BY WIND TUNNEL *

GEORGE W. GRAY

I

In their early experiments with gliders at Kitty Hawk, Wilbur and Orville Wright found that the accepted standards specifying the lifting ability of wings were wrong. They simply could not get from their gliders the lift that theory predicted. It was not until the ingenious brothers had provided themselves with a small wind tunnel, in which they could actually measure the air forces acting on various wing shapes, that they succeeded in building the first successful airplane. . . .

What was true of the Wright machine of forty-one years ago is equally true of the latest fighters and bombers. Every one of them was hatched in a wind tunnel. The top aviation demands of today are almost frighteningly exacting. They call for mechanisms so refined, packed with so much power, loaded with so many tons of fuel, armament, armor, and other matériel, capable of flight at such altitudes and speeds, that no mortal can compute in advance and lay out on paper the design that will meet all the latest requirements of the military. Each airplane as it is conceived is the heir of more than forty years of research. And yet these accumulated data of aeronautics are not enough. Each new design must be worked out individually. . . .

Wind tunnels have been useful, first of all, in discovering and developing fundamental principles of aerodynamics and in applying them to particular problems of design. Out of the tunnels have come high-speed propellers, low-drag wings, flaps which give high lift, cowls and ducts to promote the efficient cooling of the engine, and other improvements that are now standard aircraft components. . . .

Beyond this contribution of fundamental research, whose results may be applied to all aircraft, the wind tunnels have proved to be of direct value in developing the cleanness and performance characteristics of specific airplanes, and in detecting and correcting faults of design. In this capacity the American tunnels have been of high service to the nation's war effort. . . .

Indeed, everything that is discovered in the exploration of one airplane immediately becomes available for the improvement of subsequent or contemporary types and makes. The dive-recovery flaps that were developed by the NACA for the Lightning are now on the Thunderbolt and other high-speed craft. A special device for balancing ailerons on the Mustang is also serving the P-59, P-63, and A-26. . . .

II

A wind tunnel gets its results by a reversal of the conditions of flight. The test object—whether airplane, airplane part, or small-scale model—is mounted securely on rigid streamlined supports, these supports are mounted on scales, and, when the airstream is turned on, the scales "weigh" the responses of the object to the airflow. In this way it is possible to determine the amount of drag, lift, or interference that a certain shape develops. It is possible to measure aspects of stability and control, such as the tendency to pitch or roll or yaw. Practically every flying characteristic is susceptible to study by thus reversing the natural process and making the air, rather than the plane, the moving element.

America is remarkably equipped with wind tunnels. There are some eighty now in operation, distributed among twenty-seven engineering schools, ten aircraft manufacturers, the Army and Navy (each of which has four tunnels, used primarily for engineering checkup and development rather than for research), and the government's independent research agency, the National Advisory Committee for Aeronautics.

This agency was created in 1915, by act of Congress, "to supervise and direct the scientific study of the problems of flight with a view to their practical solution." It consists of fifteen non-salaried members—most of them scientists and engineers, with two representatives each from the

Army, Navy, and civil aeronautics branch of the Commerce Department. From the beginning its work has been "scientific study" at the research level. Its leadership has always been of the highest. . . .

As early as 1916 the Committee began to organize a plan of research. It selected Langley Field, Virginia, as the seat for its activities, and the Army authorities assigned a plot of ground for a laboratory. When this Langley Memorial Aeronautical Laboratory was opened in 1920, the principal item of equipment was a five-foot wind tunnel. Tunnel No. 1 has long since been dismantled to make room for more modern apparatus, but at the time it was built it seemed the last word in aerodynamic research facilities. It made many contributions to aeronautics, but perhaps the principal contribution was to open the eyes of the research staff to the inadequacy of what was then everywhere accepted as suitable equipment. Within two years the Langley engineers had designed and were beginning to build an entirely new type of wind tunnel, and this became the trail blazer for more and better tunnels to come. . . .

By 1939 the laboratory area at Langley Field was so congested with wind tunnels and auxiliary equipment, and the Army and Navy were increasing their requests for NACA technical services at so rapid a rate, that a second research center was established on the Pacific Coast—at Moffett Field, near San Francisco. It was called the Ames Aeronautical Laboratory, in honor of the late Dr. Joseph S. Ames, former president of the Johns Hopkins University, who served the NACA many years as chairman. . . .

Perhaps the most remarkable of these tunnels at Ames, certainly the most spectacular, is the 80-foot full-scale tunnel. It was completed and began operations only last June, and the substantial scientific and engineering results that have come out of its use are buried in the secrecy of wartime military research. However, the dimensions of the tunnel have been published, and it is known that the test section is large enough to admit a two-engine plane, such as the Invader, the Havoc, the Marauder, and other bombers of this category. One of the airline transports, such as a Lockheed Lodestar, could be installed here and studied at speeds up to 225 m.p.h., with the airplane's twin engines operating, propellers whirling, and the other features of flight simulated. The possible peacetime uses of this new research tool, with its enormous capacity and high versatility, are not difficult to imagine. For the first time science has the means for making direct aerodynamic studies of large two-engine airplanes at full scale.

Simply as enclosed space this Ames tunnel is impressive. It is the Mammoth Cave of architecture—a cave that turns corners and bends back on itself in a closed circuit, an immense hollow doughnut which if straightened out would be a cone 2,700 feet long—more than half a mile. The 80-foot dimension is only the width of the airstream at its narrowest part. The vista within staggers the imagination with its depth and height and breadth and its eerie shadows. Tramping through the vast cavern, with the aid of a pocket flashlight, one sees looming ahead the outline of the six gigantic fans, mounted three abreast in two rows, the embodiment of the 36,000 electrical horses which drive the big wind. The 24 million cubic feet of air within the tunnel weigh 900 tons. That is an average of only 50 pounds to each horsepower, but quite enough load when the horse is responsible for moving its 50 pounds at four times the speed of an express train. . . .

In 1940, when construction of the Ames Laboratory was just getting started, the NACA decided to establish still another center of research. . . . This Cleveland laboratory has a variety of highly specialized equipment, including two of the most remarkable wind tunnels ever built.

The first, the altitude tunnel, provides completely controlled facilities for the study of engine performance at any altitude from sea level up to the substratosphere. This means that there is a refrigeration and cooling plant to keep the temperature down to 48° below zero Fahrenheit, a pumping plant to evacuate the tunnel air to a density equivalent to that at 50,000 feet, and a fan which pushes the air around through the huge cavern at 500 m.p.h. These simultaneous processes go on while an airplane engine, mounted in the 20-foot test section, is spurting its fiery exhaust and continually adding heat and fumes to the tunnel air. To operate the tunnel at full capacity requires 52,000 horsepower, of which only 18,000 drives the fan; the remainder is needed to drive the pumps and operate the refrigeration and cooling systems.

Equally unique is the Cleveland laboratory's icing research tunnel. It is prepared to study the problem of aircraft icing wherever it shows up—in engines and engine components, on propeller blades, wings, antennae, and other parts. Just as the altitude tunnel can subject an airplane engine to the atmospheric conditions of the substratosphere, so the ice tunnel can subject it and other parts to the extreme meteorological conditions which produce dangerous icing. The tunnel has facilities for spraying water into the moving airstream and at the same time lowering the temperature to as much as 65° below zero. The top wind speed here is 320 m.p.h., and the artificial blizzards of sleet and snow which result from this combination of wind, temperature, and humidity are more than a match for nature's worst weather. . . .

III

The starting point of this development was the discovery that conclusions reached from airflow studies of models in Tunnel No. 1 could not be applied to the full size airplane. The responses of the small-scale model in this 5-foot wind tunnel were one thing, the responses of the actual airplane in the air were another, and there was no mathematical formula that would bring them into correspondence.

It is a principle of physics that the aerodynamic behavior of an object depends on its size, the speed with which it (or the air) is moving, and the air viscosity (indicated by air density). The multiple of these three factors for a given airplane or other object provides a scale index known as the Reynolds number. The Reynolds number of the Mustang fighter plane, for example, is within the range 5,000,000 to 20,000,000, which means that this is the product of multiplying (1) the size of the Mustang, by (2) its speed in level flight, by (3) the density of the air at the levels for which it is designed to fly. The Reynolds number of the Flying Fortress is 13,000,000 to 28,000,000. This is higher than the Mustang's, for although the Fortress is slower, it is so much larger than the fighter that the increase in size more than compensates for the decrease in speed. Thus, you can increase the Reynolds number of an object by increasing its size, or by increasing its speed, or by increasing the density of the air.

It was recognition of the importance of the Reynolds number that led the group at Langley to make their first contribution to the improvement of wind tunnels. "Why not put the tunnel in a sealed airtight chamber, and pump the air to higher densities?" proposed Dr. Max Munk. By compressing the air to twenty atmospheres you could use a one-twentieth-scale model and get results comparable to those that the full-scale airplane gives at atmospheric pressure. The idea, in other words, was to compress the air in the tunnel as much as you compress the airplane in the model. . . .

Since pioneering this invention, the NACA has added several tunnels of its own embodying the variable-density principle. The largest is the 19-foot tunnel completed at Langley in 1939, just in time to be of incomparable service in wartime research. . . .

But the 19-footer is comparatively new. For years the NACA's only variable-density tunnel was the original Tunnel No. 2, completed in 1923, and it has rendered yeoman service to aeronautics. It was the means of making the first systematic study of airfoils, and out of this research came the NACA family of wings, including the famous 23012 wing. When the war began in 1939, this wing was in almost universal use for transport airplanes, both in the United States and abroad; and, except for a few experimental aircraft, it was the standard wing for military airplanes.

But there were problems the variable-density tunnel could not touch. Propellers, for example, presented an enigma. They had a way of suddenly losing efficiency at high speeds; sometimes the blades would break under the pull of centrifugal force; and nobody knew the limits of safe and economical operation.

"The thing to do is to build a tunnel for propeller research," proposed Dr. Lewis to the Committee. "And I think we ought to build it big," he continued, "for this propeller problem can't be solved with small-scale models. Let's make the tunnel large enough to take an actual fuselage with its engine installation and propeller of full scale."

They designed a huge affair with a throat 20 feet in diameter. Anything over 10 feet was regarded as a giant in those days, and when the propeller-research tunnel was completed in 1926 it seemed colossal. However, as it turned out, the biggest thing about this apparatus is not its size but its record of research results. It licked the propeller problem—established the rule that the speed of rotation of propeller tips must not exceed 90 per cent of the speed of sound, and provided standards which guided propeller engineering for the next dozen years. In addition, the new tunnel explored other problems, and within a short time had contributed three major findings.

First, it showed that the exposed radial engine was a source of costly air resistance, being responsible for one-third of the drag of the entire airplane body. The researchers were able to demonstrate that merely enclosing the engine in a metal jacket immediately reduced its drag, and out of hundreds of tests with dozens of combinations came at last the NACA cowling. In this the jacket is carefully shaped both outside and inside to promote airflow, and not only is drag reduced but the cooling job is more efficiently performed. The first public use of this development came in February, 1929, when an airplane equipped with the NACA cowling made a nonstop flight from Los Angeles to New York in 18 hours and 13 minutes. Its normal speed was 157 m.p.h., but with the NACA cowling to reduce drag and promote cooling it flew at 177 m.p.h. . . .

The next contribution from the propeller-research tunnel was the discovery that a multi-engine airplane performs best when its engines are on a line with the leading edge of the wing. At the time of these investigations, engines were customarily suspended below the wing. Look at the pictures of the commercial transports, the Army and Navy bombers, Admiral Byrd's big trimotored ship in which he flew over the North Pole, and other aircraft of the twenties and early thirties, and note how fixed was the designers' idea that the place for the engine was below the wing. The NACA discovery was published in a technical report in November, 1931. It was applied by Glenn L. Martin in a two-engine bomber for the Army in 1933; and by 1934 the DC-2 transport planes had their two 700-horsepower engines (also equipped with NACA cowling) in the front-of-the-wing position, and they were making 210 m.p.h. at 8,000 feet.

A third major contribution was the demonstration of the enormous drag exacted by the landing gear. Every aerodynamicist, of course, knew that protruding landing gear cost power to pull through the air, and here and there an occasional plane had been built with facilities to fold up the landing gear or withdraw it into the body or wing. But these were sporadic and incidental efforts, and it was not until the NACA published its report in 1934 that aeronautics had an actual measurement of this inefficiency. Studies made with an actual airplane in the 20-foot tunnel showed that when the landing gear was removed the total drag diminished by one-third. After that, any designer who wanted to add speed to his airplane knew where he could get it at little cost. Today the retractable landing gear is so common it is difficult to realize that ten years ago it was a rarity. Without it, high speed aircraft would be impossible. It has been found, for example, that merely extending the landing gear of the B-29 Superfortress in flight reduces the speed of the big bomber by one-half.

The propeller-research tunnel is a landmark in aeronautical science. Probably no other single piece of research equipment has influenced as many changes in the airplane within the same space of time. . . .

IV

The primary purpose in building the types of tunnels just described was to make the scale measurements of drag, lift, and other aerodynamic factors approach those of actual flight—a condition that can be attained either by increasing the air pressure or by increasing the size of the test object. Or, as the engineers put it, they were after higher Reynolds numbers. But the Reynolds number is not the only consideration. There is another aerodynamic index, the Mach number, a speed ratio. As the Reynolds number was named for Osborne Reynolds, a Briton who distinguished himself in studies of fluid mechanics, the Mach number commemorates Ernst Mach, an Austrian who specialized in studies of high-speed phenomena. Aeronautical engineers use the term to express the ratio of aircraft speed to the speed of sound. Thus, when an engineer says that an airplane is flying at a Mach number of 0.65, he means that its speed is 65 per cent of the speed of sound. Since the speed of sound varies with altitude, the Mach number is a more fundamental expression of high-speed relationships than the number of miles per hour.

High Mach numbers first showed up in aeronautics on the tips of propellers. Work in the propeller-research tunnel at Langley determined that speeds of rotation higher than Mach number 0.90 were both inefficient and dangerous. At the time these studies were made the cruising speeds of airplanes were under 200 m.p.h., and the designers of wings, tails, and bodies needed to give little thought to the influence of Mach number. But with the development of higher-powered engines, the placing of engines in line with the wing, the adoption of cowling and retractable landing gear, speeds increased. Dr. Lewis and his researchers foresaw that in the course of a few years high-speed effects would begin to show on every part of the airplane, and the necessity of providing advance knowledge on these problems spurred them to develop new tunnels capable of producing airflows at high Mach numbers.

In 1934 a vertical tunnel was built at Langley, a tall flutelike tube emerging from a concrete test chamber, with a wind speed of 765 m.p.h. This speed was attained by discharging a jet of compressed air into the upper part of the tunnel; and by induction the sudden jet caused the air below to surge upward—like the draft up a chimney—at the high velocity. A number of significant studies were made with this vertical tunnel, but it had its handicaps. For one thing, the jet which induced the airflow was short-lived; it originated in a release of highly compressed air, and in consequence each test could last less than a minute. Also the tunnel was small, measuring only 2 feet across in its test section, and studies were limited to small-scale models. A bigger tunnel in which tests could be carried on continuously was an urgent necessity, and a group at Langley now turned aside from aeronautical research to do this special job in equipment research. The result was the 8-foot high-speed tunnel which went into operation in 1936.

This was the first high-speed tunnel of large size. Unlike the earlier jet tunnel it is horizontal, curved into the form of a large oblong ring which tapers from a maximum diameter of many yards to a minimum of 8 feet at the test section. It is here that the air attains highest velocity. An incidental problem was imposed by the tornadolike swirl; for as the airstream, moving at many hundred of miles per hour, passes through the narrowed tunnel it acts as a suction pump to pull air out of the test chamber which encloses the test section. This is the workroom of the staff operating the tunnel. As a result of the suction effect, the workroom is partially evacuated. When the wind is screaming past at maximum speed, the air in the chamber becomes so thin that it is as though the engineers were working at an altitude of 12,000 feet!

So great is this suction effect that the usual wind-tunnel structure would collapse from the pressure of the outside air. To guard against that hazard, the tunnel is made of massive concrete with walls 12 inches thick lined with steel; and the test chamber is built in the form of a beehive, also of heavy concrete and with a concrete floor 24 inches thick. The beehive architecture and the dimensions are calculated to resist the collapsing effect of the atmospheric pressure.

There is another operational hazard that had to be anticipated: the heat effect. A fan of 8,000 horsepower drives the wind at a speed approaching sonic velocity, and all this power is absorbed by the moving air in the form of heat. It was figured that if no means of cooling were provided, the inside temperature would rise ten degrees per second until it reached the stage at which the amount of heat seeping through the concrete walls would balance the input from the power plant. But it would take two hours for this equilibrium to be reached, and meanwhile a temperature of thousands of degrees would have developed within the tunnel. Everything combustible would have gone up in smoke; the steel would have melted to a liquid.

The task of providing a cooling system was entrusted to Russell G. Robinson, a young engineer on the Langley staff. He devised a ventilating tower by which a small amount of the heated air is allowed to escape at each instant of operation, while simultaneously an equal amount of fresh, cool air is taken in. This arrangement proved to be entirely successful, and is so economical that the exchange is accomplished with less than 1 per cent loss of power. Several high-speed tunnels have been built subsequent to this pioneer apparatus, and all have profited by the example of Robinson's ingenious heat-exchange system.

The 8-foot tunnel is not yet ten years old, but it has contributed to some of the key development of high-speed aircraft. One of the earliest studies resulted in a new cowling. It was found that the critical speed of the NACA cowling was 325 m.p.h.—i.e., when the airplane reached this speed, the motion of the air through and over the cowling developed shock waves and other compressibility effects which made higher speed unattainable. The 8-foot tunnel crew thereupon went to work to develop a high-speed cowling, and out of their studies came the NACA C cowl which has a critical speed of Mach number 0.65, corresponding to 500 m.p.h. at sea level. Futher research has developed newer NACA cowls with still higher critical speeds, approaching 80 per cent of the speed of sound, or around 600 m.p.h. at sea level.

In efforts to meet the problems of the efficient installation of coolers of all sorts, and eventually of jet propulsion itself, the 8-foot tunnel researchers investigated the thermocycle. The theory of the thermocycle is that if you admit air into a duct, slow the air down by expanding it, next add heat, and then speed the air up, the result will be additional thrust. This was just an idea until the 8-foot tunnel put it to the test. The thing panned out beautifully. It was demonstrated that you can pass air around an engine for cooling purposes and get enough extra thrust from the heat it absorbs to offset the drag. If the speed of the airplane is above 400 m.p.h., the radiator gives more thrust than the drag it produces, and thus becomes a source of power. This knowledge has not only been useful in improving engine cooling systems, but has also been applied in the ram jet, one of the advanced systems of power development for jet-propelled aircraft.

Another series of studies in the 8-foot tunnel tackled the propeller. It was realized that propellers of higher efficiency would be needed. As aircraft moved on into higher speed ranges, the propeller blades must be shaped to bite into the thin air of the upper atmosphere, and, moreover, to avoid the ever-threatening hazard of shock waves. From these researches came the paddle-blade type of propeller, now in use on all high-speed military aircraft.

The 8-foot tunnel was a pioneer, and its lessons guided several subsequent projects. The fastest of these is the supersonic tunnel at Langley; its test section is measured in inches, but the air hurtles through at more than 1,200 miles an hour!

V

Several years ago Eastman N. Jacobs and a group of young associates at the Langley laboratory were working on the airplane wing, trying to improve its efficiency and in particular to reduce its drag. By systematically changing the curvatures and testing them in the variable-density tunnel, they improved the shapes to such an extent that a NACA family of wings was accepted by almost all manufacturers and became standard on most of the transport and military airplanes. But the men at Langley were not satisfied. They felt that wings of much lower drag were possible. As they worked out new profiles in the tunnel and then tried them out in flight on actual airplanes, they found that the wings performed a little better in the flight tests than they did in the tunnel tests. This led to a careful evaluation of the tunnel and its limitations.

Turbulence was the element that was distorting the measurements. The atmosphere has turbulence, but it is large-scale, whereas in a wind tunnel the friction of the tunnel walls and other effects of the imprisonment of the air stir up small-scale eddies and other disturbances which cannot be balanced out in the measurements. And so, as scale effects had led to one trend in tunnel development and high-speed effects to another, the influence of turbulence now brought about still another venture in wind-tunnel design.

Jacobs and his group proceeded to design a low-turbulence tunnel. The first one built at Langley in 1938 had a turbulence only a tenth that of the variable-density tunnel previously used in airfoil research. A second and better tunnel was built in 1940, in which the turbulence was a hundredth that of the old variable-density tunnel. From these two tunnels have come a whole flock of new wings. They are remarkable for their almost uniform distribution of air pressure over the wing profile, and for the long laminar airflows which they promote. As a consequence wing drag has been cut in half, and this reduction of drag has played its part in increasing the speed of our military airplanes. Among those that can be mentioned at this time as flying on low-drag wings are the Mustang, Kingcobra, Airacomet jet plane, Invader, and Superfortress.

In addition to its low-turbulence tunnels, its full-scale, high-speed, altitude, and ice tunnels, the NACA has tunnels for the study of stability problems, others for testing the spinning characteristics of airplanes, a free-flight tunnel in which unconventional airplanes such as the flying wing and other unusual designs are investigated, and a gust tunnel. The gust tunnel makes use of models of the airplane, and in its tests the small model actually flies a course, to be interrupted in flight by a sudden gust; the behavior of the model under this disturbance is recorded photographically and also by instruments installed in its body. These records are studied for what they can teach of the design of airplanes to withstand gust loads. In the free-flight tunnel also dynamic models are used, and the miniature airplanes are put through their paces to appraise their flying characteristics. In the spinning tunnel small dynamic models are thrown into a spin and then tested to see if they can recover. The Army and Navy require that all fighter planes pass this test. . . .

1945

JETS POWER FUTURE FLYING *

WATSON DAVIS

There's power in roaring flames—whether in a windswept forest fire, your oil burner, or a jet plane of the future.

There's simplicity in a stream of speedy gas pushing an airplane forward.

Jets with their simple power are revolutionizing travel through the air—for peaceful transport or for atomic war if we fail in our attempt to get along with the other peoples of the world.

Applying jet propulsion to our airplanes is the high priority task for our research laboratories today. Already the P-80s, with turbine-jet engines, have made obsolete the best conventional fighter planes with the best internal combustion engines. Jet bombers are being flown experimentally. Jet transport planes are on the drawing boards.

The reciprocating, spark-fired internal combustion engine feeding on gasoline (look under the hood of your automobile to see one) has a rival that may drive it out of the air.

FOUR TYPES OF JETS

There are four different types of jet-propulsion units:

The turbo-jet and turbo-propeller-jet engines, which operate through the principle of the gas turbine.

The pulse-jet, used by the Germans as the propulsion unit of the V-1 "buzz" bomb.

The ram-jet, currently undergoing rapid development for use on guided missiles or other highspeed transportation.

The rocket, most highly developed in the German V-2 weapon.

Only the turbo-jet and turbo-prop-jet engines rely upon gas-turbine-driven compressors to compress the intake air. The pulse-jet and the ram-jet use oxygen of the air for burning their fuel, but compress the air by their speed. The rocket supplies its own oxygen and thus can go outside the atmosphere.

* Reprinted by permission from *Science News Letter* and from the author. Copyright 1947 by Science Service, Inc.

The principle of the combustion gas turbine is not new, but it makes possible the development of turbo-jet and turbo-prop-jet engines for aircraft. The future of marine and railroad locomotive propulsion will feel its impact. History is full of attempts to develop a satisfactory gas turbine. Early experimenters were unsuccessful. They were handicapped both by lack of knowledge which would permit design of efficient compressors and turbines, and by lack of the proper materials of construction.

WAR SPURRED RESEARCH

The wartime need for greater and greater speed in aircraft prompted intensive research that before and during the war increased our knowledge of aerodynamics. Metals were devised that would stand up for extremely high temperatures. This made possible the development of the gas turbine, in the form of the turbo-jet engine, for aircraft. This new type of engine is one of the outstanding developments since the Wrights flew the first heavier-than-air machines.

The design of the combustion gas turbine is simple. There is only one major moving part, a rotating shaft on which is mounted an air compressor and a turbine rotor. The compressor supplies air to the combustion chambers where fuel is burned continuously to increase the energy content of the compressed air by heating it. The resulting hot gases are then expanded through a turbine. The turbine rotor and shaft revolve. In the case of the turbo-jet engine, only sufficient energy is recovered by the turbine to drive the compressor, and the hot gases leaving the turbine are exhausted through nozzles to form the jet. The reaction to the jet propels the aircraft as a result of the increase in momentum of the air stream due to its rise in temperature and volume as it passes through the unit.

In the prop-jet engine, the greater part of the energy available in the hot gases from the combustion chamber is recovered by the turbine. The power thus available, over and above that required to drive the compressor is utilized to drive an air screw propeller, in the case of high-speed aircraft.

Great amounts of fuel and air consumed by the gas-turbine engine in developing its great power are astounding. Philetus H. Holt, a research director of the Standard Oil Development Co., has figured that a turbo-jet engine developing 4,000 pounds thrust, equivalent to 4,000 horsepower at 375 miles per hour, will require more than 4,000,000 cubic feet of air in an hour. At this rate, all the air in a typical six-room house would be exhausted in about nine seconds. Approximately 20 barrels of fuel are burned each hour—enough fuel, if it were gasoline, to drive an automobile 12,000 miles at a speed of 60 miles per hour, or, if heating oil, enough to heat a typical six-room house for two-thirds of a heating season.

Heat is released in the combustion chambers of the turbo-jet engine at the rate of about 20,000,000 Btu. per hour per cubic foot of combustion zone, which may be compared with a rate of one to two million Btu. per hour per cubic foot in the case of industrial furnaces. This great development of power is accomplished with a freedom from vibration unknown in reciprocating engines.

HIGH-SPEED ENGINE

Where fuel economy is of secondary importance, the turbo-jet engine far surpasses the conventional reciprocating engine when high speed at present altitudes is necessary, as is the case in fighters, interceptors and fast attack bombers. When pressurized cabins are used combined with turbo-jet power at very high altitude, fast, long-range commercial transports will be attractive to airlines. At altitudes of 40,000 feet or higher the turbo-jet unit is much more economical of fuel than at low altitudes.

Long flights of 3,000 miles, which presently take 12 to 14 hours, will be made in six to seven hours. Equipment and pilots will do double jobs; passengers will get there faster.

The turbo-propeller-jet power plant has the possibility of competing directly with the conventional reciprocating engine at present-day speeds, since improvements in design should soon give fuel economy and operating life equivalent to those of the reciprocating engine.

How soon will your airlines ticket give you such flight? Some estimate they will come in three years, others in five years and others still 10 years or longer. The rapidity of their introduction, say the engineers, will be in direct proportion to the amount and calibre of the effort expended in research and development.

Turbo-jets will do their job at double the speeds of present airlines, but aviation will turn to the ram-jet to surpass the speed of sound.

Speeds twice the speed of sound, some 1,400 miles per hour, have been achieved for short flights by the "flying stovepipe."

Jap Kamikaze "suicide" planes sparked the post-haste development of the ram-jet to power the Navy's "Bumblebee" anti-aircraft weapon that would have been shooting them down if the war had lasted.

The ram-jet idea is not new, although, like other modern jet engines, it is 20th century in its conception. Rene Lorin, a Frenchman, proposed in 1908 the use of the internal combustion engine exhaust for jet propulsion, and in his scheme the engine did not produce power in any other way. Five years later he described a jet engine where the air was compressed solely by the velocity, or ram, effect of the entering air. This is the ram-jet.

The nickname of the ram-jet, "flying stove-pipe," describes what it looks like. It is a cylindrical duct, with a varying diameter. The air enters through a tapered nosepiece and it comes in at a speed above that of sound. The ram-jet is only efficient when it goes through the air at speeds higher than the speed of sound, which is about 700 miles per hour. In the military version of the ram-jet, it is launched and brought up to speed by rockets which soon burn themselves out and give way to the ram-jet itself.

Air entering the tube when the ram-jet is in flight is slowed down to below the speed of sound. The air mixes with the fuel. The very simple device for doing this is at present one of the secrets in the ram-jet, as applied as an anti-aircraft weapon. The diffuser in the air duct stabilizes the flame and the combustion of the gases increases very rapidly through the duct. Just to the rear of the ram-jet the gases attain a speed of up to 2,000 miles per hour.

When supersonic transportation of mail, express and ultimately passengers is contemplated, the ram-jet offers a motor of great promise. The present military development of this device is by commercial and industrial agencies, under sponsorship of the Bureau of Ordnance of the Navy, with the coordination of the Applied Physics Laboratory of the Johns Hopkins University. This development may influence peacetime transportation of the future world.

In the future, liquid fuels that are produced from petroleum will be made to fit the requirements of jet engines. Particular fuel requirements for the turbo-jet engine may even bring kerosene and other distillates heavier than gasoline back into prominence.

During the war some of the jet planes were designed to burn kerosene while other jet devices operated on hundred octane gasoline. Such high octane gasoline was not actually necessary but due to the fact that much of the aviation fuel in the war areas was high octane, it was used to simplify the problem of supply.

If jet planes were used in another war emergency, a fifth of the U. S. petroleum refining capacity would be used for making jet fuels, Robert P. Russell, president of the Standard Oil Development Co., estimated recently. Designing of fuel that can be used in a variety of jet motors is as important as designing jet motors themselves. Military specifications are now being considered that will cause more of the fractions of petroleum to be used in making jet fuel. This may prove to be one of the most important decisions affecting flying power for the future.

1947

EXPLORING THE ATOM *

SIR JAMES JEANS

. . . It was towards the end of the last century that Crookes, Lenard, and above all, Sir J. J. Thomson first began to break up the atom. The structures which had been deemed the unbreakable bricks of the universe for

* From Sir James Jeans: *The Universe Around Us.* Copyright 1929, 1931 and 1944 by The Macmillan Company and used with their permission.

more than 2,000 years, were suddenly shown to be very susceptible to having fragments chipped off. A mile-stone was reached in 1897, when Thomson shewed that these fragments were identical no matter what type of atom they came from; they were of equal weight and they carried equal charges of negative electricity. On account of this last property they were called "electrons." The atom cannot, however, be built up of electrons and nothing else, for as each electron carries a negative charge of electricity, a structure which consisted of nothing but electrons would also carry a negative charge. Two negative charges of electricity repel one another, as also do two positive charges, while two charges, one of positive and one of negative electricity, attract one another. This makes it easy to determine whether any body or structure carries a positive or a negative charge of electricity, or no charge at all. Observation shews that a complete atom carries no charge at all, so that somewhere in the atom there must be a positive charge of electricity, of amount just sufficient to neutralise the combined negative charges of all the electrons.

In 1911 experiments by Sir Ernest Rutherford and others revealed the architecture of the atom, in its main lines at least. As we shall soon see, nature herself provides an endless supply of small particles charged with positive electricity, and moving with very high speeds, in the α-particles shot off from radio-active substances. Rutherford's method was in brief to fire these into atoms and observe the result. And the surprising result he obtained was that the vast majority of these bullets passed straight through the atom as though it simply did not exist. It was like shooting at a ghost.

Yet the atom was not all ghostly. A tiny fraction—perhaps one in 10,000 —of the bullets were deflected from their courses as if they had met something very substantial indeed. A mathematical calculation shewed that these obstacles could only be the missing positive charges of the atoms.

A detailed study of the paths of these projectiles proved that the whole positive charge of an atom must be concentrated in a single very small space, having dimensions of the order of only a millionth of a millionth of an inch. In this way, Rutherford was led to propound the view of atomic structure which is generally associated with his name. He supposed the chemical properties and nature of the atom to reside in a weighty, but excessively minute, central "nucleus" carrying a positive charge of electricity, around which a number of negatively charged electrons described orbits. He had to suppose that the electrons were in motion in the atom, otherwise the attraction of positive for negative electricity would immediately draw them into the central nucleus—just as gravitational attraction would cause the earth to fall into the sun, were it not for the earth's orbital motion. In brief, Rutherford supposed the atom to be constructed like the solar system, the heavy central nucleus playing the part of the sun and the electrons acting the parts of the planets.

The modern theory of wave-mechanics casts doubt on some at least of these concepts—perhaps on all, although this is still in doubt. Thus it may prove necessary to discard many or all of them before long. Yet Rutherford's concepts provide a simple and easily visualised picture of the atom, whereas the theory of wave-mechanics has not yet been able to provide a picture at all. For this reason we shall continue to describe the atom in terms of Rutherford's picture.

According to this picture, the electrons are supposed to move round the nucleus with just the speeds necessary to save them from being drawn into it, and these speeds prove to be terrific, the average electron revolving around its nucleus several thousand million million times every second, with a speed of hundreds of miles a second. Thus the smallness of their orbits does not prevent the electrons moving with higher orbital speeds than the planets, or even the stars themselves.

By clearing a space around the central nucleus, and so preventing other atoms from coming too near to it, these electronic orbits give size to the atom. The volume of space kept clear by the electrons is enormously greater than the total volume of the electrons; roughly, the ratio of volumes is that of the battlefield to the bullets. The atom has about 100,000 times the diameter, and so about a thousand million million times the volume, of a single electron. The nucleus, although it generally weighs 3,000 or 4,000 times as much as all the electrons in the atom together, is at most comparable in size with, and may be even smaller than, a single electron.

We know the extreme emptiness of astronomical space. Choose a point in space at random, and the odds against its being occupied by a star are enormous. Even the solar system consists overwhelmingly of empty space; choose a spot inside the solar system at random, and there are still immense odds against its being occupied by a planet or even by a comet, meteorite or smaller body. And now we see that this emptiness extends also to the space of physics. Even inside the atom we choose a point at random, and the odds against there being anything there are immense; they are of the order of at least millions of millions to one. Six specks of dust inside Waterloo Station represent—or rather over-represent—the extent to which space is crowded with stars. In the same way a few wasps—six for the atom of carbon—flying around in Waterloo Station will represent the extent to which the atom is crowded with electrons—all the rest is emptiness. As we pass the whole structure of the universe under review, from the giant nebulae and the vast interstellar and internebular spaces down to the tiny structure of the atom, little but vacant space passes before our mental gaze. We live in a gossamer universe; pattern, plan and design are there in abundance, but solid substance is rare.

Atomic Numbers. The number of electrons which fly round in orbits in an atom is called the "atomic number" of the atom. Atoms of all atomic numbers from 1 to 92 have been found, except for two missing numbers

85 and 87. As already mentioned, it is highly probable that these also exist, and that there are 92 "elements" whose atomic numbers occupy the whole range of atomic numbers from 1 to 92 continuously.

The atom of atomic number unity is of course the simplest of all. It is the hydrogen atom, in which a solitary electron revolves around a nucleus whose charge of positive electricity is exactly equal in amount, although opposite in sign, to the charge on the negative electron.

Next comes the helium atom of atomic number 2, in which two electrons revolve about a nucleus which has four times the weight of the hydrogen nucleus although carrying only twice its electric charge. After this comes the lithium atom of atomic number 3, in which three electrons revolve around a nucleus having six times the weight of the hydrogen atom and three times its charge. And so it goes on, until we reach uranium, the heaviest of all atoms known on earth, which has 92 electrons describing orbits about a nucleus of 238 times the weight of the hydrogen nucleus.

RADIO-ACTIVITY

While physical science was still engaged in breaking up the atom into its component factors, it made the further discovery that the nuclei themselves were neither permanent nor indestructible. In 1896 Becquerel had found that various substances containing uranium possessed the remarkable property, as it then appeared, of spontaneously affecting photographic plates in their vicinity. This observation led to the discovery of a new property of matter, namely radio-activity. All the results obtained from the study of radio-activity in the few following years were co-ordinated in the hypothesis of "spontaneous disintegration" which Rutherford and Soddy advanced in 1903. According to this hypothesis in its present form, radio-activity indicates a spontaneous break-up of the nuclei of the atoms of radio-active substances. These atoms are so far from being permanent and indestructible that their very nuclei crumble away with the mere lapse of time, so that what was once the nucleus of a uranium atom is transformed, after sufficient time, into the nucleus of a lead atom.

The process of transformation is not instantaneous; it proceeds gradually and by distinct stages. During its progress, three types of product are emitted, which are designated α-rays, β-rays, and γ-rays.

These were originally described indiscriminately as rays because all three were found to have the power of penetrating through a certain thickness of air, metal, or other substance. It was not until later that their true nature was discovered. It is well known that magnetic forces, such as, for instance, occur in the space between the poles of a magnet, cause a moving particle charged with electricity to deviate from a straight course; the particle deviates in one direction or the other according as it is charged with positive or negative electricity. On passing the various rays emitted by radio-active substances through the space between the poles of a powerful magnet, the α-rays were found to consist of particles charged with positive electricity, and the β-rays to consist of particles charged with negative electricity. But the most powerful magnetic forces which could be employed failed to cause the slightest deviation in the paths of the γ-rays, from which it was concluded that either the γ-rays were not material particles at all, or that, if they were, they carried no electric charges. The former of these alternatives was subsequently proved to be the true one.

α-Particles. The positively charged particles which constitute α-rays are generally described as α-particles. In 1909 Rutherford and Royds allowed α-particles to penetrate through a thin glass wall of less than a hundredth of a millimetre in thickness into a chamber from which they could not escape—a sort of mouse-trap for α-particles. After the process had continued for a long time, the final result was not an accumulation of α-particles but an accumulation of the gas helium, the next simplest gas after hydrogen. In this way it was established that the positively charged α-particles are simply nuclei of helium atoms; the α-particles, being positively charged, had attracted negatively charged electrons to themselves out of the walls of the chamber and the result was a collection of complete helium atoms.

The α-particles move with enormous speeds, which depend upon the nature of the radio-active substance from which they have been shot out. The fastest particles of all move with a speed of 12,800 miles a second; even the slowest have a speed of 8,800 miles a second, which is about 30,000 times the ordinary molecular velocity in air. Particles moving with such speeds as these knock all ordinary molecules out of their way; this explains the great penetrating power of the α-rays.

β-Particles. By examining the extent to which their motion was influenced by magnetic forces, the β-rays were found to consist of negatively charged electrons, exactly similar to those which surround the nucleus in all atoms. As an α-particle carries a positive charge equal in amount to that of two electrons, an atom which has ejected an α-particle is left with a deficiency of positive charge, or what comes to the same thing, with a negative charge, equal to that of two electrons. Consequently it is natural, and indeed almost inevitable, that the ejections of α-particles should alternate with an ejection of negatively charged electrons, in the proportion of one α-particle to two electrons, so that the balance of positive and negative electricity in the atom may be maintained. The β-particles move with even greater speeds than the α-particles, many approaching to within a few per cent. of the velocity of light (186,000 miles a second). . . .

γ-Rays. As has already been mentioned, the γ-rays are not material particles at all; they prove to be merely radiation of a very special kind.

Thus the break-up of a radio-active atom may be compared to the discharge of a gun; the α-particle is the shot fired, the β-particles are the smoke, and the γ-rays are the flash. The atom of lead which finally remains is the unloaded gun, and the original radio-active atom, of uranium or what not, was the loaded gun. And the special peculiarity of radio-active guns is that they go off spontaneously and of their own accord. All attempts to pull the trigger have so far failed, or at least have led to inconclusive results; we can only wait, and the gun will be found to fire itself in time. . . .

In 1920, Rutherford, using radio-active atoms as guns, fired α-particles at light atoms and found that direct hits broke up their nuclei. There is, however, found to be a significant difference between the spontaneous disintegration of the heavy radio-active atoms and the artificial disintegration of the light atoms; in the former case, apart from the ever-present β-rays and γ-rays, only α-particles are ejected, while in the latter case α-particles were not ejected at all, but particles of only about a quarter their weight, which proved to be identical with the nuclei of hydrogen atoms. . . .

Isotopes. Two atoms have the same chemical properties if the charges of positive electricity carried by their nuclei are the same. The amount of this charge fixes the number of electrons which can revolve around the nucleus, this number being of course exactly that needed to neutralise the electric field of the nucleus, and this in turn fixes the atomic number of the element. And it has for long been known that the weights of all atoms are, to a very close approximation, multiples of a single definite weight. This unit weight is approximately equal to the weight of the hydrogen atom, but is more nearly equal to a sixteenth of the weight of the oxygen atom. The weight of any type of atom, measured in terms of this unit, is called the "atomic weight" of the atom.

It used to be thought that a mass of any single chemical element, such as mercury or xenon, consisted of entirely similar atoms, every one of which had not only the same atomic number but also the same atomic weight. But Dr. Aston has shewn very convincingly that atoms of the same chemical element, say neon or chlorine, may have nuclei of a great many different weights. The various forms which the atoms of the same chemical element can assume are known as isotopes being of course distinguished by their different weights.

These weights are much nearer to whole numbers than were the old "atomic" weights of the chemists. For instance the atomic weight of chlorine used to be given as 35.5, and this was taken to mean that chlorine consisted of a mixture of atoms each 35.5 times as massive as the hydrogen atom. Aston finds that chlorine consists of a mixture of atoms of atomic weights 35 and 37 (or more accurately 34.983 and 36.980), the former being approximately three times as plentiful as the latter. In the same way a mass of mercury, of which the mean atomic weight is about 200.6, is found to be a mixture of seven kinds of atoms of atomic weights 196, 198, 199, 200, 201, 202, 204. Tin is a mixture of no fewer than eleven isotopes—112, 114, 115, 116, 117, 118, 119, 120, 121, 122, 124.

Protons and Electrons. When the presence of isotopes is taken into account, the atomic weights of all atoms prove to be far nearer to integral numbers than had originally been thought. This, in conjunction with Rutherford's artificial disintegration of atomic nuclei, led to the general acceptance of the hypothesis that the whole universe is built up of only two kinds of ultimate bricks, namely, electrons and protons. Each proton carries a positive charge of electricity exactly equal in amount to the negative charge carried by an electron, but has about 1847 times the weight of the electron. Protons are supposed to be identical with the nucleus of the hydrogen atom, all other nuclei being composite structures in which both protons and electrons are closely packed together. For instance, the nucleus of the helium atom, the α-particle, consists of four protons and two electrons, these giving it approximately four times the weight of the hydrogen atom, and a resultant charge equal to twice that of the nucleus of the hydrogen atom.

Neutrons. Until quite recently this hypothesis was believed to give a satisfactory and complete account of the structure of matter. Then in 1931 two German physicists, Bothe and Becker, bombarding the light elements beryllium and boron with the very rapid α-particles emitted by polonium, obtained a new and very penetrating radiation which they were at first inclined to interpret as a kind of γ-radiation. Subsequently Dr. Chadwick of Cambridge shewed that it possessed properties which were inconstant with this interpretation and made it clear that the radiation consists of material objects of a type hitherto unknown to science. To the greatest accuracy of which the experiments permit these objects are found to have the same mass as the hydrogen atom, while their very high penetrating power shews that if they have any electric charge at all, it can only be a minute fraction at most of the charge of the electron.

Thus it seems likely that the radiation consists of *uncharged particles* of the same mass as the proton—something quite new in a world which until recently was believed to consist entirely of charged particles. Chadwick describes these new particles as "neutrons." Whether they are themselves fundamental constituents of matter or not remains to be seen. Chadwick has suggested that they may be composite structures, each consisting of a proton and electron in such close combination that they penetrate matter almost as freely as though they had no size at all. On the other hand Heisenberg has considered the possibility that the neutron may be fundamental, the nucleus of an atom being built up solely of positively charged protons and uncharged neutrons, while the negative electrons are confined to the regions outside the nucleus. On this view there are just as many protons in the nucleus as there are electrons outside the nucleus, the number of each being the atomic number of the element, while the excess of mass needed to make up the atomic weight is provided by the inclusion of the requisite number of neutrons in the nucleus. Isotopes of the same element differ of course merely in having different numbers of neutrons in their nuclei.

Rutherford and other physicists have considered the further possibility that other kinds of neutrons, with double the mass of the hydrogen atom, may also occur in atomic nuclei, a hypothesis for which there seems to be considerable observational support.

Positive Electrons. Even more revolutionary discoveries were to come. A few years ago it seemed a piece of extraordinary good luck that in the α-particles nature herself had provided projectiles of sufficient shattering power to smash up the nucleus of the atom and disclose its secrets to the observation of the physicist. More recently nature has been found to provide yet more shattering projectiles in the cosmic radiation which continually bombards the surface of the earth—probably from outer space. This radiation has such a devastating effect on the atomic nuclei that it is difficult to make much of the resulting collection of fragments. It is, however, always possible to examine any *débris*, no matter how involved, by noticing how the constituent particles move when acted on by magnetic forces.

In 1932 C. D. Anderson made observations which suggested that this *débris* contained, among other ingredients, particles having the same positive charge as the proton, but a mass only comparable with, and possibly equal to, that of the electron. The existence of such particles has been confirmed by Blackett and Occhialini at Cambridge. The new particles may well be described as positively charged electrons, and so have been named "positrons."

As these new particles are believed to emerge from atomic nuclei, it would seem plausible to suppose that they must be normal constituents of the nuclei. Yet the recent discovery of the neutron suggests other possibilities.

We have already mentioned the hypothesis, advocated by Heisenberg and others, that the nucleus consists solely of neutrons and protons. Anderson has suggested that the proton may not be a fundamental unit in the structure of matter, but may consist of a positron and a neutron in combination. Every nucleus would then contain only neutrons and positrons, and the positrons could be driven out by bombardment in the ordinary way.

The objection to this view is that the *débris* of the nuclei shattered by cosmic radiation is found to contain electrons as well as positrons, the electrons emerging, so far as can be seen, from the same atomic nuclei as the positrons. This has led Blackett and Occhialini to propound the alternative hypothesis that the electrons and positrons are born in pairs as the result of the processes of bombardment and disintegration of atomic nuclei. At first this may seem a flagrant violation of all our views as to the permanence of matter, but we shall see shortly that it is entirely in accord with the present trend of physics.

It seems fairly certain that the positron has at most but a temporary existence. For positrons do not appear to be associated with matter under normal conditions, although they ought to abound if they were being continually produced out of nuclei at anything like the rate which the observations of Blackett and Occhialini seem to indicate. They might of course rapidly disappear from view through entering into combination with negatively charged particles to form some sort of permanent stable structure, but it seems more probable, as Blackett and Occhialini themselves suggest, that they disappear from existence altogether by combining with negative electrons. Just as a pair of electrons—one positively charged and one negatively charged—can be born out of nothing but energy, so they can die in one another's arms and leave nothing but energy behind. We shall discuss the underlying physical mechanism almost immediately.

Before the existence of the positron had been observed, or even suspected experimentally, Professor Dirac of Cambridge had propounded a mathematical theory which predicted not only the existence of the positron, but also the way in which it ought to behave. Dirac's theory is too abstrusely mathematical to be explained here, but it predicts that a shower of positrons ought gradually to fade away by spontaneous combination with negative electrons, following the same law of decay as radio-active substances. And the average life of a positron is predicted to be one of only a few millionths of a second, which amply explains why the positron can live long enough to be photographed in a condensation chamber, but not long enough to shew its presence elsewhere in the universe.

RADIATION

We have so far discussed only the material constituents of matter: we have pictured the atom as being built up of some or all of the material ingredients which we have described as electrons, protons, neutrons and positrons. Yet this is not the whole story. If it were, every atom would consist of a certain number of protons and neutrons with just sufficient electrons and positrons to make the total electric charge equal to zero. Thus, apart from the insignificant weights of electrons and positrons, the weight of every atom would be an exact multiple of the weight of a hydrogen atom. Experiment shews this not to be the case.

Electromagnetic Energy. To get at the whole truth, we have to recognise that, in addition to containing material electrons and protons, with possible neutrons and positrons, the atom contains yet a further ingredient which we may describe as electromagnetic energy. We may think of this, although with something short of absolute scientific accuracy, as bottled radiation.

If we disturb the surface of a pond with a stick, a series of ripples starts from the stick and travels, in a series of ever-expanding circles, over the surface of the pond. As the water resists the motion of the stick, we have to work to keep the pond in a state of agitation. The energy of this work is transformed, in part at least, into the energy of the ripples. We can see that the ripples carry energy about with them, because they cause a floating cork or a toy boat to rise up against the earth's gravitational pull. Thus the ripples provide a mechanism for distributing over the surface of the pond the energy that we put into the pond through the medium of the moving stick.

Light and all other forms of radiation are analogous to water ripples or waves, in that they distribute energy from a central source. The sun's radiation distributes through space the vast amount of energy which is generated inside the sun. We hardly know whether there is any actual wave motion in light or not, but we know that both light and all other types of radiation are propagated in such a form that they have many of the properties of a succession of waves.

The different colours of light which in combination constitute sunlight can be separated out by passing the light through a prism, thus forming a rainbow or "spectrum" of colours. The separation can also be effected by an alternative instrument, the diffraction grating, which consists merely of a metal mirror with a large number of parallel lines scratched evenly across its surface. The theory of the action of this latter instrument is well understood; it shews that actually the light is separated into waves of different wave-lengths. (The wave-length in a system of ripples is the distance from the crest of one ripple to that of the next, and the term may be applied to all phenomena of an undulatory nature.) This proves that different colours of light are produced by waves of different lengths, and at the same time enables us to measure the lengths of the waves which correspond to the different colours of light.

These prove to be very minute. The reddest light we can see, which is that of longest wave-length, has a wave-length of only $\frac{3}{100,000}$ inch (7.5×10^{-5} cm.); the most violet light we can see has a wave-length only half of this, or 0.000015 inch. Light of all colours travels with the same uniform speed of 186,000 miles, or 3×10^{10} centimetres, a second. The number of waves of red light which pass any fixed point in a second is accordingly no fewer than four hundred million million. This is called the "frequency" of the light. Violet light has the still higher frequency of eight hundred million million; when we see violet light, eight hundred million million waves of light enter our eyes each second.

The spectrum of analysed sunlight appears to the eye to stretch from red light at one end to violet light at the other, but these are not its true limits. When certain chemical salts are placed beyond the violet end of the visible spectrum, they are found to shine vividly, shewing that even out here energy is being transported, although in invisible form. And other methods make it clear that the same is true out beyond the red end of the spectrum. A thermometer, or other heat-measuring instrument, placed here will shew that energy is being received here in the form of heat.

In this way we find that regions of invisible radiation stretch indefinitely from both ends of the visible spectrum. From one end—the red—we can pass continuously to waves of the type used for wireless transmission, which have wave-lengths of the order of hundreds, or even thousands, of yards. From the violet end, we pass through waves of shorter and ever shorter wave-length—all the various forms of ultra-violet radiation. At wave-lengths of from about a hundredth to a thousandth of the wave-length of visible light, we come to the familiar X-rays, which penetrate through inches of our flesh, so that we can photograph the bones inside. Far out even beyond these, we come to the type of radiation which constitutes the γ-rays, its wave-length being of the order of $\frac{1}{10{,}000{,}000{,}000}$ inch, or only about a hundred-thousandth part of the wave-length of visible light. Thus the γ-rays may be regarded as invisible radiation of extremely short wave-length. We shall discuss the exact function they serve later. For the moment let us merely remark that in the first instance they served the extremely useful function of fogging Becquerel's photographic plates, thus leading to the detection of the radio-active property of matter.

It is a commonplace of modern electromagnetic theory that energy of every kind carries weight about with it, weight which is in every sense as real as the weight of a ton of coal. A ray of light causes an impact on any surface on which it falls, just as a jet of water does, or a blast of wind, or the fall of a ton of coal; with a sufficiently strong light one could knock a man down just as surely as with the jet of water from a fire hose. This is not a mere theoretical speculation. The pressure of light on a surface has been both detected and measured by direct experiment. The experiments are extraordinarily difficult because, judged by all ordinary standards, the weight carried by radiation is exceedingly small; all the radiation emitted from a 50 horse-power searchlight working continuously for a century weighs only about a twentieth of an ounce.

It follows that any substance which is emitting radiation must at the same time be losing weight. In particular, the disintegration of any radio-active substance must involve a decrease of weight, since it is accompanied by the emission of radiation in the form of γ-rays. The ultimate fate of an ounce of uranium may be expressed by the equation:

$$1 \text{ ounce uranium} = \begin{cases} 0.8653 \text{ ounce lead,} \\ 0.1345 \quad \text{"} \quad \text{helium,} \\ 0.0002 \quad \text{"} \quad \text{radiation.} \end{cases}$$

The lead and helium together contain just as many electrons and just as many protons as did the original ounce of uranium, but their combined weight is short of the weight of the original uranium by about one part in 4,000. Where 4,000 ounces of matter originally existed, only 3,999 now remain; the missing ounce has gone off in the form of radiation.

This makes it clear that we must not expect the weights of the various atoms to be exact multiples of the weight of the hydrogen atom; any such expectation would ignore the weight of the bottled-up electromagnetic energy which is capable of being set free and going off into space in the form of radiation as the atom changes its make-up. The weight of this energy is relatively small, so that the weights of the atoms must be expected to be approximately, although not exactly, integral multiples of that of the hydrogen atom, and this expectation is confirmed. The exact weight of our atomic building is not simply the total weight of all its bricks; something must be added for the weight of the mortar—the electromagnetic energy—which keeps the bricks bound together.

Thus the normal atom consists of its material constituents—protons, electrons, neutrons and positrons, or some at least of these—and also of energy, which also contributes something to its weight. When the atom re-arranges itself, either spontaneously or under bombardment, protons and electrons, or other fragments of its material structure, may be shot off in the form of α- and β-particles, and energy may also be set free in the form of radiation. This radiation may either take the form of γ-rays, or of other forms of visible and invisible radiation. The final weight of the atom will be obtained by deducting from its original weight not only the weight of all the ejected electrons and protons, but also the weight of all the energy which has been set free as radiation.

QUANTUM THEORY

The series of concepts which we now approach are difficult to grasp and still more difficult to explain, largely, no doubt, because our minds receive no assistance from our everyday experience of nature. It becomes necessary to speak mainly in terms of analogies, parables and models which can make no claim to represent ultimate reality; indeed, it is rash to hazard a guess even as to the direction in which ultimate reality lies.

The laws of electricity which were in vogue up to about the end of the nineteenth century—the famous laws of Maxwell and Faraday—required that the energy of an atom should continually decrease, through the atom scattering energy abroad in the form of radiation, and so having less and less left for itself. These same laws predicted that all energy set free in space should rapidly transform itself into radiation of almost infinitesimal wave-length. Yet these things simply did not happen, making it obvious that the then prevailing electrodynamical laws had to be given up.

Cavity-Radiation. A crucial case of failure was provided by what is known as "cavity-radiation." A body with a cavity in its interior is heated up to incandescence; no notice is taken of the light and heat emitted by its outer surface, but the light imprisoned in the internal cavity is let out through a small window and analysed into its constituent colours by a spectroscope or diffraction grating. This is the radiation that is known as "cavity-radiation." It represents the most complete form of radiation possible, radiation from which no colour is missing, and in which every colour figures at its full strength. No known substance ever emits quite such complete radiation from its surface, although many approximate to doing so. We speak of such bodies as "full radiators."

The nineteenth-century laws of electromagnetism predicted that the whole of the radiation emitted by a full radiator or from a cavity ought to be found at or beyond the extreme violet end of the spectrum, independently of the precise temperature to which the body had been heated. In actual fact the radiation is usually found piled up at exactly the opposite end of the spectrum, and in no case does it ever conform to the predictions of the nineteenth-century laws, or even begin to think of doing so.

In the year 1900 Professor Planck of Berlin discovered experimentally the law by which cavity-radiation is distributed among the different colours of the spectrum. He further shewed how his newly discovered law could be deducted theoretically from a system of electromagnetic laws which differed very sensationally from those then in vogue.

Planck imagined all kinds of radiation to be emitted by systems of vibrators which emitted light when excited, much as tuning forks emit sound when they are struck. The old electrodynamical laws predicted that each vibration should gradually come to rest and then stop, as the vibrations of a tuning fork do, until the vibrator was in some way excited again. Rejecting all this, Planck supposed that a vibrator could change its energy by sudden jerks, and in no other way; it might have one, two, three, four or any other integral number of units of energy, but no intermediate fractional numbers, so that gradual changes of energy were rendered impossible. The vibrator, so to speak, kept no small change, and could only pay out its energy a shilling at a time until it had none left. Not only so, but it refused to receive small change, although it was prepared to accept complete shillings. This concept, sensational, revolutionary and even ridiculous, as many thought it at the time, was found to lead exactly to the distribution of colours actually observed in cavity-radiation.

In 1917 Einstein put the concept into the more precise form which now prevails. According to a theory previously advanced by Professor Niels Bohr of Copenhagen, an atomic or molecular structure does not change its configuration, or dissipate away its energy, by gradual stages; on the contrary, the changes are so abrupt that it is almost permissible to regard them as a series of sudden jumps or jerks. Bohr supposed that an atomic structure has a number of possible states or configurations which are entirely distinct and detached one from another, just as a weight placed on a staircase has only a possible number of positions; it may be 3 stairs up, or 4 or 5, but cannot be 3¼ or 3¾ stairs up. The change from one position to another is generally effected through the medium of radiation. The system can be pushed upstairs by absorbing energy from radiation which falls on it, or may move downstairs to a state of lower energy and emit energy in the form of radiation in so doing. Only radiation of a certain definite colour, and so of a certain precise wave-length, is of any account for effecting a particular change of state. The problem of shifting an atomic system is like that of extracting a box of matches from a penny-in-the-slot machine; it can only be done by a special implement, to wit a penny, which must be of precisely the right size and weight—a coin which is either too small *or too large*, too light *or too heavy*, is doomed to fail. If we pour radiation of the wrong wave length on to an atom, we may reproduce the comedy of the millionaire whose total wealth will not procure him a box of matches because he has not a loose penny, or we may reproduce the tragedy of the child who cannot obtain a slab of chocolate because its hoarded wealth consists of farthings and half-pence, but we shall not disturb the atom. When mixed radiation is poured on to a collection of atoms, these absorb the radiation of just those wave-lengths which are needed to change their internal states, and none other; radiation of all other wave-lengths passes by unaffected.

This selective action of the atom on radiation is put in evidence in a variety of ways; it is perhaps most simply shewn in the spectra of the sun and stars. Dark lines similar to those which Fraunhofer observed in the solar spectrum are observed in the spectra of practically all stars and we can now understand why this must be. Light of every possible wave-length streams out from the hot interior of a star, and bombards the atoms which form its atmosphere. Each atom drinks up that radiation which is of precisely the right wave-length for it, but has no interaction of any kind with the rest, so that the radiation which is finally emitted from the star is deficient in just the particular wave-lengths which suit the atoms. Thus the star shews an *absorption spectrum* of fine lines. The positions of these lines in the spectrum shew what types of radiation the stellar atoms have swallowed, and so enable us to identify the atoms from our laboratory knowledge of the tastes of different kinds of atoms for radiation. But what ultimately decides which types of radiation an atom will swallow, and which it will reject?

It had been part of Planck's theory that radiation of each wave-length has associated with it a certain amount of energy, called the "quantum," which depends on the wave-length and on nothing else. The quantum is supposed to be proportional to the "frequency," or number of vibrations of the radiation per second, and so is *inversely* proportional to the wave-length of the radiation—the shorter the wave-length, the greater the energy of the quantum, and conversely. Red light has feeble quanta, violet light has energetic quanta, and so on.

Einstein now supposed that radiation of a given type could effect an atomic or molecular change, only if the energy needed for the change is precisely equal to that of a single quantum of the radiation. This is commonly known as Einstein's law; it determines the precise type of radiation needed to work any atomic or molecular penny-in-the-slot mechanism.

We notice that work which demands one powerful quantum cannot be performed by two, or indeed by any number whatever, of feeble quanta. A small amount of violet (high-frequency) light can accomplish what no amount of red (low-frequency) light can effect.

The law prohibits the killing of two birds with one stone, as well as the killing of one bird with two stones; the whole quantum is used up in effecting the change, so that no energy from this particular quantum is left over to contribute to any further change. This aspect of the matter is illustrated by Einstein's photochemical law: "in any chemical reaction which is produced by the incidence of light, the number of molecules which are affected is equal to the number of quanta of light which are absorbed." Those who manage penny-in-the-slot machines are familiar with a similar law: "the number of articles sold is exactly equal to the number of coins in the machine."

If we think of energy in terms of its capacity for doing damage, we see that radiation of short wave-length can work more destruction in atomic structures than radiation of long wave-length—a circumstance with which every photographer is painfully familiar; we can admit as much red light as we please without any damage being done, but even the tiniest gleam of violet light spoils our plates. Radiation of sufficiently short wave-length may not only rearrange molecules or atoms; it may break up any atom on which it happens to fall, by shooting out one of its electrons, giving rise to what is known as photoelectric action. Again there is a definite limit of frequency, such that light whose frequency is below this limit does not produce any effect at all, no matter how intense it may be; whereas as soon as we pass to frequencies above this limit, light of even the feeblest intensity starts photoelectric action at once. Again the absorption of one quantum breaks up only one atom, and further ejects only one electron from the atom. If the radiation has a frequency above this limit, so that its quantum has more energy than the minimum necessary to remove a single electron from the atom, the whole quantum is still absorbed, the excess energy now being used in endowing the ejected electron with motion.

Electron Orbits. These concepts are based upon Bohr's supposition that only a limited number of orbits are open to the electrons in an atom, all others being prohibited for reasons which Bohr's theory did not fully explain, and that an electron is free to move from one permitted orbit to another under the stimulus of radiation. Bohr himself investigated the way in which the various permitted orbits are arranged. Modern investigations indicate the need for a good deal of revision of his simple concepts, but we shall discuss these in some detail, partly because Bohr's picture of the atom still provides the best working mechanical model we have, and partly because an understanding of his simple theory is absolutely essential to the understanding of the far more intricate theories which are beginning to replace it.

The hydrogen atom, as we have already seen, consists of a single proton as central nucleus, with a single electron revolving around it. The nucleus, with about 1,847 times the weight of the electron, stands practically at rest unagitated by the motion of the latter, just as the sun remains practically undisturbed by the motion of the earth round it. The nucleus and electron carry charges of positive and negative electricity, and therefore attract one another; this is why the electron describes an orbit instead of flying off in a straight line, again like the earth and sun. Furthermore, the attraction between electric charges of opposite sign, positive and negative, follows, as it happens, precisely the same law as gravitation, the attraction falling off as the inverse square of the distance between the two charges. Thus the nucleus-electron system is similar in all respects to a sun-planet system, and the orbits which an electron can describe around a central nucleus are precisely identical with those which a planet can describe about a central sun; they consist of a system of ellipses each having the nucleus in one focus.

Yet the general concepts of quantum-dynamics prohibit the electron from moving in all these orbits indiscriminately. Bohr's original theory supposed that the electron in the hydrogen atom could move only in certain circular orbits whose diameters were proportional to the squares of the natural numbers, and so to 1, 4, 9, 16, 25, . . . Bohr subsequently modified this very simple hypothesis, and the theory of wave-mechanics has recently modified it much further.

Yet it still remains true that the hydrogen atom has always very approximately the same energy as it would have if the electron were describing one or another of these simple orbits of Bohr. Thus, when its energy changes, it changes as though the electron jumped over from one to another of these orbits. For this reason it is easy to calculate what changes of energy a hydrogen atom can experience—they are precisely those which correspond to the passage from one Bohr orbit to another. For example, the two orbits of smallest diameters in the hydrogen atom differ in energy by 16×10^{-12} erg. If we pour radiation of the appropriate wave-length on to an atom in which the electron is describing the smallest orbit of all, it crosses over to the next orbit, absorbing 16×10^{-12} erg of energy in the process, and so becoming temporarily a reservoir of energy holding 16×10^{-12} erg. If the atom is in any way disturbed from outside, it may of course discharge the energy at any time, or it may absorb still more energy and so increase its store.

If we know all the orbits which are possible for an atom of any type, it is easy to calculate the changes of energy involved in the various transitions between them. As each transition absorbs or releases exactly one quantum of energy, we can immediately deduce the frequencies of the light emitted or absorbed in these transitions. In brief, given the arrangement of atomic orbits, we can calculate the spectrum of the atom. In practice the problem of course takes the converse form: given the spectrum, to find the structure of the atom which emits it. Bohr's model of the hydrogen atom is a good model at least to this extent—that the spectrum it would emit reproduces the hydrogen spectrum almost exactly. Yet the agreement is not quite perfect, and for this reason it is now generally accepted that Bohr's scheme of orbits is inadequate to account for actual spectra. We continue to discuss Bohr's scheme, not because the atom is actually built that way, but because it provides a working model which is good enough for our present purpose.

An essential, although at first sight somewhat unexpected, feature of the whole theory is that even if the hydrogen atom charged with its 16×10^{-12} erg of energy is left entirely undisturbed, the electron must after a certain time, lapse back spontaneously to its original smaller orbit, ejecting its 16×10^{-12} erg of energy in the form of radiation in so doing. Einstein shewed that, if this were not so, then Planck's well-established "cavity-radiation" law could not be true. Thus, a collection of hydrogen atoms in which the electrons describe orbits larger than the smallest possible orbit is similar to a collection of uranium or other radio-active atoms, in that the atoms spontaneously fall back to their states of lower energy as the result merely of the passage of time.

The electron orbits in more complicated atoms have much the same general arrangement as in the hydrogen atom, but are different in size. In the hydrogen atom the electron normally falls, after sufficient time, to the orbit of lowest energy and stays there. It might be thought by analogy that in more complicated atoms in which several electrons are describing orbits, all the electrons would in time fall into the orbit of lowest energy and stay there. Such does not prove to be the case. There is never room for more than one electron in the same orbit. This is a special aspect of a general principle which appears to dominate the whole of physics. It has a name—"the exclusion-principle"—but this is about all as yet; we have hardly begun to understand it. In another of its special aspects it becomes identical with the old familiar cornerstone of science which asserts that two different pieces of matter cannot occupy the same space at the same time. Without understanding the underlying principle, we can accept the fact that two electrons not only cannot occupy the same space, but cannot even occupy the same orbit. It is as though in some way the electron spread itself out so as to occupy the whole of its orbit, thus leaving room for no other. No doubt this must not be accepted as a literal picture of things, and yet the modern theory of wave-mechanics suggests that in some sense (which we cannot yet specify with much precision) the orbits of lowest energy in the hydrogen atom are possible orbits just because the electron can completely fill them, and that adjacent orbits are impossible because the electron would fill them ¾ or 1½ times over, and similarly for more complicated atoms. In this connection it is perhaps significant that no single known phenomenon of physics makes it possible to say that at a given instant an electron is at such or such a point in an orbit of lowest energy; such a statement appears to be quite meaningless and the condition of an atom is apparently specified with all possible precision by saying that at a given instant an electron is in such an orbit, as it would be, for instance, if the electron had spread itself out into a ring. We cannot say the same of other orbits. As we pass to orbits of higher energy, and so of greater diameter, the indeterminateness gradually assumes a different form, and finally becomes of but little importance. Whatever form the electron may assume while it is describing a little orbit near the nucleus, by the time it is describing a very big orbit far out it has become a plain material particle charged with electricity.

Thus, whatever the reason may be, electrons which are describing orbits in the same atom must all be in different orbits. The electrons in their orbits are like men on a ladder; just as no two men can stand on the same rung, so no two electrons can ever follow one another round in the same orbit. The neon atom, for instance, with 10 electrons is in its normal state of lowest energy when its 10 electrons each occupy one of the 10 orbits whose energy is lowest. For reasons which the quantum theory has at last succeeded in elucidating, there are, in every atom, two orbits in which the energy is equal and lower than in any other orbit. After this come eight orbits of equal but substantially higher energy, then 18 orbits of equal but still higher energy, and so on. As the electrons in each of these various groups of orbits all have equal energy, they are commonly spoken of, in a graphic but misleading phraseology, as rings of electrons. They are designated the *K*-ring, the *L*-ring, the *M*-ring and so on. The *K*-ring, which is nearest to the nucleus, has room for two electrons only. Any further electrons are pushed out into the *L*-ring, which has room for eight electrons, all describing orbits which are different but of equal energy. If still more electrons remain to be accommodated, they must go into the *M*-ring and so on.

In its normal state, the hydrogen atom has one electron in its *K*-ring, while the helium has two, the *L*, *M*, and higher rings being unoccupied. The atom of next higher complexity, the lithium atom, has three electrons, and as only two can be accommodated in its *K*-ring, one has to wander round in the outer spaces of the *L*-ring. In beryllium with four electrons, two are driven out into the *L*-ring. And so it goes on, until we reach neon with 10 electrons, by which time the *L*-ring as well as the inner *K*-ring is full up. In the next atom, sodium, one of the 11 electrons is driven out into the still more remote *M*-ring, and so on. Provided the electrons are not being excited by radiation or other stimulus, each atom sinks in time to a state in which its electrons are occupying its orbits of lowest energy, one in each.

So far as our experience goes, an atom, as soon as it reaches this state, becomes a true perpetual motion machine, the electrons continuing to move in their orbits (at any rate on Bohr's theory) without any of the energy of their motion being dissipated away, either in the form of radiation or otherwise. It seems astonishing and quite incomprehensible that an atom in such a state should not be able to yield up its energy still further, but, so far as our experience goes, it cannot. And this property, little though we understand it, is, in the last resort, responsible for keeping the universe in being. If no restriction of this kind intervened, the whole material energy of the universe would disappear in the form of radiation in a few thousand-millionth parts of a second. If the normal hydrogen atom were capable of emitting radiation in the way demanded by the nineteenth-century laws of physics, it would, as a direct consequence of this emission of radiation, begin to shrink at the rate of over a metre a second, the electron continually falling to orbits of lower and lower energy. After about a thousand-millionth part of a second the nucleus and the electron would run into one another, and the whole atom would probably disappear in a flash of radiation. By prohibiting any emission of radiation except by complete quanta, and by prohibiting any emission at all when there are no quanta available for dissipation, the quantum theory succeeds in keeping the universe in existence as a going concern.

It is difficult to form even the remotest conception of the realities underlying all these phenomena. The recent branch of physics known as "wave mechanics" is at present groping after an understanding, but so far progress has been in the direction of co-ordinating observed phenomena rather than in getting down to realities. Indeed, it may be doubted whether we shall ever properly understand the realities ultimately involved; they may well be so fundamental as to be beyond the grasp of the human mind.

It is just for this reason that modern theoretical physics is so difficult to explain, and so difficult to understand. It is easy to explain the motion of the earth round the sun in the solar system. We see the sun in the sky; we feel the earth under our feet, and the concept of motion is familiar to us from everyday experience. How different when we try to explain the analogous motion of the electron round the proton in the hydrogen atom! Neither you nor I have any direct experience of either electrons or protons, and no one has so far any inkling of what they are really like. So we agree to make a sort of model in which the electron and proton are represented by the simplest things known to us, tiny hard spheres. The model works well for a time and then suddenly breaks in our hands. In the new light of the wave mechanics, the hard sphere is seen to be hopelessly inadequate to represent the electron. A hard sphere has always a definite position in space; the electron apparently has not. A hard sphere takes up a very definite amount of room, an electron—well, it is probably as meaningless to discuss how much room an electron takes up as it is to discuss how much room a fear, an anxiety or an uncertainty takes up, but if we are pressed to say how much room an electron takes up, perhaps the best answer is that it takes up the whole of space. A hard sphere moves from one point to the next; our model electron, jumping from orbit to orbit in Bohr's model hydrogen atom, certainly does not behave like any hard sphere of our waking experience, and the real electron—if there is any such thing as a real electron—probably even less. Yet as our minds have so far failed to conceive any better picture of the atom than this very imperfect model, we can only proceed by describing phenomena in terms of it.

1941

>>>>‹‹‹

THE DISCOVERY OF RADIUM *

MARIE SKLODOWSKA CURIE

I could tell you many things about radium and radioactivity and it would take a long time. But as we cannot do that, I shall give you only a short account of my early work about radium. Radium is no more a baby; it is more than twenty years old, but the conditions of the discovery were somewhat peculiar, and so it is always of interest to remember them and to explain them.

We must go back to the year 1897. Professor Curie and I worked at that time in the laboratory of the School of Physics and Chemistry where Professor Curie held his lectures. I was engaged in some work on uranium rays which had been discovered two years before by Professor Becquerel. I shall tell you how these uranium rays may be detected. If you take a photographic plate and wrap it in black paper and then on this plate, protected from ordinary light, put some uranium salt and leave it a day, and the next day the plate is developed, you notice on the plate a black spot at the place where the uranium salt was. This spot has been made by special rays which are given out by the uranium and are able to make

* Ellen S. Richards Monograph No. 2, Bureau of Publications of Vassar College, reprinted by permission from the publishers.

an impression on the plate in the same way as ordinary light. You can also test those rays in another way, by placing them on an electroscope. You know what an electroscope is. If you charge it, you can keep it charged several hours and more, unless uranium salts are placed near to it. But if this is the case the electroscope loses its charge and the gold or aluminum leaf falls gradually in a progressive way. The speed with which the leaf moves may be used as a measure of the intensity of the rays; the greater the speed, the greater the intensity.

I spent some time in studying the way of making good measurements of the uranium rays, and then I wanted to know if there were other elements, giving out rays of the same kind. So I took up a work about all known elements and their compounds and found that uranium compounds are active and also all thorium compounds, but other elements were not found active, nor were their compounds. As for the uranium and thorium compounds, I found that they were active in proportion to their uranium or thorium content. The more uranium or thorium, the greater the activity, the activity being an atomic property of the elements, uranium and thorium.

Then I took up measurements of minerals and I found that several of those which contain uranium or thorium or both were active. But then the activity was not what I could expect; it was greater than for uranium or thorium compounds, like the oxides which are almost entirely composed of these elements. Then I thought that there should be in the minerals some unknown element having a much greater radioactivity than uranium or thorium. And I wanted to find and to separate that element, and I settled to that work with Professor Curie. We thought it would be done in several weeks or months, but it was not so. It took many years of hard work to finish that task. There was not *one* new element; there were several of them. But the most important is radium, which could be separated in a pure state.

All the tests for the separation were done by the method of electrical measurements with some kind of electroscope. We just had to make chemical separations and to examine all products obtained, with respect to their activity. The product which retained the radioactivity was considered as that one which had kept the new element; and, as the radioactivity was more strong in some products, we knew that we had succeeded in concentrating the new element. The radioactivity was used in the same way as a spectroscopical test.

The difficulty was that there is not much radium in a mineral; this we did not know at the beginning. But we now know that there is not even one part of radium in a million parts of good ore. And, too, to get a small quantity of pure radium salt, one is obliged to work up a huge quantity of ore. And that was very hard in a laboratory.

We had not even a good laboratory at that time. We worked in a hangar where there were no improvements, no good chemical arrangements. We had no help, no money. And because of that, the work could not go on as it would have done under better conditions. I did myself the numerous crystallizations which were wanted to get the radium salt separated from the barium salt, with which it is obtained, out of the ore. And in 1902 I finally succeeded in getting pure radium chloride and determining the atomic weight of the new element, radium, which is 226, while that of barium is only 137.

Later I could also separate the metal radium, but that was a very difficult work; and, as it is not necessary for the use of radium to have it in this state, it is not generally prepared that way.

Now, the special interest of radium is in the intensity of its rays, which is several million times greater than the uranium rays. And the effects of the rays make the radium so important. If we take a practical point of view, then the most important property of the rays is the production of physiological effects on the cells of the human organism. These effects may be used for the cure of several diseases. Good results have been obtained in many cases. What is considered particularly important is the treatment of cancer. The medical utilization of radium makes it necessary to get that element in sufficient quantities. And so a factory of radium was started, to begin with, in France, and later in America, where a big quantity of ore named carnotite is available. America does produce many grams of radium every year but the price is still very high because the quantity of radium contained in the ore is so small. The radium is more than a hundred thousand times dearer than gold.

But we must not forget that when radium was discovered no one knew that it would prove useful in hospitals. The work was one of pure science. And this is a proof that scientific work must not be considered from the point of view of the direct usefulness of it. It must be done for itself, for the beauty of science, and then there is always the chance that a scientific discovery may become, like the radium, a benefit for humanity.

But science is not rich; it does not dispose of important means; it does not generally meet recognition before the material usefulness of it has been proved. The factories produce many grams of radium every year, but the laboratories have very small quantities. It is the same for my laboratory, and I am very grateful to the American women who wish me to have more of radium, and give me the opportunity of doing more work with it.

The scientific history of radium is beautiful. The properties of the rays have been studied very closely. We know that particles are expelled from radium with a very great velocity, near to that of light. We know that the atoms of radium are destroyed by expulsion of these particles, some of which are atoms of helium. And in that way it has been proved that the radioactive elements are constantly disintegrating, and that they produce, at the end, ordinary elements, principally helium and lead. That is, as you see, a theory of transformation of atoms, which are not stable, as was believed before, but may undergo spontaneous changes.

Radium is not alone in having these properties. Many having other radioelements are known already: the polonium, the mesothorium, the radiothorium, the actinium. We know also radioactive gases, named emanations. There is a great variety of substances and effects in radioactivity. There is always a vast field left to experimentation and I hope that we may have some beautiful progress in the following years. It is my earnest desire that some of you should carry on this scientific work, and keep for your ambition the determination to make a permanent contribution to science.

1922

\>\>\>\<\<\<

ATOMIC ENERGY FOR MILITARY PURPOSES *

HENRY D. SMYTH

[*FROM CHAPTER I. INTRODUCTION*]

THE CONSERVATION OF MASS AND OF ENERGY

There are two principles that have been cornerstones of the structure of modern science. The first—that matter can be neither created nor destroyed but only altered in form—was enunciated in the eighteenth century and is familiar to every student of chemistry; it has led to the principle known as the law of conservation of mass. The second—that energy can be neither created nor destroyed but only altered in form—emerged in the nineteenth century and has ever since been the plague of inventors of perpetual-motion machines; it is known as the law of conservation of energy.

These two principles have constantly guided and disciplined the development and application of science. For all practical purposes they were unaltered and separate until some five years ago. For most practical purposes they still are so, but it is now known that they are, in fact, two phases of a single principle for we have discovered that energy may sometimes be converted into matter and matter into energy. Specifically, such a conversion is observed in the phenomenon of nuclear fission of uranium, a process in which atomic nuclei split into fragments with the release of an enormous amount of energy. The military use of this energy has been the object of the research and production projects described in this report.

* From *Atomic Energy for Military Purposes* by Henry D. Smyth, published by the Princeton University Press and reprinted by permission of the publishers.

THE EQUIVALENCE OF MASS AND ENERGY

One conclusion that appeared rather early in the development of the theory of relativity was that the inertial mass of a moving body increased as its speed increased. This implied an equivalence between an increase in energy of motion of a body, that is, its kinetic energy, and an increase in its mass. To most practical physicists and engineers this appeared a mathematical fiction of no practical importance. Even Einstein could hardly have foreseen the present applications, but as early as 1905 he did clearly state that mass and energy were equivalent and suggested that proof of this equivalence might be found by the study of radioactive substances. He concluded that the amount of energy, E, equivalent to a mass, m, was given by the equation

$$E = mc^2$$

where c is the velocity of light. If this is stated in actual numbers, its startling character is apparent. It shows that one kilogram (2.2 pounds) of matter, if converted entirely into energy, would give 25 billion kilowatt hours of energy. This is equal to the energy that would be generated by the total electric power industry in the United States (as of 1939) running for approximately two months. Compare this fantastic figure with the 8.5 kilowatt hours of heat energy which may be produced by burning an equal amount of coal.

The extreme size of this conversion figure was interesting in several respects. In the first place, it explained why the equivalence of mass and energy was never observed in ordinary chemical combustion. We now believe that the heat given off in such a combustion has mass associated with it, but this mass is so small that it cannot be detected by the most sensitive balances available. . . . In the second place, it was made clear that no appreciable quantities of matter were being converted into energy in any familiar terrestrial processes, since no such large sources of energy were known. Further, the possibility of initiating or controlling such a conversion in any practical way seemed very remote. Finally, the very size of the conversion factor opened a magnificent field of speculation to philosophers, physicists, engineers, and comic-strip artists. For twenty-five years such speculation was unsupported by direct experimental evidence, but beginning about 1930 such evidence began to appear in rapidly increasing quantity. . . .

Nuclear Binding Energies

It is a general principle of physics that work must be done on a stable system to break it up. Thus, if an assemblage of neutrons and protons is stable, energy must be supplied to separate its constituent particles. If energy and mass are really equivalent, then the total mass of a stable nucleus should be less than the total mass of the separate protons and neutrons that go to make it up. This mass difference, then, should be equivalent to the energy required to disrupt the nucleus completely, which is called the binding energy. Remember that the masses of all nuclei were "approximately" whole numbers. It is the small differences from whole numbers that are significant.

Consider the alpha particle as an example. It is stable; since its mass number is four and its atomic number two it consists of two protons and two neutrons. The mass of a proton is 1.00758 and that of a neutron is 1.00893, so that the total mass of the separate components of the helium nucleus is

$$2 \times 1.00758 + 2 \times 1.00893 = 4.03302$$

whereas the mass of the helium nucleus itself is 4.00280. Neglecting the last two decimal places we have 4.033 and 4.003, a difference of 0.030 mass units. This, then, represents the "binding energy" of the protons and neutrons in the helium nucleus. It looks small, but recalling Einstein's equation, $E = mc^2$, we remember that a small amount of mass is equivalent to a large amount of energy. Actually 0.030 mass units is equal to 4.5×10^{-5} ergs per nucleus or 2.7×10^{19} ergs per gram molecule of helium. In units more familiar to the engineer or chemist, this means that to break up the nuclei of all the helium atoms in a gram of helium would require 1.62×10^{11} gram calories or 190,000 kilowatt hours of energy. Conversely, if free protons and neutrons could be assembled into helium nuclei, this energy would be released.

Evidently it is worth exploring the possibility of getting energy by combining protons and neutrons or by transmuting one kind of nucleus into another. . . .

The Need of a Chain Reaction

Our common sources of power, other than sunlight and waterpower, are chemical reactions—usually the combustion of coal or oil. They release energy as the result of rearrangements of the outer electronic structures of the atoms, the same kind of process that supplies energy to our bodies. Combustion is always self-propagating; thus lighting a fire with a match releases enough heat to ignite the neighboring fuel, which releases more heat which ignites more fuel, and so on. In the nuclear reactions we have described this is not generally true; neither the energy released nor the new particles formed are sufficient to maintain the reaction. But we can imagine nuclear reactions emitting particles of the same sort that initiate them and in sufficient numbers to propagate the reaction in neighboring nuclei. Such a self-propagating reaction is called a "chain reaction" and such conditions must be achieved if the energy of the nuclear reactions with which we are concerned is to be put to large-scale use.

Period of Speculation

Although there were no atomic power plants built in the thirties, there were plenty of discoveries in nuclear physics and plenty of speculation. A theory was advanced by H. Bethe to explain the heat of the sun by a cycle of nuclear changes involving carbon, hydrogen, nitrogen, and oxygen, and leading eventually to the formation of helium. This theory is now generally accepted. The discovery of a few $(n,2n)$ nuclear reactions (i.e., neutron-produced and neutron-producing reactions) suggested that a self-multiplying chain reaction might be initiated under the right conditions. There was much talk of atomic power and some talk of atomic bombs. But the last great step in this preliminary period came after four years of stumbling. The effects of neutron bombardment of uranium, the most complex element known, had been studied by some of the ablest physicists. The results were striking but confusing. The story of their gradual interpretation is intricate and highly technical. . . .

DISCOVERY OF URANIUM FISSION

As has already been mentioned, the neutron proved to be the most effective particle for inducing nuclear changes. This was particularly true for the elements of highest atomic number and weight where the large nuclear charge exerts strong repulsive forces on deuteron or proton projectiles but not on uncharged neutrons. The results of the bombardment of uranium by neutrons had proved interesting and puzzling. First studied by Fermi and his colleagues in 1934, they were not properly interpreted until several years later.

On January 16, 1939, Niels Bohr of Copenhagen, Denmark, arrived in this country to spend several months in Princeton, N. J., and was particularly anxious to discuss some abstract problems with A. Einstein. (Four years later Bohr was to escape from Nazi-occupied Denmark in a small boat.) Just before Bohr left Denmark two of his colleagues, O. R. Frisch and L. Meitner (both refugees from Germany), had told him their guess that the absorption of a neutron by a uranium nucleus sometimes caused that nucleus to split into approximately equal parts with the release of enormous quantities of energy, a process that soon began to be called nuclear "fission." The occasion for this hypothesis was the important discovery of O. Hahn and F. Strassmann in Germany which proved that an isotope of barium was produced by neutron bombardment of uranium. Immediately on arrival in the United States Bohr communicated this idea to his former student J. A. Wheeler and others at Princeton, and from them the news spread by word of mouth to neighboring physicists including E. Fermi at Columbia University. As a result of conversations between Fermi, J. R. Dunning, and G. B. Pegram, a search was undertaken at Columbia for the heavy pulses of ionization that would be expected from the flying fragments of the uranium nucleus. On January 26, 1939 there was a Conference on Theoretical Physics at Washington, D. C., sponsored jointly by the George Washington University and the Carnegie Institution of Washington. Fermi left New York to attend this meeting before the Columbia fission experiments had been tried. At the meeting Bohr and Fermi discussed the problem of fission, and in particular Fermi mentioned the possibility that neutrons might be emitted during the process. Although this was only a guess, its implication of the possibility of a chain reaction was obvious. . . .

General Discussion of Fission

Consider the suggestion of Frisch and Meitner in the light of the two general trends that had been discovered in nuclear structure:—first, that the proportion of neutrons goes up with atomic number; second, that the binding energy per particle is a maximum for the nuclei of intermediate atomic number. Suppose the U-238 nucleus is broken exactly in half; then, neglecting the mass of the incident neutron, we have two nuclei of atomic number 46 and mass number 119. But the heaviest stable isotope of palladium ($Z = 46$) has a mass number of only 110. Therefore to reach stability each of these imaginary new nuclei must eject nine neutrons, or four neutrons in each nucleus must convert themselves to protons by emitting electrons thereby forming stable tin nuclei of mass number 119 and atomic number 50; or a combination of such ejections and conversions must occur to give some other pair of stable nuclei. Actually, as was suggested by Hahn and Strassmann's identification of barium ($Z = 56$, $A = 135$ to 140) as a product of fission, the split occurs in such a way as to produce two unequal parts of mass numbers about 140 and 90 with the emission of a few neutrons and subsequent radioactive decay by electron emission until stable nuclei are formed. Calculations from binding-energy data show that any such rearrangement gives an aggregate resulting mass considerably less than the initial mass of the uranium nucleus, and thus that a great deal of energy must be released.

Evidently, there were three major implications of the phenomenon of fission: the release of energy, the production of radioactive atomic species and the possibility of a neutron chain reaction. The energy release might reveal itself in kinetic energy of the fission fragments and in the subsequent radioactive disintegration of the products. The possibility of a neutron chain reaction depended on whether neutrons were in fact emitted —a possibility which required investigation.

These were the problems suggested by the discovery of fission, the kind of problem reported in the journals in 1939 and 1940 and since then investigated largely in secret. The study of the fission process itself, including production of neutrons and fast fragments, has been largely carried out by physicists using counters, cloud chambers, etc. The study and identification of the fission products has been carried out largely by chemists, who have had to perform chemical separations rapidly even with sub-microscopic quantities of material and to make repeated determinations of the half-lives of unstable isotopes. We shall summarize the state of knowledge as of June 1940. By that time the principal facts about fission had been discovered and revealed to the scientific world. A chain reaction had not been obtained, but its possibility—at least in principle—was clear and several paths that might lead to it had been suggested. . . .

Suggestion of Plutonium Fission

It was realized that radiative capture of neutrons by U-238 would probably lead by two successive beta-ray emissions to the formation of a nucleus for which $Z = 94$ and $A = 239$. Consideration of the Bohr-Wheeler theory of fission and of certain empirical relations among the nuclei by L. A. Turner and others suggested that this nucleus would be a fairly stable alpha emitter and would probably undergo fission when bombarded by thermal neutrons. . . .

SUMMARY

Looking back on the year 1940, we see that all the prerequisites to a serious attack on the problem of producing atomic bombs and controlling atomic power were at hand. It had been proved that mass and energy were equivalent. It had been proved that the neutrons initiating fission of uranium reproduced themselves in the process and that therefore a multiplying chain reaction might occur with explosive force. To be sure, no one knew whether the required conditions could be achieved, but many scientists had clear ideas as to the problems involved and the directions in which solutions might be sought. . . .

[*FROM CHAPTER II. STATEMENT OF THE PROBLEM*]

THE CHAIN-REACTION PROBLEM

The principle of operation of an atomic bomb or power plant utilizing uranium fission is simple enough. If one neutron causes a fission that produces more than one new neutron, the number of fissions may increase tremendously with the release of enormous amounts of energy. It is a question of probabilities. Neutrons produced in the fission process may escape entirely from the uranium, may be captured by uranium in a process not resulting in fission, or may be captured by an impurity. Thus the question of whether a chain reaction does or does not go depends on the result of a competition among four processes:

1. escape,
2. non-fission capture by uranium,
3. non-fission capture by impurities,
4. fission capture.

If the loss of neutrons by the first three processes is less than the surplus produced by the fourth, the chain reaction occurs; otherwise it does not. Evidently any one of the first three processes may have such a high probability in a given arrangement that the extra neutrons created by fission will be insufficient to keep the reaction going. For example, should it turn out that process (2)—non-fission capture by uranium—has a much higher probability than fission capture, there would presumably be no possibility of achieving a chain reaction.

An additional complication is that natural uranium contains three isotopes: U-234, U-235, and U-238, present to the extent of approximately 0.006, 0.7, and 99.3 per cent, respectively. The probabilities of processes (2) and (4) are different for different isotopes. We have also seen that the probabilities are different for neutrons of different energies.

We shall now consider the limitations imposed by the first three processes and how their effects can be minimized.

Neutron Escape; Critical Size

The relative number of neutrons which escape from a quantity of uranium can be minimized by changing the size and shape. In a sphere any surface effect is proportional to the square of the radius, and any volume effect is proportional to the cube of the radius. Now the escape of neutrons from a quantity of uranium is a surface effect depending on the area of the surface, but fission capture occurs throughout the material and is therefore a volume effect. Consequently the greater the amount of uranium, the less probable it is that neutron escape will predominate over fission capture and prevent a chain reaction. Loss of neutrons by non-fission capture is a volume effect like neutron production by fission capture, so that increase in size makes no change in its relative importance.

The critical size of a device containing uranium is defined as the size for which the production of free neutrons by fission is just equal to their loss by escape and by non-fission capture. In other words, if the size is smaller than critical, then—by definition—no chain reaction will sustain itself. In principle it was possible in 1940 to calculate the critical size, but in practice the uncertainty of the constants involved was so great that the various estimates differed widely. It seemed not improbable that the critical size might be too large for practical purposes. Even now estimates for untried arrangements vary somewhat from time to time as new information becomes available.

Use of a Moderator to Reduce Non-Fission Capture

Thermal neutrons have the highest probability of producing fission of U-235 but the neutrons emitted in the process of fission have high speeds. Evidently it is an oversimplification to say that the chain reaction might maintain itself if more neutrons were created by fission than were absorbed. For the probability both of fission capture and of non-fission capture depends on the speed of the neutrons. Unfortunately, the speed at which non-fission capture is most probable is intermediate between the average speed of neutrons emitted in the fission process and the speed at which fission capture is most probable.

For some years before the discovery of fission, the customary way of slowing down neutrons was to cause them to pass through material of low atomic weight, such as hydrogenous material. The process of slowing down or moderation is simply one of elastic collisions between high-speed particles and particles practically at rest. The more nearly identical the masses of neutron and struck particle the greater the loss of kinetic energy by the neutron. Therefore the light elements are most effective as "moderators," i.e., slowing down agents, for neutrons.

It occurred to a number of physicists that it might be possible to mix uranium with a moderator in such a way that the high-speed fission neutrons, after being ejected from uranium and before re-encountering uranium nuclei, would have their speeds reduced below the speeds for which non-fission capture is highly probable. Evidently the characteristics of a good moderator are that it should be of low atomic weight and that it should have little or no tendency to absorb neutrons. Lithium and boron are excluded on the latter count. Helium is difficult to use because it is a gas and forms no compounds. The choice of moderator therefore lay among hydrogen, deuterium, beryllium, and carbon. Even now no one of these substances can be excluded from the list of practical possibilities. It was E. Fermi and L. Szilard who proposed the use of graphite as a moderator for a chain reaction.

Use of a Lattice to Reduce Non-Fission Capture

The general scheme of using a moderator mixed with the uranium was pretty obvious. A specific manner of using a moderator was first suggested in this country, so far as we can discover, by Fermi and Szilard. The idea was to use lumps of uranium of considerable size imbedded in a matrix of moderator material. Such a lattice can be shown to have real advantages over a homogeneous mixture. As the constants were more accurately determined, it became possible to calculate theoretically the type of lattice that would be most effective.

Reduction of Non-Fission Capture by Isotope Separation

For neutrons of certain intermediate speeds (corresponding to energies of a few electron volts) U-238 has a large capture cross section for the production of U-239 but not for fission. There is also a considerable probability of inelastic (i.e., non-capture-producing) collisions between high-speed neutrons and U-238 nuclei. Thus the presence of the U-238 tends both to reduce the speed of the fast neutrons and to effect the capture of those of moderate speed. Although there may be some non-fission capture by U-235, it is evident that if we can separate the U-235 from the U-238 and discard the U-238, we can reduce non-fission capture and can thus promote the chain reaction. In fact, the probability of fission of U-235 by high-speed neutrons may be great enough to make the use of a moderator unnecessary once the U-238 has been removed. Unfortunately, U-235 is present in natural uranium only to the extent of about one part in 140. Also, the relatively small difference in mass between the two isotopes makes separation difficult. . . .

Production and Purification of Materials

If we are to hope to achieve a chain reaction, we must reduce effect (3) —non-fission capture by impurities—to the point where it is not serious. This means very careful purification of the uranium metal and very careful purification of the moderator. Calculations show that the maximum permissible concentrations of many impurity elements are a few parts per million—in either the uranium or the moderator. When it is recalled that up to 1940 the total amount of uranium metal produced in this country was not more than a few grams and even this was of doubtful purity, that the total amount of metallic beryllium produced in this country was not more than a few pounds, that the total amount of concentrated deuterium produced was not more than a few pounds, and that carbon had never been produced in quantity with anything like the purity required of a moderator, it is clear that the problem of producing and purifying materials was a major one. . . .

Possibility of Using Plutonium

So far, all our discussion has been primarily concerned with the use of uranium itself. The element of atomic number 94 and mass 239, commonly referred to as plutonium, might be very effective. Actually, we now believe it to be of value comparable to pure U-235. We have mentioned the difficulty of separating U-235 from the more abundant isotope U-238. These two isotopes are, of course, chemically identical. But plutonium, although produced from U-238, is a different chemical element. Therefore, if a process could be worked out for converting some of the U-238 to plutonium, a *chemical* separation of the plutonium from uranium might prove more practicable than the *isotopic* separation of U-235 from U-238.

Suppose that we have set up a controllable chain reaction in a lattice of natural uranium and a moderator—say carbon, in the form of graphite. Then as the chain reaction proceeds, neutrons are emitted in the process of fission of the U-235 and many of these neutrons are absorbed by U-238. This produces U-239, each atom of which then emits a beta particle, becoming neptunium (${}_{93}Np^{239}$). Neptunium, in turn, emits another beta particle, becoming plutonium (${}_{94}PU^{239}$), which emits an alpha particle, decaying again to U-235, but so slowly that in effect it is a stable element. If, after the reaction has been allowed to proceed for a considerable time, the mixture of metals is removed, it may be possible to extract the plutonium by chemical methods and purify it for use in a subsequent fission chain reaction of an explosive nature.

Combined Effects and Enriched Piles

Three ways of increasing the likelihood of a chain reaction have been mentioned: use of a moderator; attainment of high purity of materials; use of special material, either U-235 or Pu. The three procedures are not mutually exclusive, and many schemes have been proposed for using small amounts of separated U-235 or Pu-239 in a lattice composed primarily of ordinary uranium or uranium oxide and of a moderator or two different moderators. Such proposed arrangements are usually called "enriched piles." . . .

AMOUNTS OF MATERIALS NEEDED

Obviously it was impossible in the summer of 1940 to make more than guesses as to what amounts of materials would be needed to produce:

1. a chain reaction with use of a moderator:
2. a chain-reaction bomb in pure, or at least enriched, U-235 or plutonium.

A figure of one to one hundred kilograms of U-235 was commonly given at this time for the critical size of a bomb. This would, of course, have to be separated from at least 140 times as much natural uranium. For a slow-neutron chain reaction using a moderator and unseparated uranium it was almost certain that tons of metal and of moderator would be required. . . .

HEALTH HAZARDS

It had been known for a long time that radioactive materials were dangerous. They give off very penetrating radiations—gamma rays—which are much like X-rays in their physiological effects. They also give off beta and alpha rays which, although less penetrating, can still be dangerous. The amounts of radium used in hospitals and in ordinary physical measurements usually comprise but a few milligrams. The amounts of radioactive material produced by the fission of uranium in a relatively small chain-reacting system may be equivalent to hundreds or thousands of grams of radium. A chain-reacting system also gives off intense neutron radiation known to be comparable to gamma rays as regards health hazards. Quite apart from its radioactive properties, uranium is poisonous chemically. Thus, nearly all work in this field is hazardous—particularly work on chain reactions and the resulting radioactive products. . . .

POWER VS. BOMB

The expected military advantages of uranium bombs were far more spectacular than those of a uranium power plant. It was conceivable that a few uranium bombs might be decisive in winning the war for the side first putting them into use. Such thoughts were very much in the minds of those working in this field, but the attainment of a slow-neutron chain reaction seemed a necessary preliminary step in the development of our knowledge and became the first objective of the group interested in the problem. This also seemed an important step in convincing military authorities and the more skeptical scientists that the whole notion was not a pipe dream. . . .

MILITARY USEFULNESS

If all the atoms in a kilogram of U-235 undergo fission, the energy released is equivalent to the energy released in the explosion of about 20,000 short tons of TNT. If the critical size of a bomb turns out to be practical —say, in the range of one to one hundred kilograms—and all the other problems can be solved, there remain two questions. First, how large a percentage of the fissionable nuclei can be made to undergo fission before the reaction stops; i.e., what is the efficiency of the explosion? Second, what is the effect of so concentrated a release of energy? Even if only 1 per cent of the theoretically available energy is released, the explosion will still be of a totally different order of magnitude from that produced by any previously known type of bomb. The value of such a bomb was thus a question for military experts to consider very carefully.

SUMMARY

It had been established (1) that uranium fission did occur with release of great amounts of energy; and (2) that in the process extra neutrons were set free which might start a chain reaction. It was not contrary to any known principle that such a reaction should take place and that it should have very important military application as a bomb. However, the idea was revolutionary and therefore suspect; it was certain that many technical operations of great difficulty would have to be worked out before such a bomb could be produced. Probably the only materials satisfactory for a bomb were either U-235, which would have to be separated from the 140-times more abundant isotope U-238, or Pu-239, an isotope of the hitherto unknown element plutonium, which would have to be generated by a controlled chain-reacting process itself hitherto unknown. To achieve such a controlled chain reaction it was clear that uranium metal and heavy water or beryllium or carbon might have to be produced in great quantity with high purity. . . .

[*FROM CHAPTER IV. PROGRESS UP TO DECEMBER 1941*]

THE IMMEDIATE QUESTIONS

Early in the summer of 1940 the questions of most immediate importance were:

1. Could any circumstances be found under which the chain reaction would go?
2. Could the isotope U-235 be separated on a large scale?
3. Could moderator and other materials be obtained in sufficient purity and quantity?

Although there were many subsidiary problems, as will appear in the account of the progress made in the succeeding eighteen months, these three questions determined the course of the work. . . .

THE CHAIN REACTION

Initiation of New Programs

Early in 1941 interest in the general chain-reaction problem by individuals at Princeton, Chicago and California led to the approval of certain projects at those institutions. Thereafter the work of these groups was co-ordinated with the work at Columbia, forming parts of a single large program.

Work on Resonance Absorption

There were advantages in a lattice structure or "pile" with uranium concentrated in lumps regularly distributed in a matrix of moderator. This was the system on which the Columbia group was working. As is so often the case, the fundamental idea is a simple one. If the uranium and the moderator are mixed homogeneously, the neutrons on the average will lose energy in small steps between passages through the uranium so that in the course of their reduction to thermal velocity the chance of their passing through uranium at any given velocity, e.g., at a velocity corresponding to resonance absorption, is great. But, if the uranium is in large lumps spaced at large intervals in the moderator, the amounts of energy lost by neutrons between passages from one lump of uranium to another will be large and the chance of their reaching a uranium lump with energy just equal to the energy of resonance absorption is relatively small. Thus the chance of absorption by U-238 to produce U-239, compared to the chance of absorption as thermal neutrons to cause fission, may be reduced sufficiently to allow a chain reaction to take place. . . .

The First Intermediate Experiments

About July, 1941, the first lattice structure of graphite and uranium was set up at Columbia. It was a graphite cube about 8 feet on an edge, and contained about 7 tons of uranium oxide in iron containers distributed at equal intervals throughout the graphite. . . .

Evidently the absorption of neutrons by U-238 to produce U-239 tends to reduce the number of neutrons, while the fissions tend to increase the number. The question is: Which predominates? or, more precisely, Does the fission production of neutrons predominate over all neutron-removal processes other than escape? Interpretation of the experimental data on this crucial question involves many corrections, calculations, and approximations, but all reduce in the end to a single number, the multiplication factor k.

The Multiplication Factor K

The whole success or failure of the uranium project depended on the multiplication factor k, sometimes called the reproduction factor. If k could be made greater than 1 in a practical system, the project would succeed; if not, the chain reaction would never be more than a dream. . . .

All agreed that the multiplication factor could be increased by greater purity of materials, different lattice arrangements, etc. None could say with certainty that it could be made greater than 1.

Work on Plutonium

Mention was made of the suggestion that the element 94, later christened plutonium, would be formed by beta-ray disintegrations of U-239 resulting from neutron absorption by U-238 and that plutonium would probably be an alpha-particle emitter of long half-life and would undergo fission when bombarded by neutrons. In the summer of 1940 the nuclear physics group at the University of California in Berkeley was urged to use neutrons from its powerful cyclotron for the production of plutonium, and to separate it from uranium and investigate its fission properties. Various pertinent experiments were performed and were reported by E. O. Lawrence to the National Academy Committee (see below) in May, 1941 and also in a memorandum that was incorporated in the Committee's second report dated July 11, 1941. It will be seen that this memorandum includes one important idea not specifically emphasized by others, namely, the production of large quantities of plutonium for use in a bomb.

We quote from Lawrence's memorandum as follows: "Since the first report of the National Academy of Sciences Committee on Atomic Fission, an extremely important new possibility has been opened for the exploitation of the chain reaction with unseparated isotopes of uranium. Experiments in the Radiation Laboratory of the University of California have indicated (a) that element 94 is formed as a result of capture of a neutron by uranium 238 followed by two successive beta-transformations, and furthermore (b) that this transuranic element undergoes slow neutron fission and therefore presumably behaves like uranium 235.

"It appears accordingly that, if a chain reaction with unseparated isotopes is achieved, it may be allowed to proceed violently for a period of time for the express purpose of manufacturing element 94 in substantial amounts. This material could be extracted by ordinary chemistry and would presumably be the equivalent of uranium 235 for chain reaction purposes.

"If this is so, the following three outstanding important possibilities are opened:

"1. Uranium 238 would be available for energy production, thus increasing about one hundred fold the total atomic energy obtainable from a given quantity of uranium.

"2. Using element 94 one may envisage preparation of small chain reaction units for power purposes weighing perhaps a hundred pounds instead of a hundred tons as probably would be necessary for units using natural uranium.

"3. If large amounts of element 94 were available it is likely that a chain reaction with fast neutrons could be produced. In such a reaction the energy would be released at an explosive rate which might be described as 'super bomb.' " . . .

ISOTOPE SEPARATION

The need of large samples of U-235 stimulated E. O. Lawrence at Berkeley to work on electromagnetic separation. He was remarkably successful and by December 6, 1941 reported that he could deposit in one hour one microgram of U-235 from which a large proportion of the U-239 had been removed. . . .

The Centrifuge and Gaseous Diffusion Methods

Though we have made it clear that the separation of U-235 from U-238 might be fundamental to the whole success of the project, little has been said about work in this field. Such work had been going on since the summer of 1940 under the general direction of H. C. Urey at Columbia. . . .

After careful review and a considerable amount of experimenting on other methods, it had been concluded that the two most promising methods of separating large quantities of U-235 from U-238 were by the use of centrifuges and by the use of diffusion through porous barriers. In the centrifuge, the forces acting on the two isotopes are slightly different because of their differences in mass. In the diffusion through barriers, the rates of diffusion are slightly different for the two isotopes, again because of their differences in mass. Each method required the uranium to be in gaseous form, which was an immediate and serious limitation since the only suitable gaseous compound of uranium then known was uranium hexafluoride. In each method the amount of enrichment to be expected in a single production unit or "stage" was very small; this indicated that many successive stages would be necessary if a high degree of enrichment was to be attained.

By the end of 1941 each method had been experimentally demonstrated in principle; that is, single-stage separators had effected the enrichment of the U-235 on a laboratory scale to about the degree predicted theoretically. K. Cohen of Columbia and others had developed the theory for the single units and for the series or "cascade" of units that would be needed. Thus it was possible to estimate that about 5,000 stages would be necessary for one type of diffusion system and that a total area of many acres of diffusion barrier would be required in a plant separating a kilogram of U-235 each day. Corresponding cost estimates were tens of millions of dollars. For the centrifuge the number of stages would be smaller, but it was predicted that a similar production by centrifuges would require 22,000 separately driven, extremely high-speed centrifuges, each three feet in length at a comparable cost.

Of course, the cost estimates could not be made accurately since the technological problems were almost completely unsolved, but these estimates as to size and cost of plant did serve to emphasize the magnitude of the undertaking. . . .

PRODUCTION AND ANALYSIS OF MATERIALS

By the end of 1941 not very much progress had been made in the production of materials for use in a chain-reacting system. The National Bureau of Standards and the Columbia group were in contact with the Metal Hydrides Company of Beverly, Massachusetts. This company was producing some uranium in powdered form, but efforts to increase its production and to melt the powdered metal into solid ingots had not been very successful.

Similarly, no satisfactory arrangement had been made for obtaining large amounts of highly purified graphite. The graphite in use at Columbia had been obtained from the U. S. Graphite Company of Saginaw, Michigan. It was of high purity for a commercial product, but it did contain about one part in 500,000 of boron, which was undesirable. . . .

To summarize, by the end of 1941 there was no evidence that procurement of materials in sufficient quantity and purity was impossible, but the problems were far from solved. . . .

NATIONAL ACADEMY COMMITTEE REPORT

The third report (of a National Academy Committee, November 6, 1941) was specifically concerned with the "possibilities of an explosive fission reaction with U-235." Although neither of the first two National

Academy reports indicated that uranium would be likely to be of decisive importance in the war, this possibility was emphasized in the third report. We can do no better than quote portions of this report.

"Since our last report, the progress toward separation of the isotopes of uranium has been such as to make urgent a consideration of (1) the probability of success in the attempt to produce a fission bomb, (2) the destructive effect to be expected from such a bomb, (3) the anticipated time before its development can be completed and production be underway, and (4) a preliminary estimate of the costs involved.

"1. *Conditions for a fission bomb. A fission bomb of superlatively destructive power will result from bringing quickly together a sufficient mass of element U-235.* This seems to be as sure as any untried prediction based upon theory and experiment can be. Our calculations indicate further that the required masses can be brought together quickly enough for the reaction to become efficient . . .

"2. *Destructive effect of fission bombs.* (*a*) *Mass of the bomb. The mass of U-235 required to produce explosive fission under appropriate conditions can hardly be less than 2 kg nor greater than 100 kg.* These wide limits reflect chiefly the experimental uncertainty in the capture cross section of U-235 for fast neutrons . . . (*b*) *Energy released by explosive fission.* Calculations for the case of masses properly located at the initial instant indicate that between 1 and 5 per cent of the fission energy of the uranium should be released at a fission explosion. This means from 2 to 10×10^8 kilocalories per kg of uranium 235. *The available explosive energy per kg of uranium is thus equivalent to about 300 tons of TNT.*

"3. *Time required for development and production of the necessary U-235.* (*a*) *Amount of uranium needed.* Since the destructiveness of present bombs is already an important factor in warfare, it is evident that, if the destructiveness of the bombs is thus increased 10,000-fold, they should become of decisive importance.

"The amount of uranium required will, nevertheless, be large. If the estimate is correct that 500,000 tons of TNT bombs would be required to devastate Germany's military and industrial objectives, *from 1 to 10 tons of U-235 will be required to do the same job.*

"(*b*) *Separation of U-235. The separation of the isotopes of uranium can be done in the necessary amounts.* Several methods are under development, at least two of which seem definitely adequate, and are approaching the stage of practical test. These are the methods of the centrifuge and of diffusion through porous barriers. Other methods are being investigated or need study which may ultimately prove superior, but are now farther from the engineering stage.

"(*c*) *Time required for production of fission bombs.* An estimate of time required for development, engineering and production of fission bombs can be made only very roughly at this time.

"If all possible effort is spent on the program, one might however expect fission bombs to be available in significant quantity within three or four years.

"4. *Rough estimate of costs.* (The figures given in the Academy report under this heading were recognized as only rough estimates since the scientific and engineering data to make them more precise were not available. They showed only that the undertaking would be enormously expensive but still in line with other war expenditures. . . .")

[*FROM CHAPTER VI. THE METALLURGICAL PROJECT AT CHICAGO IN 1942*]

INTRODUCTION

As has been made clear, the information accumulated by the end of 1941 as to the possibility of producing an atomic bomb was such as to warrant expansion of the work, and this expansion called for an administrative reorganization. It was generally accepted that there was a very high probability that an atomic bomb of enormous destructive power could be made, either from concentrated U-235 or from the new element plutonium. It was proposed, therefore, to institute an intensive experimental and theoretical program including work both on isotope separation and on the chain-reaction problems. It was hoped that this program would establish definitely whether or not U-235 could be separated in significant quantities from U-238, either by electromagnetic or statistical methods; whether or not a chain reaction could be established with natural uranium or its compounds and could be made to yield relatively large quantities of plutonium; and whether or not the plutonium so produced could be separated from the parent material, uranium. It was hoped also that the program would provide the theoretical and experimental data required for the design of a fast-neutron chain-reacting bomb.

The problems of isotope separation had been assigned to groups under Lawrence and Urey while the remaining problems were assigned to Compton's group, which was organized under the cryptically named "Metallurgical Laboratory" of the University of Chicago. . . .

OBJECTIVES

In accordance with the general objectives just outlined, the initial objectives of the Metallurgical Laboratory were: first, to find a system using normal uranium in which a chain reaction would occur; second, to show that, if such a chain reaction did occur, it would be possible to separate plutonium chemically from the other material; and, finally, to obtain the theoretical and experimental data for effecting an explosive chain reaction with either U-235 or with plutonium. The ultimate objective of the laboratory was to prepare plans for the large-scale production of plutonium and for its use in bombs.

ORGANIZATION OF THE WORK

The laboratory had not only to concern itself with its immediate objectives but simultaneously to bear in mind the ultimate objectives and to work toward them on the assumption that the immediate objectives would be attained. It could not wait for a chain reaction to be achieved before studying the chemistry of plutonium. It had to assume that plutonium would be separated and to go ahead with the formulation of plans for its production and use. Consequently problems were continually redefined as new information became available, and research programs were reassessed almost from week to week. . . .

PROCUREMENT OF MATERIALS

General

It has been made clear that the procurement of materials of sufficient purity was a major part of the problem. As far as uranium was concerned, it seemed likely that it would be needed in highly purified metallic form or at least as highly purified uranium oxide. The other materials which were going to be needed were either graphite, heavy water, or possibly beryllium. It was clear at this time that, however advantageous heavy water might be as a moderator, no large quantities of it would be available for months or years. Beryllium seemed less advantageous and almost as difficult to get. Therefore the procurement efforts for a moderator were centered on graphite. . . .

Uranium Ore

Obviously there would be no point in undertaking this whole project if it were not going to be possible to find enough uranium for producing the bombs. Early indications were favorable, and a careful survey made in November, 1942, showed that immediate delivery could be made of adequate tonnages of uranium ores. . . .

Graphite Procurement

At the beginning of 1942 graphite production was still unsatisfactory but it was, of course, in quite a different condition from the metal production since the industrial production of graphite had already been very large. The problem was merely one of purity and priority. Largely through the efforts of N. Hilberry, the National Carbon Company and the Speer Carbon Company were both drawn into the picture. Following suggestions made by the experts of the National Bureau of Standards, these companies were able to produce highly purified graphite with a neutron absorption some 20 per cent less than the standard commercial materials previously used. . . .

The First Self-Sustaining Chain-Reacting Pile

By the fall of 1942 enough graphite, uranium oxide, and uranium metal were available at Chicago to justify an attempt to build an actual self-sustaining chain-reacting pile. But the amount of metal available was small —only about 6 tons—and other materials were none too plentiful and of varying quality. These conditions rather than optimum efficiency controlled the design.

The pile was constructed on the lattice principle with graphite as a moderator and lumps of metal or oxide as the reacting units regularly spaced through the graphite to form the lattice. Instruments situated at various points in the pile or near it indicated the neutron intensity, and movable strips of absorbing material served as controls. . . .

The pile was first operated as a self-sustaining system on December 2, 1942. So far as we know, this was the first time that human beings ever initiated a self-maintaining nuclear chain reaction. Initially the pile was operated at a power level of ½ watt, but on December 12 the power level was raised to 200 watts. . . .

Conclusion

Evidently this experiment, performed on December 2 just as a reviewing committee was appraising the Chicago project, answered beyond all shadow of doubt the first question before the Metallurgical Laboratory; a self-sustaining nuclear chain reaction had been produced in a system using normal uranium. . . .

Relation Between Power and Production of Plutonium

The immediate object of building a uranium-graphite pile was to prove that there were conditions under which a chain reaction would occur, but the ultimate objective of the laboratory was to produce plutonium by a chain reaction. Therefore we are interested in the relation between the power at which a pile operates and the rate at which it produces plutonium. The relation may be evaluated to a first approximation rather easily. . . .

The first chain-reacting pile that we have described operated at a maximum of 200 watts. Assuming that a single bomb will require the order of one to 100 kilograms of plutonium, the pile that has been described would have to be kept going at least 70,000 years to produce a single bomb. Evidently the problem of quantity production of plutonium was not yet solved.

The Chemistry of Plutonium

The second specific objective of the Metallurgical Laboratory was to show that, if a chain reaction did occur, it would be feasible to separate the plutonium chemically from the other material with which it is found. . . .

Successful microchemical preparation of some plutonium salts and a study of their properties led to the general conclusion that it was possible to separate plutonium chemically from the other materials in the pile. This conclusion represents the attainment of the second immediate objective of the Metallurgical Laboratory. Thus, by the end of 1942, plutonium, entirely unknown eighteen months earlier, was considered an element whose chemical behavior was as well understood as that of several of the elements of the old periodic table. . . .

On the basis of the evidence available it was clear that a plutonium production rate somewhere between a kilogram a month and a kilogram a day would be required. At the rate of a kilogram a day, a 500,000 to 1,500,000 kilowatt plant would be required. (The ultimate capacity of the hydroelectric power plants at the Grand Coulee Dam is expected to be 2,000,000 kw.) Evidently the creation of a plutonium production plant of the required size was to be a major enterprise even without attempting to utilize the thermal energy liberated. Nevertheless, by November, 1942, most of the problems had been well defined and tentative solutions had been proposed. . . .

[*FROM CHAPTER VII. THE PLUTONIUM PRODUCTION PROBLEM AS OF FEBRUARY 1943*]

The Scale of Production

The first decision to be made was on the scale of production that should be attempted. For reasons of security the figure decided upon may not be disclosed here. It was very large.

The Magnitude of the Problem

The production of one gram of plutonium per day corresponds to a generation of energy at the rate of 500 to 1,500 kilowatts. Therefore a plant for large-scale production of plutonium will release a very large amount of energy. The problem therefore was to design a plant of this capacity on the basis of experience with a pile that could operate at a power level of only 0.2 kilowatt. As regards the plutonium separation work, which was equally important, it was necessary to draw plans for an extraction and purification plant which would separate some grams a day of plutonium from some tons of uranium, and such planning had to be based on information obtained by microchemical studies involving only half a milligram of plutonium. To be sure, there was information available for the design of the large-scale pile and separation plant from auxiliary experiments and from large-scale studies of separation processes using uranium as a stand-in for plutonium, but even so the proposed extrapolations both as to chain-reacting piles and as to separation processes were staggering. In peacetime no engineer or scientist in his right mind would consider making such a magnification in a single stage, and even in wartime only the possibility of achieving tremendously important results could justify it. . . .

Choice of Plant Site

Once the scale of production had been agreed upon and the responsibilities assigned, the nature of the plant and its whereabouts had to be decided. The site in the Tennessee Valley, known officially as the Clinton Engineer Works, had been acquired by the Army. . . .

Reconsideration at the end of 1942 led General Groves to the conclusion that this site was not sufficiently isolated for a large-scale plutonium production plant. At that time, it was conceivable that conditions might arise under which a large pile might spread radioactive material over a large enough area to endanger neighboring centers of population. In addition to the requirement of isolation, there remained the requirement of a large power supply which had originally determined the choice of the Tennessee site. To meet these two requirements a new site was chosen and acquired on the Columbia River in the central part of the State of Washington near the Grand Coulee power line. This site was known as the Hanford Engineer Works. . . .

Nature of the Lattice

The lattices we have been describing heretofore consisted of lumps of uranium embedded in the graphite moderator. There are two objections to such a type of lattice for production purposes: first, it is difficult to remove the uranium without disassembling the pile; second, it is difficult to concentrate the coolant at the uranium lumps, which are the points of maximum production of heat. It was fairly obvious that both these difficulties could be avoided if a rod lattice rather than a point lattice could be used, that is, if the uranium could be concentrated along lines passing through the moderator instead of being situated merely at points. . . .

Loading and Unloading

Once the idea of a lattice with cylindrical symmetry was accepted, it became evident that the pile could be unloaded and reloaded without disassembly since the uranium could be pushed out of the cylindrical channels in the graphite moderator and new uranium inserted. The decision had to be made as to whether the uranium should be in the form of long rods, which had advantages from the nuclear-physics point of view, or of relatively short cylindrical pieces, which had advantages from the point of view of handling. In either case, the materials would be so very highly radioactive that unloading would have to be carried out by remote control, and the unloaded uranium would have to be handled by remote control from behind shielding.

Possible Materials; Corrosion

If water was to be used as coolant, it would have to be conveyed to the regions where heat was generated through channels of some sort. Since graphite pipes were not practical, some other kind of pipe would have to be used. But the choice of the material for the pipe, like the choice of all the materials to be used in the pile, was limited by nuclear-physics considerations. The pipes must be made of some material whose absorption cross section for neutrons was not large enough to bring the value of k below unity. Furthermore, the pipes must be made of material which would not disintegrate under the heavy density of neutron and gamma radiation present in the pile. Finally, the pipes must meet all ordinary requirements of cooling-system pipes: they must not leak; they must not corrode; they must not warp. . . .

While the choice of material for the piping was very difficult, similar choices—involving both nuclear-physics criteria and radiation-resistance criteria—had to be made for all other materials that were to be used in the pile. For example, the electric insulating materials to be used in any instruments buried in the pile must not disintegrate under the radiation. In certain instances where control or experimental probes had to be inserted and removed from the pile, the likelihood had to be borne in mind that the probes would become intensely radioactive as a result of their exposure in the pile and that the degree to which this would occur would depend on the material used. . . .

Protection of the Uranium from Corrosion

The most efficient cooling procedure would have been to have the water flowing in direct contact with the uranium in which the heat was being produced. Indications were that this was probably out of the question because the uranium would react chemically with the water, at least to a sufficient extent to put a dangerous amount of radioactive material into solution and probably to the point of disintegrating the uranium slugs. Therefore it was necessary to find some method of protecting the uranium from direct contact with the water. Two possibilities were considered: one was some sort of coating, either by electroplating or dipping; the other was sealing the uranium slug in a protective jacket or "can." Strangely enough, this "canning problem" turned out to be one of the most difficult problems encountered in such piles.

Water Supply

The problem of dissipating thousands of kilowatts of energy is by no means a small one. How much water was needed depended, of course, on the maximum temperature to which the water could safely be heated and the maximum temperature to be expected in the intake from the Columbia River; certainly the water supply requirement was comparable to that of a fair-sized city. Pumping stations, filtration and treatment plants all had to be provided. Furthermore, the system had to be a very reliable one; it was necessary to provide fast-operating controls to shut down the chain-reacting unit in a hurry in case of failure of the water supply. If it was decided to use "once-through" cooling instead of recirculation, a retention basin would be required so that the radioactivity induced in the water might die down before the water was returned to the river. The volume of water discharged was going to be so great that such problems of radioactivity were important, and therefore the minimum time that the water must be held for absolute safety had to be determined. . . .

Shielding

The radiation given off from a pile operating at a high power level is so strong as to make it quite impossible for any of the operating personnel to go near the pile. Furthermore, this radiation, particularly the neutrons, has a pronounced capacity for leaking out through holes or cracks in barriers. The whole of a power pile therefore has to be enclosed in very thick walls of concrete, steel, or other absorbing material. But at the same time it has to be possible to load and unload the pile through these shields and to carry the water supply in and out through the shields. The shields should not only be radiation-tight but air-tight since air exposed to the radiation in the pile would become radioactive.

The radiation dangers that require shielding in the pile continue through a large part of the separation plant. Since the fission products associated with the production of the plutonium are highly radioactive, the uranium after ejection from the pile must be handled by remote control from behind shielding and must be shielded during transportation to the separation plant. All the stages of the separation plant, including analyses, must be handled by remote control from behind shields up to the point where the plutonium is relatively free of radioactive fission products. . . .

[*FROM CHAPTER IX. GENERAL DISCUSSION OF THE SEPARATION OF ISOTOPES*]

FACTORS AFFECTING THE SEPARATION OF ISOTOPES

By definition, the isotopes of an element differ in mass but not in chemical properties. . . . For most practical purposes, therefore, the isotopes of an element are separable only by processes depending on the nuclear mass. . . .

Except in electromagnetic separators, isotope separation depends on small differences in the average behavior of molecules. Such effects are used in six "statistical" separation methods; (1) gaseous diffusion, (2) distillation, (3) centrifugation, (4) thermal diffusion, (5) exchange reactions, (6) electrolysis. Probably only (1), (3), and (4) are suitable for uranium; (2), (5), and (6) are preferred for the separation of deuterium from hydrogen. In all these "statistical" methods the separation factor is small so that many stages are required, but in the case of each method large amounts of material may be handled. All these methods had been tried with some success before 1940; however, none had been used on a large scale and none had been used for uranium. The scale of production by electromagnetic methods was even smaller but the separation factor was larger. There were apparent limitations of scale for the electromagnetic method. There were presumed to be advantages in combining two or more methods because of the differences in performance at different stages of separation. The problem of developing any or all of these separation methods was not a scientific one of principle but a technical one of scale and cost. These developments can therefore be reported more briefly than those of the plutonium project although they are no less important. A pilot plant was built using centrifuges and operated successfully. No large-scale plant was built. Plants were built for the production of heavy water by two different methods. . . .

[*FROM CHAPTER X. THE SEPARATION OF THE URANIUM ISOTOPES BY GASEOUS DIFFUSION*]

Work at Columbia University on the separation of isotopes by gaseous diffusion began in 1940, and by the end of 1942 the problems of large-scale separation of uranium by this method had been well defined. Since the amount of separation that could be effected by a single stage was very small, several thousand successive stages were required. It was found that the best method of connecting the many stages required extensive recycling so that thousands of times as much material would pass through the barriers of the lower stages as would ultimately appear as product from the highest stage.

The principal problems were the development of satisfactory barriers and pumps. Acres of barrier and thousands of pumps were required. The obvious process gas was uranium hexafluoride for which the production and handling difficulties were so great that a search for an alternative was undertaken. Since much of the separation was to be carried out at low pressure, problems of vacuum technique arose, and on a previously unheard-of scale. Many problems of instrumentation and control were solved; extensive use was made of various forms of mass spectrograph.

The research was carried out principally at Columbia under Dunning and Urey. In 1942, the M. W. Kellogg Company was chosen to develop the process and equipment and to design the plant and set up the Kellex Corporation for the purpose. The plant was built by the J. A. Jones Construction Company. The Carbide and Carbon Chemicals Corporation was selected as operating company.

A very satisfactory barrier was developed although the final choice of barrier type was not made until the construction of the plant was well under way at Clinton Engineer Works in Tennessee. Two types of centrifugal blower were developed. . . .

[*FROM CHAPTER XI. ELECTROMAGNETIC SEPARATION OF URANIUM ISOTOPES*]

By the end of December, 1941, when the reorganization of the whole uranium project was effected, Lawrence had already obtained some samples of separated isotopes of uranium and in the reorganization he was officially placed in charge of the preparation of further samples and the making of various associated physical measurements. However, just as the Metallurgical Laboratory very soon shifted its objective from the physics of the chain reaction to the large-scale production of plutonium, the objective of Lawrence's division immediately shifted to the effecting of large-scale separation of uranium isotopes by electromagnetic methods. This change was prompted by the success of the initial experiments at California and by the development at California and at Princeton of ideas on other possible methods. . . .

The calutron mass separator consists of an ion source from which a beam of uranium ions is drawn by an electric field, an accelerating system in which the ions are accelerated to high velocities, a magnetic field in which the ions travel in semicircles of radius depending on ion mass, and a receiving system. The principal problems of this method involved the ion source, accelerating system, divergence of the ion beam, space charge, and utilization of the magnetic field. The chief advantages of the calutron were large separation factor, small hold-up, short start-up time, and flexibility of operation. By the fall of 1942 sufficient progress had been made to justify authorization of plant construction, and a year later the first plant units were ready for trial at the Clinton Engineer Works in Tennessee.

Research and development work on the calutron were carried out principally at the Radiation Laboratory of the University of California, under the direction of Lawrence. Westinghouse, General Electric, and Allis Chalmers constructed a majority of the parts; Stone and Webster built the plant, and Tennessee Eastman operated it.

Since the calutron separation method was one of batch operations in a large number of largely independent units, it was possible to introduce important improvements even after plant operation had begun.

In the summer of 1944 a thermal-diffusion separation plant was built at the Clinton Engineer Works to furnish enriched feed material for the electromagnetic plant and thereby increase the production rate of this latter plant. The design of the thermal-diffusion plant was based on the results of research carried out at the Naval Research Laboratory and on the pilot plant built by the Navy Department at the Philadelphia Navy Yard.

Although research work on the calutron was started later than on the centrifuge and diffusion systems, the calutron plant was the first to produce large amounts of the separated isotopes of uranium. . . .

[*FROM CHAPTER XII. THE WORK ON THE ATOMIC BOMB*]

The entire purpose of the work described in the preceding chapters was to explore the possibility of creating atomic bombs and to produce the concentrated fissionable materials which would be required in such bombs. . . . Security considerations prevent a discussion of many of the most important phases of this work. . . .

In the choice of a site for this atomic-bomb laboratory, the all-important considerations were secrecy and safety. It was therefore decided to establish the laboratory in an isolated location and to sever unnecessary connection with the outside world.

By November, 1942, a site had been chosen—at Los Alamos, New Mexico. It was located on a mesa about 30 miles from Santa Fe. One asset of this site was the availability of considerable area for proving grounds, but initially the only structures on the site consisted of a handful of buildings which once constituted a small boarding school. There was no laboratory, no library, no shop, no adequate power plant. The sole means of approach was a winding mountain road. That the handicaps of the site were overcome to a considerable degree is a tribute to the unstinting efforts of the scientific and military personnel.

J. R. Oppenheimer has been director of the laboratory from the start. . . .

Naturally, the task of assembling the necessary apparatus, machines and equipment was an enormous one. Three carloads of apparatus from the Princeton project filled some of the most urgent requirements. A cyclotron from Harvard, two Van de Graaff generators from Wisconsin, and a Cockcroft-Walton high-voltage device from Illinois soon arrived. As an illustration of the speed with which the laboratory was set up, we may record that the bottom pole piece of the cyclotron magnet was not laid until April 14, 1943, yet the first experiment was performed in early July. Other apparatus was acquired in quantity; subsidiary laboratories were built. Today this is probably the best-equipped physics research laboratory in the world. . . .

By definition, an explosion is a sudden and violent release of a large amount of energy in a small region. To produce an efficient explosion in an atomic bomb, the parts of the bomb must not become appreciably separated before a substantial fraction of the available nuclear energy has been released, since expansion leads to increased escape of neutrons from the system and thus to premature termination of the chain reaction. Stated differently, the efficiency of the atomic bomb will depend on the ratio of (a) the speed with which neutrons generated by the first fissions get into other nuclei and produce further fission, and (b) the speed with which the bomb flies apart. Using known principles of energy generation, temperature and pressure rise, and expansion of solids and vapors, it was possible to estimate the order of magnitude of the time interval between the beginning and end of the nuclear chain reaction. Almost all the technical difficulties of the project come from the extraordinary brevity of this time interval.

No self-sustaining chain reaction could be produced in a block of pure uranium metal, no matter how large, because of parasitic capture of the neutrons by U-238. This conclusion has been borne out by various theoretical calculations and also by direct experiment. For purposes of producing a nonexplosive pile, the trick of using a lattice and a moderator suffices—by reducing parasitic capture sufficiently. For purposes of producing an explosive unit, however, it turns out that this process is unsatisfactory on two counts. First, the thermal neutrons take so long (so many micro-seconds) to act that only a feeble explosion would result. Second, a pile is ordinarily far too big to be transported. It is therefore necessary to cut down parasitic capture by removing the greater part of the U-238—or to use plutonium.

Naturally, these general principles—and others—had been well established before the Los Alamos project was set up.

Critical Size

The calculation of the critical size of a chain-reacting unit is a problem that has already been discussed in connection with piles. Although the calculation is simpler for a homogeneous metal unit than for a lattice, inaccuracies remained in the course of the early work, both because of lack of accurate knowledge of constants and because of mathematical difficulties. For example, the scattering, fission, and absorption cross sections of the nuclei involved all vary with neutron velocity. The details of such variation were not known experimentally and were difficult to take into account in making calculations. By the spring of 1943 several estimates of critical size had been made using various methods of calculation and using the best available nuclear constants, but the limits of error remained large.

The Reflector or Tamper

In a uranium-graphite chain-reacting pile the critical size may be considerably reduced by surrounding the pile with a layer of graphite, since such an envelope "reflects" many neutrons back into the pile. A similar envelope can be used to reduce the critical size of the bomb, but here the envelope has an additional role: its very inertia delays the expansion of the reacting material. For this reason such an envelope is often called a tamper. Use of a tamper clearly makes for a longer lasting, more energetic, and more efficient explosion. The most effective tamper is the one having the highest density; high tensile strength turns out to be unimportant. It is a fortunate coincidence that materials of high density are also excellent as reflectors of neutrons.

Efficiency

As has already been remarked, the bomb tends to fly to bits as the reaction proceeds and this tends to stop the reaction. To calculate how much the bomb has to expand before the reaction stops is relatively simple. The calculation of how long this expansion takes and how far the reaction goes in that time is much more difficult.

While the effect of a tamper is to increase the efficiency both by reflecting neutrons and by delaying the expansion of the bomb, the effect on the efficiency is not as great as on the critical mass. The reason for this is that the process of reflection is relatively time-consuming and may not occur extensively before the chain reaction is terminated.

Detonation and Assembly

It is impossible to prevent a chain reaction from occurring when the size exceeds the critical size. For there are always enough neutrons (from cosmic rays, from spontaneous fission reactions, or from alpha-particle-induced reactions in impurities) to initiate the chain. Thus until detonation is desired, the bomb must consist of a number of separate pieces each one of which is below the critical size either by reason of small size or unfavorable shape. To produce detonation, the parts of the bomb must be brought together rapidly. In the course of this assembly process the chain reaction is likely to start—because of the presence of stray neutrons—*before* the bomb has reached its most compact (most reactive) form. Thereupon the explosion tends to prevent the bomb from reaching that most compact form. Thus it may turn out that the explosion is so inefficient as to be relatively useless. The problem, therefore, is twofold: (1) to reduce the time of assembly to a minimum; and (2) to reduce the number of stray (predetonation) neutrons to a minimum.

Some consideration was given to the danger of producing a "dud" or a detonation so inefficient that even the bomb itself would not be completely destroyed. This would, of course, present the enemy with a supply of highly valuable material. . . .

Method of Assembly

Since estimates had been made of the speed that would bring together subcritical masses of U-235 rapidly enough to avoid predetonation, a good deal of thought had been given to practical methods of doing this. The obvious method of very rapidly assembling an atomic bomb was to shoot one part as a projectile in a gun against a second part as a target. The projectile mass, projectile speed, and gun caliber required were not far from the range of standard ordnance practice, but novel problems were introduced by the importance of achieving sudden and perfect contact between projectile and target, by the use of tampers, and by the requirement of portability. None of these technical problems had been studied to any appreciable extent prior to the establishment of the Los Alamos laboratory. . . .

In April, 1943, the available information of interest in connection with the design of atomic bombs was preliminary and inaccurate. Further and extensive theoretical work on critical size, efficiency, effect of tamper, method of detonation, and effectiveness was urgently needed. Measurements of the nuclear constants of U-235, plutonium, and tamper material had to be extended and improved. In the cases of U-235 and plutonium, tentative measurements had to be made using only minute quantities until larger quantities became available.

Besides these problems in theoretical and experimental physics, there was a host of chemical, metallurgical and technical problems that had hardly been touched. Examples were the purification and fabrication of U-235 and plutonium, and the fabrication of the tamper. Finally, there were problems of instantaneous assembly of the bomb that were staggering in their complexity.

The new laboratory improved the theoretical treatment of design and performance problems, refined and extended the measurements of the nuclear constants involved, developed methods of purifying the materials to be used and, finally, designed and constructed operable atomic bombs. . . .

1945

THE SCIENTIFIC MEANING OF CHANCE *

GILBERT N. LEWIS

. . . Do you believe in miracles? Let us consider a box with a one-gram weight resting on its floor. Let us place this box in a bath maintained at an extremely constant temperature, we will say 65° F, and let the whole be protected by the most perfect mechanism that we can think of to shield it from external jars. Let us, in other words, shut it off from all external influences, leaving only a small hole through which we may observe. We may look into the box millions of times and always find the weight upon the floor, and we then state this to be a law of nature. But the time will come when we look in and find the weight some distance from the floor. It will

* Reprinted by permission from *The Yale Review.* Copyright 1926 by The Yale Publishing Association, Inc.

not happen often, but we can calculate with a high degree of accuracy the chance of finding it, let us say, ten centimeters or more from the floor. This chance is so very small that I cannot express it in any ordinary way. We state chances as fractions, but to denote this chance I should have to put down a decimal point and zero after zero, and should spend my whole lifetime before I could write down a number not a zero. But the calculation is none the less exact.

The chance becomes larger if I consider smaller weights and lesser heights from the floor. Let the height be one hundred million times as small and the weight also one hundred million times as small, and then the calculation shows that if we look every second we shall find the weight as far off the floor as this 6.32 times in every million years. If you bet five to one on the appearance of this phenomenon in a million years, you might lose at first, but you would come out ahead in the long run.

If we take a still smaller weight the chance goes up very rapidly, and if we examine particles which are just visible with a good miscroscope, we find them hopping about in what is known as the Brownian movement, and which we now know to be identical with that thermal agitation which all molecules or groups of molecules exhibit, and which always increases with increasing temperature. From a study of these movements Perrin was able to draw some extremely important deductions with the aid of the same formula as I have used in these calculations.

If the jumping of the one-gram weight was a miracle, here in the Brownian movement thousands of such miracles are constantly occurring before our eyes. It is not true that things left to themselves approach a constant state, but only that they approach a state which ordinarily appears constant to us because of the dullness of our perceptions.

It was Maxwell who made the ingenious suggestion of a little demon who could see and distinguish between the individual molecules. Let us consider, as a type of irreversible phenomenon, the mixing of two gases. A container with a partition in the middle has oxygen on one side, nitrogen on the other. If a small hole is made in the partition, the gases mix by diffusion, so that ultimately we cannot distinguish between the contents of the two sides. This, according to the ideas of classical thermodynamics, is a completely irreversible phenomenon. But suppose the demon stationed at the orifice with a small shutter which he can open or close at will, and suppose that he decides to let only oxygen molecules pass in one direction and only nitrogen molecules in the other. Can he not through this exercise of *conscious choice* ultimately restore the original condition, with all the oxygen on the one side and all the nitrogen on the other? That such a reversal of a so-called irreversible process may occur, even without a demoniacal agency, was first recognized by Willard Gibbs, who announced that such a reversal is not an impossibility but only an improbability; and this idea was most successfully developed by Boltzmann.

In order to illustrate the modern statistical view of thermodynamics, let us consider a fresh pack of cards, all sorted, for example, ace, king, queen of spades, ace, king, queen of clubs, and so on. Such a grouping of the cards is easily described and easily discernible. If I spread the pack before you, one-half is obviously black, the other red. If I should put this pack into some sort of shuffling and dealing machine the first deals might give some very singular hands, but as the process continued, a point would be reached where we would say that the pack was well shuffled. Now, any one of the particular arrangements obtained by shuffling is just as improbable *a priori* as the first well-sorted arrangement, and by this we mean that if we note the arrangement, card by card, in a well-shuffled pack, this identical arrangement is no more likely to recur than the arrangement of the fresh pack. Nevertheless, while the number of possible well-sorted or easily *describable* arrangements is very small, there is an enormous number of arrangements of a *nondescript* character. As the shuffling continues, the arrangement constantly changes; there is no approach to any one particular arrangement, but, on the other hand, it rarely happens that a remarkably distinguished arrangement occurs. If one picks up a bridge hand with thirteen trumps, he will probably tell of it to all his friends, and indeed such a hand is a very rare fluctuation from the general run of nondescript hands.

There is a psychological element in all this. If we look down from a window upon a street of New York and see the people emerging from a subway exit, some occurrence may draw our attention to one group of ten people. We make note of their faces and their clothes. They thus become in some measure familiar to us, and it strikes us as remarkable that these ten people are about to melt into the crowds of the great city and will never again meet together. Yet all through the day each will be one of a group which differs from the first only in that we have not become acquainted with its members.

Since the rules of chance arrangement contain every essential feature of the second law of thermodynamics, let me further illustrate by considering a box containing ten black balls at the left and ten white balls at the right. If we shake the box, there will still perhaps be only a few black balls to the right, but if we continue to shake, they will soon be well mixed. Yet as the mixing continues we do not come nearer and nearer to the even distribution of five blacks and five whites on each side. On the contrary, the arrangement of six and four occurs more frequently than that of five and five, and occasionally greater fluctuations from the mean occur. Indeed, if we have the patience to shake the box two or three hundred thousand times we shall probably come to the original well-sorted arrangement, all whites on one side and all blacks on the other; and if we have recorded the result of each shaking, the record will show no particular dissymmetry with respect to the earlier and to the later shakings.

If instead of the twenty balls we had taken a million grains of white and black sand, the mixing would have appeared to be more thorough, but the fluctuations, although not so evident, would still be there, and if we should take an enormously greater number of particles we would have a complete analogy to the mixing of the molecules of oxygen and nitrogen. And here again we must assume the existence of fluctuations from the mean, sometimes small, sometimes great, and after the lapse of a vast period of time even so great as to give once more pure oxygen and pure nitrogen. Here again if there were a way of recording these fluctuations between the original distribution of pure oxygen and pure nitrogen until we arrive once more at the same distribution, there would be nothing in all these fluctuations which would not be symmetrical with respect to past and future.

Are all cases of irreversible phenomena as simple as this? For many years I have found this one of the most perplexing and tantalizing of scientific questions. As long as it was supposed that radiation, even from a single atom, goes out in a way which can never be entirely reversed, there seemed an insurmountable obstacle to the view that all irreversible processes are mere mixings and shufflings, with no element of novelty except that which arises from the vast number of elementary processes involved. But if we now regard radiation also as a process of exchange of energy between two atoms, the emitting and absorbing atoms playing symmetrical parts, this obstacle is removed.

We then find not even a shred of truth left in the statement that an isolated system moves towards a state of equilibrium. It will move towards it and move away from it, and in the long run as often in one direction as in the other. It is only when we start far away from the state of equilibrium, that is, when we start with some state of unusual distinction, and when we follow the system a little way along its path, that we can state that it will as a rule proceed towards more *nondescript* states.

The second law of thermodynamics has come to be regarded as one of the most powerful and inexorable of nature's laws. It is beginning to dominate chemistry and the biological sciences, and its sway extends from the pure sciences into the various domains of technology. Now, however, that we have looked behind the scenes, it almost seems as though it were all a sham, like some silly clown garbed in the ermine of royalty. Stripped of its finery, we find that the second law states that if a pack of cards is thrown into a shuffling machine, the chances are that it will become shuffled.

If this discovery comes to us as a great disillusionment it is only because our minds are tinged from infancy with the hoary superstition of the absolute. We say, "If this great law is not always true what becomes of our other exact laws?" But can we have no reverence for any institution without making the childish assumption of its infallibility? Can we not see that exact laws, like all the other ultimates and absolutes, are as fabulous as the crock of gold at the rainbow's end? We have a sense of contentment as we travel day by day through the beautiful and fertile lands into which we are led by one of these will-o'-the-wisps. It is only after someone cries, "I have caught it in my hands," that we experience the bitterness of disappointment.

Our respect for the great law of entropy need be no less because it has its exceptions, nor yet because it can be reduced to the obvious. Think of all the propositions of Euclidean geometry which can be reduced to the simple statement that there are parallel lines and that there are circles. Familiarity breeds contempt only for artificiality and pretense; and the law of entropy becomes a greater law as we now must limit it by the following statement: an isolated system always proceeds in the direction of greater entropy, provided that it be so far removed from the state of equilibrium that the chance fluctuations in that state may be ignored.

A law of nature becomes a better law when we can predict the exceptions to it. If someone tells you that the sun will continue to rise and set through all future time, you are not deceived by the finality of this statement. You know that here and there through the galaxy of stars many cataclysms occur which would wipe out whole solar systems. If through a study of the average frequency of such occurrences, or through a study of the movements of all known bodies in the neighborhood of the sun, we predict that the earth will be safe for another trillion years, we have far more information than is furnished by the trivial statement that the sun will go on rising forever. . . .

1926

SPACE, TIME AND EINSTEIN *

PAUL R. HEYL

Whether we understand it or not, we have all heard of the Einstein theory, and failure to understand it does not seem incompatible with the holding of opinions on the subject, sometimes of a militant and antagonistic character.

Twenty-four years have elapsed since Einstein published his first paper on relativity, dealing principally with certain relations between mechanics and optics. Since that time a new generation has grown up to whom pre-Einstein science is a matter of history, not of experience. Eleven years after his first paper Einstein published a second, in which he broadened and extended the theory laid down in the first so as to include gravitation.

* Publication approved by the Director of the Bureau of Standards of the U. S. Department of Commerce. Reprinted from *The Scientific Monthly*. Copyright 1929 by The Science Press.

And now again, thirteen years later, in a third paper, Einstein has broadened his theory still farther so as to include the phenomena of electricity and magnetism.

In view of the rekindling of interest in Einstein because of the appearance of his latest paper it may be worth while to reëxamine and restate the primary foundations upon which his theory rests.

The general interest taken in this subject is frequently a matter of wonder to those of us who must give it attention professionally, for there are in modern physical science other doctrines which run closely second to that of Einstein in strangeness and novelty, yet none of these seems to have taken any particular hold on popular imagination.

Perhaps the reason for this is that these theories deal with ideas which are remote from ordinary life, while Einstein lays iconoclastic hands on two concepts about which every intelligent person believes that he really knows something—space and time.

Space and time have been regarded "always, everywhere and by all," as independent concepts, sharply distinguishable from one another, with no correlation between them. Space is fixed, though we may move about in it at will, forward or backward, up or down; and wherever we go our experience is that the properties of space are everywhere the same, and are unaltered whether we are moving or stationary. Time, on the other hand, is essentially a moving proposition, and we must perforce move with it. Except in memory, we can not go back in time; we must go forward, and at the rate at which time chooses to travel. We are on a moving platform, the mechanism of which is beyond our control.

There is a difference also in our measures of space and time. Space may be measured in feet, square feet or cubic feet, as the case may be, but time is essentially one-dimensional. Square hours or cubic seconds are meaningless terms. Moreover, no connection has ever been recognized between space and time measures. How many feet make one hour? A meaningless question, you say, yet something that sounds very much like it has (since Minkowski) received the serious attention of many otherwise reputable scientific men. And now comes Einstein, rudely disturbing these old-established concepts and asking us to recast our ideas of space and time in a way that seems to us fantastic and bizarre.

What has Einstein done to these fundamental concepts?

He has introduced a correlation or connecting link between what have always been supposed to be separate and distinct ideas. In the first place, he asserts that as we move about, the geometrical properties of space, as evidenced by figures drawn in it, will alter by an amount depending on the speed of the observer's motion, thus (through the concept of velocity) linking space with time. He also asserts in the second place that the flow of time, always regarded as invariable, will likewise alter with the motion of the observer, again linking time with space.

For example, suppose that we, with our instruments for measuring space and time, are located on a platform which we believe to be stationary. We can not be altogether certain of this, for there is no other visible object in the universe save another similar platform carrying an observer likewise equipped: but when we observe relative motion between our platform and the other it pleases our intuition to suppose our platform at rest and to ascribe all the motion to the other.

Einstein asserts that if this relative velocity were great enough we might notice some strange happenings on the other platform. True, a rather high velocity would be necessary, something comparable with the speed of light, say 100,000 miles a second; and it is tacitly assumed that we would be able to get a glimpse of the moving system as it flashed by. Granting this, what would we see?

Einstein asserts that if there were a circle painted on the moving platform it would appear to us as an ellipse with its short diameter in the direction of its motion. The amount of this shortening would depend upon the speed with which the system is moving, being quite imperceptible at ordinary speeds. In the limit, as the speed approached that of light, the circle would flatten completely into a straight line—its diameter perpendicular to the direction of motion.

Of this shortening, says Einstein, the moving observer will be unconscious, for not only is the circle flattened in the direction of motion, but the platform itself and all it carries (including the observer) share in this shortening. Even the observer's measuring rod is not exempt. Laid along that diameter of the circle which is perpendicular to the line of motion it would indicate, say, ten centimeters; placed along the shortened diameter, the rod, being itself now shortened in the same ratio, would apparently indicate the same length as before, and the moving observer would have no suspicion of what we might be seeing. In fact, he might with equal right suppose himself stationary and lay all the motion to the account of our platform. And if we had a circle painted on our floor it would appear flattened to him, though not to us.

Again, the clock on the other observer's platform would exhibit to us, though not to him, an equally eccentric behavior. Suppose that other platform stopped opposite us long enough for a comparison of clocks, and then, backing off to get a start, flashed by us at a high speed. As it passed we would see that the other clock was apparently slow as compared with ours, but of this the moving observer would be unconscious.

But could he not observe our clock?

Certainly, just as easily as we could see his.

And would he not see that our clock was now faster than his? "No," says Einstein. "On the contrary, he would take it to be slower."

Here is a paradox indeed! *A*'s clock appears slow to *B* while at the same time *B*'s clock appears slow to *A*! Which is right?

To this question Einstein answers indifferently:

"Either. It all depends on the point of view."

In asserting that the rate of a moving clock is altered by its motion Einstein has not in mind anything so materialistic as the motion interfering with the proper functioning of the pendulum or balance wheel. It is something deeper and more abstruse than that. He means that the flow of time itself is changed by the motion of the system, and that the clock is but fulfilling its natural function in keeping pace with the altered rate of time.

A rather imperfect illustration may help at this point. If I were traveling by train from the Atlantic to the Pacific Coast it would be necessary for me to set my watch back an hour occasionally. A less practical but mathematically more elegant plan would be to alter the rate of my watch before starting so that it would indicate the correct local time during the whole journey. Of course, on a slow train less alteration would be required. The point is this: that a timepiece keeping local time on the train will of necessity run at a rate depending on the speed of the train.

Einstein applies a somewhat similar concept to all moving systems, and asserts that the local time on such systems runs the more slowly the more rapidly the system moves.

It is no wonder that assertions so revolutionary should encounter general incredulity. Skepticism is nature's armor against foolishness. But there are two reactions possible to assertions such as these. One may say: "The man is crazy" or one may ask: "What is the evidence?"

The latter, of course, is the correct scientific attitude. To such a question Einstein might answer laconically: "Desperate diseases require desperate remedies."

"But," we reply, "we are not conscious of any disease so desperate as to require such drastic treatment."

"If you are not," says Einstein, "you should be. Does your memory run back thirty years? Or have you not read, at least, of the serious contradiction in which theoretical physics found itself involved at the opening of the present century?"

Einstein's reference is to the difficulty which arose as a consequence of the negative results of the famous Michelson-Morley experiment and other experiments of a similar nature. The situation that then arose is perhaps best explained by an analogy.

If we were in a boat, stationary in still water, with trains of water-waves passing us, it would be possible to determine the speed of the waves by timing their passage over, say, the length of the boat. If the boat were then set in motion in the same direction in which the waves were traveling, the apparent speed of the waves with respect to the boat would be decreased, reaching zero when the boat attained the speed of the waves; and if the boat were set in motion in the opposite direction the apparent speed of the waves would be increased.

If the boat were moving with uniform speed in a circular path, the apparent speed of the waves would fluctuate periodically, and from the magnitude of this fluctuation it would be possible to determine the speed of the boat.

Now the earth is moving around the sun in a nearly circular orbit with a speed of about eighteen miles per second, and at all points in this orbit light waves from the stars are constantly streaming by. The analogy of the boat and the water-waves suggested to several physicists, toward the close of the nineteenth century, the possibility of verifying the earth's motion by experiments on the speed of light.

True, the speed of the earth in its orbit is only one ten-thousandth of the speed of light, but methods were available of more than sufficient precision to pick up an effect of this order of magnitude. It was, therefore, with the greatest surprise, not to say consternation, that the results of all such experiments were found to be negative; that analogy, for some unexplained reason, appeared to have broken down somewhere between mechanics and optics; that while the speed of water-waves varied as it should with the speed of the observer, the velocity of light seemed completely unaffected by such motion.

Nor could any fault be found with method or technique. At least three independent lines of experiment, two optical and one electrical, led to the same negative conclusion.

This breakdown of analogy between mechanics and optics introduced a sharp line of division into physical science. Now since the days of Newton the general trend of scientific thought has been in the direction of removing or effacing such sharp lines indicating differences in kind and replacing them by differences in degree. In other words, scientific thought is monistic, seeking one ultimate explanation for all phenomena.

Kepler, by his study of the planets, had discovered the three well-known laws which their motion obeys. To him these laws were purely empirical, separate and distinct results of observation. It remained for Newton to show that these three laws were mathematical consequences of a single broader law—that of gravitation. In this, Newton was a monistic philosopher.

The whole of the scientific development of the nineteenth century was monistic. Faraday and Oersted showed that electricity and magnetism were closely allied. Joule, Mayer and others pointed out the equivalence of heat and work. Maxwell correlated light with electricity and magnetism. By the close of the century physical phenomena of all kinds were regarded as forming one vast, interrelated web, governed by some broad and far-reaching law as yet unknown, but whose discovery was confidently expected, perhaps in the near future. Gravitation alone obstinately resisted all attempts to coordinate it with other phenomena.

The consequent reintroduction of a sharp line between mechanics and optics was therefore most disturbing. It was to remove this difficulty that Einstein found it necessary to alter our fundamental ideas regarding space and time. It is obvious that a varying velocity can be made to appear constant if our space and time units vary also in a proper manner, but in introducing such changes we must be careful not to cover up the changes in velocity readily observable in water-waves or sound waves.

The determination of such changes in length and time units is a purely mathematical problem. The solution found by Einstein is what is known as the Lorentz transformation, so named because it was first found (in a simpler form) by Lorentz. Einstein arrived at a more general formula and, in addition, was not aware of Lorentz's work at the time of writing his own paper.

The evidence submitted so far for Einstein's theory is purely retrospective; the theory explains known facts and removes difficulties. But it must be remembered that this is just what the theory was built to do. It is a different matter when we apply it to facts unknown at the time the theory was constructed, and the supreme test is the ability of a theory to predict such new phenomena.

This crucial test had been successfully met by the theory of relativity. In 1916 Einstein broadened his theory to include gravitation, which since the days of Newton had successfully resisted all attempts to bring it into line with other phenomena. From this extended theory Einstein predicted two previously unsuspected phenomena, a bending of light rays passing close by the sun and a shift of the Fraunhofer lines in the solar spectrum. Both these predictions have now been experimentally verified.

Mathematically, Einstein's solution of our theoretical difficulties is perfect. Even the paradox of the two clocks, each appearing slower than the other, becomes a logical consequence of the Lorentz transformation. Einstein's explanation is sufficient, and up to the present time no one has been able to show that it is not necessary.

Einstein himself is under no delusion on this point. He is reported to have said, "No amount of experimentation can ever prove me right; a single experiment may at any time prove me wrong."

Early in the present year Einstein again broadened his theory to include the phenomena of electricity and magnetism. This does not mean that he has given an electromagnetic explanation of gravitation; many attempts of this kind have been made, and all have failed in the same respect—to recognize that there is no screen for gravitation. What Einstein has done is something deeper and broader than that. He has succeeded in finding a formula which may assume two special forms according as a constant which it contains is or is not zero. In the latter case the formula gives us Maxwell's equations for an electromagnetic field; in the former, Einstein's equations for a gravitative field. . . .

Einstein's aim from the first has been to bring order, not confusion; to exhibit all the laws of nature as special cases of one all-embracing law. In his monism he is unimpeachably orthodox.

But there are other monistic philosophers besides scientific men. You will recall Tennyson's vision of

> One law, one element,
> And one far-off, divine event
> To which the whole creation moves.

1929

PHYSICS

History and Biography

CAJORI, FLORIAN, *History of Physics* (New York, The Macmillan Company, 1929).

CAMPBELL, LEWIS, and GARNETT, WILLIAM, *The Life of James Clerk Maxwell* (London, The Macmillan Company, 1882).

CREW, HENRY, *The Rise of Modern Physics* (Baltimore, The Williams & Wilkins Company, 1928).

CROWTHER, J. A., *The Life and Discoveries of Michael Faraday* (London, Society for Promoting Christian Knowledge, 1918).

CURIE, ÈVE, *Madame Curie* (New York, Doubleday & Co., Inc., 1938; also Pocket Books).

DARROW, F. L., *Masters of Science and Invention* (New York, Harcourt, Brace and Company, Inc., 1923).

EINSTEIN, ALBERT, and INFELD, LEOPOLD, *The Evolution of Physics* (New York, Simon & Schuster, 1938).

FRANKLIN, BENJAMIN, *Autobiography*, edited by Carl Van Doren (New York, The Viking Press, 1945).

GLASSER, OTTO, *Wilhelm Conrad Röntgen and the Early History of the Röntgen Rays* (Springfield, Ill., Charles C. Thomas, 1934).

HART, IVOR B., *The Great Physicists* (London, Methuen & Co., Ltd., 1927).

JEANS, SIR JAMES, *The Growth of Physical Ideas* (New York, The Macmillan Co., 1948).

LUCRETIUS, *On the Nature of Things*, translated by Arthur S. Way (London, The Macmillan Co., 1933).

MABEE, CARLETON, *The American Leonardo, a Life of S. F. B. Morse* (New York, Alfred A. Knopf, Inc., 1943).

MACH, ERNST, *History and Root of the Principle of the Conservation of Energy* (Chicago, The Open Court, 1911).

———, *Science of Mechanics—a Critical and Historical Exposition of Its Principles* (Chicago, The Open Court, 1907).

MAGIE, WILLIAM F., *A Source Book in Physics* (New York, McGraw-Hill Book Company, Inc., 1935).

MORE, LOUIS T., *Isaac Newton* (New York, Charles Scribner's Sons, 1934).

———, *The Life and Works of the Honourable Robert Boyle* (New York, Oxford University Press, 1944).

PUPIN, MICHAEL, *From Immigrant to Inventor* (New York, Charles Scribner's Sons, 1924).

STRUTT, ROBERT J., *Life of Lord Rayleigh* (New York, Longmans, Green & Co., 1924).

TAYLOR, LLOYD W., *Physics, the Pioneer Science* (Boston, Houghton Mifflin Company, 1941).

THOMSON, J. A., *Count Rumford of Massachusetts* (New York, Farrar & Rinehart, Inc., 1935).

THOMPSON, SILVANUS P., *Michael Faraday, His Life and Work* (New York, Cassell & Co., 1901).

THOMSON, J. J., *Recollections and Reflections* (London, George Bell & Sons, Ltd., 1936).

TURNER, D. M., *Makers of Science, Electricity and Magnetism* (London, Oxford University Press, 1927).

General

BOYS, C. V., *Soap Bubbles and the Forces Which Mould Them* (New York, Young, 1902).

DARROW, KARL K., *The Renaissance of Physics* (New York, The Macmillan Company, 1936).

DUNNING, J. R., and PAXTON, H. C., *Matter, Energy and Radiation* (New York, McGraw-Hill Book Company, Inc., 1941).

GRAY, GEORGE W., *The Advancing Front of Science* (New York, Whittlesey House, 1937).

HELMHOLTZ, HERMANN VON, *On the Relation of Natural Science to Science in General* (New York, Atkinson, 1900).

KELVIN, LORD (WILLIAM THOMSON), *Popular Lectures and Addresses* (London, The Macmillan Company, 1889–94).

LEMON, HARVEY B., *From Galileo to Cosmic Rays* (Chicago, University of Chicago Press, 1935).

PLANCK, MAX, *The Philosophy of Physics* (New York, W. W. Norton & Company, 1936).

SULLIVAN, J. W. N., *The Bases of Modern Science* (London, Ernest Benn, Ltd., 1928).

SWANN, W. F. G., *The Architecture of the Universe* (New York, The Macmillan Company, 1934).

WIGNER, E. P., editor, *Physical Science and Human Values* (Princeton, Princeton University Press, 1947).

WRIGHT, HAROLD, *University Studies*—Cambridge, see article entitled "The Craft of Experimental Physics" by P. M. S. Blackett (London, I. Nicholas & Watson, 1933).

Light

BRAGG, SIR WILLIAM, *The Story of Electromagnetism* (London, G. Bell & Sons, 1941).

———, *The Universe of Light* (London, G. Bell & Sons, 1933).

COHEN, I. B., *Benjamin Franklin's Experiments;* a new edition of *Franklin's Experiments and Observations on Electricity* (Cambridge, Harvard University Press, 1941).

FARADAY, MICHAEL, *The Chemical History of a Candle* (New York, Harper & Brothers, 1903).
———, *Experimental Researches in Electricity* (New York, E. P. Dutton & Co., Inc., 1912; Everyman).
FLEMING, J. A., *Waves and Ripples in Water, Air and Aether* (London, The Sheldon Press, 1923).
HERTZ, HEINRICH, *Electric Waves: Being Researches on the Propagation of Electric Action with Finite Velocity through Space*, translated by D. E. Jones (New York, The Macmillan Company, 1893).
HOWELL, J. W., and SCHROEDER, H., *History of the Incandescent Lamp* (New York, Maqua Co., 1927).
HUYGHENS, CHRISTIAN, *Treatise on Light*, translated by Silvanus P. Thompson (Chicago, University of Chicago Press, 1945).
LUCKIESH, MATTHEW, *Torch of Civilization: the Story of Man's Conquest of Darkness* (New York, G. P. Putnam's Sons, 1940).
MICHELSON, A. A., *Light Waves and Their Uses* (Chicago, University of Chicago Press, 1903).
MILLER, DAYTON C., *Sparks, Lightning, Cosmic Rays* (New York, The Macmillan Company, 1934).
STOKES, SIR G. G., *On Light* (London, The Macmillan Company, 1887).
THOMPSON, SILVANUS P., *Light Visible and Invisible* (New York, The Macmillan Company, 1897).
TYNDALL, JOHN, *Light and Electricity* (New York, D. Appleton and Co., 1893).

Heat

BOLTON, H. C., *Evolution of the Thermometer* (Philadelphia, Chemical Publishing Co., 1900).
MAXWELL, J. C., *Matter and Motion* (London, Society for Promoting Christian Knowledge, 1920).
———, *Theory of Heat* (London, Longmans, Green & Co., 1871).
TYNDALL, JOHN, *Heat, a Mode of Motion* (New York, D. Appleton and Co., 1873).

Sound

HELMHOLTZ, HERMANN VON, *On the Sensations of Tone*, translated by Alexander J. Ellis (New York, Longmans, Green & Co., 1895).
KNUDSEN, VERN O., *Architectural Acoustics* (New York, John Wiley & Sons, Inc., 1932).
MILLER, DAYTON C., *Anecdotal History of the Science of Sound to the Beginning of the 20th Century* (New York, The Macmillan Company, 1935).
———, *The Science of Musical Sounds* (New York, The Macmillan Company, 1916).

Relativity

DINGLE, HERBERT, *Relativity for All* (London, Methuen & Co., Ltd., 1922).
EINSTEIN, ALBERT, *Relativity: the Special and the General Theory*, translated by Robert W. Lawson (New York, Henry Holt and Company, Inc., 1920).
FRANK, PHILLIP, *Einstein, His Life and Times* (New York, Alfred A. Knopf, Inc., 1947).
GAMOW, GEORGE, *Mr. Tompkins in Wonderland* (New York, The Macmillan Company, 1940).

HEYL, PAUL R., *The Common Sense of the Theory of Relativity* (Baltimore, The Williams & Wilkins Company, 1924).

The Atom

GAMOW, GEORGE, *Mr. Tompkins Explores the Atom* (New York, The Macmillan Company, 1944).
HARRISON, GEORGE R., *Atoms in Action* (New York, William Morrow and Company, Inc., 1941).
HECHT, SELIG, *Explaining the Atom* (New York, The Viking Press, 1947).
HEYL, PAUL R., *Electrons—Nature's Building Blocks* (Indianapolis, P. R. Mallory, 1943).
MILLIKAN, ROBERT A., *The Electron, Its Isolation and Measurement* (Chicago, University of Chicago Press, 1924).
MILLS, JOHN, *Electronics, Today and Tomorrow* (New York, D. Van Nostrand Company, Inc., 1944).
ROBERTSON, JOHN K., *Atomic Artillery: Modern Alchemy for Everyman* (New York, D. Van Nostrand Company, Inc. 1937).
SMYTH, HENRY DEW., *Atomic Energy for Military Purposes* (Princeton, Princeton University Press, 1945).
SOLOMON, ARTHUR K., *Why Smash Atoms?* (Cambridge, Harvard University Press, 1946).

Aeronautics

BLACK, ARCHIBALD, *The Story of Flying* (New York, Whittlesey House, 1943).
CLEVENGER, CLOYD P., *Modern Flight* (New York, Noble and Noble, Inc., 1941).
GRAY, GEORGE W., *Frontiers of Flight* (Alfred A. Knopf, 1948).
JORDANOFF, ASSEN, *Power and Flight* (New York, Harper & Brothers, 1944).
LEY, WILLY, *Rockets: the Future of Travel Beyond the Stratosphere* (New York, The Viking Press, 1944).
MILBANK, JEREMIAH JR., *The First Century of Flight in America* (Princeton, Princeton University Press, 1943).
SHIELDS, BERT A., *Air Pilot Training* (New York, Whittlesey House, 1939).
SMITH, HENRY L., *Airways: the History of Commercial Aviation in the United States* (New York, Alfred A. Knopf., 1942).
WRIGHT, BAILEY AYERS, and others, *Flight, a General Survey of Fundamentals of Aviation* (Chicago, American Technical Society, 1941).

Applications in Engineering and Industry

ANDRADE, E. N. DAC., *Engines* (New York, Harcourt, Brace and Company, Inc., 1928).
APPLEYARD, R., *Pioneers of Electrical Communication* (London, The Macmillan Company, 1930).
BLACK, ARCHIBALD, *The Story of Bridges* (New York, Whittlesey House, 1936).
——, *The Story of Tunnels* (New York, Whittlesey House, 1937).
BURTON, E. F., and KOHL, W. H., *The Electron Microscope* (New York, Reinhold Publishing Company, 1942).
DAVIS, WATSON, *The Story of Copper* (New York, The Century Co., 1924).
DEFOREST, LEE, *Television, Today and Tomorrow* (New York, The Dial Press, 1942).

EASTMAN KODAK Co., *Elementary Photographic Chemistry* (Rochester, Eastman Kodak Co., 1941).

———, *How to Make Good Pictures: the Complete Handbook for the Amateur Photographer* (Rochester, Eastman Kodak Co., 1943).

FISKE, BRADLEY A., *Invention, the Master-Key to Progress* (New York, E. P. Dutton & Co., Inc., 1921).

FLEXNER, JAMES T., *Steamboats Come True: American Inventors in Action* (New York, The Viking Press, 1944).

HENRY, ROBERT S., *This Fascinating Railroad Business* (New York, The Bobbs Merrill Co., 1943).

HOLLAND, MAURICE, *Industrial Explorers* (New York, Harper & Brothers, 1928).

HOLMES, RICHARD E., *Air Conditioning in Summer and Winter* (New York, McGraw-Hill Book Company, Inc., 1938).

HYLANDER, C. J., and HARDING, ROBERT, JR., *An Introduction to Television* (New York, The Macmillan Company, 1941).

Joint Board on Science Information Policy for: O.S.R.D., War Dept. & Navy Dept. *Radar, a Report on Science at War* (Washington, Office of War Information, 1945).

MACKENZIE, C. D., *Alexander Graham Bell* (Boston, Houghton Mifflin Company, 1928).

MACLAREN, MALCOLM, *The Rise of the Electrical Industry during the Nineteenth Century* (Princeton, Princeton University Press, 1943).

MEES, C. E. K., *Photography* (New York, The Macmillan Company, 1942).

PARKER, CHARLES M., *Steel in Action* (Lancaster, Pa., Jacques Cattell Press, 1943).

PHILLIPS, CHARLES J., *Glass, the Miracle Maker, Its History, Technology and Applications* (New York, Pitman Pub. Corp., 1941).

STANGLE, WILLIAM H., *An Air Conditioning Primer, the A-B-C of Air Conditioning* (New York, McGraw-Hill Book Company, Inc., 1940).

STEINMAN, DAVID B., and WATSON, SARA RUTH, *Bridges and Their Builders* (New York, G. P. Putnam's Sons, 1941).

TAFT, ROBERT, *Photography and the American Scene, a Social History* (New York, The Macmillan Company, 1938).

USHER, ABBOTT P., *A History of Mechanical Inventions* (New York, McGraw-Hill Book Company, 1929).

WEIL, B. H., and ANHORN, V. J., *Plastic Horizons* (Lancaster, Pa., Jacques Cattell Press, 1944).

VI

CHEMISTRY

SCIENCE, as you have seen repeatedly in these pages, knows no national boundaries. Like music, it speaks a universal language. Lavoisier, founder of modern chemistry, was a Frenchman. During the Revolution, his country, with the cry "The Republic has no need of savants," cut off his head. Priestley, with Lavoisier one of the giants of modern chemistry, was an English clergyman who fled to America as a result of political persecution. Mendelejeff, whose Periodic Table brought order out of chaos in chemistry, was a Russian born in Siberia. He made a balloon ascension in 1887 to observe a solar eclipse. The comment of his peasant neighbors is worth repeating: "He flew on a bubble and pierced the sky and for this the authorities made him a chemist." Willard Gibbs, whose Phase Rule is a landmark in physical chemistry, lived a quiet, secluded life as a New England teacher. August Kekulé, the German, one of the founders of organic chemistry, was an intuitive genius. Here is his own picture of how, while on a visit to London, he made one of his great discoveries:

> I sank into a reverie. The atoms flitted about before my eyes. I had always seen them in movement, these little beings, but I had never succeeded in interpreting the manner of their movement. That day I saw how two small ones often joined into a little pair; how a larger took hold of two smaller, and a still larger clasped three or even four of the small ones, and how all spun round in a whirling round-dance. I saw how the larger ones formed a row and only at the end of the chain smaller ones trailed along. The cry of the conductor, "Clapham Road," woke me up from my reverie, but I occupied part of the night in putting at least sketches of these dream-products on paper. Thus originated the structure-theory.

In the first two articles in this section, you will find incorporated a number of classic examples of chemical research. Ida Freund, in her brilliant essay "The Methods of the Inductive Sciences," lets three outstanding chemists explain the exact methods which they used to solve specific problems and to test the accuracy of the solutions. This article complements those by Huxley and Davis in the first section. President Conant of Harvard puts the case method to different use in the selection on "Combustion" from his important new book *On Understanding Science.* In explaining the strategy and tactics of science, President Conant believes, to quote from his book, that "The stumbling way in which even the ablest of the early scientists had to fight through thickets of erroneous observations, misleading generalizations, inadequate formulations, and unconscious prejudices is the story which . . . needs telling."

Another great advance in chemistry is recorded in "The Periodic Classification of the Elements." Here Professor Ehret reproduces Mendelejeff's first periodic table of 1872, as well as one of the latest (1947) tables, and shows that the intervening development is a striking example of the coöperative nature of scientific progress.

In "The Task of the Organic Chemist," G. Ross Robertson of the University of California offers a broad examination of the whole subject of organic chemistry—some astonishing statistics on the trillions of possible organic compounds, material on physical chemistry and how the gap between physical and organic chemistry has gradually lessened, the importance of Pregl's technique of microanalysis, and the possibilities for the future of organic chemistry which the electron microscope holds.

In "Order and Chaos in the World of Atoms," B. C. Saunders and R. E. D. Clark of Cambridge write with characteristic British clarity of the chemical world as it appears to us today. The bonds that hold chemicals together and the architectural feats the chemist must accomplish to make new compounds, are described with figures of speech of great vividness. Here the border line between physics and chemistry becomes barely discernible.

How are the discoveries discussed in these articles to be used by the applied scientist? Robert E. Rose, who has headed the Du Pont Laboratories, describes the industrial use of some of the more important chemical compounds in "The Foundations of Chemical Industry." More specifically, Willis A. Gibbons, research expert at the United States Rubber Company, tells how "Bouncing Molecules" do the job that makes them so important in daily living and world politics.

Finally, Linus Pauling of the California Institute of Technology takes us to another boundary of the field of chemistry. As medicine becomes a more mature, more exact science, it relies more and more on chemical research. Not only is "Molecular Architecture and Medical Research" an inspiring article in itself, but it gives a hint of a development which the future may hold—in which the sciences of living things may learn to express themselves in chemical and physical terms, mathematically defined.

THE METHOD OF THE INDUCTIVE SCIENCES *

IDA FREUND

The object of all the Natural Sciences is the acquisition of knowledge concerning the natural objects surrounding us, as we apprehend them by our senses; of the changes occurring in these objects, together with the laws governing these changes; and of the more proximate or more ultimate causes, to the operation of which are due the individual phenomena and the general laws comprising these. The method now commonly employed for this object is that of proceeding from the observation and the study of the individual phenomena to the detection of uniformities in these, that is, to the law; from that which refers to one to that which refers to many; from the special to the general, by the process termed *Induction.* And the knowledge thus acquired is next utilised in the inverse process, in which from the general laws obtained by induction, inferences are drawn for the purpose of explaining the observed phenomena and of foretelling the occurrence of others. This process, termed *Deduction,* proceeds on the principle that what is asserted to be true of all similar phenomena of a special kind will also be true of any one individually; it argues from the many to the one; from the general to the special. But the inferences thus drawn according to the laws of thought are again checked and verified by appeal to the actual facts, by the study of the phenomena the course of which deduction foretells; and exact coincidence between what actually happens and what had been foretold theoretically, is made the test for the correctness of the inductive and deductive processes by which these inferences had been arrived at.

Knowledge of the objects surrounding us has been stated to be the common object of all natural sciences. But as knowledge grew, the need for classification and specialisation became evident, and thus there arose a division between the sciences, in which Chemistry has taken for its province one side of the study of the materials of which these objects are composed. Leaving Physics, the science most closely related to it, to investigate the properties common to all kinds of matter and differing only in degree, such as density, power of conducting an electric current, etc., Chemistry deals with the properties which belong to certain kinds of matter and not to others, which characterise one kind of matter and differentiate it from all other matter.

For instance, it is a common property of all kinds of matter to undergo change in volume on the application of heat, but each substance has its own characteristic coefficient of expansion; on the other hand it is a specific

* From *The Study of Chemical Composition* by Ida Freund, Cambridge University Press. Reprinted by permission from the publishers.

property of the solid called red precipitate, that above a certain temperature the further addition of heat transforms it into liquid mercury and gaseous oxygen.

A not uncommon description of Chemistry as "the science dealing with the study of all the different homogeneous kinds of matter met with in nature, and with the permanent changes these can undergo when transformed into other kinds of matter" gives the basis for the usual subdivision of this science into two parts, (I.) descriptive and classificatory, (II.) theoretical. Of these the first has to do with the investigation of the properties peculiar to each of the different kinds of matter, and the classification of all matter according to these properties; that is, the putting together of those kinds of matter which agree in having in common a greater or lesser number of properties, and the separation of these from all the other kinds of matter which do not possess those particular properties. The second is mainly concerned with the facts and laws observed in the study of chemical change, and of the composition of the substances undergoing or resulting from the change.

Thus theoretical chemistry has to deal with two kinds of problems: (i) with those which relate to the changes that matter can undergo, and to the laws regulating these changes; and since change can only be realised by a comparison of the initial and the final condition, (ii) with those referring to its composition. Function and composition are therefore the two kinds of phenomena studied in theoretical chemistry. Mechanical analogies are dangerous, but the comparison of these two aspects of theoretical chemistry to dynamics and statics respectively may be ventured on because it has at any rate become justified by long-established use. To keep these two sets of problems completely separate would be very difficult and unsatisfactory, whatever the form chosen for the presentation of the subject, but when that of the historical development is adopted it becomes practically impossible. And hence, though the subject of this book is professedly the theoretical chemistry of composition, the discussion of dynamical problems cannot and will not be altogether excluded.

The general remarks made at the outset concerning the method now followed in the building up of the Natural Sciences apply of course in every detail to the special case of theoretical chemistry. But before showing how this method has operated in the development of this particular branch of science, it may be advisable to discuss separately the processes involved, their sequence and interdependence.

The beginning is made by the recognition of individual phenomena, leading to what is called the knowledge of facts. This knowledge may be gained either by direct observation of the phenomena occurring in nature, or of those which have been caused by some act undertaken by ourselves for that purpose. "Observation" and "Experiment" are the names given to these two modes of collecting knowledge of facts.

"When we merely note and record the phenomena which occur around us in the ordinary course of nature we are said to *observe*. When we change the course of nature by the intervention of our will and muscular powers, and thus produce unusual combinations and conditions of phenomena, we are said to *experiment*. Sir John Herschel has justly remarked that we might properly call these two modes of experience 'passive' and 'active' observation—an experiment differs from a mere observation in the fact that we more or less influence the character of the events which we observe." (Jevons, *Principles of Science.*)

The different behaviour of iron, which rusts in air, and of gold, which remains unchanged, had no doubt been observed as a natural occurrence long before experiments were performed in which these metals were exposed to the influence of heat, of water, of acids, etc., and the comparative effect produced on them by these various agents noted. Important and valuable as is the observation of naturally occurring phenomena, yet for the advance of science, experiment is paramount.

"When Galileo let balls of a particular weight, which he had determined himself, roll down an inclined plane; or when Torricelli made the air carry a weight, which he had previously determined to be equal to that of a certain column of water; when at a still later stage Stahl changed metal into calx, and calx back again into metal, by first withdrawing something and then restoring it; then a new light was flashed on all students of nature. . . . Reason, holding in one hand its principles according to which concordant phenomena alone can be admitted as laws of nature, and in the other hand the experiment which it has devised according to those principles, must approach nature for instruction; but not as a pupil, to be taught just what the master pleases, but as a judge, who forces the witnesses to answer the questions he puts to them. . . . Thus after many centuries of groping, the study of nature was first made to walk along the sure path of a science." (Kant's *Critique of Pure Reason*, Second Preface.)

Before they can become material for the building up of a science, it is essential that the occurrences themselves should be correctly apprehended, and that the relation between an effect observed and that which caused it should be ascertained.

"In order that the facts obtained by observation and experiment may be capable of being used in furtherance of our exact and solid knowledge, they must be apprehended and analysed according to some Conceptions which, applied for this purpose, give distinct and definite results, such as can be steadily taken hold of and reasoned from." (Whewell, *Philosophy of the Inductive Sciences.*)

To illustrate the two distinct points involved in the above:

We all have heard about the sea-serpent, but should not find anything about such an animal in a treatise on zoology, and that because the tales concerning it cannot be looked upon as trustworthy evidence. No doubt there is a great difference in the number of occurrences reported to the Society for Psychical Research and that used by it as the basis of its work. And to give a chemical example: Regnault had by the action of caustic potash on ethylene chloride (a substance consisting of carbon, hydrogen, and chlorine, and prepared by the direct union of olefiant gas and chlorine) obtained a new substance differing from the parent one in that the elements of hydrochloric acid had been withdrawn, but still containing carbon, hydrogen, and chlorine. This substance was termed vinyl-chloride,[1] and at one time it was of the utmost interest to chemists to establish beyond doubt whether another substance having a percentage composition identical with that of Regnault's compound but different properties, did or did not exist. It was maintained by certain chemists that by an altogether different process they had obtained a substance having the percentage composition of vinyl-chloride but entirely different properties.[2] The experiments relating to the production of this substance were repeated by Kekulé and Zincke, who found "that the most remarkable property of this remarkable compound was its non-existence." (Schorlemmer, *Rise and Development of Organic Chemistry*.)

And if caution is required as to what should and what should not be accepted as "facts," it is none the less so as regards the relation between causes and effects. A certain effect undoubtedly does occur, but what has been its real cause? The correct correlation may be a matter of considerable difficulty, because the conditions under which a certain effect is observed to occur are always very complex; a large number of these may be effective at the same time, and it does not follow that those which are most easily apprehended are also those which are really determinant. The correct solution of such a problem, though relating to one fact only, the referring of an effect observed to the real cause producing it, involves the same mental and experimental processes, and the same sequence of these, as does the treatment of a whole collection of facts; and hence a detailed consideration of some such typical cases becomes important. A short account will therefore be given of certain investigations, undertaken with the object of assigning to a phenomenon observed its true cause, from which will be deduced the general method followed in all such cases.

In 1770, very early in his career, Lavoisier presented to the Académie des Sciences a paper entitled "On the Nature of Water and on the Experiments Adduced in Proof of the Possibility of Its Change into Earth." [3] This paper exhibits as well as any of his later ones the peculiar characteristics of Lavoisier's method and style, that is, it is marked by the display of extraordinary genius. Lavoisier thus enunciates the object of the investigation:

---

[1] $C_2H_4Cl_2 + KOH = C_2H_3Cl + KCl + H_2O$
ethylene chloride; vinyl chloride

[2] $C_2H_4O + COCl_2 = C_2H_3Cl + CO_2 + HCl$
aldehyde + phosgene; ↓ supposed different compound, proved to be a mixture of aldehyde and phosgene.

[3] *Œuvres*, II. (p. 1).

"I find myself confronted with the task of settling by decisive experiments a question of interest in physics, namely, whether water can be changed into earth, as was thought by the old philosophers, and still is thought by some chemists of the day."

He begins by investigating whether the fact stated is correct, whether earth (solid matter) is really produced in an operation in which, at any rate apparently, water plays the determining part. This fact he finds vouched for historically. Plants had been made to grow, deriving their increase in weight seemingly only from the water supplied to them. Van Helmont had planted a willow weighing 5 lbs. in 200 lbs. of earth thoroughly dried before weighing, then moistened with distilled water, and always fed with such water only. A suitable hood kept out dust, and after five years the willow was found to weigh 169 lbs. and 3 ozs., whilst the earth after again being dried and then weighed, had lost 2 ozs. only. Hence 164 lbs. of willow were assumed to have been produced from water only. Similar experiments seemed very popular and they all led to the same inference. But still more to the point were the observations of Boyle, Becher, Stahl and others, all of whom had found as the result of experiment that water, no matter how often it had been distilled previously,—that is, made to undergo an operation in which the gasifiable water could be separated from any non-volatile solid held by it in solution—yet left on evaporation an earthy residue. But Lavoisier is not content to simply accept the fact; he repeats the experiment and finds that in distilling rain water, a very pure form of water, from a glass vessel, he obtains an earthy residue; and he at once goes further, ascertaining a fact well calculated to throw some light on the cause of the phenomenon investigated. He compares the density of the distillate with that of the original rain water and finds it practically identical:

"I thought that I might infer from this experiment one of two things, either that the earth which I had separated by the distillation was of such a nature that it could be held in solution in the water without increasing its density, or at least without increasing it as much as other substances would do; or else that this earth was not yet in the water when I had determined its density, that it had been formed during distillation, in short that it was a product of the operation. To decide with certainty which of these views I should adopt, no means has seemed to me more suitable than to repeat precisely the same experiment in hermetically sealed vessels, keeping exact count of the weight of the vessel and of that of the water used in the experiment.

For if it should be a case of the fire matter passing through the glass and combining with the water, there must needs occur after many distillations an increase in the total weight of the matter, that is to say, in the combined weight of the water, the earth and the vessel. The same thing should not occur if the earth had been formed at the expense of the water or of the vessel; but if so, there must needs also be found a diminution in the weight of one or the other of these two substances, and this diminution must be exactly equal to the quantity of earth separated."

Here then we find Lavoisier enumerating the various possible causes for the formation of the earth, and in each case drawing the inference as to what would be the influence of the operation of this particular cause on the weights of the whole system and of its component parts. The paragraph just quoted, when cast into tabular form, would present itself thus:

Earth is formed by the repeated distillation of water in a hermetically sealed glass vessel

cause:	the earth has its origin in something external to the vessel and its contents	the earth has its origin in the vessel and its contents themselves
inference:	as the earth forms, the weight of the vessel and its contents should increase.	as the earth forms, the weight of the vessel and its contents should remain the same.

cause:	the earth comes from the vessel	the earth comes from the water	the earth comes from the vessel and the water
inference:	the vessel loses weight, and this loss is exactly equal to the weight of earth formed.	the weight of the vessel remains the same.	the vessel loses weight, but not to the extent of the weight of earth formed.

It is evident then what quantities must be determined experimentally, in order to settle to which of these theoretical inferences the actually occurring phenomenon corresponds, and hence what is the cause sought for.

A special glass vessel termed a pelican, the use of which for repeated distillation goes back to alchemical times, was employed.

John French, in *The Art of Distillation,* 1650, gives this illustration:

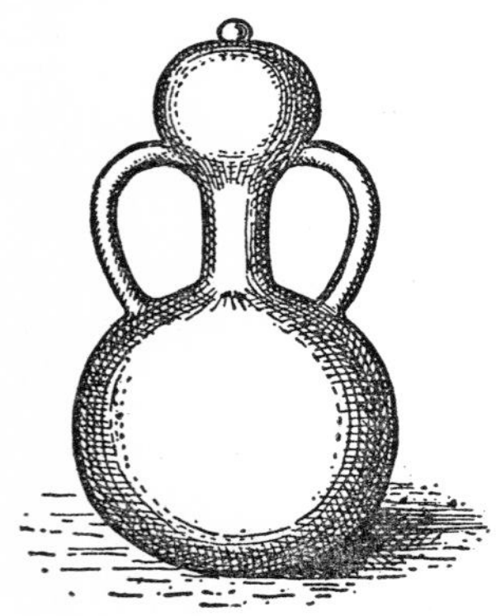

FORM OF A PELICAN

"The matter must be put in at the top, which afterwards must be closed up."

"A pelican is a flask devised for the circulation, the rising and falling back, of liquids, and therefore adapted for distillation, for which purpose it is provided with handle-like tubes reaching almost to the top, and curving back into the sides, like a pelican plucking at its own breast. The lower bulb is the larger of the two, and communicates with the neck, which terminates in a small top with an opening. But of this vessel also there are very many different varieties." [1]

The pelican was weighed empty in a balance specially constructed for the purpose, and surpassing in sensitiveness the instruments of that time. A certain amount of water purified by repeated distillation was introduced into the pelican, the whole heated gently on a sand-bath, and

[1] "Pelecanus est ampulla circulatoria, ascensui descensuiq.; atque ita vario discursui spirituum apta, cuius gratia ansata est canalibus, prope caput productis, et in latus reflexis, instar pelicani pectus suum fodientis. Venter inferius grandior est; inde quasi in

the stopper closing the vessel lifted from time to time to allow the air to escape. As soon as it could be assumed that all the air had been expelled, the stopper was fixed in securely and the pelican with the water contained in it weighed. The whole apparatus was then surrounded by sand, and heating was begun on October 24th, 1768; for 25 days no change was noticed, on December 20th solid particles were observed floating about, the quantity of these was seen to increase until on February 1st, 1769, the experiment was stopped, lest by some accident the results of this long operation should be lost. The whole apparatus was then weighed again. The values obtained in the different weighings were:

	Livres	*Onces*	*Gros*	*Grains* [1]
Weight before heating on Oct. 24, 1768, of the empty pelican	1	10	7	21·50
Weight before heating on Oct. 24, 1768, of the pelican and water	5	9	4	41·50
∴ Weight of the water	3	14	5	20·00
Weight after heating from Oct. 24 to Feb. 1st, of the pelican, water and earth	5	9	4	41·75
∴ Change in weight	0	0	0	0·25

"The weight at the end differs only by one quarter of a grain [2] from that determined before the operation; but so trifling a difference can be neglected because the accuracy of the balance is not great enough to allow me to answer for so small a quantity. . . . From the fact that no increase had been found in the total weight of the matter, it was natural to conclude that it was not fire matter, nor any other extraneous body, that had penetrated the substance of the glass and combined with the water to form the earth. It remained to determine whether the earth owed its origin to a destruction of a portion of the water, or of the glass; and nothing was easier. With the precautions I had taken it was only a case of determining whether it was the weight of the vessel or that of the water contained in it that had suffered diminution."

The pelican was next unstoppered, a process attended with difficulty, and thereby affording conclusive proof that the vessel had been securely closed, no air having been able to leak in. It was emptied, and the water, together with the solid suspended in it, carefully preserved in a glass vessel. The empty pelican was weighed with the following results:

	Livres	*Onces*	*Gros*	*Grains*
Weight of the vessel in which water had been distilled 100 days	1	10	7	4·12
Original weight of the vessel	1	10	7	21·50
∴ Loss of weight sustained by the vessel ...	0	0	0	17·38

"Therefore it was clearly shown that it was the substance of the glass itself which had supplied the earth separated from the water during the digestion, that what had happened was merely a solution of the glass; but in order to completely

collum coit, cui caput paruum cum foramine impositum est, quamquam etiam in hac vase mira sit varietas." (Libavius, *Alchymia*, 1595.)

[1] Old French measures: 1 livre = 16 onces à 8 gros à 72 grains;
1 livre = 489·5058 grams; 1 once = 30·59 grams; 1 grain = 0·053 gram.

[2] 1 quarter grain = ·013 gram.

accomplish my object, it still remained for me to compare the weight of the earth which had separated from the water during the digestion, with the diminution in weight sustained by the pelican. These two quantities should of course be equal, and if there had been found a considerable excess in the earth, it would have become necessary to conclude from it that it had not been furnished by the glass alone."

The weight of this earth was ascertained by adding together the weight of the solid actually suspended in the water, and that obtained from the water by evaporating it in another glass vessel.

Weight of earth	20·40	grains
Loss of weight of the pelican	17·38	"
Difference	3	"

"But the diminution in weight of the pelican was only 17 4/10 grains, and hence there is an excess of three grains in the weight of the earth which cannot be attributed to the solution of the particles of the pelican. A little reflection on the conditions of the operation will however make it easy to see what is the origin of this excess, and how indeed it was a necessity of the case. It will have been noted that on removal from the pelican, the water had been poured into a glass vessel, and that it had afterwards been transferred for evaporation to a glass retort. But these different operations could not have been accomplished without solution of a small portion of the substance of these two vessels."

He concludes, "It follows from the experiments described in this memoir that the greater part, possibly the whole, of the earth separated from rain water by evaporation, is due to the solution of the vessels in which it has been collected and evaporated."

In the Bakerian Lecture given by Sir H. Davy before the Royal Society in 1806, the subject of which was, "On Some Chemical Agencies of Electricity," [1] is found an investigation concerning the products of the electrolysis of water. Besides hydrogen and oxygen there are also formed acid and alkali. Davy states this as a fact:

"The appearance of acid and alkaline matter in water acted on by a current of electricity at the opposite electrified metallic surfaces, was observed in the first chemical experiments made with the column of Volta."

The fact itself was therefore well established; it had been observed by Davy himself, as well as by other investigators. The problem requiring solution was, to ascertain whether the acid and alkali were derived from the water, and if they were not, whence they came. In pre-Lavoisierean times the action of the electric current itself might have been looked upon as a possible generating cause, but the day for such interpretations had gone. Davy, in his attempt to settle this question, had to make other plausible hypotheses for explaining the fact observed. He had to pass in review all the possible guesses as to the cause of the production of the acid and the alkali. These substances might have been contained as constituents in the

[1] London, *Phil. Trans. R. Soc.* 1807 (p. 1).

water itself, or they might have been derived from the vessels in which the electrolysis occurred, or from the surrounding air. These were practically the only possible, or at any rate they were the most obvious assumptions. Davy first set himself the task of accounting for the formation of the alkali, which always appeared at the negatively charged pole. He had observed before that when electrolysis in a glass vessel had proceeded for a considerable time, the vessel in which the alkali was formed seemed corroded, and probably it was this that led him to his first assumption, namely, that the alkali came from the vessel. If correct, this assumption would lead to the necessary inference that varying the material of the vessel should have an influence on the amount of alkali produced; and if such an influence could be actually proved, it would become very likely that the assumption made was correct. Following this out experimentally, Davy performed the electrolysis in agate cups connected by a strand of amianthus (fine asbestos), the cups and the connecting material having been carefully cleaned by boiling in distilled water. There appeared a great deal of acid and very little alkali, the amount of alkali yielded under otherwise the same conditions in glass vessels being about twenty times as great; and moreover it was noted that whilst the amount of acid produced increased continuously, and depended mainly on the time the current had been passing, the amount of alkali produced in a glass vessel increased at first rapidly, then more and more slowly, and that when the same glass vessel was used for a second similar experiment very much less alkali was produced. Hence it would appear that a glass vessel favoured the production of alkali, but that a definite amount of glass could yield a limited amount of alkali only, whilst the production of the acid was not influenced by the substitution of agate for glass, and seemed to depend for its formation on some store of matter which, at any rate in the course of the experiments made, did not sensibly diminish. The electrolysis was next carried out in gold cones, with the result that the amount of the alkali produced was minute, that of the acid as great as ever. It should here be mentioned that in the course of the experiments Davy proved the acid to be nitrous acid, the alkali soda. The results obtained so far seemed to indicate that the production of the alkali was mainly, but not entirely, due to the material of the glass vessels. But whence came the minute trace of alkali obtained on electrolysis in the gold cones? The water used for electrolysis had been distilled in glass vessels, and this seemed to afford a possible explanation. Davy says:

"It was now impossible to doubt that the water contained some substance in very minute quantities, capable of causing the appearance of fixed alkali, but which was soon exhausted, and the question that immediately presented itself was: Is this substance saline matter carried over in distillation?"

Here then a second guess is made, namely, that a minute quantity of saline matter, yielding alkali on electrolysis, is contained in the water as an impurity, produced by the solvent action of the water on the glass of the still, and carried over mechanically with the steam. This supposition was put to an experimental test by evaporating in a silver vessel some of the distilled water used for electrolysis. A small quantity of solid matter was left. This solid might or might not have been the origin of the alkali produced. Further experiment must decide. Some of the solid was thrown into the gold cone in which electrolysis had produced its maximum effect of alkalinity; a great increase of alkalinity could be observed at once. Hence it was proved that when water originally distilled from glass vessels is electrolysed in glass vessels, the alkali produced is due mainly to the electrolysis of the saline matter dissolved from the glass by the water, and also in a small degree to the saline matter dissolved in water distilled from and preserved in glass vessels. A final test of the truth of these two assumptions was made by electrolysing in the agate and gold vessels water which had been distilled in silver vessels. No alkali whatever was formed, but as much acid as before, and Davy sums up the results by saying:

"To detail any more operations of this kind will be unnecessary; all the facts prove that the fixed alkali is not generated from the water but evolved either from the solid materials employed, or from saline matter in the water."

But all the same he performs a further experiment to test his explanation deductively.

"I was now able to determine distinctly that the soda produced in glass tubes came principally from the glass, as I had always supposed."

Into the gold cup in which electrolysis is being carried out with water producing no alkali, he drops a piece of glass, and the result is the immediate formation of alkali.

The source of the acid formed at the positive pole is next investigated.

"I had never made any experiments in which acid matter having the properties of nitrous acid was not produced, and the longer was the operation the greater was the quantity that appeared."

The experiments already made have shown that the material of the vessels and saline matter dissolved in the water do not account for this acid. Hence, of the most obvious guesses enumerated before as to its possible cause, there is left practically only the influence of the air, or generation from the water itelf. The fact that the acid produced is nitrous acid makes it in itself probable that the oxygen liberated at the positive pole, together with the nitrogen of the air, should prove the true cause. Davy tests this supposition, from which follows the inference that removal of the air should prevent the formation of the acid, and he finds that when carrying out the electrolysis under the receiver of an air-pump, the yield of acid is diminished.

"I repeated the experiment under more conclusive circumstances. I arranged the apparatus as before [gold cones and water distilled in silver vessels]; I exhausted the receiver and filled it with hydrogen gas from a convenient air-holder; I made a second exhaustion and again introduced hydrogen that had been carefully prepared. The process was conducted for twenty-four hours, and at the end of this time neither of the portions of the water altered in the slightest degree the tint of litmus. It seems evident then that water chemically pure is decomposed by electricity into gaseous matter alone, into oxygen and hydrogen."

One more investigation shall now be described, one of comparatively recent date, in further illustration of the method used to establish the correct connection between an effect observed and the cause to which this effect is due.

In his wonderfully exact determinations of the densities of certain elementary gases, Lord Rayleigh found that nitrogen derived from the atmosphere had a density about ½ per cent. greater than that of nitrogen obtained by the decomposition of chemical compounds. . . . This then was the question to which an answer had to be found and was found: What is the cause of the difference between the densities of the nitrogen derived from the two sources? [1] Guesses had to be made; the inferences drawn from all the possible answers had each to be passed in review, and put to the test of experiment. The causes producing the observed difference in density could be of two kinds: (i) the lighter gas might contain an admixture of some gas, known or unknown, of density less than ordinary nitrogen, or (ii) the heavier gas might contain an admixture of some gas, known or unknown, heavier than ordinary nitrogen. The lighter gas possibly contained in the chemical nitrogen might, for instance, have been hydrogen derived from the decomposition of the substances from which the nitrogen had been prepared, and which all contained hydrogen; or it might have been a special form of nitrogen differing from ordinary nitrogen in being made up of less complex ultimate particles.[2]

"When the discrepancy of weights was first encountered, attempts were naturally made to explain it by contamination with known impurities. Of these the most likely appeared to be hydrogen, present in the lighter gas in spite of the passage over red-hot cupric oxide.[3] But inasmuch as the intentional introduction of hydrogen into the heavier gas, afterwards treated in the same way with cupric oxide, had no effect upon its weight, this explanation had to be abandoned. . . . At this stage it seemed not improbable that the lightness of the gas extracted from chemical compounds was to be explained by partial dissociation of nitrogen molecules into detached atoms. In order to test this suggestion both kinds of gas were submitted to the action of the silent electric discharge, with the result that both retained their weights unaltered. This was discouraging, and a further experiment pointed still more markedly in the negative direction. . . . On stand-

[1] Rayleigh and Ramsay, "Argon, a New Constituent of the Atmosphere," London, *Proc. R. Soc.* 57, 1895 (p. 265). *Nature,* London, 51, 1895 (p. 347).

[2] Dissociated nitrogen.

[3] The preparation and purification of the chemical nitrogen used for the density determination always involved passage over red-hot cupric oxide.

ing, the dissociated atoms might be expected to disappear, in partial analogy with the known behaviour of ozone. With this idea in view, a sample of chemically prepared nitrogen was stored for eight months. But at the end of this time the density shewed no sign of increase, remaining exactly as at first. . . . Regarding it as established that one or other of the gases must be a mixture, containing, as the case might be, an ingredient much heavier or much lighter than ordinary nitrogen, we had to consider the relative probabilities of the various possible interpretations. Except upon the already discredited hypothesis of dissociation, it was difficult to see how the gas of chemical origin could be a mixture. . . . The simplest explanation in many respects was to admit the existence of a second ingredient in air from which oxygen, moisture and carbonic anhydride had already been removed. The proportional amount required was not great. If the density of the supposed gas were double that of nitrogen, ½ per cent. only by value would be needed; or if the density were but half as much again as that of nitrogen, then 1 per cent. would still suffice. But in accepting this explanation, even provisionally, we had to face the improbability that a gas surrounding us on all sides, and present in enormous quantities, could have remained so long unsuspected."

The next stage was to put the supposition that atmospheric nitrogen contains an admixture of a heavier gas to the test of experiment. The methods employed for the purpose of trying to separate out from atmospheric nitrogen something denser than chemical nitrogen were the physical one of diffusion, whereby it could not be expected that more than a very partial separation could be effected, and by means of which a gas denser than atmospheric nitrogen was actually obtained; and the chemical one of the absorption of the nitrogen. Amongst substances which under suitable conditions combine directly with nitrogen—the number of these is very small—are oxygen and magnesium. Nitrogen mixed with excess of oxygen and sparked in contact with an alkali which will absorb the nitrous acid as soon as it is formed, can be completely converted into the latter, the residual oxygen being of course easily removed in the ordinary way; nitrogen is also fairly readily absorbed when passed over heated magnesium, a nitride of magnesium being formed. The application of the two chemical methods yielded in each case a residual gas incapable of combining with oxygen or magnesium, and the amount of which was proportional to the amount of atmospheric nitrogen originally taken, thus doing away with the possibility of its being derived from the substances employed in the process of absorption. This gas was denser than atmospheric nitrogen, had a characteristic spectrum, and a definite boiling point and freezing point, different from those of any other hitherto known substance. Thus the suspected new constituent of air was isolated; but in order to further strengthen the proof that the greater density of atmospheric nitrogen was due to the presence in it of this new substance, which its discoverers named Argon, theoretical deductions concerning the relative properties of chemical nitrogen, atmospheric nitrogen and argon were tested by observation of the actual properties.

(i) From the data:

D = density of chemical nitrogen = 1·2505.

D_1 = " " atmospheric " = 1·2572.

a = proportional volume of argon in atmospheric nitrogen = ·0104 [this value was determined incidentally in the course of the isolation of the argon].

d, the density of argon, can be calculated by the formula

$$ad + [1 - a]\ D = D_1$$

$$\therefore d = D + \frac{D_1 - D}{a} = 1{\cdot}8945,$$

which makes the specific gravity of argon (referred to $N = 14$ or $O = 16$) = 20·6.

The specific gravity of argon, as found experimentally for a sample obtained by means of magnesium, was 19·9, a very good agreement considering the not very great accuracy with which *a* was known, and the difficulty of getting the argon used in the actual density determinations quite free from nitrogen.

(ii) Chemically prepared nitrogen was submitted to the very same processes which in the case of atmospheric nitrogen had yielded about 1 per cent. by volume of the unabsorbable residue termed Argon, that is, chemical nitrogen was sparked over an alkali with excess of oxygen, or passed over heated magnesium, and was in every case practically completely absorbed.

Hence an element present in enormous quantities, but till then not suspected, was conclusively proved to exist, and to be the cause of the difference in density between chemical and atmospheric nitrogen, a difference revealed by most accurate measurements of a physical quantity, aptly described by Lord Rayleigh as "the triumph of the last place of decimals."

What is it that the three investigations just described have in common? Their object was to ascertain the causes producing certain effects observed: the production of earth from water, the production of acid and alkali on the electrolysis of water, the difference in density between two gases till then supposed to be the same.

In each case the actual occurrence of the effect had first to be proved beyond doubt.

Next taking into account all the pertinent phenomena observed incidentally (the identical density of the water before and after the distillations in which the earth is produced, the corrosion of the glass vessels in which the alkali is formed electrolytically, the specific difference in the substances from which the two kinds of nitrogen had been produced), and all the conditions of the experiment as far as they could be realised, hypotheses were framed, that is guesses were made concerning the possible causes of the effects observed. Each of these hypotheses had to be shown to afford an explanation of the particular effect it referred to, which is merely a thinking process; thus Lavoisier's possible explanations were that the earth formed came from the water (least likely after the result of the density determinations), or from the fire through the pores of the glass vessel, or from the vessel itself; Davy had the choice between the hypotheses of making the water, or the air, or the material of the vessels the origin of the acid and alkali formed; Lord Rayleigh had to pass in review the assumptions that a lighter or a heavier gas was mixed with one or other of his differing specimens of nitrogen.

Then followed the testing of the adequacy of the hypotheses to the purpose for which they had been devised. The deductive inferences drawn from each of them were put to an experimental test, and, according as the result yielded was positive or negative, hypotheses were retained or rejected, rejection of course leading to a reduction in the number. Since the total weight of a closed vessel containing water in which earth had been formed, had not altered, the origin of the earth could not be in the fire matter; change of material of the containing vessel, and the substitution of purer water for some containing a solid in solution, was found to have no influence on the amount of the nitric acid formed by electrolysis of the water, and hence the acid was not likely to be derived from either the water itself or the containing vessel; hydrogen purposely added to nitrogen was completely removed by the process ordinarily followed in the preparation of the chemical nitrogen, and hence the cause sought could not be the presence of hydrogen as an impurity in the lighter gas. It may happen that all hypotheses but one are eliminated when tested by a first set of deductions. It may be that they are all eliminated; if so fresh ones must be sought, and if these should share the same fate, the phenomenon remains for the time being unexplained, though the work done will not be lost, future investigators being spared the framing and testing of hypotheses already proved unsuccessful. Or it may be that two or more hypotheses will all stand the test of a first set of inferences; when this happens the two hypotheses must be tested further and further, until an inference is drawn, which, according to the one, would give a result different and easily distinguished from that yielded by the other. An experiment, in this case called a *crucial* experiment (from *crux*, the fingerpost at a bifurcation of a road), is called upon to decide.

"Instances of the Fingerpost [or of the Cross-roads], borrowing the term from the fingerposts which are set up where roads part, to indicate the several directions . . . I also call Decisive and Judicial. . . . I explain them thus. When in the investigation of any nature, the understanding is so balanced as to be uncertain as to which of two or more natures the cause of the nature in question should be assigned, on account of the frequent and ordinary concurrence of many natures, Instances of the Fingerpost show the union of the natures with the nature in question to be sure and indissoluble, of the other to be varied and separable; and thus the question is decided, and the former nature is admitted as the cause, while the latter is dismissed and rejected. . . . These Instances of the Fingerpost . . . for the most part . . . are expressly and designedly sought for and applied, and discovered only by earnest and active diligence. . . . Let the nature in question be Weight or Heaviness. Here the road will branch into two, thus. It must needs be that heavy or weighty bodies either tend of their own nature to the centre of the earth, by reason of their proper configuration; or else that they are attracted by the mass and body of earth itself as by the congregation of kindred substances, and move to it by sympathy. If the latter of these be the cause, it follows that the nearer heavy bodies approach to the earth, the more rapid and violent is their motion to it; and that the further they are from the earth, the feebler and more tardy is their motion. . . . With regard to this then, the following would be an instance of the Fingerpost. Take a clock moved by leaden weights, and another moved by the compression of an iron spring; let them be exactly adjusted . . . ; then place the clock moving by weights on the top of a very high steeple. . . . Repeat the experiment in the bottom of a mine. . . . If the virtue of the weights is found diminished on the steeple and increased in the mine, we may take the attraction of the mass of the earth as the cause of weight." (Bacon, *Novum Organum*, Book II, xxxvi.)

The function of such crucial experiments may be illustrated from the investigations just described. In Lavoisier's experiment on the change of water into earth, the hypothesis of the extraneous origin of the earth was eliminated when the constancy of the weight of the whole system had been proved; but this left it open whether the earth was derived from the vessel, from the water, or from both. The weighing of the earth itself and of the vessel supplied the crucial experiments required to give the answer.[1] The inferences were: (i) if derived from the vessel, the weight of earth formed must be exactly equal to the loss of weight of the vessel; (ii) if derived from the water, the weight of the vessel must not have changed; (iii) if derived from both the vessel and the water, the weight of earth formed must exceed the loss in weight of the vessel. The result of the actual experiments gave the answer that the earth came from the material of the vessel only.

One hypothesis and one only having been found to give a satisfactory explanation of the phenomenon investigated, the hypothesis becomes an actually ascertained fact, which may or may not be further verified by the testing of more deductive inferences. Lavoisier could state that water is not changed into earth, and that when earth appears, this is due to the solvent action of water on glass vessels; Davy was able to state that the alkali and acid formed when water is electrolysed were derived from the material of the vessels and from the air, and that under suitable conditions pure water yields oxygen and hydrogen only; Rayleigh and Ramsay could actually isolate a heavier gas from atmospheric nitrogen.

These investigations, described in illustration of general principles, were here utilised with reference to what is the first step in the acquisition of scientific knowledge, namely the correct recognition of individual facts, and the connection between an effect produced and the cause producing it. But isolated facts, however clearly recognised and however great in

[1] Here, as always, the decision between three possible answers necessitates two experiments.

number, do not yet constitute a science. Classification steps in and makes these facts the basis of generalisations. Classification consists in selecting some one property, putting together all the objects or all the phenomena which possess this property, and separating them from all the others which do not; it consists in the putting together of what is like in some way and the separating of it from what is unlike in that respect. The chemist, in dealing with the permanent changes produced in matter, inquires into the various causes which produce them; for instance, he may select for separate consideration those changes which all have the common property of being the result of the action of heat. In the study of a number of facts brought together because of their being in some way of the same kind, we may recognise that the same cause produces in a greater or lesser number of cases the same effect, and such a recognition leads to a generalisation. The following may serve as definitions:

"*Classification* is the arrangement together of any series of objects [or of occurrences] which are like and the separation of those which are unlike, in order to facilitate the operations of the mind in clearly conceiving and retaining in memory the character of the objects in question" (Huxley).

"*Generalisation* is the recognition of a certain common nature between a greater or lesser number of facts and the extension of what has been observed in a limited number of cases to a multitude of yet unexamined cases."

But in considering how classification and generalisation are actually used in physical science, it is found that practically the one always involves the other. When we put together the objects or phenomena which have something in common, *i.e.*, when we classify, we have in this very act recognised a common nature, *i.e.*, generalised. Again, when we have recognised that a certain cause produces with many or with all substances the same effect, that is, when we generalise, we had prior to this to supply ourselves with the necessary material for so doing; we had to bring together for separate consideration all the phenomena which possessed the class-characteristic of the operation of the same cause, and the generalisation itself is after all nothing but a class-characteristic, appertaining to a more or less extensive class according as to whether the generalisation is a more or less wide one. In classifying all metals into noble (not changed when heated in air) and base (changed when heated in air) the alchemists really founded a classification on the generalisation that some metals when heated in air are changed and others not; and again the generalisation that all gases when heated expand equally, is bound up with the recognition of the class-characteristics of gases.

Generalisation leads to laws. Law is the statement of a definite relation between cause and effect, which by observation and experiment we have ascertained to hold for a number of cases belonging to a certain class of facts, and which we therefore assume will hold for any other case belonging to the same class of facts. The law may be of a qualitative nature only. Thus the name of acid has been given to a number of substances which all agree in possessing certain definite properties, *e.g.* a certain effect on the sense of taste, the power of changing certain vegetable colouring matters to red, the destruction of the alkaline nature of substances such as potash and soda, effervescence with carbonates, solution of metals such as zinc and magnesium accompanied by the evolution of hydrogen. The investigation of the composition of a number of acids, and of the nature of the change termed neutralisation in which, by the inter-action with other substances, such as soda, carbonates, zinc or magnesium, these characteristic properties are destroyed, has led to a generalisation embodied in the law "all acids contain hydrogen replaceable by metal," with the result, that now when a new substance is discovered which has the functional class-characteristics of an acid, *e.g.* sour taste, turning certain vegetable colouring matter red, etc., etc., we should assume that it also possessed the class-characteristic of composition embodied in the above law. We should expect it to contain hydrogen, and to be capable of yielding a compound which contained metal in place of some of this hydrogen at any rate.

But the generalisation to be embodied in a law may be of a quantitative nature. It is one thing to make the generalisation that all gases expand equally under the influence of heat, another to find the value for this common coefficient of expansion. Berthollet had in 1809 demonstrated that hydrogen diffuses much more rapidly than any other gas; but it remained for Graham first to show, in 1828, that the diffusion of all gases is inversely as some function of their density, apparently the square root; and then to definitely establish, in 1838, that "the diffusion, or spontaneous intermixture, of two gases in contact, . . . is, in the case of each gas, inversely proportional to the square root of the density of that gas."

"Experiments may be of two kinds: experiments of simple fact, and experiments of quantity. . . . [In the latter] the conditions will vary, not in quality, but quantity, and the effect will also vary in quantity, so that the result of quantitative induction is also to arrive at some mathematical expression involving the quantity of each condition, and expressing the quantity of the result. In other words, we wish to know what function the effect is of its conditions. We shall find that it is one thing to obtain the numerical results, and quite another thing to detect the law obeyed by those results, the latter being an operation of an inverse and tentative character." (Jevons, *Principles of Science.*)

The discovery of such laws likewise necessitates the framing and the testing of hypotheses. The history of the Inductive Sciences affords many examples of how such laws have emerged, only after much labour, as the survival of the fittest of many hypotheses. The law of refraction lends itself admirably to showing the successive steps in such discoveries, and the place amongst these of hypotheses.

It was known to the ancients that a ray of light, in passing from one medium into another, was refracted, *i.e.*, that rectilinear propagation ceased and that the ray was bent. The amount of this bending was actually measured for certain cases by Ptolemy (2nd century A.D.), and the general fact recognised that when light passes from air to glass—from a less dense to a more dense medium—the angle of refraction is less than the angle of incidence, *i.e.* the ray is bent towards the perpendicular; and the corresponding angles were given. In the middle ages observations were made, and more or less correct tables constructed, in which angles of incidence and the corresponding angles of refraction were recorded. Kepler (1604) attempted to reduce to rule the measured quantities of refraction. He is known to have made as many as 17 suppositions as to the law connecting the value of the angle of incidence with that of the angle of refraction,—17 guesses as to what function the one was of the other. These suppositions, or guesses, or hypotheses, he had to test deductively by comparing the actually measured angles of refraction corresponding to certain angles of incidence with those calculated according to his hypothetical law. All his hypotheses proved erroneous, including one according to which the angle of refraction should be partly proportional to the angle of incidence and partly proportional to the secant of that angle, and which gave values agreeing to within ½ degree with the experimental ones. In 1621 Snell discovered the real relation. If he knew of the work done on the subject before, he must of course have been much helped thereby, being saved from spending time on the testing of hypotheses already proved inadequate. His supposition that the sine of the angle of refraction is directly proportional to the sine of the angle of incidence rose from a hypothesis to a law, once it had been proved deductively that it always gave theoretical values identical with those actually measured, and that no other supposition did likewise.[1]

Such a development of a hypothesis into a law is characterised by Mill in the following manner:

"It appears, then, to be a condition of a genuinely scientific hypothesis, that it be not destined always to remain an hypothesis, but be certain to be either proved or disproved by . . . comparison with observed facts. . . . In hypotheses of this character, if they relate to causation at all, the effect must be already known to depend on the very cause supposed, and the hypothesis must relate only to the precise mode of dependence; the law of the variation of the effect according to the variations in the quantity or in the relations of the cause. With these may be classed the hypotheses which do not make any supposition with regard to causation, but only with regard to the law of correspondence between facts which accompany each other in their variations, though there may be no relation of cause and effect between them. Such were the different false hypotheses which Kepler made respecting the law of the refraction of light. It was known that the direction of the line of refraction varied with every variation

[1] These facts concerning the discovery of the law of refraction are taken from Whewell, *History of the Inductive Sciences.*

in the direction of the line of incidence, but it was not known how; that is, what changes of the one corresponded to the different changes in the other. In this case any law, different from the true one, must have led to false results. . . . In all these cases, verification is proof; if the supposition accords with the phenomena there needs no other evidence of it." (Mill, *System of Logic.*)

A whole group of laws may furnish the material for further generalisation and may be embraced in a more general law. For instance the statement, "the elements combine in ratios which are those of their combining weights, or of simple whole multiples of these" is a further generalisation from the three laws of chemical combination, and includes them all.

Generalisation and the formulation of laws is the response to the desire of the human mind for simplicity, for the power to comprise a number of apparently isolated facts under one aspect. But this desire goes further, and leads to attempts to find some ultimate reason for the phenomena observed. Some fundamental properties are assigned to that which is the vehicle of the phenomena studied; in chemistry, which is the science dealing with the composition and the transformation of matter, we postulate certain properties of that matter; in optics—a science in which the phenomena are not inseparably connected with matter, *i.e.*, that which exhibits mass or the property of being attracted by the earth—the hypothetical properties are those of an all-pervading medium called the luminiferous ether, the existence of which is assumed for the purposes of the case. It is by virtue of these hypothetical properties that the cause of the individual phenomena observed and of the more or less general laws deduced from these, must be such as it is and no other. Such an assumption devised for such a purpose constitutes a scientific hypothesis. The nature of hypotheses, and their function in the discovery of individual facts and laws, has already been discussed, but they must now be considered in their bearings on great divisions or the whole of a science. It has been said several times in what has preceded, that a hypothesis is simply a guess which may be right or may be wrong, and that this process of guessing must be continued until a right one has been found. But how shall we know which is right? or put somewhat differently, what are the requirements of a good hypothesis?

1. It must explain *all* the phenomena and laws which classification has brought together in a particular branch of science, that is, it must be inductively true. The examples given before show how the efficiency of a hypothesis, for explaining an individual fact (p. 414) or law (p. 418), can be tested, and within a larger scope, the method is the same. The laws must seem natural consequences of the cause assumed in the hypothesis.

"To discover a Conception of the mind which will justly represent a train of observed facts is, in some measure, a process of conjecture, . . . and the business of conjecture is commonly conducted by calling up before our minds several suppositions, selecting that one which most agrees with what we know of the observed facts. Hence he who has to discover the laws of nature may have to invent many suppositions before he hits upon the right one; and among the endowments which lead to his success, we must reckon that fertility of invention which ministers to him such imaginary schemes, till at last he finds the one which conforms to the true order of nature. A facility in devising hypotheses, therefore, is so far from being a fault in the intellectual character of a discoverer, that it is, in truth, a faculty indispensable to his task. . . . But if it be an advantage for the discoverer of truth that he be ingenious and fertile in inventing hypotheses which may connect the phenomena of nature, it is indispensably requisite that he be diligent and careful in comparing his hypotheses with the facts, and ready to abandon his invention as soon as it appears that it does not agree with the course of actual occurrences. This constant comparison of his own conceptions and supposition with observed facts under all aspects forms the leading employment of the discoverer; this candid and simple love of truth, which makes him willing to suppress the most favourite production of his own ingenuity as soon as it appears to be at variance with realities, constitutes the first characteristic of his temper. He must have neither the blindness which cannot, nor the obstinacy which will not, perceive the discrepancy of his fancies and his facts. He must allow no indolence, or partial views, or self-complacency, or delight in seeming demonstration, to make him tenacious of the schemes which he devises, any further than they are confirmed by their accordance with nature. The framing of hypotheses is, for the enquirer after truth, not the end, but the beginning of his work. Each of his systems is invented, not that he may admire it and follow it into all its consistent consequences, but that he may make it the occasion of a course of active experiment and observation. And if the results of this process contradict his fundamental assumptions, however ingenious, however symmetrical, however elegant his system may be, he rejects it without hesitation. He allows no natural yearning for the offspring of his own mind to draw him aside from the higher duty of loyalty to his sovereign, Truth, to her he not only gives his affections and his wishes, but strenuous labour and scrupulous minuteness of attention." (Whewell, *Philosophy of the Inductive Sciences.*)

2. But in science there is no finality; facts accumulate, knowledge grows; and hence the second requirement of a good hypothesis is, that it should, without any or with only slight modifications in its original form, explain the phenomena and laws discovered after its promulgation in the particular branch of science to which it refers. Lavoisier explained the properties of acids by the hypothesis of the acidifying principle being oxygen, the name of which (ὀξύς, γεννάω = acid, I generate) still bears witness to this view. This hypothesis held sway until the time of the proof of the elementary nature of chlorine, which involved that of the absence of oxygen from hydrochloric acid, a compound of hydrogen and chlorine, and hence led to the complete abandonment of what in the history of science is known as Lavoisier's Oxygen Theory of Acids.

Sometimes the original hypothesis is modified to adapt it to the new demands made upon it, but the less strain it need bear in this way, the greater is its inherent probability.

"When the hypothesis, of itself and without adjustment for the purpose, gives us the rule and reason of a class of facts not contemplated in its construction, we have a criterion of its reality, which has never yet been produced in favour of falsehood. . . . [In *true* hypotheses] all the additional suppositions tend to simplicity and harmony; the new suppositions . . . require only some easy modification of the hypothesis first assumed, the system becomes more coherent as it is further extended. The elements which we require for explaining a new class of facts are already contained in our system. . . . In *false* theories, the contrary is the case. The new suppositions are something altogether additional;—not suggested by the original scheme, perhaps difficult to reconcile with it. Every such addition adds to the complexity of the hypothetical system, which at last becomes unmanageable, and is compelled to surrender its place to some simpler explanation." (Whewell, *Philosophy of the Inductive Sciences.*)

3. A good hypothesis must indicate the lines of future research in that its deductions referring to phenomena not known before are verified when put to the test of experiment; that is, it must be deductively true and suggestive.

"The hypotheses which we accept ought to explain phenomena which we have observed. But they ought to do more than this; our hypotheses ought to foretell phenomena which have not yet been observed; . . . because if the rule prevails, it includes all cases; and will determine them all, if we can only calculate its real consequences. Hence it will predict the results of new combinations, as well as explain the appearances which have occurred in old ones. And that it does this with certainty and correctness, is one mode in which the hypothesis is to be verified as right and useful." (Whewell, *Philosophy of the Inductive Sciences.*)

"By deductive reasoning and calculation, we must endeavour to anticipate such new phenomena, especially those of a singular and exceptional nature, as would necessarily happen if the hypothesis be true." (Jevons, *Principles of Science.*)

The discovery of the three elements, gallium, scandium and germanium, the properties of which were foretold with the closest approximation to truth from the application of the system according to which the properties of all elements are assumed to be a periodic function of their atomic weights, is a striking example of the deductive application of hypotheses. Amongst other such brilliant results stands out prominently the discovery of radium. M. Becquerel found in 1896 that compounds of uranium spontaneously and continuously emit some radiation which, among other properties, has that of making air a conductor of electricity. This effect, the quantity of which can be determined with great accuracy, was used by Mme. Curie to measure the amount of radiation produced by various compounds of uranium and of thorium, which latter had meanwhile been found to emit the same kind of radiation.

"The radio-activity of compounds of thorium and uranium, measured under different conditions, shows that it is not influenced by any change of physical state or chemical composition. . . . The chemical combinations and mixtures containing uranium and thorium are active in proportion to the amounts of the metal contained."

The subsequent testing of a large number of rocks and minerals showed that certain minerals which contained uranium and thorium, *e.g.* pitchblende (oxide of uranium), chalcolite (double phosphate of copper and uranium), possess radio-activity much greater than that "theoretically" due to the amount of uranium present.

"These facts did not accord with previous conclusions, according to which no mineral should be as active as the element thorium or uranium."

Hence the inference:

"It appeared probable that if pitchblende, chalcolite, etc. possess so great a degree of activity, these substances contain a small quantity of a strongly radio-active body, differing from uranium and thorium and the simple bodies actually known. I thought that if this were indeed the case, I might hope to extract this substance from the ore by the ordinary methods of chemical analysis."

The search was made, and resulted (1898) in the proof of the existence of several hitherto unknown substances, characterised by their great radio-activity, and in fact discovered and isolated by this property. To the substance so far obtained in greatest amount was given the name radium.

It should be specially noted that it is not a necessary requirement of a good hypothesis that the assumptions made should ever be capable of sensual realisation, that is of demonstrative proof. "The suppositions made must not in themselves be absurd, that is contradictory to the laws of nature or of mind held true" (Jevons), that is all. We need not even stipulate that the suppositions made should be true, it is not by its truth that we judge a hypothesis, but by its utility: by the simplicity of its postulates; by the extensiveness of the phenomena to which it applies; and most important of all, by its adaptability to deductive application. And nothing is more dangerous to the proper appreciation of scientific methods than confusion concerning the nature and relative importance of experimental data and of scientific hypotheses. The first is the real, the unalterable, the ruler; the second is the assumed, the changeable, the servant, the tool which has to be thrown away when it is no longer able to cope with the work demanded from it, or when a better, because a simpler and more adaptable one, is devised.

But when a hypothesis fulfils all these demands, when in a simple manner it correlates knowledge, when it is so elastic as to let the new at once fall into its proper place by the old, and when under its directions the quest for further knowledge becomes a direct advance along clearly indicated paths, then the hypothesis takes rank as a theory.

Thus we have the Undulatory Hypothesis of Light, which assumes the existence of an all-pervading medium of definite properties in which light is propagated by transversal waves. This hypothesis explained satisfactorily the phenomena and laws of rectilinear propagation, of reflection and refraction, of the colours of thin plates and of diffraction fringes; and when confronted with the additional phenomena of polarisation and of double refraction, it could deal with these also without encumbering itself by new and recondite assumptions, but simply by settling a point which in its original conception had been left open, namely the direction of the vibration in the wave-front; and lastly it was able to foretell the phenomena of internal and external conical refraction, phenomena so strange and so unique that it is safe to say they might never have been discovered had they not been looked for, in order to test the result of deduction. Hence we have the Undulatory Theory of Light, which comprises very nearly the whole science of optics, all the phenomena and laws arrived at inductively and explained by the wave hypothesis, and all such as have been discovered as the result of deductive inference from it.

So also we have a Kinetic Hypothesis of Gases, which assumes that the constituent particles are perfectly elastic, that they are at such a distance apart as not to influence each other, that they occupy a space which is negligible when compared with that occupied by the gas as a whole, and that they are in a continuous state of motion, subject to the ordinary laws of dynamics. And there is the Kinetic Theory which comprises: (i) All the empirical laws of gaseous pressure, temperature, and diffusion, with their explanation in terms of the above hypothesis. (ii) Deductions from the hypothesis, such as equality of the numbers of constituent particles in equal volumes of different gases, or the difference of the ratio between the two specific heats of a gas according to the number of constituent parts contained in each molecule, inferences which are in perfect accordance with experimental results and the interpretation of these. . . .

To sum up the subject matter of this chapter. It consists in an attempt to characterise the method of the inductive sciences, to show that the sequence of the processes employed is: (1) the collection of facts, which corresponds with finding an answer to the question—*what* happens? (2) the classification of these facts, and the generalisation from these classified facts, which yields the laws and which answers the question—*how* do these things happen? (3) the explanation of all that has been found to occur in terms of a hypothesis devised for this purpose, which supplies an answer to the question, *why* [1] do these things happen? and finally the welding together of all these processes in the theory of the science.

1904

[1] Objection has been raised against the separation of the processes here given under (2) and (3), and it has been urged that even in the devising and applying of hypotheses we are only following out the "how"; that the "why" is beyond the range of what science can deal with.

COMBUSTION *

JAMES B. CONANT

TWO FURTHER PRINCIPLES IN THE TACTICS AND STRATEGY OF SCIENCE

. . . Let us now turn to the second case history to be considered in this chapter. It is an example drawn from the history of chemistry in the second half of the eighteenth century, and, it is only fair to warn the reader, a most complicated case. Perhaps too much effort is required to master the facts involved to make this a good example for the layman. But I believe it should be included in the course I am proposing because in it two important principles in the Tactics and Strategy of Science are illustrated in a peculiarly striking fashion. These principles are as follows:

First, a useful concept may be a barrier to the acceptance of a better one if long-intrenched in the minds of scientists.

Second, experimental discoveries must fit the time; facts may be at hand for years without their significance being realized; the total scientific situation must be favorable for the acceptance of new views.

THE OVERTHROW OF THE PHLOGISTON THEORY

The case history which illustrates excellently these two important points might be entitled "the overthrow of the phlogiston theory" or "Lavoisier's work on combustion in the 1770's." As indicated by the first phrase the case also affords a classic example of the mustering of evidence pro and con when two rival concepts are in collision. This phenomenon though frequent is usually so transient in the history of science as to be hard to capture for purposes of historical study. In the investigation of combustion the normal progress of science was, so to speak, delayed; this fact, in a sense, accounts for why a study of this difficult passage in scientific history is of special significance to those interested in the Tactics and Strategy of Science.

The easiest way to understand the revolution in chemistry associated with the name of Lavoisier is first to describe the phenomena in question in terms of modern concepts; then to show how for nearly a hundred years everyone was thoroughly confused. This pedagogic device would have to be used by the instructor in the course I am suggesting. It involves the dogmatic statement of a certain amount of popularized physics and chemistry, but I doubt if the presentation would be much more arbitrary in this respect than most freshman courses. Indeed, some of the material might be said to be common knowledge today.

Almost every high-school graduate "knows" (I put quotation marks

* From *On Understanding Science* by James B. Conant, Yale University Press, reprinted by permission from the publishers.

around the word) that air is primarily a mixture of oxygen gas and nitrogen gas; furthermore, when a candle or a match or a cigarette "burns," heat and light are being evolved by a chemical reaction involving oxygen. This is called "combustion." If we burn enough material in a closed space, the combustion stops because the oxygen is used up. What burns? Some but not all of the students will say that in the cases mentioned it is a group of carbon compounds, and some will add that the products of combustion are carbon dioxide, CO_2 and water, H_2O. Anyone who has an elementary knowledge of chemical symbols usually loves to share the information! Suppose you heat molten tin in air at a high temperature for a long time, and the bright metal becomes covered with a scum, obviously not a metal. What has happened? A combination with oxygen—an oxide is formed—the bright boys and girls answer. Correct. Suppose we heat this nonmetallic substance, an oxide, with carbon. What would happen? The carbon would combine with the oxygen, giving an oxide of carbon and leaving the metal. This is what happens in making iron from iron ore, the very bright boy tells you.

All very simple and plain. And you can set students to work in high-school laboratories to prove it. Yet it is an historic fact that at the time of the American Revolution not one philosopher or experimentalist out of one hundred could have given you an inkling of this explanation which we now designate as "correct." Instead, they would have talked learnedly of "phlogiston," a name probably totally unfamiliar to all but the chemists who read this book. Nearly a hundred years after Newton, and still everyone was thoroughly bewildered by such a simple matter as combustion! This fact needs to be brought home to all who would understand science and who talk of the "scientific method."

The chemical revolution was practically contemporary with the American Revolution and, of course, just preceded the French Revolution. Lavoisier, the man who singlehanded but building on the work of others made the revolution, lost his head at the hands of the Revolutionary Tribune in 1794 (though he was by no means hostile to the basic aims of the great social and political upheaval). Whether or not he was betrayed by a scientific colleague (Fourcroy) who at least was an ardent supporter of the extreme party then in power, is an intriguing historical question; its study would be a by-product of this case history in which certain students would take great interest. Likewise, the fact that another prominent figure in the final controversy was Priestley, a Unitarian clergyman, who was made an honorary citizen by the French Assembly and then fled to America in the very year of Lavoisier's execution to escape a reactionary English mob, adds zest to the story. There is no lack of material to connect science with society in the late eighteenth century, though the connection I think is more dramatic than significant; at all events, for keeping up students' interest it can hardly be surpassed.

THE CLASSIC EXPERIMENT ON THE ROLE OF OXYGEN IN COMBUSTION

The chemical revolution took place during the years 1772–78. By the later date Lavoisier had made clear to the scientific world the role of oxygen in combustion. His classic experiment, often described in elementary textbooks, was as follows: Mercury heated in common air produces a red material (an oxide we would say, a "calx" to the chemists of the eighteenth century). In a closed space about one fifth of the air disappears. The red material weighs more than the metal from which it was formed. Therefore, something has disappeared from the air and combined with the metal. The red material, the oxide or calx, is next strongly heated in an enclosed space with the sun's rays brought to a focus by a large lens or "burning glass," a gas is evolved and the metal regenerated. The new gas is the "something" which disappeared from the original air, for the amount is the same, and the calx has lost weight in the right amount. The new gas (oxygen) mixed with the residue from the first experiment yields a mixture which is identical with common air.

The experiments are simple, the proof appears to be complete. (Lavoisier, of course, generalized far beyond the case of mercury.) But the new conceptual scheme was by no means accepted at once with great acclaim. Quite the contrary. Lavoisier had to drive home his points with telling arguments. Slowly his French contemporaries were won over, but Priestley and Watt of the steam-engine fame and Cavendish and scores of others continued to cling to the phlogiston theory for a decade. Priestley's case is particularly interesting. This English experimenter had actually provided Lavoisier with an important clue when in 1774 he told him about his preparation of oxygen gas by heating red oxide of mercury. But Priestley died in 1804 without ever being converted to the new doctrine.

Why was there this reluctance to modify ideas in the light of beautifully clear experiments, and why were the men of the eighteenth century so long in getting on the right track? There were two reasons: first, one conceptual scheme—the phlogiston theory—had acquired an almost paralyzing hold on their minds; and second, elucidating the facts necessary to overthrow the theory involved experiments with gases which were then extremely difficult.

THE SIGNIFICANCE OF THE PHLOGISTON THEORY

The phlogiston theory in its day was, we must first realize, a long step forward. In the sixteenth and seventeenth centuries those who were interested in making some sense out of what we now call chemistry were wandering in a bewildering forest. From the alchemists and the practical men, particularly the metal makers, they had acquired a mass of apparently unrelated facts and strange ideas about "elements." The earth, air, fire,

and water concept of Aristotle was still hovering over them. Boyle in his *Skeptical Chymist* did a little, but not much, to clear a space in the tangled underbrush of fact and fancy so closely interwoven and cemented by strange words. Let us look at some of the common phenomena that had to be explained by Newton and his contemporaries, that is to say, fitted into a conceptual scheme. Metals could be obtained by heating certain materials with charcoal (the ancient art of winning metals from their ores). Metals were at first sight very much the same; they had similar superficial properties. Even today the classification of metal and nonmetal appeals at once to a layman. Other solids were called "earths" (oxides for us today) or else, like charcoal or sulfur, they were "combustible principles." Some earths when heated with charcoal yielded metals. This process could be reversed, for often but not always the metal (for example, tin) on heating yielded an earthlike substance. From such an artificial earthlike substance (an oxide in modern terms) the metal could be regained if the earth was heated with charcoal. A pure earth of this sort might be called a calx, the process of forming it by heating a metal was "calcination."

How were all these facts, inherited from the Middle Ages and before, to be fitted together? By the introduction of a principle called phlogiston, closely related to Aristotle's old element, fire—closely related, yet the relationship was never clear. To those who sought for clarity it seemed evident that there must be some common principle involved in the process of making various metals from their calces and vice versa. Therefore, let us call this something phlogiston, they in effect declared. When phlogiston was added to a calx you had a metal, when you removed it from a metal a calx was formed; phlogiston was in a sense a metalizing principle. Note there is a commonsense assumption more or less implied in this line of reasoning: except for gold, and occasionally a few other metals, calces *not* metals occur in nature. Therefore, these calces were the simpler materials, something must be added to them to make them metals. Since metals were so alike, the "something" was obviously the same in all cases. We shall call it phlogiston, said Becher and his pupil Stahl in a series of books published in 1703–31.

Here was a key to unlock a maze, and it was immediately accepted. Here was a concept which provided a pattern into which a mass of otherwise unrelated phenomena could be fitted. Substances were rich or poor in phlogiston, this seemed easy to establish. What was phlogiston itself? It probably was never to be seen. Substances rich in phlogiston easily took fire and, indeed, fire was perhaps a manifestation of phlogiston, or worked with it at least. For some, fire was still an element. Charcoal was a phlogiston-rich material and on heating with a metallic calx gave up its phlogiston to the calx, making a metal. By itself charcoal burned, the phlogiston appearing as fire or combined with the air. Sulfur, using the word in its modern sense, was found free in nature; it burned when heated and yielded an acid, vitriolic acid (sulfuric acid in modern terms). Clearly, this sulfur was only vitriolic acid highly "phlogisticated"; the burning set the phlogiston free and yielded the acid.

We can write these changes in diagrammatic form to illustrate how the chemists of the eighteenth century thought:

Calx + phlogiston (from charcoal) ⟶ metal.
Metal heated in air ⟶ calx + phlogiston (to the air).
Charcoal burned yields phlogiston to the air accompanied by fire.
Phlogisticated vitriolic acid (sulfur to us) burns yielding phlogiston (to the air) + vitriolic acid (sulfuric acid).

There was one very simple flaw in all this argument and the interesting fact is that this flaw was known and talked about for fifty years before the phlogiston theory was even shaken, much less overthrown. This is a beautiful illustration of the principle in the Tactics and Strategy of Science referred to at the beginning of this section, namely, that a scientific discovery must fit the times. As early as 1630 (note the date—before Boyle was born) a Frenchman, Jean Rey, studied the calcination of tin and showed that the calx weighed more than the tin from which it was formed. More than that, he gave an explanation closely in accord with Lavoisier's ideas of 150 years later. For he said, "this increase in weight comes from the air, which in the vessel has been rendered denser, heavier, and in some measure adhesive . . . which air mixes with the calx . . . and becomes attached to its most minute particles. . . ." Boyle confirmed the increase in weight of metals in calcination in 1673 but added no support to Rey's shrewd guess (it was little more) as to the reason. In fact, if anything, he led subsequent investigators down the wrong path. At least in retrospect it seems that if he had followed up only a little more boldly his own experiments, the phlogiston theory might never have been proposed or, if proposed, never accepted seriously. Yet it is all too easy to imagine that even a still greater genius than Boyle could have discovered oxygen and revealed its role in combustion and calcination in the seventeenth century. Too much physics as well as chemistry lay under wraps which were only slowly removed by the labors of many men.

At all events, Boyle put forward the hypothesis that fire, the Aristotelian principle, had passed through the walls of the glass vessel used and combined with the metal, thereby giving it weight. This was, of course, not the same as the phlogiston theory formulated a generation later; in a sense it was the opposite because according to Boyle something was *added* to the metal in calcination, namely, fire. While in the phlogiston theory something, namely, phlogiston, was *removed*. But Boyle's writings did focus attention on the heat and flame (a characteristic of fire and calcination) rather than on the air which had figured in Rey's explanation.

A SCIENTIFIC DISCOVERY MUST FIT THE TIMES

Rey's ideas about the air seem to have been lost in the subsequent 150 years, but not the facts of calcination. That a calx weighed more than the metal was well known throughout the eighteenth century, but this fact was *not* recognized as being fatal to the phlogiston theory. Here is an important point. Does it argue for the stupidity of the experimental philosophers of the day as a few writers once would have us think? Not at all; it merely demonstrates that in complex affairs of science, one is concerned with trying to account for a variety of facts and with welding them into a conceptual scheme; one fact is not by itself sufficient to wreck the scheme. In discussing Galileo's failure and Torricelli's successful interpretation of lift pumps, I referred to the principle that a conceptual scheme is never discarded merely because of a few stubborn facts with which it cannot be reconciled; a concept is either modified or replaced by a better concept, never abandoned with nothing left to take its place.

Not only was it known in 1770 that a calx weighed more than the metal from which it was formed (which means to us that something must have been taken up in its formation), but Boyle himself back in the 1660's showed that air was necessary for fire. John Mayow and Robert Hooke at about the same date had written about burning and the respiration of animals in terms of air being "deprived of its elastic force by the breathing of animals very much in the same way as by the burning of flame." Stephen Hales, fifty years later, spoke the same language. But these men were all ahead of their times. As we reread their papers we see in spite of strange words and ill-defined ideas they had demonstrated that air in which material had been burned or animals had respired would no longer sustain fire or life; furthermore, they showed that there was an actual diminution of the volume of the air in such cases. All of which seems to force the right explanation to our eyes; not so to the chemists of the eighteenth century.

Air which would no longer support combustion had merely become so rich in phlogiston it could take up no more, the "phlogistonists" declared. Indeed, when Priestley discovered how to prepare essentially pure nitrogen, it was quite natural for him to regard it as completely "phlogisticated air," because nitrogen will not support combustion. Likewise, when he discovered how to prepare essentially pure oxygen gas by heating red oxide of mercury, he called it "dephlogisticated air." He found this gas to be like common air, though a candle burned in it more brightly than even in common air. Upon the whole, said Priestley, it may safely be concluded, "that the purest air is that which contains the least phlogiston: that air is impure (by which I mean that it is unfit for respiration, and for the purpose of supporting flame) in proportion as it contains more of that principle." This letter was read to the Royal Society on May 25, 1775.

And in the same year in another letter he spoke of his newly discovered oxygen as "[an air] that is five or six times better than common air, for the purposes of respiration, inflammation and, I believe, every other use of common atmospherical air. As I think I have sufficiently proved that the fitness of air for respiration depends on its capacity to receive the *phlogiston* exhaled from the lungs this species of air may not improperly be called, *dephlogisticated air*."

EXPERIMENTAL DIFFICULTIES WITH GASES

A chemist reading the papers of the phlogistonists clutches his head in despair; he seems to be transported to an Alice-through-the-looking-glass world! But if he is patient and interested he soon recognizes that much of the difficulty stemmed from the experimenters' inability to handle and characterize different gases. This fact illustrates once again the third point of the principles outlined in the last chapter, the difficulty of experimentation. Metals and calxes, inflammable substances like sulfur, charcoal, and phosphorus, the chemists of the eighteenth century could recognize and manipulate since they were solids. Even some liquids like vitriolic acid, water, and mercury were quite definite individuals. But two gases, neither of which would support fire, like nitrogen and carbon dioxide, were often hopelessly confused; or two which burned, like hydrogen and carbon monoxide. Nearly all gases look alike except for the few which are colored. They are compressible and subject to thermal expansion to about the same degree. Their densities, i.e., the weight of a unit volume, differ but that was something not easy to determine in those days. Indeed, in the eighteenth century the distinction between weight and density (i.e., weight per unit volume) even for solids and liquids was often confused. The chemical properties of each gas are characteristic and the way each gas is prepared is different; and it was these differences that finally led to a straightening out of some of the tangled skein.

To understand the difficulties of the chemists of 175 years ago, imagine yourself an elementary student in a laboratory given glass bottles of air, of oxygen, of nitrogen, and one containing air saturated with ether vapor, and asked to tell whether or not all the "airs" or gases in the bottles are identical. The air containing the ether vapor (actually still largely air) will be the only one at first recognized as distinct. A student does not know how to proceed to examine these gases except by looking at them, smelling them, or testing their solubility in water. And from Boyle's day to Priestley's the experimenters were largely in the same predicament. They spoke of different "airs," but hardly knew whether the differences were real or due to the presence of some impurity. Thus, Priestley, writing in 1777, said:

"Van Helmont and other chymists who succeeded him, were acquainted with the property of some *vapours* to suffocate, and extinguish flame, and of others to be ignited. . . . But they had no idea that the substances (if, indeed they knew that they were *substances*, and not merely *properties*, and *affections* of bodies which produced those effects) were capable of being separately exhibited in the form of a *permanently elastic vapour* . . . any more than the thing that constitutes *smell*. In fact they knew nothing at all of any air besides *common air*, and therefore they applied the term to no other substances whatever. . . ."

The history of the study of gases covers a hundred years from Boyle's day. A number of important improvements in techniques were made. They were brought to a focus by Priestley who in 1772 carried out extensive and very original experiments with "airs." He improved still further several techniques of handling these airs or gases which enormously simplified the experimental procedures. Before Priestley's work only three "different airs" were known. In a few years he had discovered eleven more, including oxygen. Here is another illustration of the importance of techniques, though here we meet with an evolutionary rather than a revolutionary change.

Though Priestley was the chief figure in extending the knowledge of gases, his stubborn refusal to accept the consequences of his own discoveries has already been mentioned. It is not necessary in this chapter to discuss either Priestley or Lavoisier as individuals, though the instructor using the case history of combustion would certainly wish to do so. Nor do I propose to digress by examining the priority problems involved in the work of these two men and the Swedish chemist, Scheele, who also discovered oxygen. Such matters fall within the province of the historian of science. For the purposes of the present exposition the important questions are: Why did it take the scientists of the eighteenth century so long to get on the right road? And why were there so many stubborn travelers on the wrong road after the right one had been discovered?

THE PHLOGISTON THEORY, A BLOCK TO A NEW CONCEPT

It is sometimes said that the experimenters before Lavoisier's day did not carry out quantitative experiments, that is, they did not use the balance. If they had, we are told, they would have discovered that combustion involves an increase in weight and would have rejected the phlogiston theory. This is nonsense. Rey, as I have already explained, long before the beginning of the phlogiston period showed that a calx weighed more than a metal. Quantitative experiments, though, of course, not very accurate ones, were repeatedly made. Everyone knew that a calx weighed more than the metal from which it was formed. No straightforward statement of the phlogiston theory could accommodate this fact. Yet the phlogiston theory was so useful that few if any in the mid-eighteenth century were looking to overthrow it or disprove it. Rather, they were interested in reconciling one inconvenient set of facts with what seemed from their point of view an otherwise admirable conceptual scheme. How they twisted and squirmed to accommodate the quantitative facts of calcination with the phlogiston theory makes an interesting chapter in the history of science. The eighteenth-century accounts are often confusing. Fortunately their many details need not concern the readers of this book; nor except in broad outline need they concern one teaching the principles of the Tactics and Strategy of Science with the aid of the eighteenth-century studies on combustion.

The principle which emerges is one already encountered, namely, that it takes a new conceptual scheme to cause the abandonment of an old one: when only a few facts appear to be irreconcilable with a well established conceptual scheme, the first attempt is *not* to discard the scheme but to find some way out of the difficulty and keep it. Likewise the proponents of new concepts are rarely shaken by a few alleged facts to the contrary. They seek at first to prove them wrong or to circumvent them. Thus Lavoisier persisted with his own new concept in spite of the fact that certain experiments seemed to be completely inexplicable in its terms. It was later found that the interpretation of the experiments was in error. Not so in the case of the calcination of metals: there could be no doubt in the mind of anyone by 1770 that the increase in weight during calcination was real. There was also no doubt that there should be a loss in weight according to the phlogiston theory. Or at best no change in weight if phlogiston were an imponderable substance like fire.

ATTEMPTS TO RECONSTRUCT THE PHLOGISTON THEORY

One attempt to get out of the dilemma of calcination took refuge in a confusion between weight and density (calxes are less dense than metals, but the total weight in the calcination increased). This was soon put right by clear thinking. Another attempt involved assigning a negative weight to phlogiston. This illustrates how desperately men may strive to modify an old idea to make it accord with new experiments. But in this case the modification represented not a step forward but several steps to the rear! What was gained by accommodating the quantitative aspect of calcination was lost by following the consequences of negative weight to a logical conclusion. What manner of substance or principle could phlogiston be that when it was added to another material the total mass or weight diminished? The idea that phlogiston had negative weight strained the credulity, and for the most part this logical extension of the phlogiston theory (logical in one sense, highly illogical in another) was never widely accepted. But before we laugh too hard at the investigators of the eighteenth century, let us remember that before the nineteenth century heat was considered a corporeal substance and the whole concept of the atomic and molecular theory of matter lay over the distant horizon.

To some of the chemical experimenters, the dilemma presented by the quantitative facts of calcination seems to have been accepted as just one of those things which cannot be fitted in. And this attitude is much more common in the history of science than most historians would have you believe. Indeed, it is in a way a necessary attitude at certain stages of development of any concept. The keen-minded scientist, the real genius, is the man who keeps in the forefront of his thoughts these unsolved riddles. He then is ready to relate a new discovery or a new technique to the unsolved problems. He is the pioneer, the revolutionist. And it is this combination of strategy and tactics in the hands of a master which is well worthy of study if one would try to understand science through the historical approach.

LAVOISIER'S CLUE

To recount the history of Lavoisier's development of his new theory, and the way in which the new discoveries of the time were fitted into his scheme would mean the recital of a long story. Such an account would be out of place in this volume, though a considerable portion of it would be involved in a thorough study of the case histories at hand. Let me take a few moments of the reader's time, however, to point out how Lavoisier first seems to have taken the right turn in the road. In a famous note of 1772, he wrote as follows:

"About eight days ago I discovered that sulphur in burning, far from losing weight, on the contrary gains it; . . . it is the same with phosphorus; this increase of weight arises from a prodigious quantity of air that is fixed during the combustion and combines with the vapours.

"This discovery, which I have established by experiments that I regard as decisive, has led me to think that what is observed in the combustion of sulphur and phosphorus may well take place in the case of all substances that gain in weight by combustion and calcination: and I am persuaded that the increase in weight of metallic calces is due to the same cause. . . ."

Here we seem to see the mental process at work to which I referred a few moments ago: the perception that a new fact properly interpreted enables one to explain an old dilemma, an outstanding unsolved problem. In a sense, in this note Lavoisier outlined the whole new chemistry, as he always later claimed. (The note was deposited sealed with the Secretary of the French Academy on November 1, 1772.) To be sure, at first Lavoisier mistook the gas evolved in the reduction of a calx with charcoal (carbon dioxide, the "fixed air" of that day) with the gas absorbed in calcination. The study we can now make of his notebooks as well as his later publications makes it plain that it was not until after Priestley's discovery of oxygen and Lavoisier's repetition of some of Priestley's experiments with the new gas that the nature of the gas absorbed in calcination became clear. It was only then that all the pieces of the puzzle fitted together, with the newly discovered oxygen occupying the central position in the picture. But at the outset Lavoisier recognized that something was absorbed from the air. Unconsciously he was retracing the steps Jean Rey had taken nearly 150 years earlier and which had never been followed up. Rey's almost forgotten book was called to Lavoisier's attention shortly after his first publications of his new theory.

An interesting question that will at once come to the mind of many is the following: why did the study of sulfur and phosphorus lead Lavoisier to the right type of explanation? Why after experiments with those substances did he set out full of confidence on a set of planned experiments along a new line? This is one of those historical riddles which can never be answered, but concerning which it is not entirely profitless to speculate. I suggest that the key word in Lavoisier's note of November 1, 1772, is "prodigious"—"this increase of weight arises from a prodigious quantity of air that is fixed." If this is so, we have again another illustration of how experimental difficulties or the lack of them condition the evolution of new concepts. To determine whether air is absorbed or not during the calcination of a metal is not easy; the process takes a long time, a high temperature, and both the increase in weight and the amount of oxygen absorbed are small. But with phosphorus and sulfur the experiment was relatively easy to perform (the materials burn at once on ignition with a burning glass); furthermore, the effect observed is very large. The reason for this in terms of modern chemistry is that sulfur and phosphorus have low atomic weights of 32 and 31 (oxygen is 16), and in the combustion 1 atom of phosphorus combines with 5 of oxygen; 1 atom of sulfur with 3 of oxygen. The atomic weight of the metals is high, the number of atoms of oxygen combining with them, fewer. Thus 62 weights of phosphorus will yield $62 + (5 \times 16) = 142$ parts of combustion product; while in the case of tin, the atomic weight is 118 and only 2 atoms of oxygen are involved. Thus 118 weights of tin would yield only $118 + (2 \times 16) = 150$ weights of calx or an increase of only about 25 per cent. Note that with phosphorus the increase is more than double. The corresponding differences would be reflected in the volume of oxygen absorbed, and furthermore, since the calcination of tin was a long process at a high temperature in a furnace, no entirely satisfactory way of measuring the volume of air absorbed was at hand in 1770.

QUANTITATIVE MEASUREMEMENTS AND ACCIDENTAL ERRORS

As a matter of fact, until Lavoisier was put on the track of the gas prepared by heating mercuric oxide by Priestley, he had a hard time proving that metallic calxes did gain in weight *because* of absorption of something from the air. The method he used was to repeat certain experiments of Boyle with a slight modification. Both the modification and the difficulties are of interest and point an obvious moral to the tale. Boyle had sealed tin in a glass vessel and heated the vessel a long time on a charcoal fire (which he says is a very dangerous operation as the glass may well explode). Boyle then removed the vessel from the fire and after cooling opened the glass, reweighed the vessel and noted the increase in weight. This was one of the many well-known experiments showing that the calx weighed more than the metal. (Boyle, the reader will recall, believed the increase to be due to the fire particles which passed through the glass). Now, said Lavoisier, where Boyle went wrong was in not weighing the vessel *before* opening it. For if his explanation were right and the fire had passed through the glass and combined with the tin, the increase would have occurred before the air was admitted. While if oxygen were involved, the increase in weight would occur *after* the air was admitted. The results obtained by Lavoisier on repeating this experiment were as expected, but were far from being as striking as those obtained with phosphorus for the reasons just explained. The increase was 10 parts in a total of 4,100 in one experiment and 3 parts in about the same amount in another! We now know that the difficulties of weighing a large glass vessel with a high degree of accuracy are great, due to film moisture and electrical charges. It is, therefore, not surprising that the glass retort, after heating, varied in weight from day to day almost as much as the total gain in weight in one of the two experiments.

These tough facts of experimentation are of great importance. To me, they indicate strongly that even if Boyle had weighed his vessel before and after admitting the air, the uncertainties of his figures would probably have been so great as to confuse him and subsequent investigators. *Important advances in science are based on quantitative measurements only if the measured quantity is large as compared with possible systematic and accidental errors.* The principle of significant figures which plays so large a part in later scientific history is foreshadowed in a crude way by this episode involving the combustion of phosphorus and the calcination of tin. Therefore, in considering the case history at hand the instructor would undoubtedly wish to enlarge at some length on the whole problem of the controlled variable and the role of quantitative measurements.

LAVOISIER AND PRIESTLEY'S STUBBORN FACTS

For students who had some prior knowledge of chemistry, say a good high-school course, the study of the last days of the phlogiston theory might be rewarding. For the controversy between Lavoisier and Priestley not only illustrates with what tenacity an able man may cling to a hopeless position, but also the boldness with which the innovator pushes forward. Even if a few facts appear to be to the contrary, he still pushes his new ideas just as his conservative opponent stoutly maintains his own tenets in spite of contradictory evidence. In such tugs of war which are the commonest experience in science, though usually in highly restricted areas and with limited significance, the innovator is by no means always right. This point needs to be made perfectly clear. Several case histories to this end would be worth recounting. A few dramatic instances would be in order where some bold man put forward a new idea based on alleged facts which turned out to be erroneous or erroneously interpreted.

The record of Lavoisier was the opposite. For the facts he ignored were indeed not facts at all. Priestley's main points against Lavoisier's views were based on a mistaken identification of two different gases. This fact again emphasizes the difficulties of experimentation. Two gases, both inflammable, carbon monoxide and hydrogen, were at that period confused, even by the great experimenters with gases. Assuming their identity Priestley could ask Lavoisier to account for phenomena which were indeed inexplicable according to the new chemistry, but could be accommodated in the phlogiston theory, now being twisted more each day to conform to new discoveries. Not until long after Lavoisier's execution in 1794 was the relationship between the two gases straightened out. Therefore, Lavoisier was never able to respond to the most weighty of Priestley's arguments against his doctrine. He merely ignored the alleged facts, much as Priestley ignored the unexplained gain in weight or calcination. Each undoubtedly believed that some way would be found around the difficulty in question. Lavoisier's hopes, not Priestley's, proved well founded. So proceeds the course of science. Sometimes it turns out that difficulties with a concept or conceptual scheme are wisely ignored, sometimes unwisely. To suppose, with some who write about the "scientific method," that a scientific theory stands or falls on the issue of one experiment is to misunderstand science indeed.

A study of the overthrow of the phlogiston theory is thus seen to be more than a single case history; it is a related series of case histories. The student's knowledge of chemistry or willingness to take time to obtain this knowledge would be the limiting factor on the use of this material. Even without prior study of chemistry, I believe, a profitable excursion into this complicated bit of scientific history could be undertaken. From such an excursion would come a deeper appreciation of the two principles to which I earlier referred in this chapter. Having studied the phlogiston theory no one would fail to realize that old concepts may present barriers to the development of new ones; having traced the course of the history of experiments with gases and calcination, no one could fail to realize that scientific discoveries must fit the times if they are to be fruitful. In addition, other principles of the Tactics and Strategy of Science are constantly recurring throughout the somewhat lengthy story: the influence of new techniques, the difficulties of experimentation, the value of the controlled experiment, the evaluation of new concepts from experiment—all these are to be found illustrated more than once by those who have patience to study a strange and often neglected chapter in the history of science.

1947

THE PERIODIC CLASSIFICATION OF THE ELEMENTS *

WILLIAM F. EHRET

. . . The history of attempts to classify elements by their atomic weights extends back for more than a century, and, as might be expected, is intimately bound up with the advances that were made in the determination of atomic weights and in the discovery of new elements. In all, it forms one of the most interesting chapters in the history of chemistry, and furnishes, over and over again, examples of the application of both the inductive and deductive methods in science.

Earliest to notice any connection between atomic weights and the grouping of elements was Döbereiner, who, in 1829, pointed out that if one arranged chemically related elements in groups of three, there was an almost constant difference between the atomic weights of the elements in the group. In other words, the atomic weight of the intermediate member was approximately the *arithmetic mean* of the weights of the end-members. Thus, for the following three groups, the differences average about 47.

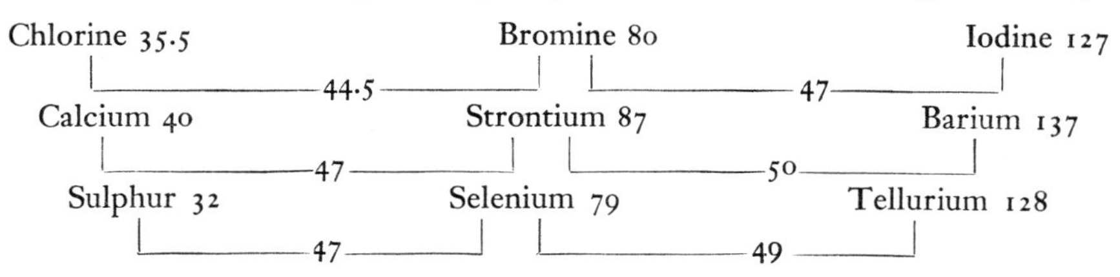

This was an intriguing regularity, and efforts were made to extend the scheme as new elements were discovered or the atomic weights of known ones were rectified. . . .

By 1863, more elements were known and the atomic weights of many had been corrected. In this year, Newlands drew attention to a *periodicity* that existed in the properties of the lighter elements, then known,[1] when they were arranged in increasing order of atomic weight. In his sequence, reading from left to right:

Li	Be	B	C	N	O	F
Na	Mg	Al	Si	P	S	Cl
K	Ca	Cr	Ti	Mn	Fe	

* From *Smith's College Chemistry*, Sixth Edition by William F. Ehret. Copyright 1947 by D. Appleton-Century Company, Inc.

[1] The family of elements formed by the inert gases helium, neon, etc., it must be noted, was not discovered until many years subsequent to Newlands' time.

Newlands noticed that every succeeding eighth element had properties similar to the first. . . . On account of the fact that each element resembles most closely the seventh element beyond or before it in the list, the relation was called the *law of octaves*. After chlorine the octaves become less easy to trace. Potassium (39) follows chlorine and corresponds satisfactorily to sodium, but it is not until seventeen successive elements have been set down that we reach one closely resembling chlorine, namely, bromine. . . .

Mendelejeff adjusted the difficulty which the heavier elements had presented to Newlands, and developed the whole conception so completely that the resulting system of classification—the periodic system—has been connected with his name ever since. The table shown below is the one published by him in 1872. It will be noted that it contains only 63 of the 96 elements now known, and five of these were in doubt (marked "?").

The chief change made by Mendelejeff from the arrangement in simple octaves is to be found in his fourth, sixth, and tenth series or periods. To each of these octaves he added four elements which he put into an eighth group; thus, the elements Fe, Co, Ni, and Cu were lumped together at the end of the fourth series. In a later table, series four and five were combined to make a "long series," and Fe, Co, and Ni were inserted as "transition ele-

MENDELEJEFF'S PERIODIC CLASSIFICATION OF THE ELEMENTS (1872)
(Numbers in Parenthesis Are the Atomic Weights)

Group →	I	II	III	IV	V	VI	VII	VIII
Type → Compound	R_2O	RO	R_2O_3	RO_2 H_4R	R_2O_5 H_3R	RO_3 H_2R	R_2O_7 HR	RO_4
SERIES 1	H(1)							
2	Li(7)	Be(9.4)	B(11)	C(12)	N(14)	O(16)	F(19)	
3	Na(23)	Mg(24)	Al(27.3)	Si(28)	P(31)	S(32)	Cl(35.5)	
4	K(39)	Ca(40)	–(44)	Ti(48)	V(51)	Cr(52)	Mn(55)	Fe(56), Co(59), Ni(59), Cu(63)
5	[Cu(63)]	Zn(65)	–(68)	–(72)	As(75)	Se(78)	Br(80)	
6	Rb(85)	Sr(87)	?Yt(88)	Zr(90)	Nb(94)	Mo(96)	–(100)	Ru(104), Rh(104), Pd(106), Ag(108)
7	[Ag(108)]	Cd(112)	In(113)	Sn(118)	Sb(122)	Te(125)	I(127)	
8	Cs(133)	Ba(137)	?Di(138)	?Ce(140)	—	—	—	
9	—	—	—	—	—	—	—	
10	—	—	?Er(178)	?La(180)	Ta(182)	W(184)	—	Os(195), Ir(197), Pt(198), Au(199)
11	[Au(199)]	Hg(200)	Tl(204)	Pb(207)	Bi(208)	—	—	
12	—	—	—	Th(231)	—	U(240)		

ments" between the two octaves making up the long series. Similarly, series 6 and 7, and 10 and 11, were combined to make long series, each with its set of transition elements in group VIII, and each beginning with a metal resembling lithium and sodium. The periodicity in valence, referred to above, fell in with this plan fairly well.

At the time Mendelejeff made the table shown above, one place had to be left blank in the fourth series and two in the fifth, as a trivalent element (Sc) was lacking in the fourth, and a trivalent (Ga) and quadrivalent one (Ge) in the fifth. These places have since been filled, as we shall presently see. The sixth and seventh series, which were later made into one long series, were rather complete, lacking only an element in group VII. . . . In the remaining series there were many blanks, but the order of atomic weights and the valences enabled Mendelejeff satisfactorily to place most of the elements that were known (see, however, the rare earths, below). The chemical relations of the elements of the eighth period to those of the sixth justify the position assigned to each. Cesium, for example, is the most active of the alkali metals, and barium has always been classed with strontium.

On page 440 there appears a modern version of Mendelejeff's periodic table. At first sight, the resemblance between the old and the new tables is not striking, but that is merely because of a change in the form of presentation and because half again as many elements are included as in the original table. For convenience, in the new table, the elements in the "long periods" have been stretched out in one line rather than in two (octaves) placed one immediately under the other. This requires doubling the number of groups, by dividing them into sub-groups, marked *a* and *b*, which may seem to make for a less compact table, but the change presents certain important advantages. . . .

Five fundamental changes have been made in the table since it was first published by Mendelejeff. *First*, is the addition of another group, the family of the *inert gases* of the atmosphere. These elements were unknown before 1894, but fall logically into a new group at the right-hand side of the table, as here given. *Secondly*, the anomalous ninth series has been dropped, and the eighth, tenth, and eleventh have been combined to form one long period, the sixth in the new table. *Thirdly*, an entirely new group of elements, fourteen in number, called the *rare earths* (position Nos. 58–71) has been appended to the table. Most of these elements were unknown to Mendelejeff. They all resemble lanthanum (No. 57) in properties, and may be placed to one side, leaving lanthanum to stand as their prototype. *Fourthly*, each element has received an *atomic number* which, beside indicating its position in the table, is of fundamental significance in that it gives the number of electrons possessed by the atoms of the element. . . . The number of electrons, and their arrangement, determine almost all the properties of the element and thus govern its position in the table. *Finally*, another group of elements, the *actinide series* (Nos. 90–96), has recently

PERIODIC CLASSIFICATION OF THE ELEMENTS

The atomic number is given above the symbol of the element; the atomic weight, to no more than four significant figures, below the symbol.

Group →	I_a	II_a	III_b	IV_b	V_b	VI_b	VII_b	VIII_b			I_b	II_b	III_a	IV_a	V_a	VI_a	VII_a	VIII_a
Type → Compounds	R_2O RH	RO RH_2	R_2O_3	RO_2	R_2O_5	RO_3	R_2O_7	RO-R_2O_3-RO_2-RO_3 (RO_4)			R_2O	RO	R_2O_3	RO_2 RH_4	R_2O_5 RH_3	RO_3 H_2R	R_2O_7 HR	
PERIODS 1	1 H 1.008																	2 He 4.003
2	3 Li 6.940	4 Be 9.02											5 B 10.82	6 C 12.01	7 N 14.01	8 O 16.00	9 F 19.00	10 Ne 20.18
3	11 Na 23.00	12 Mg 24.32											13 Al 26.97	14 Si 28.06	15 P 30.98	16 S 32.06	17 Cl 35.46	18 A 39.94
4	19 K 39.10	20 Ca 40.08	21 Sc 45.10	22 Ti 47.90	23 V 50.95	24 Cr 52.01	25 Mn 54.93	26 Fe 55.85	27 Co 58.94	28 Ni 58.69	29 Cu 63.57	30 Zn 65.38	31 Ga 69.72	32 Ge 72.60	33 As 74.91	34 Se 78.96	35 Br 79.92	36 Kr 83.7
5	37 Rb 85.48	38 Sr 87.63	39 Y 88.92	40 Zr 91.22	41 Cb 92.91	42 Mo 95.95	43 Tc 99	44 Ru 101.7	45 Rh 102.9	46 Pd 106.7	47 Ag 107.9	48 Cd 112.4	49 In 114.8	50 Sn 118.7	51 Sb 121.8	52 Te 176.6	53 I 126.9	54 Xe 131.3
6	55 Cs 132.9	56 Ba 137.4	57* La 138.9	72 Hf 178.6	73 Ta 180.9	74 W 183.9	75 Re 186.3	76 Os 190.2	77 Ir 193.1	78 Pt 195.2	79 Au 197.2	80 Hg 200.6	81 Tl 204.4	82 Pb 207.2	83 Bi 209.0	84 Po 210	85 At 211	86 Rn 2 22
7	87 Fr 223	88 Ra 226.1	89† Ac 227.1															
*Rare Earth Elements → 58-71				58 Ce 140.1	59 Pr 140.9	60 Nd 144.3	61 Il	62 Sm 150.4	63 Eu 152.0	64 Gd 156.9	65 Tb 159.2	66 Dy 162.5	67 Ho 164.9	68 Er 167.2	69 Tm 169.4	70 Yb 173.0	71 Lu 175.0	
†Actinide Series → 90-96				90 Th 232.1	91 Pa 231	92 U 238.1	93 Np 237	94 Pu 239	95 Am 241	96 Cm 242								

been introduced for reasons similar to those which compelled the addition of the rare earths. The elements in the actinide group are all radioactive and some of their physical and chemical properties are not yet known. Nevertheless, sufficient justification appears to exist to bracket them with the corresponding rare earth elements, for example, Nd with U, Ce with Th, *etc.*

Examination of the modern table reveals no unoccupied positions. Only one element, No. 61, provisionally called illinium Il, awaits a permanent designation. It, and technetium Tc (No. 43), are recently discovered by-products of the operation of atomic energy piles. Elements 93 and 94, neptunium and plutonium, were made in large quantity in connection with the atomic bomb and energy schemes developed during World War II. Minute amounts of two additional "transuranic" elements, Nos. 95 and 96 (americium and curium), have been made by nuclear transformations in the laboratory.

In the modern periodic table *each chemical family occupies a separate group* which is designated by a Roman numeral and a sub-letter. Thus we shall sometimes refer to the elements in group II_b when we mean zinc, cadmium, and mercury, or we may speak of the elements in the a-groups when we wish to include all elements falling in the groups marked with a subscript *a*.

Under each group number appears a type formula for an oxide, and sometimes a hydride, formed by each element in that group, *e.g.*, the element calcium forms the oxide CaO and the hydride CaH_2. . . .

The step-like heavy line, noticed in the table, separates the elements that are commonly considered *metals*, to the left, from the *non-metals* on the right. This cannot be considered a hard and fast division, for elements next to the line, as As, Sb, or Te, are *on* the border, and exhibit properties intermediate between those of the metals and the non-metals. It is evident that as we proceed through the periods, and the elements become heavier, fewer and fewer of them fall into the non-metallic category.

One-half of the elements are segregated by heavy lines in the form of rectangles in two sections of the table. Actually this is only *one* large section, since, as was mentioned above, the rare earth elements and the actinide series should be placed with their prototypes Nos. 57 and 89. The members of this large group are called *transition elements*, and they have a number of common characteristics. . . .

If we examine the physical properties of *successive elements*, or of corresponding compounds of successive elements, *of any one family* we almost always find a uniform *gradation* observable. . . . Thus the melting-points of the alkali metals are as follows:

Li 186°, Na 97.5°, K 62.3°, Rb 38.5°, Cs 26°.

That the *chemical relations* of the elements vary just as do the physical properties of the simple substances is easily shown. Thus, each period, except the first, begins with an active metallic (positive) element and, barring group VIII_a, ends with an active non-metallic (negative) element, the intervening elements showing a more or less continuous variation between these limits. Again, the elements at the top are the least metallic of their respective columns. As we descend, the members of each group are more markedly metallic (in the first columns), or, what is the same thing, less markedly non-metallic (in the latter columns).

Anticipating the discovery of some more exact mode of stating the relationship in each case, and remembering that similar values of each property (whether chemical or physical) recur *periodically*, usually at intervals corresponding to the length of an "octave" or period, the principle which is assumed to underlie the whole, the *periodic law*, may be stated thus: *The properties of the elements are periodic functions of their atomic weights.* We shall recognize this as a rather general "law," and use it as a working hypothesis, not as a rigorous mathematical tool. In a strict sense, a periodic function is one that repeats itself at regular intervals; in our table, however, repetition of properties appears after periods of 2, 8, 8, 18, 18, and 32 elements. Furthermore, to be more rigorous, we should arrange our elements according to atomic number and not atomic weight, for in several different places in the table the ascending order of atomic weights has not been followed. . . .

The system has found application chiefly in four ways:

1. In the *prediction of new elements.* Mendelejeff (1871) drew attention to the blank then existing between calcium (40) and titanium (48). He predicted that an element to fit this place would have an atomic weight 44 and would be trivalent. From the nature of the surrounding elements, he very cleverly deduced many of the physical and chemical properties of the unknown element and of its compounds. He named it eka-boron (Sanskrit *eka,* "one"). In 1879 Nilson discovered scandium (45.1), and its behavior corresponded *in practically every detail* with that predicted for eka-boron. Mendelejeff also described accurately two other elements, likewise unknown at the time. They were to occupy vacant places between zinc and arsenic, and were named eka-aluminum and eka-silicon. In 1875 Lecoque de Boisbaudran found gallium, and in 1888 Winkler discovered germanium, and these blanks were filled. . . .

2. By enabling us to decide on the *correct values for the atomic weights* of some elements, when the equivalent weights have been measured, but no volatile compound is known. Thus, the equivalent weight of indium was found, by experiment, to be 38 and, as the element was supposed to be bivalent, it received the atomic weight 76. It was quite out of place near arsenic (75), however, being decidedly a metallic element. But as a trivalent element with the atomic weight 115, it fell quite logically into a vacant space between cadmium and tin. Later work fully justified the change. More recently, when radium was discovered, it was found to have

the equivalent weight 113 and to resemble barium. Consequently we assume that, like barium, it is bivalent, and assign it to fill a vacant place under this element, in the last series.

3. By *suggesting problems for investigation.* The periodic system has been of constant service in the course of inorganic research, and has often furnished the original stimulus to such work as well.

For example, the first experimental determinations of the atomic weights of the *platinum metals* placed them in the order, Ir (197), Pt (198), Os (199), although the resemblance of osmium to iron and ruthenium would have led us to expect that this element should come first. For similar reasons platinum should come last, under palladium. A reinvestigation of the atomic weights, suggested by these considerations, was undertaken by Seubert, and the old values were found in fact to be very inaccurate. Seubert obtained: Os = 191, Ir = 193, Pt = 195.

In the same way, incorrect values of many physical properties have been detected, and have been rectified by more careful work.

Originally *lead,* although it fell in the fourth column, possessed only one compound PbO_2 in which it seemed to be undoubtedly quadrivalent. Search for salts of the same form, however, speedily yielded the tetrachloride $PbCl_4$, tetracetate, and many others. The existence of osmium tetroxide OsO_4, and a corresponding compound of ruthenium, suggests that other compounds of the elements of the eighth group, displaying the valence eight, may be capable of preparation.

4. By furnishing a comprehensive *classification of the elements,* arranging them so as to exhibit the relationships among the physical and chemical properties of the elements themselves and of their compounds. . . .

The periodic table of 1872 is now mainly of historic interest. It was reproduced in this chapter primarily to remind us that progress in science, as in every human endeavor, is generally made in a slow, evolutionary manner. Thousands of minds and hands have labored since Mendelejeff's time to bring the classification to its present state of perfection, yet the basic pattern has remained unchanged. To Mendelejeff we must extend special praise for his ingenuity in laying the groundwork for a classification which is not excelled by any other in science or the arts. This achievement seems all the more remarkable when it is recalled that he was familiar with little more than half the elements and that the physical and chemical data available in his time were decidedly meager. Yet thousands had worked before Mendelejeff's time to gather even this data which made it possible for him to proceed. Thus the table, as it stands today, is a monument to the diligence of many generations of chemists, and shows, perhaps more clearly than do some other achievements, that *science is a coöperative venture* in which man has met with signal success.

1947

>>>><<<<

THE TASK OF THE ORGANIC CHEMIST *

G. ROSS ROBERTSON

According to a rough estimate based on published records, there have now been "discovered" about 450,000 organic chemical compounds. In 1883 the number was but 15,000; in 1910 it was 150,000; in 1936, 350,000. Most of this collection has been amassed by investigators in universities and research institutes. If one might delve into the confidential records of Imperial Chemical Industries, Ltd., Interessen Gemeinschaft Farbenindustrie A.G., or E. I. du Pont de Nemours and Company, substantial additions to the list would undoubtedly come to light.

The publications describing this mass of work are rapidly becoming the despair of chemical libraries. Beilstein's colossal *Handbook of Organic Chemistry*, now in its fourth edition, attempts to keep abreast of the task of abstracting this material in brief. Although Beilstein's publisher has now fallen twenty-four years behind current reports of laboratory work, the price of his *Handbook* has already passed $1,500.

The term "discovery" applied to a chemical compound of carbon was particularly appropriate in earlier periods of the world's history, when scientists of a primitive sort literally discovered such useful things as camphor, alcohol, and sugar. Even today it is significant in such projects as the identification of vitamin K and penicillin.

In modern industrial technology a new compound may turn up by accident; for example, the beautiful new phthalocyanine pigment which will stand red heat. Most of the prolific family of organic compounds, however, are the result of a definite synthetic program calling for precise chemical architectural design as well as competent service from the scientific building contractor. At least, such has been the fashion since September, 1860.

The date which marked the emergence of organic chemistry from chaos to order would have been 1811, and not 1860, had it not been for the inertia of the human mind. It was in 1811 that the obscure Italian physicist Avogadro gave to the world the uninteresting but extremely important statement that equal volumes of gases contain equal numbers of molecules. No one paid any attention to Avogadro. As a result, organic chemists muddled along for forty-nine years without realizing that the key to the riddle of chemical formulation lay before them. Not even H_2O, the formula of water, was established; some learned scholars insisted that it should be HO.

At the close of a particularly dull international chemical convention in Karlsruhe in the fall of 1860, Stanislao Cannizzaro, a bright young

* From *Science in the University*, University of California Press. Copyright 1944 by the Regents of the University of California.

chemistry professor from Genoa, distributed copies of propaganda pamphlets drawing attention to his old compatriot Avogadro. Most of the pamphlets reached the wastebasket, but a few competent chemists read and learned. What they read was not nominally "organic" chemistry, but rather a proof establishing the relative weights of the atoms of which the submicroscopic molecules of sugar, alcohol, morphine, and so forth, are composed. It was as if a secret code for communications had been broken, resulting in a flood of clarified knowledge.

The Structural Formula. So came to light the structural formula and its limitless opportunities for variation in design. It became possible to specify a particular arrangement of atoms which meant a useful drug, a gorgeous dye, or a potent insecticide; and, more important, to demonstrate the course of manufacture in the laboratory or manufacturing plant. Without such chemical architecture the conversion of ineffective natural gasoline, whose molecular design is suggestive of strings of beads, into modern aviation gasoline, designed more like bunches of grapes, would have been impossible.

Like most scientific analogies, the bead-string and grape comparisons are inadequate. Atoms of carbon, hydrogen, oxygen, nitrogen, and a very few other chemical elements found in organic compounds, may be interconnected in much more complex patterns, in chains both open and endless, simple and branched. Each arrangement, absolutely precise with respect to number, weight, and volume of constituent parts, and with respect to connections, represents a chemical compound, and may occasionally represent a new ten-million-dollar industry.

The number of different arrangements of atoms in molecules may not be infinite, but it certainly is large. Not long ago a chemist who apparently derives entertainment from mathematics demonstrated that there could be 62,491,178,805,831 different compounds of carbon and hydrogen, every one of which has the condensed chemical formula $C_{40}H_{82}$. Each of these would obey the chemical laws relating to possible interatomic connections.

This already astronomical computation, which refers only to the 40-82 combination, may be repeated for thousands of other condensed formulas, and always with a total count of impressive proportions. Following so preposterous an inventory of possibilities, one may introduce oxygen and nitrogen into the game, and then the arithmetic really begins to expand. For every one of these chemical compounds a perfectly definite "blueprint" or structural formula may be laid out without laboratory trial, though not always with assurance of success in actual production. The chemical architect may thus produce a beautiful series of pictures covering all reasonable possibilities. Unfortunately, he has difficulty in telling which theoretical picture belongs to a given newly discovered organic compound.

Photography of Small Things. Many a pioneer in organic chemistry has wished that he might turn a supermicroscope upon an unknown substance before him and actually see the details of individual atoms. Years of laboratory practice supported by blind but well-directed logic had already told him what *kinds* of atoms and what *relative numbers* of these atoms existed in the uniform molecules massed indistinguishably before his eyes; but the *absolute size* and *arrangement* of these atoms called for more scientific aid.

Eventually it was Millikan, through the famous oil-drop experiment, who indirectly told the organic chemist the sad news about the size of his molecules. From Millikan's figures, and later from X-ray spectrography, one finds, for example, a molecule of the common drug aspirin to be only nine Ångstrom units long. This means that no less than 28,000,000 aspirin molecules laid end to end would be required to span the distance of one inch. Or, getting down to really little things, the average distance from center to center of the individual atoms in that molecule will run about 1/150,000,000 of an inch. Unfortunately for the would-be chemical microscopist, the shortest waves of visible light run more than 3,000 Ångstrom units in wave length, rendering visual perception or even photography of the individual molecule by conventional technique entirely impossible. A 9-Ångstrom-unit molecule on a 5,000-unit wave of visible light disturbs the light about as much as a cork bothers the waves of the open Pacific.

The chemist was thus completely baffled. He was therefore compelled to devise extensive and ingenious, but very tedious, experiments from which he could reason what the structure of molecules must be. It often required ten years or more to work out the configuration of a molecule which could have been comprehended in less than one hour if the chemist had been able to use the technique of the botanist with a powerful microscope. The brilliant dyestuff magenta, whose molecular structure was attacked by some of Germany's leading chemists about 1860, was not deciphered until 1878, when at last the great scientist Emil Fischer was able to write down the graphic formula. Next came the shorter task of learning how to make the substance most effectively in the laboratory. Only then could the chemical engineers and manufacturers rush into the long-awaited production program.

Electron Optics. Sentenced to a lifetime of blind experimentation, the researcher in organic chemistry was deeply stirred by the comparatively recent announcement of the electron microscope, which breaks over the barriers heretofore prohibiting high-powered magnification. Electron beams are focused by means of a magnetic field simulating a lens, instead of light beams through a glass lens. In theory at least, the new instrument permits resolution of objects distant from each other not 5,000 Ångstrom units, but down to 1 Ångstrom unit or less. Such an achievement would render the details of a molecular atom cluster distinguishable.

Four years ago no scientist of repute would have risked the prediction that the electron microscope would ever produce a photograph in which two atoms, 1½ Angstrom units apart, could be distinguished as two separate objects. But the campaign toward just such a goal is in vigorous progress, whether the researchers publicly admit it or not. The investigators have long passed the stage where they display, with pride, photographs which merely demonstrate that electron resolution is superior to light resolution.

At the present writing the electron microscopist is far below the boundary zone of resolution by light, and is already able to distinguish objects only 40 Angstrom units apart. The path of research from 40 units to 1 unit, however, presents obstacles insurmountable with present-day technique. The necessity of high voltage, which destroys the object whose photograph is desired; difficulty in producing the stable, highly constant magnetic field needed for creation of an unblurred photographic image; difficulties of working in a high vacuum—all these grow in significance as magnification is increased. It is true, nevertheless, that submicroscopic virus molecules, which to the chemist are objects of giant size, have already been photographed; but the journey from a virus molecule to an aspirin molecule, electronically speaking, will be long, weary, and discouraging. The scientist who finally gives the organic chemist the instrument in which he can photograph the ordinary small molecule, be it sugar, vitamin, or strychnine, will have achieved something far beyond any Nobel Prize accomplishment yet recorded. The present writer humbly ventures the guess that the first photographic revelations of atomic linkages will not be conventional facsimile pictures, but rather some new types of electronic photographs from which the organic chemist can interpret structure just as he has reasoned without visual evidence in past years. Like X-ray spectrograms, they will not look like structural models portrayed in textbooks. . . .

The Role of the Physical Chemist. Near the turn of the century some chemists grew impatient with the German style of program calling for more and more synthetic compounds. A few of the more extreme thinkers in the group began, "off the record," to make sarcastic comparisons with the art of breeding guinea pigs. They observed that at least 95 per cent, meaning about 95,000 of the known compounds, had not yet come into any practical use. Instead of making more compounds, they preferred to investigate the habits of a few substances.

This new group, styled physical chemists, were not taken too seriously by the German technical authorities. Chemistry was organic chemistry. Even in the year 1938 one found in Heidelberg and Munich that the physical chemist was set aside in an "institute" by himself, and could be quite confident that he would never be director of the university chemistry department.

For the first third of the twentieth century, roughly speaking, the physical chemist and the organic chemist went their separate ways. The physical chemist considered his colleague to be somewhat more of an artisan than a fundamental scientist, while the organic chemist was confident that the physical chemist spent so much time on underlying theory that he never did anything practical with organic compounds.

It is perhaps not surprising that the United States, newest major center of chemical thought, took the leadership in the new science of physical chemistry, and holds it today. California in particular was outstanding through the leadership of Gilbert N. Lewis and Arthur A. Noyes. In 1920 or 1925 no one in chemical circles would have thought of either of these scientists as a researcher in organic chemistry. To Lewis, however, goes the credit for presenting, in 1916, a concept nominally belonging to physical chemistry but later proving to be most fruitful in the interpretation of organic chemistry.

Prior to Lewis, the organic chemist was satisfied to spread out upon paper a group of capital letters representing atoms of carbon, hydrogen, and so on, and then to insert connecting lines between these letters to represent bonds holding the atoms together in a chemical compound. Such was the structural formula. No one concerned himself greatly with the physical meaning of these interatomic bonds. To be quite frank, even today the hormone or vitamin researcher, absorbed in the task of isolating and deciphering rarer and rarer natural compounds, is prone to be impatient and inconsiderate of the modern lore of electronic bonds.

Mechanism of Chemical Reactions. Following the original suggestion of Lewis, it was soon universally conceded that the chemical bond is in some way to be identified as a pair of electrons. From this concept has grown a new body of knowledge dealing with chemical bonds, in which another California physical chemist, Linus Pauling, has taken the lead. As a result of this activity the two branches of chemistry, organic and physical, have come together. Inspired by Lewis and Pauling, a new tribe of young scientists in chemistry, well grounded in the art as well as the extensive detailed facts of organic chemistry, have come upon the scene. These young scientists are not primarily interested in the breeding of new chemical guinea pigs for pigs' sake. They are, instead, directing their attention to the processes by which molecular structure is changed; they seek to unravel the mechanism by which chemical bonds are made and broken.

One can almost hear a vigorous protest from organic chemists of former days, such as Williamson of London, von Baeyer of Munich, or Nef of Chicago, at the assumption that study of the mechanism of chemical reactions is just a modern idea of the nineteen-forties. Hundreds of pages were written twenty, forty, and sixty years ago in which the supposed maneuvers of atoms from molecule to molecule were outlined. A hydrogen atom wandered from its companion carbon atom over to an oxygen atom; then the atomic chain broke and a piece moved over to a new position; a new chemical bond appeared in such a place—so ran the paragraphs of supposed explanation.

In the light of modern physical chemistry most of these historic explanations were pure speculation. Their value was largely pedagogical and inspirational. They were not based upon dependable scientific measurements. To be sure, the present-day investigators, like their predecessors, do not hesitate to picture atomic maneuvers, but their analysis of chemical strategy is based on new tools and new techniques, prominent among which is the science of kinetics.

Speed of Chemical Reaction. One of the most useful tricks of the kineticist is his scheme of dissecting what looks like one chemical process into two, three, or even four successive reactions. The researcher then usually discovers that one of these atomic moves is surprisingly slow. It is thus revealed as the "bottleneck" of the whole scheme, and may be responsible for the notorious inefficiency of the synthetic process under investigation.

Reaction-rate experimentation is not always personally convenient. Perhaps an instrument must be read hourly for a continuous stretch of thirty or forty hours, necessitating the addition of a reasonably comfortable cot and an alarm clock to the laboratory equipment. The old-fashioned organic chemist, if not too feverishly enthusiastic, could interrupt his researches at normal bedtime. If he had not obtained a product by that time, he might continue next day. If the process did not go well, he simply reported the procedure as impractical. What he often overlooked, by contrast with the modern physical-organic chemist, was the possibility that his recalcitrant reaction was merely *slow,* not impossible. Thus came to the fore the science of catalysis, in which methods of accelerating slow processes are of critical importance.

Still more subtle is the problem arising where two or more competing chemical reactions may take place in one reaction mixture of organic chemicals, particularly where the desired reaction is slow and the undesired process fast. This situation was exemplified in a recent brilliant industrial development in a California petroleum laboratory where the knotty problem of synthetic glycerol (glycerine) was untangled virtually by a neat practical application of physical-organic chemistry.

The organic compound propylene, cheaply obtainable in huge quantities from petroleum-cracking plants, was known to react with chlorine in a classical manner, leading to a relatively unimportant product. By appropriate alteration of physical conditions the industrial research staff have speeded up—relatively—another reaction which leads to glycerol, leaving the expected classical reaction harmlessly behind. Unfortunately for the present market the chlorine required in the new process has been held up by military priority regulation; but with the return of international peace the new synthetic glycerol is expected to serve as a long-desired commercial balance wheel to stabilize the price of the compound and encourage manufacturers to build industries upon glycerol as they dared not do under the fickle market conditions of the past.

Useful and Useless Compounds. The inference that 95 per cent or more of known organic compounds are useless may seem valid from the standpoint of the ultimate consumer, but it draws a loud protest from the organic chemist. Not all useful things are in retail stores.

When an investigator tries to identify a complex natural substance, he often pulls the unknown molecule to pieces, isolates and purifies the pieces, and then searches for data on these fragments. It is then very convenient to have a depository, a chemical museum, let us say, containing scores of thousands of well-described compounds ready for comparison. Once these fragments are recognized, the main problem is well along toward solution. It is not even necessary to have the actual substances at hand. Accurate descriptions, traced through Beilstein, do very well.

It was in this manner that R. R. Williams, an American investigator, finally solved the mystery of vitamin B_1, ending twenty-six years of patient research by many chemists and opening the present era of widespread public vitamin consumption. Williams found that common photographers' sodium sulfite would neatly split the B_1 molecule into two parts. By trimming these parts he was able to produce substances which could be identified in chemical literature. It is thus presumptuous to declare that any organic compound is entirely useless.

Chemistry on a Small Scale. In earlier days the seeker of naturally occuring organic compounds chose substance obtainable in abundance, such as tartaric acid from grapes or nicotine from tobacco. There was ample material for the quantitative chemical analysis necessary to establish the condensed or empirical formula. Such an analysis required scarcely one-half gram, or about one-sixtieth of an ounce, for the two check determinations. With the advent of twentieth-century research on vitamins and hormones there was introduced perforce a new style of chemistry on an almost microscopic scale. The records of research on the auxins, or plant-growth hormones, offer a striking illustration of material on a small scale versus costs on a large scale.

During the period 1930–1935 inclusive, Kögl, Haagen-Smit, and associates in Holland spent $56,000 (American cost equivalent) on the isolation and identification of auxins A and B, organic compounds whose remarkable power of stimulating plant growth had been observed by Went, the plant physiologist associated in the investigation. The total yield of auxin A for the six years was approximately 700 milligrams; of auxin B, about 300. This output of crystalline hormones totals about one-thirtieth of an ounce, and if piled together would not have filled a small teaspoon. By old-fashioned reckoning there would have been enough auxin A for about three analyses, and by skimping a bit one might have performed the necessary two analyses on the 30 milligrams of auxin B. But so wasteful a performance would have left nothing for the real scientific campaign to decipher the structural formula. After all, the whole proposal for analysis is absurd since Kögl and Haagen-Smit never had enough material in one single year to perform a full-scale determination, and would have been reluctant to save up material lest the earlier supply deteriorate in storage. Actually the auxin problem was solved in brilliant style, but the solution would have been impossible but for the prior research of Fritz Pregl of the University of Graz, Austria.

In 1923 a Nobel Prize was awarded to Pregl for a seemingly simple feat of laboratory technique. Pregl merely cut the size of an analytical sample from 200 milligrams to 2 milligrams. To permit such an operation the famous Kuhlmann chemical balance, sensitive to 0.001 milligram, or about 1/30,000,000 of an ounce, had to be invented. Of course such a cold arithmetical summary of Pregl's accomplishment does not begin to do justice to the beautiful technique developed by the Austrian investigator.

Thus heralded to international fame, Pregl attracted students from research laboratories the wide world over. The master himself is dead and his luckless university has been thrust into academic oblivion by political tyranny, but Pregl's disciples have carried his technique of microanalysis into their laboratories throughout America.

A little simple arithmetic will reveal the value of Pregl's technique to Kögl and Haagen-Smit with their precious 1,000 milligrams of auxins. Even more grateful for such assistance must have been Richard Kuhn, the research genius of Heidelberg who analyzed and deciphered vitamin B_2 (riboflavin), which is now being put into vitamin-enriched bread as well as the ubiquitous pills. Kuhn worked up the albumin of no less than 33,000 eggs, from which he finally isolated just 100 milligrams of the potent vitamin. It is to be remembered that for his brilliant achievements with elusive organic compounds Kuhn was awarded a Nobel Prize in 1939, though on orders from Berlin he declined it.

Large and Small Atoms. It is true that the analytical organic chemist, trying to decipher molecular structure, may curse his luck in having to deal with molecules of such minute dimensions. To the physiologist, however, who thinks of organic chemistry as a constructive or operative process, the story is very different.

Recent research in the chemistry of vision has shown that chemical reaction involving only nine molecules of ordinary size has been detected by the human eye. This leads to a whimsical speculation on the kind of physiology we would have if atoms and molecules of organic compounds were larger—large enough to suit the convenience of the chemical microscopist, who would like a minimum of 5,000 Ångstrom units instead of 1½ such units between atoms.

But the physiologist reminds us that chemistry is a science of three dimensions. Cubing 1½ gives a space of about 3⅓ cubic Ångstrom units, while cubing 5,000 yields 125,000,000,000 such space units. It is thus evident that the brain, or the human retina, or any other highly developed living tissue, has roughly forty billion times as many atoms as the hypothetical matter of grosser structure. It would thus be out of the question for retina or brain to detect and record either the multitude of details of visual perception or any other of the finely elaborated activities which constitute human life if the organism were constructed of the larger atoms. In other words, the higher ranges of evolution would be chemically impossible. Perhaps there is a chemical reason why the elephant is wiser than the gnat. He is just composed of more atoms.

Crystals or Tar. The conventional, old-fashioned organic chemist of 1880, 1900, or even 1920 insisted on having his solid preparations crystalline, as evidence of purity if nothing else. When luck was bad, a variety of molecules appeared in place of the single species, and the useless mess was characterized as "tar." Some young researcher, name now forgotten, long ago summarized the situation briefly:

Bubble, bubble, little tar!
How I wonder what you are!
If I knew I'd famous be.
Won't you crystallize for me?

After cursing tars for at least four generations, organic chemists finally decided that there might be something in the idea of variety instead of uniformity in structural formula. They suspected, furthermore, that the despised tar not only contained many kinds of molecules, but that these were probably very large molecules. It proved not difficult to string certain molecules together in chains, clusters, and checkerwork designs in random, extremely variant quantities. In this way the precise crystal was replaced by the amorphous synthetic resin or "plastic" which now so greatly intrigues public interest.

If the average molecular weight of the synthetic resin is kept moderately low, a thermoplastic product is obtained. This material does not melt, but merely softens with moderate heat. The famous "Plexiglas," so popular for curved shatter-proof windows in military aircraft, is a good example. If the plastic molecules are allowed to grow extensively in three dimensions, the thermosetting product is obtained, suitable for distributor caps or noiseless timing gears in a hot automobile motor.

The idea of stringing molecules together in enormous supermolecules, while a late development by mankind, is an old story in plant and animal life. Cotton, silk, and wool are all excellent illustrations, and it was this very fact which led the Du Pont research organization to attempt an artificial counterpart as a possible substitute for silk. In the resulting product, nylon, one of the characteristic chemical reactions presumably used by the silkworm was employed on a new type of synthetic raw material. The importance of the result is not so much the degree of success at the moment by nylon in competition with silk; it is rather the opportunity to change materials or chemical reactions as either public experience or laboratory test may suggest. Such changes are scarcely practical when the producer is a silkworm. We may therefore predict a troubled future for the silk industry, and busy days for Du Pont.

It is of course true that the kineticist, the photochemist, the X-ray spectrographer, the electron-diffraction expert, and others physically minded are contributing valuable testimony to the increasingly difficult task of running down rarer and rarer organic compounds. It must be conceded, however, that a hundred years and more of practice in standard organic chemical methods are not brushed aside in a day. It is still true that most of the practical results of 1944 come from straight chemical experiments in glass vessels of the organic laboratory, followed by analysis and reasoning just as Justus von Liebig reasoned in 1844. But we know a far greater number of standard reactions, and more technique, than the skillful Liebig. There is still no royal road to the structural formula.

1944

ORDER AND CHAOS IN THE WORLD OF ATOMS *

B. C. SAUNDERS AND R. E. D. CLARK

HOW ATOMS ARE HELD TOGETHER

Magnetism

By far the most important of all forces between atoms are those caused by electricity. Curiously enough the electric forces which we meet in everyday life are often exceedingly small, so it was only natural that their enormous significance remained unrealised for a long time. It seems scarcely possible to suppose that the gigantic atomic forces which hold a lump of steel together can really be of the same character as the minute force which makes the fur of a cat stand on end when it is stroked, or makes our fountain pen pick up pieces of paper. . . . Yet such, in fact, is the case. . . .

At one time it was thought that magnetic forces were among the most powerful in nature—thus Gilbert supposed that the universe was held together by means of them. Eventually, however, it was found that such forces are, after all, relatively insignificant—although, of course, very much greater than those due to gravity. Some idea of the smallness of magnetic forces may be gauged from the fact that under comparable conditions in the atom, ten thousand times as much force can be obtained from a given quantity of electricity by allowing electric charges to attract one another, as can be obtained by utilising the magnetic forces to which the same amount of electricity can give rise.

* From *Order and Chaos in the World of Atoms* by B. C. Saunders and R. E. D. Clark, English Universities Press, Ltd., reprinted by permission from the publishers.

At first sight this is a surprising statement, for it is magnetism which runs our factories and pulls our electric trains, while electro-magnets lift pieces of steel weighing many tons. But it is none the less true that magnetic forces are incomparably smaller than the electric forces which we shall next come to consider. It is very curious how deceptive appearances may be. In the atomic world, magnetic forces, which in our ordinary world appear very great, become very small. On the other hand electric forces, which to us appear very small, become very great.

So far as ordinary materials are concerned, magnetic properties are rather uncommon except in iron and a small number of alloys. The fact that a coil of wire carrying a current becomes a magnet, suggests conversely that in a magnetic substance like iron an electric current is probably circulating continuously. Since the core of an atom is surrounded by orbital electrons which may be regarded as revolving round the core, it seems natural to suppose that the resulting electric current is the cause of magnetism. It has been proved, however, that the magnetism is not caused by the rotation of the electrons round the core of the atom, but by the electrons themselves. They are not to be thought of as mathematical points of no size, but as occupying a certain amount of space. This being so, an electron can rotate about its own axis, and so possesses what is called a "spin." In most ordinary substances there is an equal number of electrons spinning in opposite directions, but in iron and magnetic substances generally, there is an odd number of electrons so that the spin of one of them is not compensated and is able to give rise to magnetic properties.

Spins are, of course, a pictorial way of representing reality and the tendency in recent years has been to ascribe less and less reality to pictures of this kind. However, whether the "spins" be real or not, there is no doubt that individual particles of electricity behave as tiny coils carrying electric currents.

Magnetic forces produced in this way are so weak that they are quite incapable of holding atoms together, at all events at the ordinary temperature. For this reason, they, like gravitation, come outside the realm of chemistry.

Physical Forces

In order of strength, the next type of attraction between atoms is known as the van der Waals' force—named after van der Waals who first discovered how it arises. This is the force which holds most liquids and solids together—the force which prevents our cups of tea from disappearing into thin air, which keeps our newspapers from disintegrating when we touch them and the force of which we make good use whenever we have occasion to use a pot of paste or glue. In short they are the ordinary *physical* as distinct from chemical forces and, for simplicity, we shall refer to them in future as *physical forces.* (Although convenient, this term is not, of course, accurate. Physical forces would normally cover gratitation, magnetism etc., and we shall use [quotes] thus—"physical"—to show that the word is being used in a restricted sense.)

Like magnetism, "physical" forces are really nothing more nor less than electric forces. They come into being in the following way.

We have seen that atoms consist of a positively charged centre with negative charges surrounding it. Now if an atom, *A*, is alone, the positive charge will place itself, on an average, exactly in the centre of the negative charges. But if, at some distance away, there happens to be another atom, *B*, a rather complicated state of affairs will arise. The constituent parts of the *A* atom will, according to the sign of their electrical charges, attract or repel the constituent parts of the *B* atom and *vice versa*. The two centres taken alone will repel each other since both have positive charges; the two negative "outsides" (or "*shells*") will also repel one another because they too have like charges. But, on the other hand, the shells of the *A* atom will attract the centre of the *B* atom, while the shells of the *B* atom will attract the centre of the *A* atom. The result is that the positive centres of the atoms become displaced (the atoms are then said to be *polarised*) and no longer occupy the geometrical centres of the atoms.

With so many attractions and repulsions the resulting situation is naturally very complicated. Yet mathematicians have been able to work out what will happen in a case of this kind. They find that the resulting force between the atoms is not very large, but that, on the whole, two such atoms will always attract one another slightly. Though small, the force is, however, far greater than that of gravitation and a good deal larger than that of magnetism.

In a gas the molecules are always in a state of violent agitation which, however, becomes less as the temperature is lowered. If we imagine a gas being cooled down slowly there eventually comes a time when the agitation becomes just insufficient to keep the atoms apart. It is at this point that a gas becomes a liquid, and the weak forces which we have just described begin to hold the atoms together. On the basis of these simple principles mathematicians have been able to calculate the boiling-points of all the inert gases from a consideration of their properties in the gaseous state, and in every case the predictions have turned out to be very close to the observed values.

The resulting "bonds" between the atoms of the type described above are usually very weak, but in the case of large molecules of complex and unsymmetrical shapes the "bonds" become very much stronger. It often happens in such cases that substances with large surfaces will attach other molecules to themselves with great tenacity, and we shall see later that there are even cases in which union by "physical" bonds is so strong that true chemical bonds are invariably the first to break. These "physical" forces are, therefore, of importance to the chemist.

Electrically Charged Atoms

Having discussed the ways in which electricity can disguise itself, we may now describe the straightforward electric bonds which, from a chemical point of view, are of much greater importance than the forces already discussed.

If two electrically charged objects, one positive and one negative, are held apart and the distance between them varied, it is found that the force with which they attract one another depends upon their distance apart. At great distances the force is very small but becomes greater as the charges approach each other until, at a certain point, it reaches a maximum value. After that the force becomes less and is very soon replaced by a repulsion.

The meaning of these facts is, of course, easy to understand. Just the same thing would happen if, for instance, we imagined two large tennis balls attracting one another as a result of gravitation. If the balls were far apart they would attract each other but slightly, but the force would become greater the nearer they were allowed to approach. If, however, they came too near, they would begin to get in each other's way and the balls, by ceasing to be spherical, would resist further compression. The attraction would, therefore, cease abruptly and be replaced by a repulsion. . . .

Instead of two atoms there are a large number—many millions, in fact. And if these millions of particles are of two kinds, one positive and the other negative, each particle tries to arrange matters so that it is a certain distance from a particle of the opposite kind. . . .

The result is that all the particles arrange themselves in the form of a lattice structure, and it has been found that the exact type of structure formed depends upon the relative sizes of the particles. If one charged particle (called an *ion,* see below) is very large and the other very small we get one arrangement: if on the other hand the two ions are much the same size, then another kind of lattice structure is formed. The different kinds of possible structures can be illustrated very satisfactorily by means of balls of different sizes, which are found to pack together to give structures identical with those which actually occur in the realm of the atoms.

So we see that in a crystal the forces or "bonds" which hold the atoms together may consist of nothing more than simple electrical attractions. This kind of bond or *valency* [1] is usually termed the *electro-valent bond* or *ionic bond.* This type of link could be considered as being produced by the transfer of an electron from one atom to another. Every atom attempts to gather eight electrons in its outer shell—this being the stable arrangement. This is sometimes done by adding electrons and sometimes by losing electrons. Thus in sodium chloride, the sodium atom loses an electron (negative

[1] The simple definition of valency, quite independent of any theory as to the nature of the binding, is as follows: The *valency* of an atom is the number of atoms of hydrogen with which it can combine. Thus chlorine has a valency of one, oxygen two, nitrogen three and carbon four.

charge) from its outer shell, which is then transferred to the outer shell of the chlorine atom. In this way the sodium atom becomes positively charged (*positive ion*). The chlorine has also now eight electrons in its outer shell and having acquired a negative charge is called a *negative ion* (Fig. 1). W. H. and W. L. Bragg employing X-ray analysis have shown that in solid sodium cloride, each sodium ion is surrounded symmetrically by six chlorine ions, and each chlorine ion by six sodium ions and so on throughout the structure.

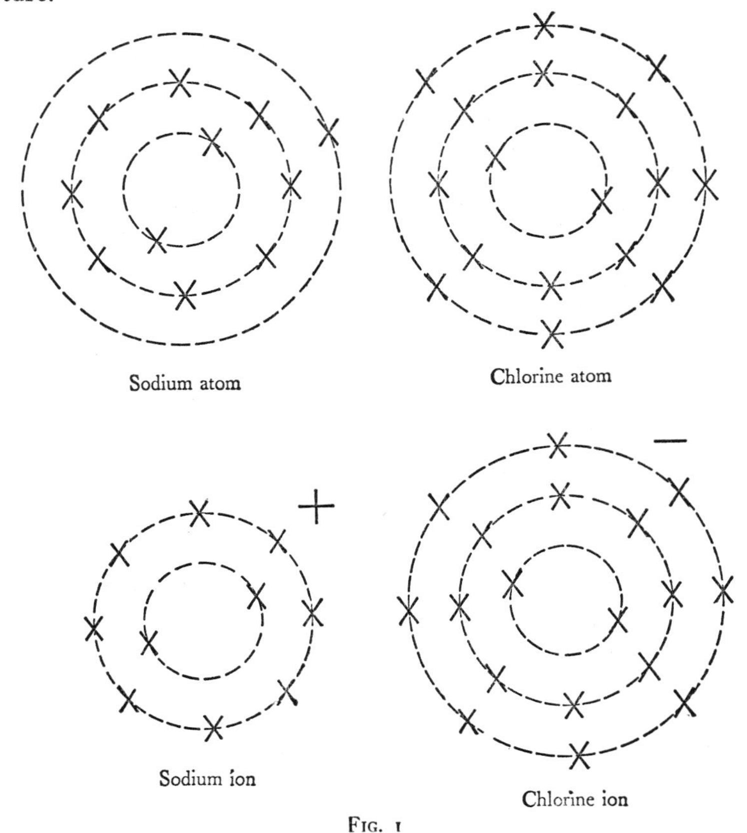

FIG. 1

Sodium Chloride

From what has been said it is clear that the electro-valent bond is one which can be exerted between a given ion and all its neighbours of the opposite sign. This type of bond is therefore in no way spatially directed.

The Metallic Bond

Metals, which can give rise only to one kind of ion with a positive charge, are held together in a somewhat different way. The metallic atoms give up electrons which are free to move about in a metal—thus accounting for a high electrical conductivity. It is these electrons which are liberated from the hot filament of an ordinary wireless valve.

The "gas" of free electrons and the lattice structure of positive ions attract one another strongly, and it is for this reason that metals are unusually rigid and compact forms of matter.

Directional Forces (Co-valent Bonds)

Another way in which atoms can be joined to one another can be illustrated as follows.

Floating about on the surface of a cup of tea a crowd of tiny bubbles may often be seen. These bubbles attract one another and often collect in groups at the side of the cup. The force which holds them together bears some resemblance to the bond which we have just been considering. The bubbles have come as near to one another as they can without losing their individuality and we can think of them as being held in place as a result of their mutual attractions—which in this case are due to the surface tension of the tea.

As the bubbles are in contact they cannot as a rule come any closer to one another. Yet, in point of fact, they sometimes *do* come closer, for, after two bubbles have been in contact for a short time, they sometimes suddenly turn into one larger one. The film which at first divided them now envelops them both and they are no longer two bubbles but one.

Atoms are rather like bubbles in some respects though not in all. They have an inner nucleus or core which the bubbles lack, but they are covered with a sheath of electrons just as the bubbles are covered with a film of liquid. The analogy suggests that if two atoms are pressed very close together, the sheath will give way at the point of contact and so the same electrons will envelop both atoms. Now this is precisely what happens with certain atoms. But two such atoms are not made into one larger atom as happens in the case of the bubbles, for the atoms still have their inner cores intact and, in fact, it is only a few of the outermost electrons which have been shared in the process—the inner electrons still remain in association with their own atom cores. (See Fig. 2, in which the outermost electrons alone are shown.)

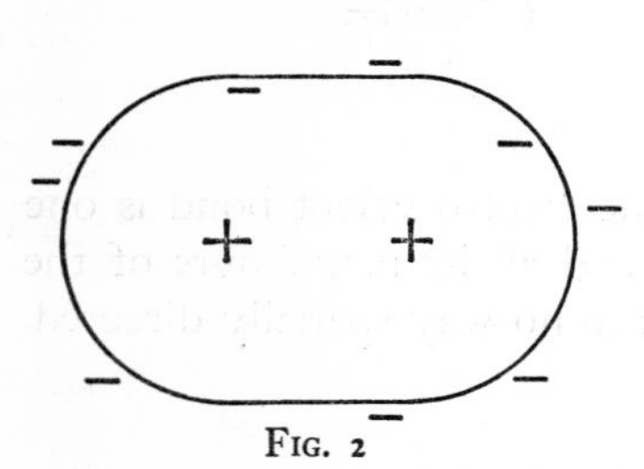

FIG. 2

This is a rather picturesque way, perhaps, of explaining a wholly new kind of bond, but let us now explain the matter in another way.

Carbon tetrachloride is a liquid compound and is composed of one carbon atom and four chlorine atoms (CCl_4). Carbon has four electrons in its outer shell and would like to have eight. Chlorine has seven such electrons and would also like to obtain eight. The simplest way of completing these octets is for the carbon atom to share each of its outer electrons with a chlorine atom. (Fig. 3.) It should be noted that the carbon atom has not *transferred* one electron to each chlorine atom (cf. sodium chloride, pp. 456–457, but each chlorine atom shares equally two electrons with the carbon atom. This type of bond is known as the *co-valent link*.

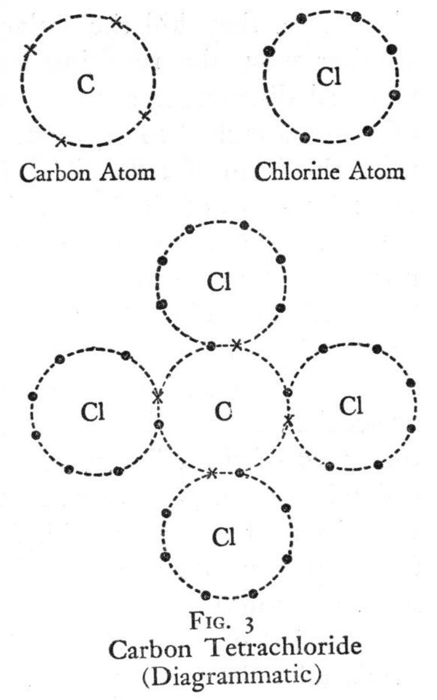

FIG. 3
Carbon Tetrachloride
(Diagrammatic)

When two atoms are joined in the above way, the shared negative charge is nearly all concentrated between them. We may picture a negative charge forcing its way in between two positive charges and thus, as it were, holding two mutually repelling enemies together. Referring again to Fig. 3, it must be realised that there is no essential difference between the electrons[1] around the carbon nucleus and those around the chlorine nucleus, and that the dotted circles in no sense indicate the actual orbits of the electrons.

Chemists have worked hard in order to discover the reason why atoms are sometimes pushed together sufficiently close to make them coalesce, while at other times they remain apart in the manner we have previously described (electro-valent bond). As a result many interesting facts have been discovered, and it is now possible to say what kind of bond a new compound is likely to contain, even before the compound has been made. Apart from the intrinsic nature of the elements concerned, a factor which counts for a good deal is that of size. If one kind of atom is much smaller than its neighbor, a considerable number of the smaller atoms will be able to fit round the larger one, and a whole group of them will manage to penetrate the shell of the larger atom, where one alone would have failed to do so. But there are also other causes into which it is hardly necessary to enter here. . . .

THE CHEMIST AS ARCHITECT

. . . We have examined the nails and the glue of chemistry—those forces which prevent the atoms from breaking apart, despite the violent agitation to which they are so often subjected. Now we shall seek to learn how man can control and utilise these forces, in order to build up minute atom-structures for his own benefit. . . .

To-day we are just beginning to establish many relationships between shapes and properties which were undreamed of in the seventeenth century. It is found that if certain atoms are arranged to form a model of a partic-

[1] Crosses and dots are used simply to make the origin of the electrons clearer.

ular shape, they kill the malaria parasite; if other atoms are arranged in another way, the resulting structure kills the *spirochætes* which cause venereal diseases; if a molecule is long and thin, with a particular type of group attached to one end, it spreads on water to give a thin film; if it takes the form of a flat plate, it makes an excellent solid lubricant. Many other instances of similar relationships could also be cited.

Facts such as these are sufficient to demonstrate the enormous importance of the study of molecular architecture. It is true that we still have little or no idea why a particular class of compound (that is to say a group of substances in which all the atoms are arranged according to the same general plan) should act as a cure for malaria, or produce anæsthesia or accelerate the action of the kidneys or even alter our subjective sense of the speed of time. But the fact is that relationships of this kind do exist, and when enough is known about them it should be possible to predict what kind of structure will, for example, kill a certain parasite most effectively. It remains for the chemist to synthesise a compound having the required structure. . . .

In the last chapter we saw that there were two main kinds of chemical bonds (the electro-valent bond and the co-valent bond). Corresponding to these, there are, in general, two distinct ways in which atom-structures may be built up. As an example of the first kind we may consider ordinary salt. We can make this compound by putting together the elements sodium and chlorine in the right proportions and, as we have seen, there is then formed a crystal lattice in which the two kinds of atoms are arranged in a very symmetrical manner. The resulting structure is the only one which can be formed in the circumstances, and it is *always* formed whenever the experiment is carried out.

In other cases, it sometimes happens that the atoms can be packed together in two or three different ways. As a rule there is a slight energy difference between these arrangements, and the arrangement which is associated with the least possible quantity of energy is the one produced. Though normally stable, this structure may, under very different physical conditions, possess more energy than formerly, so that a previously unstable structure now becomes stable. Thus carbon usually crystallises as graphite (the material of which "lead" pencil is made), but under great pressure the atoms arrange themselves in another way and diamonds are formed instead.

There is also another way in which atom-structures of this kind can be made. Instead of taking an element *A* and an element *B* and bringing them together to give the compound *AB*, it is possible to start with compounds such as *AC* and *BD* which, when brought together, will give rise to *AB* and *CD* (double decomposition).

Thus there is little opportunity for variations in the game of atom-building in cases of this kind. The sodium and chlorine have already, so to speak, decided on the shape of the structure which they will make when they are brought together. Nothing the chemist can do will induce them to take up any other shape. The chemist merely occupies the rôle of the farmer who plants the seed in the earth, but he cannot by his own effort determine that one seed shall produce maize, another wheat and another barley. These differences depend upon the seed, not upon the sower. In the same way, where electro-valent links are concerned, the subsequent arrangement of the atoms depends upon the atoms themselves, not upon the chemist. Only in rare instances are there two or three possible arrangements, and it is only then that the chemist by exercising his very limited choice can begin to fancy himself master of all he surveys.

When we consider the second (co-valent) kind of bond, the situation is very different. A molecule of ordinary sugar contains a dozen carbon atoms, eleven oxygen atoms and twenty-two hydrogen atoms—which is not nearly as many atoms as are contained in numerous other compounds. At once we ask ourselves whether the properties of these three elements are such that, when mixed together, they will give rise to sugar, just as sodium and chlorine when mixed together gave rise to salt. So we try the experiment, and place carbon, hydrogen and oxygen in a flask in the right proportions and see what happens.

Reaction can certainly be made to occur under certain conditions, but no sugar is formed. It does not matter whether we heat the mixture, or cool it, or pass electricity through it, or shine light upon it, or employ any other means, not a trace of sugar makes its appearance. And what applies to sugar, applies to practically all organic compounds; the only exceptions being a few exceedingly simple substances, which, with a good deal of difficulty, can be prepared directly provided the conditions are exactly right. (Often high pressures are needed, together with traces of substances known as *catalysts* which make certain reactions take place more easily, although the catalysts themselves are not changed during these reactions).

Thus, in the case of sugar, the individual atoms have clearly no power of themselves to combine to give a molecule or group of atoms of the particular shape of the sugar molecule. If they do so at all, it must be because they have been constrained to shape themselves in this way by reason of an external influence. And it is exactly this external influence which the chemist is in a position to supply.

Thus the chemist finds himself confronted with two types of structure which differ in an important way. The nature of this difference can most easily be explained by means of a simple analogy.

If we take some wooden spheres and throw them into a box we find that on being shaken they tend to take up one or other of two possible arrangements (Fig. 4). If, however, we are permitted to stick them together with strong glue, there is now no limit to the shapes we can make: chains, curves, spirals, circles, crosses etc. all become possible. Yet these artificial shapes are not really stable since none of them could have come into position of its own accord merely by throwing the spheres together.

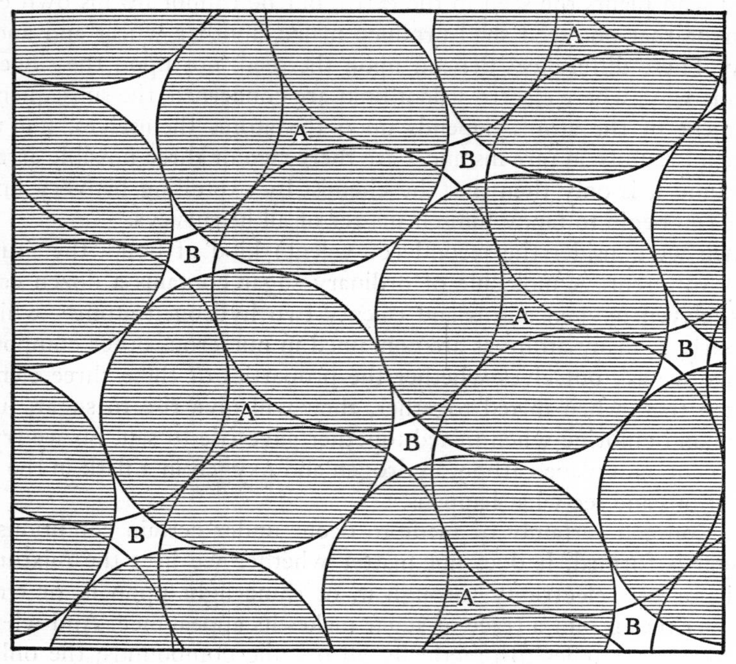

FIG. 4

Diagram illustrating the two ways in which spheres can pack together. Shaded circles represent lower layer of spheres: unshaded upper layer. A third layer can be added either (1) by placing the next layer in positions marked *A* or (2) in positions marked *B*. In this way two distinct kinds of cubic lattices can be produced.

Thus the spheres can be arranged in the form of definite structures either with the aid of glue or by utilising the force of gravity (which was the force made use of when the spheres were thrown together). Now the difference between these two cases lies in the fact that the glue exerts a force in a specified direction while the force of gravity acts uniformly on all the particles. . . . We have learned that co-valency is a directional bond wheras electro-valency is not. It is this fact, therefore, which is responsible for the limitless forms which can be built up by co-valencies and to the very limited number produced by electro-valencies.

So far the analogy of the wooden spheres has stood us in good stead, but it breaks down at one point. It is possible to use the same spheres in order to make models which illustrate either a co-valent or an electro-valent structure, but with atoms this is not always so. Most of the metals give rise to electro-valent bonds and most of the non-metals are joined by co-valent bonds. Of these the co-valent bonds are much more interesting, because of the greater variety of structures to which they can give rise.

Although the latter kind of bond can be formed with a large number of elements, carbon possesses a power of making them which is unique. With most other elements it is found that if more than a very limited number of atoms is connected together, the whole system becomes unstable and breaks up. But with carbon the state of affairs is different. No matter how many links have already been formed in a molecule, there is no restriction to more and yet more atoms joining together in the same way until truly gigantic molecules are produced. Owing to this property of carbon, the number of compounds of this element greatly exceeds those of all the other elements put together. For this reason the discussion which follows has reference chiefly to carbon compounds, for in practice it is only with this element that a large variety of complicated molecular structures can be made. . . .

Ordinary physical analogies suggest that the number of possible combinations of A and B atoms rises enormously with the number of atoms which one molecule contains. If we have two spheres we can stick them together in one way only. . . . If, on the other hand, we have half a dozen spheres, we can arrange them in a straight line, a circle, a cross, etc. So clearly the more spheres we have at our disposal the greater the variety of shapes we can make with them. . . .

With two and also with three carbon atoms surrounded by hydrogen atoms, there is still only one possibility in each case, but with ten carbon atoms there are no less than 75 possible arrangements or, as we say, 75 "*isomerides*." After that the numbers rise at an enormous rate:

Number of carbon atoms.	*Number of possible arrangements.*
1, 2, 3	1
4	2
5	3
10	75
20	$3{\cdot}6 \times 10^{6}$
30	$4{\cdot}1 \times 10^{9}$
40	$6{\cdot}2 \times 10^{13}$
60	$2{\cdot}2 \times 10^{22}$

These figures apply to simple structures of carbon and hydrogen only. Let us suppose, however, that just one of the hydrogen atoms is replaced by something else—for instance, by an atom of chlorine. The possible number of structures now becomes very much greater, and with ten carbon atoms there are 1,553 forms instead of 75, while all the other figures are correspondingly larger. With two of the hydrogen atoms replaced by two atoms of, say, chlorine, the numbers are larger still, and they are again greatly increased if the two atoms replacing the hydrogens are not identical.

When we consider substances as complex as the dye-stuffs—though the dye-stuffs are not as a matter of fact nearly as complicated as many common chemical compounds with which we are all familiar—the number of different forms is enormous. . . .

Structures as complex as the proteins give rise to an even larger number of possibilities. Protein molecules are built up by the linking together of simple molecules known as *amino-acids* (they derive their name from the fact that they contain both a basic and an acidic group). At least twenty-five of these acids have been isolated from naturally occurring proteins. Supposing, however, the number to be only twenty-one, it would be possible to link them together in 10^{2700} ways, and thus create this number of chemically distinct protein molecules.

It is difficult to think of any helpful analogy which will give us an idea of the magnitude of the latter number, but perhaps it is worth making an attempt, even though it is foredoomed to failure. Let us start with the number of electrons in the entire universe—about 10^{79} according to Eddington. Next we multiply this by a million, and the answer by a million, and the answer by a million . . . Then we shall have to go on repeating the words "Multiply the answer by a million" until we have covered nearly ten pages of this book, and then at last we shall have arrived at a number somewhere in the neighbourhood of 10^{2700}—although, of course, we shall still have no real conception of the meaning of these uninteresting pages! . . .

Empirical Methods

Although man's achievements in the realm of atomic architecture have been extraordinarily successful, it is nevertheless only too true that chemical processes are in some respects of a somewhat clumsy nature. We should not think highly of a carpenter who tried to construct tables and chairs by shutting his eyes and throwing wood, nails and glue around his workshop more or less at random. Yet, in effect, this is what the chemist does when investigating a new reaction.

The reason for the chemist's behaviour is not far to seek. Glue and nails and pieces of wood are visible objects which we can pick up and put in the right place. Atoms, however, are so small that we cannot see what we are doing with them, and so we are obliged to resort to the use of indirect methods.

However, there is much more to it than that. A blind carpenter *might* with a great deal of trouble be able to make chairs and tables by throwing the necessary parts about in his workshop. But he would have to spend a great deal of time learning how to do it, and he would need to be very intelligent in order to profit by his mistakes. Some of the problems which he would encounter are not difficult to imagine. He would probably find that if he threw the table legs too vigorously, they would bounce off again, even if they hit the right target; on the other hand, if he were too phlegmatic, the legs might never reach their destination.

As he continued his researches, he would soon find many further problems waiting to be tackled: he would, for instance, have to discover the optimum conditions of "concentration" in his workshop—for if the workshop were too full of the constituent parts, operations would be hampered by congestion, whereas if it were too empty the chances of successful "collisions" would diminish and the parts would have less chance of joining together.

In the same way the chemist has to take the greatest care that his atoms and molecules hit one another with just the right degree of violence. This is done by carefully controlling the temperature. Likewise the chemist must often spend much time ascertaining the right concentration for a particular reaction to take place. One way of controlling the concentration is by altering the pressure. If the pressure is raised it has the effect of squeezing the atoms or molecules together, while if it is lowered the molecules are pulled farther apart. It is found that if substances which are reacting are able to give rise to more than one set of products, then a large proportion of that product which would normally occupy the smallest volume is obtained if the pressure is made very high. On the other hand, if the pressure is made as low as possible, the more bulky product predominates.

Perhaps the analogy need not be pursued much farther. The synthetic chemist has yet other tricks up his sleeve, though not very many. One further thing he can do is to use electricity in various forms, though considering the high hopes that were once entertained, the application of electricity has proved rather disappointing on the whole. Strong electric fields make certain molecules take up particular positions in space—we shall have more to say about this later—and this may alter the way in which they react with one another. Sometimes, too, as in the preparation of ozone from oxygen, the electric field breaks down molecules into atoms which are highly reactive, but this process is of assistance in producing only exceedingly simple molecules. Then again, electricity can be made to liberate atoms or groups of atoms in an active form ideally suited to take part in chemical reactions. It is often used, for instance, to supply hydrogen atoms in the process known as "reduction" by which oxygen is removed from, or hydrogen is added to, a molecule.

Yet another technique is to spread substances out in thin layers. The reason why this is so successful can best be understood by reverting to our blind carpenter once more. If he were to fill his carpenter's shop with table-tops and throw the legs into their midst, he would probably obtain many "tables" with legs which were not all attached to the same side of the table top. To increase his "yield" of perfect tables he might, therefore, prefer to spread the table-tops neatly over the floor before starting operations. In this way the formation of freak tables would be altogether prevented.

Now this is exactly what the chemist often does. Many reactions occur on solid surfaces much more satisfactorily than in the liquid state. For this reason an enormous amount of labour is expended in research designed to determine the best kind of surfaces on which to spread molecules. Sometimes hot wires are used, or the surfaces of various rare oxides mixed in suitable proportions, or liquids are emulsified and made stable by the addition of special substances, or again finely powdered minerals which have a large surface are used.

A vast amount of empirical information is now available with regard to the best surfaces for different reactions. Unfortunately the theoretical aspect of the problem has not advanced so far, and we still have little idea why platinum, nickel and oxides of rare elements like vanadium are so extraordinarily effective in promoting surface reactions.

With regard to reactions on liquid surfaces, extremely important work has been done at Cambridge in recent years, particularly by Rideal and Schulman. It has been found possible to spread chemical compounds over surfaces of water and then cause reactions to take place on the lower portions of the molecules. The reactions can be followed by noting changes in the area of the films on water. . . .

Synthesis

We have now begun to understand how a chemical reaction works, and have pictured the way in which molecules fly about striking one another in wild confusion, undergoing disintegration or exchanging part of their structures as a result of the collisions.

It is obvious that a process of this kind can rarely produce much increase in complexity, for the turbulent molecules are more likely to break one another into simpler components than to build themselves into more complex structures. Usually a chemical reaction can, at the best, produce but a small rise in complexity, and if the chemist desires to build a complex structure, he must in general proceed slowly and deliberately, employing one reaction after another, so that the building process may be accomplished stage by stage.

Let us try to picture the synthesis of a complex molecule. In order to see what is happening, we shall imagine an entire laboratory magnified a hundred million times, so that the carbon atoms are now about an inch across and plainly visible, and the brobdingnagian chemist is one hundred thousand miles high. We shall look on while this giant tries to build molecules which have the shape of, shall we say, chairs.

To begin with, of course, the giant makes the simpler components of his molecular model. After many fruitless attempts he finds the conditions under which a fair proportion of his atoms come together to make legs—each consisting, perhaps, of four atoms arranged in a straight line.

The giant soon finds that this is only the beginning of his difficulties. We can see as we look at the most successful mixture he has produced that it contains not merely legs but all kinds of other shapes in addition—the latter of which will have to be removed lest they interfere with the next stage of the process.

To us it seems an easy matter to remove the unwanted shapes by hand, but we must remember that when the giant looks at the mixture he can see nothing of what we can see. His hands are enormous, and since his gigantic eyes are fifteen hundred miles across, as large as planets, it is no wonder if objects but two or three inches in diameter make no impression upon his retina. He will have to think of some other way of "purifying" his product. Perhaps he will invent a machine to separate the shapes, or perhaps he will decrease the violence of the movements in his mixture in the hope that all the straight objects will collect together in bundles, leaving the other objects floating about in a "liquid" condition.

Sure enough, the giant at length finds a way out of the difficulty, and he obtains a specimen of legs unmixed with any other shapes. Then the main frame of the chair is made in similar fashion, perhaps in several stages. Finally these constituent parts are mixed and shaken vigorously, which causes some of them to join together in the manner desired by the giant.

Though easily described, all this takes a good deal of time and is very difficult to perform. After each of the many stages which are involved, the giant is obliged to devise a means of purifying his product, otherwise he can proceed no farther. At first he experiences relatively little difficulty in doing this, for he finds that the simple shapes often pack together in bundles if they are not shaken together too vigorously. Again, he finds, in other instances, that if he shakes his mixed models with extreme violence, some of them leap out of the mixture before others, thus effecting a partial separation which can be made complete by repeating the process sufficiently often. But as the shapes become larger and more complicated, the giant finds greater and greater difficult in separating them: indeed he is often quite unable to do so at all. As a result, he is often obliged to abandon promising ways of making the structures he wants, and is forced to try his hand at more roundabout methods instead. On other occasions he is obliged to abandon his two favourite ways of effecting separation, and is compelled to use more tedious methods in their place when he is lucky enough to discover them.

Thus, after many failures, the giant succeeds perhaps in making something with the shape of a chair and separating it from the misshapen chairs which are inevitably formed at the same time. For the giant it involves untold labour to make a model so simple that we ourselves could have put it together in a few minutes by the simple expedient of joining the "atoms" together, just as a child joins pieces of "Meccano" without the slightest difficulty. But the giant is too large and clumsy to do what we can do.

Of course our picture of the brobdingnagian giant clumsily trying to make chairs many millions of times too small for him to use sounds like the phantasies of a wonderland. But it is not so: it is a tolerably exact picture of the methods employed by the chemist when starting an investigation, and it does not suggest that the art of building up new molecules is any more difficult than is actually the case.

It would take thousands of years of continuous effort to find out how to make chairs out of "atoms" in the manner described above, and the result is that no single individual could ever succeed in doing so. In the case of real molecules, thousands of years of labour have indeed already been expended: bodies of research workers in every country have devoted their entire time to problems such as this. They alter the conditions in every conceivable way; they try experiments again and again. Their results are often failures—instead of building structures in the way they intend, they find they have pulled them to pieces or joined them up the wrong way round or, more often still, they believe they have made the right shapes out of the atoms, but they can find no way of separating the substances they require from others which they do not require.

Finally, however, the correct experimental conditions gradually evolve, and once these are clearly established, the chemist can build up the required molecule with remarkable precision and certainty. It then becomes possible for any other chemist with the necessary manipulative skill to repeat successfully the work of the original investigator in a very much shorter space of time.

But chemists have one great advantage—they have a relatively enormous literature in which they can find out what has been done previously and where others have had success. Thus, to any single individual, synthesis is often only a question of adding one group of atoms to a molecule which has already been made, and not of having to start again from the constituent atoms every time. Yet even this may be extremely difficult. . . .

1942

THE FOUNDATIONS OF CHEMICAL INDUSTRY *

ROBERT E. ROSE

PRELUDE: THE JUGGLERS

All of us have seen the juggler who entertains by throwing one brightly colored ball after the other into the air, catching each in turn and throwing it up again until he has quite a number moving from hand to hand. The system which he keeps in motion has an orderly structure. He changes it by selecting balls of different colors, altering the course or the sequence of the balls, or by adding to or diminishing the number with which he plays.

* From *Chemistry In Industry*, edited by H. E. Howe, The Chemical Foundation, reprinted by permission from the publishers.

With this figure in mind let us use our imaginations. Before us we have an assemblage of hundreds of thousands of jugglers varying in their degree of accomplishment; some handle only one ball, others, more proficient, keep several in motion, and there are still others of an astounding dexterity who play with an hundred or more at once. The balls they handle are of ninety different colors and sizes. The jugglers do not keep still but move about at varying rates; those handling few and light balls move more quickly than those handling many or heavier ones. These dancers bump into each other and when they do so in certain cases they exchange some of the balls which they are handling or one juggler may take all of those handled by another, but in no case are the balls allowed to drop.

THE VANISHING POINT

Now imagine the moving group to become smaller and smaller until the jugglers cease to be visible to us, even when they dance under the highest power microscope. If someone who had not seen them were to come to you and say that he proposed undertaking the problem of finding out how the balls were moving and what were the rules of the exchanges made, and further that he proposed utilizing his knowledge to control what each minute juggler was doing, you would tell him that his task was hopeless. If the chemist had listened to such advice there would be no chemical industry and you would lose so much that you would not be living in the way you are.

The jugglers are the electromagnetic forces of matter, the balls are the atoms, and each group in the hands of the juggler is a molecule of a substance. In reality, of course, instead of each molecule being represented by one unit we should multiply our jugglers by trillions and trillions.

THE MASTERY OF MOLECULES

The chemist, without even seeing them, has learned to handle these least units of materials in such a way as to get the arrangements which are more useful from those less useful. This power he has acquired as the outcome of his life of research, his desire to understand, even though understanding brought him no material gain, but mere knowledge. Because of his patience and devotion he has built a number of industries; all have this in common—they serve to rearrange atoms of molecules or to collect molecules of one kind for the service of man.

THE GREAT QUEST

The study of the substances of the earth's crust, of the air over and of the waters under earth, which has led us to our present knowledge of the electron, atom, and molecule, has been more adventurous than many a great journey made when the world was young and the frontier of the unknown was not remote from the city walls. Into the unknown world of things upon the "sea that ends not till the world's end" the man of science ventured, and he came back laden with treasure greater than all the gold and precious stones ever taken from the earth. He gave these to others and he fared forth again without waving of flags, without the benediction of holy church, with no more than the courage of him who would win Nature, who had chosen a harder road than that of the great, made famous because of subduing other men. He took no arms upon his quest, scarcely enough food to keep body and soul together, but instead, fire, glass, and that most astounding of all tools, the balance. As he pushed farther and farther on his great venture and as more and more joined his little band, he brought more and more back to those who did not understand in the least what he was doing, until now the lives of all men are made easier if not happier by these strange, most useful, and most potent things of which he is the creator by reason of the understanding his journeys have given him—a power much greater than any mere black magic.

This is the story of some of the strange treasure found by him in the far lands that are about us—treasure found by learning the secret of the jugglers' dance—the dance of the least little things out of which all we know is fashioned.

SULFURIC ACID

The Great Discovery

In Sicily and other parts of the earth where there are volcanoes, lumps of a yellow crumbly "stone" are found, called brimstone (a corruption of *brennisteinn* or burning stone). This material was regarded as having curative properties; if it was burned in a house the bad odors of the sickroom of primitive times were suppressed. Also the alchemists found that it took away the metallic character of most metals and they considered it very important in their search for the philosopher's stone, the talisman that was to turn all things to gold. The alchemists found also that sulfur, when burned over water, caused the water to become acid, and one of them found further that if the burning took place in the presence of saltpeter the acid which was produced was much stronger; indeed, if concentrated it was highly corosive. A useless find, it seemed, of interest only to the alchemist who hoped to become rich beyond the dreams of avarice, and immortal as the gods. But the chemist made this discovery of more importance to the condition of the human race than that of Columbus, because by it he gave man a kingdom different from any that could have been his by merely discovering what already existed upon earth. That is the wonder of the chemist's work; he finds that which is not upon the earth until he discovers it; just as the artist creates so does the chemist. If he did not, there would be no chemical industry to write about.

Experiment to Manufacture

Having investigated this acid, he found it a most valuable new tool with which many new and interesting things could be made, and much could be done that before had been impossible. It became necessary, then, if all men were to profit as the chemist always wishes them to do by his power, that sulfuric acid should be made easily and cheaply in large quantities. The first attempt at commercial manufacture was in 1740; before that each experimenter made what little he needed for himself. The process, that mentioned above, was carried out in large glass balloons. It was a costly method and tedious. Then in 1746 lead chambers were substituted for the glass and the industry progressed rapidly.

The whole object of this most basic of all chemical industries can be written in three simple little equations.

Sulfur		Oxygen		Sulfur Dioxide
S	+	O_2	=	SO_2
Sulfur Dioxide		Oxygen		Sulfur Trioxide
SO_2	+	O_2	=	SO_3
Sulfur Trioxide		Water		Sulfuric Acid
SO_3	+	H_2O	=	H_2SO_4

Of the three elements necessary, oxygen occurs uncombined in the air of which it forms one-fifth by volume; it is also present combined with other elements in very large quantities in water, sand, and generally throughout the earth's crust, which is nearly half oxygen in a combined condition.

The Raw Materials

The great storehouse of hydrogen on the earth is water, of which it forms one-ninth, by weight. Sulfur is not so widely distributed in large quantities but it is very prevalent, being present in all plants and animals and also in such compounds as Epsom salts, gypsum, and Glauber's salt. In the free condition, i.e., as sulfur itself, it is found in volcanic regions and also where bacteria have produced it by decomposing the products of plant decay. There is one other source of sulfur that is quite important, a compound with iron which contains so much sulfur that it will burn.

The problem then was to take these substances and from them group the elements in such order as to produce sulfuric acid.

Since sulfur burns readily, that is, unites with oxygen to form sulfur dioxide, one might expect it to take up one more atom of oxygen from the air and become sulfur trioxide. It does, but so slowly that the process would never suffice for commercial production. But there is a way of speeding up the reaction which depends on using another molecule as a go-between, thus making the oxygen more active. The principle is that of the relay. Suppose an out-fielder has to throw a ball a very long way. The chances are that the ball will not be very true and that it may fall short of reaching the base. If there is a fielder between, he can catch the ball and get it to the base with much greater energy.

The chemist uses as a go-between a catalyst (in one process), oxides of nitrogen. Molecules of this gas throw an oxygen atom directly and unfailingly into any sulfur dioxide molecule they meet, then equally certainly they seize the next oxygen atom that bumps into them and are ready for the next sulfur dioxide molecule. Since molecules in a gas mixture bump into each other roughly five billion times a second, there is a very good chance for the exchange to take place in the great lead chambers of approximately a capacity of 150,000 cubic feet into which are poured water molecules (steam), oxygen molecules (air), and sulfur dioxide, to which are added small quantities of the essential oxides of nitrogen.

The Acid Rain

A corrosive, sour drizzle falls to the floor and this is chamber acid. It is sold in a concentration of 70 to 80 per cent. The weak chamber acid is good enough for a great many industrial purposes and is very cheap. If it is to be concentrated this must be done in vessels of lead up to a certain concentration and then in platinum or gold-lined stills if stronger acid is needed. Naturally this is expensive and every effort was made to find a method of making strong sulfuric acid without the necessity of this intermediate step. Especially was this true when the dyestuffs industry began to demand very large quantities of tremendously strong sulfuric acid which was not only 100 per cent but also contained a considerable amount of sulfur trioxide dissolved in it (fuming sulfuric acid).

The difficulty was overcome by using another catalyst (platinum) in the place of the oxides of nitrogen. If sulfur dioxide and oxygen (air) are passed over the metal the two gases unite to form sulfur trioxide much more rapidly and in the absence of water. Since platinum is very expensive and its action depends on the surface exposed, it is spread on asbestos fibers and does not look at all like the shiny metal of the jeweler. This method is known as the contact process and the product is sulfur trioxide, which represents the highest possible concentration of sulfuric acid and can be led into ordinary oil of vitriol (98 per cent sulfuric acid) and then diluted with water and brought to 98 per cent acid or left as fuming acid, depending on the requirements of the case. The perfection of this process was the result of some very painstaking research because when it was tried at first it was found that the platinum soon lost its virtue as a catalyst, and it was also discovered that the reason for this was the presence of arsenic in the sulfur dioxide. To get rid of every trace of arsenic is the hardest part of the contact process.

Vitriol

Next time you visit a laboratory ask to be shown a bottle of concentrated sulfuric acid. You will see a colorless, oily liquid, much heavier than water, as you will notice if you lift the bottle. A little on your skin will raise white weals and then dissolve your body right away; paper is charred by it as by fire. When it touches water there is a hissing.

Sulfuric Acid and Civilization

A dreadful oil, but its importance to industry is astonishing. If the art of making it were to be lost tomorrow we should be without steel and all other metals and products of the metallurgical industry; railroads, airplanes, automobiles, telephones, radios, reënforced concrete, all would go because the metals are taken from the earth by using dynamite made with sulfuric acid; and for the same reason construction work of all kinds, road and bridge building, canals, tunnels, and sanitary construction work would cease.

We should have to find other ways to produce purified gasoline and lubricating oil. The textile industry would be crippled. We should find ourselves without accumulators, tin cans, galvanized iron, radio outfits, white paper, quick-acting phosphate fertilizers, celluloid, artificial leather, dyestuffs, a great many medicines, and numberless other things into the making of which this acid enters at some stage.

If at some future date, however, all of our sulfur and all of our sulfur ores are burned up the chemist will yet find ways of making sulfuric acid. Possibly he may tap the enormous deposits of gypsum which exist in all parts of the earth. This has been done to some extent already but is not a process which is cheap enough to compete with sulfuric acid made from sulfur.

NITRIC ACID

It is essential that all the heavy chemicals, that is, the most used acids, alkalies, and salts, should be made so far as possible from readily available cheap material. We use air, water, and abundant minerals on this account. Nitric acid caused the chemical industry much concern until it was found possible to make it from air, because until then its source was Chile saltpeter, or sodium nitrate, a mineral occurring in a quantity only in the arid Chilean highlands. However, this source of supply is still the most important and the process used is one of great interest.

Having made oil of vitriol, the chemist found that he could produce other acids, one of the most important of these being liberated from saltpeter by the action of sulfuric acid. When nitric acid is made in this fashion we find that the sulfuric acid is changed into sodium sulfate and remains behind in the still. One might think from this that sulfuric acid is stronger and on that account that it drives out nitric acid, but in fact this preparation depends on a very simple principle, one of great importance.

Another Dance

We may best illustrate it by returning to our former simile. Let us assume a sodium nitrate juggler moving rather slowly. He is bumped into by a sulfuric acid juggler moving at about the same rate. They exchange some of the atoms with which they are playing and in consequence one juggler holds sodium hydrogen sulfate while the other holds nitric acid.

$$NaNO_3 + H_2SO_4 \rightarrow NaHSO_4 + HNO_3$$

The nitric acid molecule does not slow down the juggler as much as the sodium hydrogen sulfate and therefore this particular dancer moves away quite fast. Suppose millions of these exchanges to be taking place; then the nitric acid molecules will continue to dance away and will not come back to exchange their atoms any more. If we keep them all in by putting a lid on, then they are forced to go back and we get no more than a sort of game of ball in which the hydrogen and sodium atoms are passed back and forth. If, on the other hand, we open the lid and put a fire under the pot, the nitric acid molecules move faster and sooner or later all of them are driven out.

Nitric acid is now made from the air in more than one way so that we are entirely independent of the beds of Chile saltpeter no matter what might happen to them. Without nitric acid we could not make guncotton, dynamite, TNT, picric acid, ammonium nitrate, and the other explosives which are so enormously important to our civilization. In addition, we would lose all our brilliant dyes and most of our artificial silk, from which it is easy to see that this substance is of great importance to all of us.

SALT, THE JEWEL BOX

Soda

Among the treasures to which man fell heir as the most important inhabitant of the earth was one of innumerable little cubes made of sodium and chloride, crystals of salt. These he noticed whenever seawater evaporated and he soon found, if he lived on a vegetable diet as he did in some places, that the addition of these to his food made it much more pleasant and savory. In fact, it is a necessity for the health of the human body. Hunting peoples do not use it so much because they live almost entirely on meat, which contains sufficient salt. Next it was found that salt could be employed for preserving fish and meat, and thus man was able to tide over the periods in which hunting was poor. For ages and ages it was put to no other use. Nobody but a chemist would have thought of doing anything with it. In order to understand the whole of what he did and the part which salt plays in industry owing to the chemist's activity we must go back a little.

Soap as a Hair Dye

Very early it was found that the ashes of a fire (and fires at that time were always made of wood) were useful in removing grease from the hands. They were the earliest form of soap and it is surprising how long they remained the only thing used. Our records go to show that the Romans were the first of the more civilized peoples to find out how to make real soap, and they learned it from the Gauls, who used the material which they made from wood ashes and goat's tallow for washing their hair and beards because they believed that this gave them the fiery red appearance which they thought was becoming. The Romans saw the advantage of soap over wood ashes and a very considerable trade in the making of various kinds of soaps arose, but the difficulty always was with the production of the ashes because it takes quite a lot of ashes to make even a small quantity of soap. The advantage of having something more abundant to take the place of the ashes was evident. But the real stimulus which led to the discovery of soda ash came from a different source.

Glass from Ashes and Sand

It was found that ashes heated with sand formed glass. It was also found that the ashes of marine plants, or plants occurring on the seashore, gave a much better glass than that which could be made from the ashes of land plants. In consequence of this, as the art of glass making grew, barilla, the ashes of a plant growing in the salt marshes of Spain, became an increasingly important article of commerce and upon it depended the great glass factories of France and Bohemia. Owing to the political situation which arose at the end of the eighteenth century, France found herself in danger of losing her supremacy in the art of making glass because England cut off her supply of the Spanish ashes. For some reason the French ruler at the time had vision enough to see that it might be possible to make barilla artificially from some source within the kingdom of France and he offered a prize to any one who would make his country independent of Spain. We have seen that the chemist's business is the transmutation of one kind of material into another, and naturally it was the chemist who came forward with a solution of the problem. Since this process is now supplanted by a more economical one, we will merely outline it here.

Limestone to Washing Soda

Remember that it is essential to start from some abundant common material. Le Blanc, the chemist who solved the problem, knew that the Spanish ashes contained sodium carbonate, the formula of which we write as Na_2CO_3; that is, it is a combination of sodium, carbon, and oxygen.

There are a great many carbonates in nature and among these is that of calcium which we know as chalk, limestone, or marble, depending on the way in which it crystallizes. In this we have a substance of the formula $CaCO_3$. Suppose, then, we write the two compounds side by side: Na_2CO_3, $CaCO_3$. Evidently the only difference is that in one we have two atoms of sodium (Na_2) in place of one of calcium (Ca) in the other. Salt contains sodium and is very common. If, then, we can get the sodium radical from the sodium chloride and the carbonate radical from the limestone and join the two pieces we will get sodium carbonate, which is what we want. What Le Blanc did was to treat sodium chloride with sulfuric acid. This gave him sodium sulphate and hydrochloric acid. Then he heated the sodium sulfate with coke or charcoal and limestone, after which he extracted the mass with water and found that he had sodium carbonate in solution.

The steps do not sound difficult but it was really a great feat to make them commercially possible. In the first stage when sulfuric acid acted on the salt, hydrochloric acid was given off and this was a great nuisance. The amount of it produced exceeded any use that could be found for it and it was poured away; being highly acid it undermined the houses in the neighborhood and caused a great deal of trouble. Later, it became the most valuable product of the process because it was converted into bleaching powder by a method that we will take up subsequently.

Industry a Result of Chemical Discovery

It is interesting to learn that this process which France invented in her extremity became one of the largest industrial developments in England. It caused the flourishing there of the sulfuric acid industry because this acid was necessary for the process and, as we have seen, sulfuric acid is tremendously valuable in a great variety of directions. It also made possible the development of an enormous textile industry because the making of cloth needs soap and bleach, both of which were first supplied in abundance as a consequent of Le Blanc's discovery.

To return to the story of the chemist's transformations of salt, the present process for the conversion of this compound into sodium carbonate is by the action of ammonia and carbon dioxide upon a saturated solution of it, the carbon dioxide being obtained from limestone. When these three substances are brought together a change takes place which can best be described by the following equation:

$$\underset{\text{Ammonia}}{NH_3} + \underset{\text{Water}}{H_2O} + \underset{\text{Carbon Dioxide}}{CO_2} = \underset{\text{Ammonium Bicarbonate}}{NH_4HCO_3}$$

$$\underset{\text{Salt}}{NaCl} + \underset{\text{Ammonium Bicarbonate}}{NH_4HCO_3} = \underset{\text{Sodium Bicarbonate}}{NaHCO_3} + \underset{\text{Ammonium Chloride}}{NH_4Cl}$$

The change that takes place depends on the fact that sodium bicarbonate is comparatively insoluble and separates out. It is collected and then heated, the heat causing it to turn into sodium carbonate, carbon dioxide, and water.

$$2\ NaHCO_3 = Na_2CO_3 + CO_2 + H_2O$$

In this process the essential thing is to keep the ammonia in the system, because it is used over and over again and, if it escapes, an expense arises out of all proportion to the value of the carbonate which must be sold at a price of about two cents per pound. The ammonia goes out of the reaction, as indicated in the equation, in the form of ammonium chloride and this is returned to the process by allowing quicklime, made by heating limestone in kilns, to decompose the chloride. The other part of the limestone (the carbon dioxide) is also used in the process, as shown in the first equation. We start then with salt, water, and limestone, and we finish with calcium chloride and sodium carbonate.

Caustic Soda

This is not all that the chemist was able to do with salt. In soap making much better results are obtained if, instead of using wood ashes which give us nothing but an impure soft potash soap, we use sodium hydroxide or caustic soda. Now, caustic soda is something which does not occur in nature because it always combines with the carbon dioxide of the air or with some acid material and disappears. The old method of making it was to take the soda of the Le Blanc process and to treat it with slaked lime. In this way we can make about a 14 per cent solution of caustic soda which is then evaporated if it is required in a more concentrated form. This method of making caustic soda was sufficiently economical to give us all that we needed at very reasonable prices, but eventually a better method was discovered.

Caustic soda is $NaOH$, that is to say, it is water (H_2O) in which one of the hydrogens has been replaced by sodium. If in any way we could make this reaction take place, $NaCl + HOH = NaOH + HCl$, we would get directly two products which we want. Unfortunately, it is impossible to get salt to exchange atoms in this way with water. However, a study of salt solutions showed that the atoms of sodium and chlorine were actually separated when in solution and that they also acquired a property which would allow of their segregation. They became electrically charged and it is always possible to attract an electrically charged body by using a charged body of opposite sign. If, then, we put the positive and the negative pole of a battery or another source of electricity in a solution of salt the chlorine will wander away to the positive and the sodium will wander to the negative pole.

Electrons

What takes place can best be described by a rough analogy. Suppose two automobiles of different makes are running side by side, keeping together because of the friendship which exists between the two parties. Now suppose these two machines have an accident in which, by a freak, one wheel is torn off one car and added to the other. Assume that the occupants of the car are not damaged and that the cars can still run; also that the fifth wheel is a distinct nuisance. If there were two garages at considerable distances, one of which specialized in taking off extra wheels and the other did nothing but put on missing wheels, and the accident were a common one involving thousands of machines, then it would be natural for the cars to move in opposite directions to these two garages and if we assume that all the wheels are interchangeable, then there might be a traffic between the garages, by another road perhaps, the wheels being sent from one to the other.

This very rough picture is intended to describe the fact that when the sodium and chlorine atoms of salt are separated by water the electrons of which they are composed are distributed in such a way that there is an extra one in the chlorine which (an electron being negative) makes the chlorine particle negative, while the sodium lacks one electron and therefore becomes positive since it was neutral before. The result, then, of this electrolysis or use of the electric current in separating the charged atoms of sodium chloride (the ions as they are called) is that sodium and chlorine are given off at the two poles. Now, chlorine is not very soluble in water and can be collected as a gas. The sodium, on the other hand, as each little particle is liberated, reacts with the water about it to give hydrogen and sodium hydroxide. Therefore, we have accomplished what we set out to do, only instead of getting sodium hydroxide and hydrogen chloride we get sodium hydroxide, chlorine, and hydrogen.

Electricity

The success of this method is due to discoveries in another field of science. Only when Michael Faraday's researches on the nature of the electric current made available another source of energy different from heat, was it possible for the chemist to carry out what has just been described; at first only in a very small way but, as the production of electricity became more and more economical, ever on a larger scale until now the industry is a most important one.

Chlorine

So far we have directed our attention almost entirely to the sodium atom of salt; the other part of the molecule, the chlorine, is also extremely valuable to us. It used to be set free by oxidizing hydrochloric acid of the

Le Blanc process with manganese dioxide. Now, as we have just seen, we get it directly from a solution of salt by electrolysis.

Uses of Caustic Soda

The two servants which the chemist has conjured out of salt by using electricity are extremely valuable, though if they are not handled rightly they are equally as dangerous as they are useful when put to work. Caustic soda is a white, waxy-looking solid which is extremely soluble in water and attracts moisture from the air. It is highly corrosive, destroying the skin and attacking a great many substances. When it is allowed to act on cellulose in the form of cotton the fiber undergoes a change which results in its acquiring greater luster so that the process of mercerizing, as it is called, is valuable industrially. The manufacture of artificial silk made by the viscose method depends on the fact that caustic soda forms a compound with cellulose. Practically all the soap manufactured at the present time is produced by the action of caustic soda on fat. The by-product of this industry is glycerol which is used in making dynamite. In fact, soda is just as important among alkalies as sulfuric acid is among acids.

Uses of Chlorine

Chlorine, the partner of sodium, is a frightfully destructive material. It attacks organic substances of all kinds, destroying them completely, and it also attacks all metals, even platinum and gold, though fortunately, if it is quite dry, it does not react with iron, and on that account it can be stored under pressure in iron cylinders. Although it is such a deadly gas if allowed to run wild, yet it is extremely useful and its discovery has been very greatly to the advantage of the human race. First of all, it is employed in the manufacture of bleaching powder, a product which enables the cotton industry to work far more intensively than it otherwise could. Formerly cotton was bleached by laying it on the grass, but that is much too slow for our present mode of life. In fact, we have no room for it because it has been calculated that the cotton output of Manchester, England, would require the whole country as a bleaching field and this is obviously impossible. Then came the discovery that this same compound could be used in purifying our water supplies of dangerous disease-breeding bacteria and this has reduced the typhoid death rate from that of a very dangerous epidemic disease to a negligible figure. Now, whenever the water supply of a city is questionable, chlorine is pumped right into the mains or else a solution made from bleaching powder is used. Twenty parts of bleaching powder per million is sufficient to kill 90 to 95 per cent of all the bacteria in the water. For medical use, a solution of hypochlorous acid, which is the active principle of bleaching powder, has been developed into a marvelous treatment for deep-seated wounds, and recoveries which formerly would have been out of the question are now possible.

Chlorine is also used in very large amounts in making organic chemicals which the public enjoys as dyestuffs or sometimes does not enjoy as pharmaceuticals or medicines.

All in all, the products obtained from the little salt cube are of extreme necessity and importance to every one of us and their utilization shows what can be done when men of genius devote themselves to the acquisition of real knowledge and then translate their discoveries into commercial enterprises for the benefit of humanity.

CHEMISTRY AND UNDERSTANDING

The brief story for which we have space indicates but very dimly the real interest and fascination the chemist has in handling matter. His knowledge has increased to such a point that he can build you a molecule almost to order to meet any specifications. To be without any knowledge of chemistry is to go through life ignorant of some of the most interesting aspects of one's surroundings; and yet the acquisition of some knowledge of this subject is by no means hard. There are any number of books which tell the story in simple language if you do not wish to study the science intensively. On the other hand, all that you need is a real interest and a willingness to think as you read.

1924

BOUNCING MOLECULES *
(AND RUBBER)

WILLIS A. GIBBONS

The controlled release of atomic energy is the greatest scientific development of our time. But in our preoccupation with this great achievement let us not forget other aspects of atoms which have more intimate relation to our daily life and well-being. Think of the vast and useful array of properties which characterize the matter forming our bodies and all animate nature—the air we breathe, the water we drink, the materials we use in our work or play. How can we explain all these forms of matter? The properties of all these different forms of matter are largely the properties of their molecules, and these properties are in turn determined by the nature and arrangement of the atoms which compose the molecules. Many different kinds of molecules occur naturally and man has made many new kinds.

Of all the various known materials, rubber is one of the most remark-

* From *The Scientists Speak*, edited by Warren Weaver. Reprinted by permission from Boni & Gaer, Inc. Copyright 1947 by Boni & Gaer, Inc.

able. It has a unique assortment of physical properties—great elasticity, stretchability, and toughness. Rubber has contributed directly to many modern inventions such as the motorcar. So vital is rubber to our civilization that it was a near catastrophe when the supply of natural rubber was cut off by the war. Fortunately we were able to produce synthetic rubber promptly enough so that our war effort was not retarded.

The peculiar properties of rubber have excited the curiosity of scientists. As a result of their efforts we now have a good idea of the structure of the molecules of rubber, both natural and synthetic.

Let us assume that we are wearing extraordinary spectacles, so powerful that we can see the molecules of matter and the atoms of which they are composed. The rubber molecule is exceedingly complicated, so suppose we look first at something comparatively simple: for example, a molecule of ordinary paraffin wax. We would see that the paraffin wax is made up of two kinds of atoms—carbon and hydrogen. The carbon atoms are linked together in a chainlike arrangement and the separate hydrogen atoms are attached directly to the carbon atoms.

There may be from 25 to 50 carbon atoms in the chain. That is paraffin wax. Now let us look at a molecule of rubber. It too consists of carbon and hydrogen, and most of the carbon atoms are again fixed together to form a chain. However, we have some difficulty in seeing the rubber molecule as a whole, for two reasons. First, it is very long; if we have the patience to count the carbon atoms we shall find that there are several thousand of them in the chain. The second difficulty in looking at the entire rubber molecule is that it, like all its fellow molecules, is kinked, twisted, and in a general state of disorder. If our spectacles are so powerful that the paraffin or rubber molecules appear to have the thickness of a good sized rope, say one inch in diameter, the paraffin molecule will appear to be about 15 inches long. Rubber molecules under the same conditions would appear to be some 30 to 150 feet in length, provided of course we could untangle them so as to see the entire molecule at a glance.

As would be expected, these giant chainlike molecules of rubber behave very differently from the short molecules of paraffin wax. If a large assemblage of rubber molecules—in other words, a piece of rubber—is stretched, the long chains are brought into alignment one with another. In fact, the aligning operation is the stretching operation. As you hold the piece of rubber in your hand, the kinked and twisted molecules are in a state of constant movement. Individual atoms vibrate without losing their relative positions in the molecule. Whole sections of the molecule also oscillate. This motion increases as the temperature rises; actually the warmth in the substance which we feel with our hands is the movement of the atoms and groups of atoms. When we stretch the rubber, we enforce some semblance of order. We thus restrict some of the motions of the molecules as though they were confined in a smaller space, and accordingly the remaining movements become more rapid; that is, the temperature rises.

The molecules tend to resist this straightening out. When the stretched rubber is released, matters revert to about their original state—the rubber contracts and the molecules resume their unruly ways. Likewise, if we suddenly compress the rubber it will resist; in other words it bounces.

We have seen that the paraffin wax and rubber both consist of chains of carbon atoms, although of very different length. This chainlike arrangement permits the molecules to slip past one another when force is applied to them. In other words, both materials are plastic. Plasticity is important because it permits convenient manufacturing processes such as molding.

The giant threadlike molecules of rubber can be fastened together by cross links. When it is thus cross-linked, rubber ceases to be plastic. This process is called vulcanization, and sulfur is the usual cross-linking material. The properties of the vulcanized rubber vary with the number of the cross-links. If there are relatively few, the rubber is soft and flexible, and will stretch easily. With a greater number of cross-links the rubber becomes stiffer and harder and more force is required to stretch it.

Seen through our magic spectacles, the cross-linked or vulcanized rubber seems more complicated than the unvulcanized material. Adjoining chains are linked together at irregular intervals by atoms of sulfur, but the linking is not merely a matter of joining two chains together in a structure similar to a tire chain. The linking extends to three dimensions and probably is not at all regular. The process of vulcanization was discovered a hundred years ago but our knowledge of it is still incomplete.

The plastic properties of rubber permit us to put it into any desired shape; the cross-linking or vulcanization operation sets the material in that shape. These changes of state are all-important to the utilization of rubber as a structural material.

What we have said thus far applies to both the natural and synthetic rubber molecules. However, there are some differences which can be observed. If the chainlike molecule is built in a regular fashion, that is, if the atoms of carbon and hydrogen are so arranged that a regular repeating order exists, the stretched rubber will show certain peculiar properties. For example, when stretched natural rubber is examined in an X-ray spectrograph it gives a regular pattern similar to the one we see when an ordinary crystalline structure is examined in the X-ray. This means that stretched rubber molecules have an orderly repeating arrangement, like a crystal. The orderly pattern is not apparent when the tension of the rubber is released, and the molecule is no longer straight. In somewhat the same way the pattern of a plaid necktie is not evident when the tie is crushed into a shapeless mass, but becomes evident when the tie is pulled out straight.

Some of the synthetic rubbers, however, do not show this effect when they are examined by the X-ray. There is no regular pattern, and we believe that this is a consequence of the molecular structure. We believe that the atoms in the chain of synthetic rubber are not so orderly in their arrangement as is the case with natural rubber. This difference is particularly in evidence when natural rubber is compared with the type of synthetic rubber known as GR-S—a variety produced from butadiene and styrene. GR-S is the synthetic rubber that was manufactured in large amounts during the recent war, which provided tires and other articles used in the war effort. Despite its lack of orderly arrangement of atoms, this synthetic rubber has proved to be highly satisfactory for most of the important uses.

A task which remains for the rubber technologists to solve is that of producing synthetic molecules having a more orderly arrangement of atoms in the chain. When that is attained, we shall have a man-made rubber which should more closely resemble the natural product.

Science has made rapid advances in recent years in its ability to explain the physical properties of substances in terms of the arrangement of the atoms in their molecules, and these advances are a tribute to the work done by the chemists and the physicists. The success which has attended these efforts to explain the nature of the material world prompts us to believe that still greater discoveries lie ahead, for there are yet many mysteries that await understanding. Many of these discoveries will be made by the young people of America who in increasing numbers are devoting themselves to careers of science.

1947

MOLECULAR ARCHITECTURE AND MEDICAL PROGRESS *

LINUS PAULING

The molecule of Penicillin G contains forty-one atoms. This wonderful substance, penicillin, opposes certain deadly bacteria, and in a few years it has saved the lives of tens of thousands of people. DDT kills insects; and it has been the means of stopping epidemics by destroying mosquitos, lice, and other agents which transmit infectious disease. Morphine, ether, and other anesthetics allay pain and put us to sleep. Still other substances, such as adrenaline, stimulate the heart and wake us up.

Why? Why do these various drugs have these different effects on our bodies? What is the secret of the specific response which each invokes?

* From *The Scientists Speak*, edited by Warren Weaver. Reprinted by permission from Boni & Gaer, Inc. Copyright 1947 by Boni & Gaer, Inc.

We do not know the full answer to this question, but we are sure that, for each substance, part of the answer lies in the details of the structure of the molecules of the substance. To find the full answer we must first of all determine the precise arrangement of the forty-one atoms in the molecule of penicillin, and of the twenty-eight atoms in the molecule of DDT. This knowledge is needed as the first step toward understanding the power of penicillin to kill bacteria, and the power of DDT to destroy insects. And so for morphine, adrenaline, and all the rest—the secret of their physiological action lies in their molecular architecture.

Our task, however, is really two-fold. First, we must determine the structure of the drugs which produce these physiological effects. And second, we must determine the structure of the enzymes, nerve fibers, and tissues of the living organism which react to these drugs in their characteristic ways.

Much progress has already been made on the first of these problems. Chemists have worked out the architecture of many substances which have medicinal effects. In the case of chloroform, for example, it has long been known that its molecule consists of five atoms—one atom of carbon, one of hydrogen, and three of chlorine. Back in the 1880's, chemists found that the three chlorine atoms and the one hydrogen atom are compactly arranged in space around the carbon atom. The three chlorine atoms may be considered as lying at the three corners of the base of a three-sided pyramid, with the hydrogen atom at the apex, the carbon atom being inside the pyramid at its center. The chemists also discovered that each of the four outer atoms is held by a very powerful chemical affinity to the single carbon atom within. This general picture was obtained by chemical methods developed long ago. But within our time, beginning in the 1930's, scientists have obtained a far more precise knowledge of the structure of the chloroform molecule. They have even determined the submicroscopic distances which separate the carbon atom, within the molecule, from the four atoms which are grouped around it.

In order to measure such distances we have to give up our familiar units of measurement—they are too coarse for this molecular world. We make use of a special yardstick known as the Angstrom unit. In the span of the familiar household inch there are two hundred and fifty-four million of these tiny units. This, then, is our molecular yardstick, the Angstrom—a unit which measures one two-hundred-fifty-four-millionth part of an inch.

It is difficult to visualize this dimension. To get some picture of what it means, let us examine a wineglass full of liquid chloroform, and let us assume that everything is magnified by this linear factor 254 million, which converts one Angstrom unit into an inch and which correspondingly magnifies one inch into four thousand miles. On this scale, a man would be about two hundred and fifty thousand miles tall—which is the distance from the earth to the moon. On the same scale, the wineglass would be as big as the earth, and the chloroform molecules filling the glass would each measure about seven inches across.

The shape of the chloroform molecule, you remember, is that of a triangular pyramid, with the carbon atom inside and the four-corner points of the pyramid occupied by the three atoms of chlorine and the one atom of hydrogen. On our magnified scale, we can picture the inside carbon atom as about the size of a walnut, the three chlorine atoms as small oranges, and the hydrogen as a tangerine. On this same scale, the distance from the walnut, representing the carbon atom, to each of the oranges, representing the chlorine atoms, is 1.76 inches—a distance corresponding in molecular dimensions to 1.76 Angstrom units. Similarly, the distance from the walnut—the carbon atom—to the tangerine—the hydrogen atom—is 1.09 inches—corresponding, on the molecular scale, to 1.09 Angstrom units.

Our giant wineglass, as big as the earth, would be filled to the brim with billions of billions of these seven-inch molecules. And these molecules would not be resting quietly on each other in the wineglass, but would be jostling one another and rolling over one another in vigorous motion. Very often one of the molecules, at the surface of the liquid, would break away from its neighbors and would escape into the air, where it might impinge on a nerve ending within our nose, and cause us to become aware of the characteristic odor of chloroform; or it might, with many others, be inhaled, and cause us to lapse into unconsciousness.

Chloroform is not the only molecule whose dimensions are known. In recent years scientists have determined with similar accuracy the structures of several hundred substances.

These substances represent a variety of architectural complexities—ranging from small molecules of only two or three atoms to much more complex molecules built of fifty or sixty atoms. Most of our knowledge of the structure of these substances has necessarily been obtained by indirect means.

I remember, as a boy in Oregon, looking at a distant arc light through the fabric of an open umbrella. I could see the light, itself, and above it and below it, and to the right and left, there appeared something more—a pattern of spectra, the familiar colors of the rainbow. This pattern of colors was caused by the interference and reinforcement of the light waves which passed through the meshes of the fabric, and the angular spread of the pattern was determined by the ratio of the wave length of the light to the distance between the meshes of the cloth. Knowing the wave length of the light, one could use the observed pattern to calculate the distance from one thread to the next. One could also infer from the nature of the diffraction pattern the type of weave, and thus determine the structure of the cloth.

The investigator of molecular structure follows a similar procedure. He may, for example, use a beam of electrons—instead of the rays from the distant arc light.

The molecules of the chemical compound which he seeks to measure are analogous to the fabric of the umbrella. When the beam of electrons passes through the molecules, the electron waves are scattered into a diffraction pattern which is photographed—and by analyzing this photographed pattern the scientist learns how the atoms are arranged in the molecule and how they are spaced with reference to one another. The structure of a number of drugs has been analyzed in just this way.

But working out the architecture of drugs and other chemical compounds is only half the job. There remains the task of determining the structure of that part of the living creature on which the drug or other chemical acts. And this task is extremely difficult, because of the extreme complexity of many constituents of living matter. For example, the molecule of penicillin consists of forty-one atoms—but the molecule of hemoglobin, one of the important constituents of the red blood cell, consists of ten thousand atoms. Other protein molecules are larger still. Some containing twenty thousand, one hundred thousand, even one million atoms to a single molecule have been weighed. But although we can weigh them, we do not yet know the exact architecture of a single one of these protein molecules.

This then is the great problem of modern chemistry—the determination of the molecular architecture of the proteins and other complex constituents of the living organism. *This problem must be solved.* The progress of medicine depends on its solution.

When once a real understanding of the physiological activity of chemical substances is obtained—when we know what are the structural features of the penicillin molecule which give it its power, what is the method of attack of the poliomyelitis virus on the molecules of the nerves of the victim of infantile paralysis, what relation the cancer-producing molecules of polynuclear aromatic hydrocarbons bear to the molecules determining cell division—when we know these things, then medical progress will be swift. The medical research man then will be a molecular architect. He will be able to draw the atomic blueprints for promising pharmacological compounds in order that chemists may synthesize them and biologists may test them. He will be able to analyze and to interpret the structures of enzymes, tissues, and viruses to learn the mechanism of disease and hence the way of combatting diseases.

When this time comes—and it is coming—medicine will indeed have become an exact science.

1947

>>>‹‹‹

CHEMISTRY

History and Biography

Boyle, Robert, *The Sceptical Chymist* (New York, E. P. Dutton & Co., Inc., 1911; Everyman).

Child, Ernest, *The Tools of the Chemist: Their Ancestry and American Evolution* (New York, Reinhold Publishing Corporation, 1940).

Conant, J. B., *On Understanding Science* (New Haven, Yale University Press, 1947).

Davy, Sir Humphrey, *Elements of Chemical Philosophy* (Philadelphia, Bradford and Inskeep, 1812).

Findlay, Alexander, *A Hundred Years of Chemistry* (New York, The Macmillan Company, 1937).

Freund, Ida, *The Study of Chemical Composition* (Cambridge, Cambridge University Press, 1904).

Harrow, Benjamin, *Eminent Chemists of Our Time* (New York, D. Van Nostrand Company, Inc., 1920).

Holt, A., *A Life of Joseph Priestley* (London, Oxford University Press, 1931).

Jaffe, Bernard, *Crucibles* (New York, Simon & Schuster, Inc., 1930).

Leonard, J. N., *Crusaders of Chemistry: Six Makers of the Modern World* (New York, Doubleday & Co., Inc., 1930).

Marsh, J. E., *The Origins and the Growth of Chemical Science* (London, John Murray, 1929).

Masson, Irvine, *Three Centuries of Chemistry: Phases in the Growth of a Science* (London, Benn Brothers, Ltd., 1925).

Mees, C. E. K., *The Path of Science* (New York, John Wiley & Sons, Inc., 1946).

Ramsay, Sir William, *Essays Biographical and Chemical* (New York, E. P. Dutton & Co., Inc., 1908).

———, *The Gases of the Atmosphere: The History of Their Discovery* (London, The Macmillan Company, 1915).

Russell, Richard, *The Works of Geber* (London, J. M. Dent & Sons Ltd., 1928).

Smith, Edgar P., *Chemistry in America* (New York, D. Appleton and Co., 1914).

Tilden, Sir William A., *Famous Chemists* (New York, E. P. Dutton & Co., Inc., 1921).

———, *Sir William Ramsay: Memorials of His Life and Work* (London, The Macmillan Company, 1918).

Vallery-Radot, René, *Pasteur*, translated by Mrs. R. L. Devonshire (New York, Garden City Pub. Co., Inc., 1926).

General

Dyer, Walter S., *A Practical Survey of Chemistry* (New York, Henry Holt and Company, Inc., 1941).

Grady, Roy I., and Chittum, J. W., *The Chemist at Work* (Easton, Pa., The Jour. of Chem. Ed., 1940).

Hogg, John C., *An Introduction to Chemistry* (New York, Oxford University Press, 1938).

Hogg, John C., and Bickel, C. L., *Elementary Experimental Chemistry* (New York, Oxford University Press, 1937).

Holmes, H. N., *Out of the Test Tube* (New York, Emerson Books, Inc., 1941).

Kendall, James, *General Chemistry: a Cultural Course Based Upon the Texts of the Late Alexander Smith* (New York, D. Appleton-Century Company, Inc., 1936).

Offner, Monroe M., *Fundamentals of Chemistry and their Applications in Modern Life* (Philadelphia, The Blakiston Company, 1944).

Sadtler, Samuel S., *Chemistry of Familiar Things* (Philadelphia, J. B. Lippincott Co., 1927).

Saunders, B. C., and Clark, R. E. D., *Order and Chaos in the World of Atoms* (London, English Universities Press, 1942).

Weeks, Mary Elvira, *Discovery of the Elements* (Easton, Pa., Jour. of Chem. Ed., 1945).

Wendt, Gerald, *Chemistry* (New York, John Wiley & Sons, Inc., 1942).

Organic and Inorganic

Alexander, Jerome, *Colloid Chemistry: Principles and Applications* (New York, D. Van Nostrand Company, Inc., 1937).

Bragg, Sir William H., *X Rays and Crystal Structure* (London, George Bell & Sons, Ltd., 1924).

Deming, Horace G., *In the Realm of Carbon: the Story of Organic Chemistry* (New York, John Wiley & Sons, Inc., 1930).

Hawley, Gessner G., *Seeing the Invisible* (New York, Alfred A. Knopf, Inc., 1947).

———, *The Story of Colloids* (New York, Alfred A. Knopf, Inc., 1947).

Haynes, William, *The Stone that Burns: the Story of the American Sulphur Industry* (New York, D. Van Nostrand Company, Inc., 1942).

Little, Arthur D., *The Handwriting on the Wall* (Boston, Little, Brown & Company, 1928).

Wilson, Charles Morrow, *Trees and Test Tubes: the Story of Rubber* (New York, Henry Holt and Company, Inc., 1943).

Chemistry in Industry

Deming, Horace G., *General Chemistry: an Elementary Survey Emphasizing Industrial Applications of Fundamental Principles* (New York, John Wiley & Sons, Inc., 1944).

Howe, H. E., editor, *Chemistry in Industry* (New York, The Chemical Foundation, 1924).

Li, Kuo Ch'in, and Wang, Chung Yu, *Tungsten: Its History, Geology, Ore-Dressing, Metallurgy, Chemistry, Analysis, Applications and Economics* (New York, Reinhold Publishing Corporation, 1943).

Naylor, N. M., and Le Vesconte, Amy, *Introductory Chemistry with Household Applications* (New York, D. Appleton-Century Company, Inc., 1941).

Read, William Thornton, *Industrial Chemistry* (New York, John Wiley & Sons, Inc., 1943).

Riegel, Emil R., and others, *Industrial Chemistry* (New York, Reinhold Publishing Corporation, 1942).

THE AUTHORS

AITKEN, ROBERT GRANT
Formerly Director of the Lick Observatory and formerly President of the American Astronomical Society, Professor Aitken has specialized in work on faint satellites, comets and binary stars.

BELL, ERIC TEMPLE
He is not only Professor of Mathematics at the California Institute of Technology and the author of such popular works on science as *Men of Mathematics*, but also the author of thrillers with titles like *The Purple Sapphire.*

BOWEN, IRA SPRAGUE
The Director of the Mount Wilson–Palomar Observatories, which house the 200-inch telescope, has been associated for years with the California Institute of Technology. He is a specialist in extreme ultraviolet spectroscopy and in nebular spectra.

BUMSTEAD, HENRY ANDREWS
The late Dr. Bumstead was Professor of Physics at Yale and Director of the Sloane Physical Laboratory.

CLARK, R. E. D.
Member of the Department of Chemistry, University Chemical Laboratory, Cambridge, England.

CONANT, JAMES B.
President Conant of Harvard was formerly Professor of Organic Chemistry at Harvard. During the recent war, he was Chairman of the National Defense Reseach Committee.

COPERNICUS, NICHOLAS
The founder of modern astronomy, whose book *De Orbium Cœlestium Revolutionibus*, published in 1543 and presented to the author on his deathbed, overthrew the Ptolemaic system which had reigned for many centuries.

CURIE, MARIE SKLODOWSKA
Her laborious work on the isolation of radium, done in collaboration with her husband, is a monument in the history of science, and opened a new epoch in physics.

DALY, REGINALD A.
Professor-emeritus of Geology at Harvard, the recipient of many scientific honors, one of the world's leading authorities on petrology and geophysics.

DAVIS, WATSON
Author of *The Story of Copper* and *Science Picture Parade*, editor of numerous books including *The Advance of Science*, contributor to many magazines and technical publications, Mr. Davis has been since 1933 Director of Science Service, this country's foremost organization for the dissemination of scientific information to newspapers and magazines and to the public.

DAVIS, W. M.
The specialist on the physical geography of the land and seas, who was Professor of Geology at Harvard. He died in 1934.

DINGLE, HERBERT

Professor Dingle is one of Great Britain's noted astrophysicists, a former Vice-President of the Royal Astronomical Society. He is also a master of lucid and vigorous prose, a fact which becomes evident on a reading of the short selection from his work here published.

DUBRIDGE, LEE ALVIN

President of the California Institute of Technology since 1946. As Director of the Radiation Laboratory at the Massachusetts Institute of Technology, he was one of the leaders in the country's wartime research. He is an authority on waves and on photoelectric phenomena.

DURAND, WILLIAM F.

Professor-emeritus of Mechanical Engineering at Stanford University. One of the great modern pioneers on hydrodynamics, aerodynamics and thermodynamics. Responsible for much early research on the resistance and propulsion of ships and airplanes, and the performance of screw and air propellers.

EDDINGTON, SIR ARTHUR

Sir Arthur's recent death was a great loss to modern astronomy. Plumian Professor of Astronomy at Cambridge and Director of the Cambridge Observatory, he was recognized as one of the greatest modern astronomers. His work on the internal constitution of the stars and his substantiation of the relativity theory by the observation of the effect of gravity on the path of a star's rays are among his outstanding achievements. He also wrote such well-known books as *The Nature of the Physical World* and *New Pathways in Science.*

EDMAN, IRWIN

Professor of Philosophy at Columbia since 1935, Dr. Edman has written voluminously not only for scholarly publications but also for such popular magazines as *The Atlantic*, *Harper's* and *The New Yorker*. He is also a poet of some note and the author of *Candle in the Morning*, *Philosopher's Quest,* and other popular books.

EHRET, WILLIAM F.

Professor of Chemistry at New York University since 1936. He has done extensive research in X-ray, crystal structure analysis, and in phase equilibria in saturated salt solutions.

FOSDICK, RAYMOND B.

As President of the Rockefeller Foundation, a post which he recently resigned, he has had a profound effect on the development of experimental science throughout the world.

FRANKLIN, BENJAMIN

This famous American philosopher and statesman needs no identification.

FREUND, IDA

Her *Study of Chemical Composition*, done as Staff Lecturer and Associate of Newnham College, Cambridge, is an excellent study of method and historical development.

FURNAS, C. C.

An American Olympic athlete in his college days, C. C. Furnas has been Associate Professor of Chemical Engineering at Yale and is now Director of the Cornell Aeronautical Laboratory. His book, *The Next Hundred Years,* was a popular best seller.

GALILEI, GALILEO

The famous Italian physicist and astronomer who died in 1642. His research on falling bodies, his astronomical observations, his construction of a thermometer in 1597 and a telescope in 1609, and his insistence on observation in science as opposed to dependence on authority have marked him as one of the greatest minds in human history.

GAMOW, GEORGE

Professor Gamow's sprightly books *Mr. Tompkins in Wonderland* and *Mr. Tompkins Explores the Atom* have combined literary imagination with sound scientific theory. Now at George Washington University, he specializes in research on nuclear physics and its application to stellar evolution.

GEIKIE, SIR ARCHIBALD

Born in 1835, he was one of the greatest of the Scottish geologists. He was director of the geological survey of Scotland and director-general of the geological survey of the United Kingdom. He wrote many books including a *Textbook of Geology* which is a classic.

GIBBONS, WILLIS A.

One of our leading authorities on synthetic rubber as well as on many phases of the treatment of rubber, a director of research at the United States Rubber Company, who contributed largely to our efforts during the recent war.

GRAY, GEORGE W.

One of the foremost popularizers of science, Mr. Gray is noted for the accuracy and authenticity of his writing. He is the author of many books and articles on science.

HELMHOLTZ, HERMANN VON

The celebrated German physiologist and physicist, especially known for his discoveries in optics and acoustics. He invented the ophthalmoscope in 1851.

HEYL, PAUL R.

Until his retirement in 1942, was associated with the Bureau of Standards in Washington. His work on the absolute determination of gravity is a model of careful and accurate research. His many books and articles on scientific subjects were likewise models of accurate and interesting exposition.

HOTCHKISS, W. O.

President-emeritus of the Rensselaer Polytechnic Institute, he has had long experience in commercial mining and geology, in academic work and as Deputy Director of the Specialist Corps of the United States Army.

HUGGINS, SIR WILLIAM

English astronomer who lived from 1824 to 1910 and whose original experiments in spectrum analysis resulted in great advances in the early days of astrophysics.

HUXLEY, T. H.

The celebrated nineteenth-century biologist and writer on scientific subjects. He it was who, more than any other single individual, popularized the Darwinian theory and defeated the attempts to discredit it.

JEANS, SIR JAMES

Formerly President of the Royal Astronomical Society and of the British Association for the Advancement of Science and Secretary of the Royal Society, Sir James was most widely known in the United States for his popular volumes, *The Universe Around Us*, *The Mysterious Universe*, *The Stars in Their Courses*, and other books addressed to the informed layman. He did important work on the dynamical theory of gases, the mathematical theory of electricity and magnetism, and problems of cosmogony and stellar dynamics.

JONES, SIR H. SPENCER

It is interesting to note that one of the finest articles yet written on the 200-inch telescope in California is by a British scientist, the Astronomer Royal since 1933 and a past President of the Royal Astronomical Society.

KNOPF, ADOLPH

Professor of Geology at Yale, the author of important original research in the field he discusses in this book.

LA FARGE, OLIVER

Mr. La Farge is not only an ethnologist but also an authority on the American Indian and the author of popular novels like *Laughing Boy* which won the Pulitzer Prize in 1929.

LANGEWIESCHE, WOLFGANG

A well-known popular scientific writer whose own work in aeronautics lends authenticity to his descriptions of research in this and related fields.

LEWIS, GILBERT N.

Formerly Professor of Chemistry at the University of California, winner of the Davy, Willard Gibbs and Arrhenius medals as well as many other scientific awards, he was an authority on thermodynamic theory and its application to chemistry, and worked in many other scientific fields with great distinction. He died in 1946.

LILIENTHAL, DAVID E.

His work as Director of TVA and as Chairman of the Atomic Energy Commission have made him world famous.

LOWES, JOHN LIVINGSTON

Formerly Professor of English at Harvard, John Livingston Lowes was one of the world's greatest authorities on a number of aspects of English literature. His studies of such English poets as Coleridge and Chaucer were recognized as outstanding.

MACELWANE, JAMES B., S.J.

One of a group of Jesuit scientists who have been outstanding in seismological research. He is Professor of Geophysics at St. Louis University, and has written over a hundred papers on seismology and other subjects.

MOULTON, F. R.

Dr. Moulton, who is now Administrative Secretary of the American Association for the Advancement of Science, was formerly Professor of Astronomy at the University of Chicago. He is one of the authors of a widely known theory of the origin of the solar system and a leading authority on celestial mechanics.

NEWTON, HUMPHREY

No relation to Sir Isaac, he was the latter's personal assistant and amanuensis.

NEWTON, SIR ISAAC

His achievements, mentioned in the text of this book, have made him generally recognized as the greatest scientific genius who ever lived. He was born in 1642 and died in 1727.

PAULING, LINUS

Chairman of the Division of Chemistry and Chemical Engineering at the California Institute of Technology, winner of the Willard Gibbs Medal and other honors, an outstanding worker in the application of chemistry to biological problems.

POINCARÉ, HENRI
Until his death in 1912, he was one of the great mathematicians and scientific philosophers of modern times. He was a member of the French Academy, Professor of Mathematics and Astronomy at the Sorbonne and the author of monumental works in mathematical physics and celestial mechanics.

ROBERTSON, G. ROSS
Associate Professor of Chemistry at the University of California, a specialist in chemical apparatus and appliance design as well as in various phases of organic chemistry.

ROSE, ROBERT E.
Formerly Director of the Technical Laboratory, E. I. duPont de Nemours and Co., a specialist in dyes, alkylated sugars and glucosides, and wood decay.

RUSSELL, BERTRAND
Mathematician, philosopher, lecturer and teacher of note, now at Trinity College, Cambridge, Bertrand Russell is the author of many books including *Mysticism and Logic, Sceptical Essays, The Scientific Outlook* and, with Alfred North Whitehead, the monumental *Principia Mathematica.*

SAUNDERS, B. C.
Member of the Department of Chemistry, University Chemical Laboratory, Cambridge, England.

SMYTH, HENRY D.
Chairman of the Department of Physics at Princeton, a specialist in molecular structure and the ionization of gases, he is the author of the famous Smyth Report, from which the selection in this book is taken.

WHIPPLE, FRED L.
A member of the staff of the Harvard Observatory, Dr. Whipple is the discoverer of six comets and has done original research on such subjects as meteors, spectrophotometry, novæ, the earth's upper atmosphere, and stellar evolution.

WHITEHEAD, ALFRED NORTH
Another great modern mathematician who at the time of his death was Professor-emeritus of Philosophy at Harvard. For many years he was a lecturer on mathematics at the University of London but in 1924 came to America. His works on philosophy, science and mathematics are conceded to have had a profound effect on the course of contemporary thought.

ZOBELL, CLAUDE E.
Specialist in bacterial physiology and marine microbiology, Assistant Director of the Scripps Institution of Oceanography.

Index